J. C. Archer

12/11/90

Handbook of Engineering Design

Roy D Cullum, FIED
Editor of *Materials + Manufacture*

Butterworths

London   Boston   Singapore   Sydney   Toronto   Wellington

 PART OF REED INTERNATIONAL P.L.C.

First published 1988
  Reprinted 1989

© **Butterworth and Co. (Publishers) Ltd, 1988**
excepting Chapter 16 © R. A. Berry, 1988

British Library Cataloguing in Publication Data
Cullum, Roy D.
  Handbook of engineering design.
  1. Engineering design
  I. Title
  620′.00425   TA174
  ISBN 0–408–00558–0

Library of Congress Cataloging in Publication Data
Handbook of engineering design.
  Includes bibliographies and index.
  1. Engineering design—Handbooks, manuals, etc.
I. Cullum, Roy D.
TA174.H24   1987   620′.00425   87–10373
ISBN 0–408–00558–0

Photoset by TecSet Ltd, Wallington, Surrey
Printed and bound in England by Hartnolls Ltd, Bodmin, Cornwall

Preface

The purpose of a handbook is to provide a reader with information from a chosen specialised area. The *Handbook of Engineering Design* is no exception. It does not claim to turn the reader into a designer or a designer into a better designer. It does, however, offer designers the opportunity to gain accurate information more quickly than is possible by going through past publications and past papers in the hope of finding something relevant to a current design.

The handbook contains both new and previously published material. Its major aim is to draw the reader's attention to past activities which may have some aspect relevant to a current design and which will help the reader to avoid the pitfalls to which past designs may have been victim. All the publications cited in the text are listed at the end of each chapter, and I make no apology for drawing on those authors whose experience in specific fields is greater than my own.

RDC

Acknowledgements

Chapter 2
This chapter was prepared with the help of Alloy and Metal Stockholders Ltd, Barpoint Ltd, BSC Stainless, Fagersta Ltd, Sanderson and Kayser Ltd, and Sandvik Ltd.

Chapter 4
Acknowledgement is due to *Engineers Digest* and to the Glacier Metal Co. Ltd, GKN Bound Brook Ltd, Le Carbone (GB) Ltd, Railko Ltd, British Timken, INA Bearing Co. Ltd, RHP Ltd, Cooper Roller Bearing Co. Ltd, and Norbrac Carbon Ltd. Grateful acknowledgement is also due to SKF (UK) Ltd for permission to extract information from their *Ball Bearing Journals* 192 and 194 for use in this chapter.

Chapter 6
Acknowledgement is due to Atlas Copco Ltd for material used in section 6.5.

Chapters 8, 11, 12, 13,
These chapters are reproduced from the *Chartered Mechanical Engineer* by permission of the Institution of Mechanical Engineers.

Chapter 9
This chapter was prepared with the technical assistance of Associated Spring, Barnes Group Inc, with material drawn from their copyright publication *Design Handbook of Springs and Custom Metal Parts*.

Contents

Contributors

Richard Bell

R. A. Berry
Rolls Royce Ltd, Bristol

David Bryant

Roy D. Cullum
Publication Services, Worthing

D. L. Duffett
CAD Centre, Cambridge

The late Murray K. Forbes
Serck Heat Transfer (Heavy Engineering Division), Birmingham

V. H. Hamblett
Fluid consultant

G. S. Haviland
Loctite Corporation, USA

Eric Hemming
Past President, Institution of Engineering Designers

J. W. P. Jaffe
Principal Consultant, Technical Audit Ltd

Franklin M. Keeley

V. T. Morgan
GKN Bound Brook Ltd, Lichfield

D. H. Morton-Jones
Department of Chemistry, University of Lancaster

Peter Polak
Department of Mechanical Engineering, University of Sheffield

K. Sharples
Sharples Stress Engineers Ltd, Preston, Lancashire

H. C. Town

Barry T. Turner
Barry T. Turner Associates, Dunchurch, Warwickshire

A. C. Wordsworth
Lloyd's Register of Shipping, Experimental Laboratories, Crawley

D. W. Wyatt

PART 1

1

Stages in design

1.1 Disciplined creativity

Much has been written about teaching design, but in the final analysis good design skills can be acquired only by experience. To be a successful designer one must have a sympathetic understanding of all the factors that go to create an engineering product. Ideally a designer should have experienced the problems with which his design is intended to cope, and the discipline imposed in making a product that can handle the problems. He should also experience the satisfaction or frustration of using it. From these extremes the designer creates and practices his craft. Jones (1973) notes seven stages in a general design methodology and these he summarises as:

(1) recognition that the problem exists;
(2) study of its parameters and their conversion to recognisable terms;
(3) preparation by assimilating existing knowledge and searching for other data;
(4) analysis with the intention of satisfying a feasible enquiry;
(5) synthesis — manipulation of the analysis to yield available solutions;
(6) evaluation by which a solution is chosen;
(7) presentation — the method by which the solution is communicated.

Within these seven phases one must include the important considerations of cost, aesthetics and ergonomic factors. One or more of these considerations will be paramount, depending on the purpose for which the product is intended. Successful design is a compromise between all the factors involved, and a designer must have as wide a knowledge as possible of these factors to arrive at a successful compromise.

Pitts (1973) suggests that all the parameters essential to the design should be listed in the form of specification, and this must always be formulated by the designer and not by the customer. A critical look at the problem in hand is a necessary first step in creating a correct attitude to the design. A customer may list many items he feels to be valuable as part of his requirements but each item must be examined carefully by the designer and, before transfer to the specification, many of the customer's items will be found to be irrelevant to the design. Pitts quotes a trivial example, a request for a wooden tool cabinet. The customer's real need is for a tool cabinet, but by specifying that it should be wooden the customer has attempted to take a design decision.

All the items in the designer's specification are unlikely to be of equal significance, and Pitts illustrates the relative importance of a vacuum cleaner component compared with an aircraft control component (Figure 1.1).

It is often argued that before commencing a design one should examine the literature relating to that particular product or process. By seeing what has been done before one has the opportunity to accept an existing design or a modification of one. Previous designs may also act as a stimulus to producing a better design. Any new design should be an improvement on what has gone before. Unless the specification requires it, there is little point in simply using an existing design.

There are no hard and fast rules that a designer can apply in designing a product, since each product has to be assessed on its own merits and requirements. Nevertheless he has to consider the aesthetics, the quality, the cost and the time scale in which the product has to be produced. Reliability, quality assessment and safety are all important aspects that the designer must consider. There may be other considerations, such as ease of transportation — there is little point in building a first-rate chemical plant if it cannot be broken down and transported to its destination.

Degree of importance

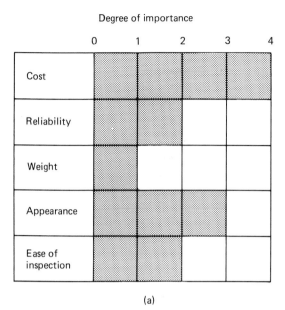

(a)

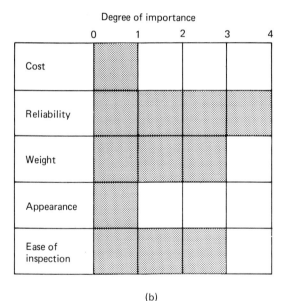

(b)

Figure 1.1 (a) The importance of some items from a vacuum cleaner component specification; (b) the importance of some items from an aircraft control component specification.

1.2 Economics

The designer should not fail to recognise the pound, dollar or franc as an engineering unit as significant as the kilogram or the metre. In spite of the development of economic science and the introduction of improved costing techniques, economics still ap-

pears somewhat nebulous when compared with the more predictable calculations of applied mechanics. This point is emphasised by the reluctance of component manufacturers to provide an indication of price as part of their product data. The underlying principle of economic manufacture is economy of effort. In design a specific requirement usually has to be fulfilled and the designer is only concerned with meeting this requirement in the most economical way possible, although the need for sales appeal may warrant some expenditure on aesthetics.

Problem recognition and the ability to analyse the requirements to be specified are especially important in design economics. For example, there is little to be gained by designing a component for use within a system which has a greater life than the system itself, or by designing a component in a measuring device to meet an accuracy of 1% when the overall accuracy of the system is only 15%. In other words the designer should be asking himself what the minimum satisfactory requirements are. Figure 1.2 shows diagramatically some of the costs which have to be borne by the price of the finished product. The contributions made to the whole by the various sub-divisions will depend largely on the particular product being manufactured and the production throughput.

Good design costs money, and a perfect design would require unlimited financial resources and unlimited time. It is the designer's responsibility to decide the amount of time he can effectively afford to devote to his problem. His decision must take account of the final market price of the product, the numbers to be produced and the rate for his own services and design office overheads.

1.3 Safety

While design is normally governed by economic considerations, exceptions do exist to this rule. One such is safety. Here the designer finds himself under a moral obligation to the community. For example, in the aerospace industry a defective design can result in loss of life on a massive scale. Under the Health and Safety at Work Act a designer can be held responsible if the operator of a particular piece of equipment he has designed falls victim to it, even though the accident may be the result of misuse. It therefore behoves the designer not only to consider all the other wide ramifications of his design but also to ensure that his product is safe in use, even when abused. Pitt (1973) summarises the situation thus:

(1) The designer must compare his efforts with those of the manufacturer and consider any moral implications of his work.
(2) In general, pre-production development is less expensive than that carried out during service.

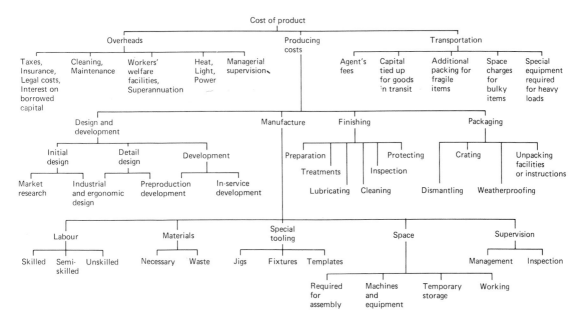

Figure 1.2 The breakdown of product costs

1.4   Method of manufacture

All manufacturing processes, no matter how automated they are, require some degree of human intervention. To divide labour into the three arbitrary categories of skilled, semi-skilled and unskilled might at first sight seem illogical. But since the cost of labour, or the cost of avoiding its use, may account for the greatest proportion of a product's price, the designer should *be aware* of its capabilities and limitations. It is therefore important that at the conception of the design, the designer is aware of the methods by which the product may be made. And again there has to be an inter-relation between the method by which a product is produced and its life and future reliability. Durability and dependability depend not only on the design of the product, but on the choice of material and the way in which it is manufactured. For example, it may prove more expensive to buy in an extruded section which requires a minimum amount of machining, but it may be infinitely more reliable than a product bent from sheet material which requires the services of a welder or riveter to make it into the final product.

In a different sphere, forgings and castings may provide an integrity to a component but they can be fearfully expensive, and the number of items produced has a profound influence on the decision as to whether this method of production should be considered.

The designer also has to take into account whether the product he has designed requires any special tooling. One design may be easy to manufacture although the initial material may be expensive to buy. On the other hand, it may be considered cheaper to produce an expensive tool to provide a large number of identical parts at a much cheaper unit cost. Pitt summarises this aspect thus:

(1)   The skill of labour is more often related to the quantities required.
(2)   Every line on a drawing requires time and effort to interpret and implement.

The prices of materials are largely governed by their availability and the effort and the energy necessary to provide them. Availability, which can seriously affect price stability, is frequently overlooked by designers. Designers must also consider what degree of waste is involved in manufacturing a product. Normally scrap prices reflect very little return, and in some cases scrap prices are negligible.Therefore the art of the designer has to be directed towards providing the minimum amount of waste from any raw material from which his product is made. It is not unknown for a sheet metal part to be reduced by a millimetre or two without detriment to the product's ability to perform its function and thus allow two products to be cut from a single sheet, where otherwise two sheets would have been used.

1.5   Reliability

Much has been made in recent years of reliability and its prediction. Reliability and the degree to which efforts are made to ensure it depends on the product's final requirement and its application. Pronikov (1973) makes the point that the performance characteristics of any piece of equipment, its accuracy, reliability and durability, are influenced by its design, by the materials from which it is made and the processes used in its manufacture. Methods of inspection, assembly and testing, load and environmental conditions as well as age, all contribute to changes in performance and service. Manufacturing processes cause statistical variations in dimensions and material properties. Service variations are random, but their probable effects can be assessed.

Pronikov sets out several basic concepts and aspects of dependability and durability. Efficiency is that state of a product in which it is capable of fulfilling its set function with characteristics that depend on the requirements of a technical specification. Dependability is the ability of the product to fulfil its specified function while maintaining its service indices within given limits for a required interval of time. Life is the calendar operated period of an assembly or component, whereas its specific life is the operating time of the product in hours or in other unit functions of time such as amount of work done, kilometres covered, number of cycles, etc. Failure is an event which defines a breakdown in the efficiency of the machine or in one of its elements. Failure criteria given in the technical specification should always be limited to a given type of product. Reliability is the ability of the product to maintain the specified efficiency within given limits for a certain time or specific life without enforced stops. Durability is the ability of the product to maintain efficiency within a limiting value with the necessary breaks for maintenance and overhaul. Economic factors are extremely important when assessing reliability, because although an increase in the reliability and durability of a machine involves certain additional material costs it is, on the other hand, possible to obtain increased efficiency and capital investment from reduced labour costs for repair and maintenance of the machine and reduced losses due to downtime. Pronikov suggests that an economic criterion of reliability can be the sum of costs involved in the manufacture and operation of the machine related to its optimum service life.

1.6 Aesthetics

The designer also has to consider aesthetics and make a realistic appraisal of the problems involved in achieving good aesthetic design. The basic sensation of recognition or response to stimuli is typically regarded as an outward expression of quality. But since appearance is the first point of contact with the prospective purchaser it is necessary to establish the priority of aesthetic freedom as part of the general design process. Jones (1973) suggests the simplest economic definition would require appearance to reflect function and quality in relation to environment without greatly increasing cost, remembering that in some cases form will be implicitly defined by function. It is easy to demolish the fallacious argument that only function or only form matters. In one case a judgement will already have been made on a visual appraisal, on the other hand there is no functional advantage in a machine or product imitating the aesthetic standards of handcrafts.

It is instructive to reflect on the psychological effect of appearance; the harmonic or discordant response to line and shape emphasises its expressive nature. It is frequently enhanced by some type of decoration; colour or texture are typical methods of modifying impressions of shape and mass. The real problem is how the designer can exercise a degree of aesthetic judgement, of which appearance is one manifestation, in a situation where the sophistication expected of twentieth century designs, often based on parameters such as optimum mass-to-volume ratio, gives little opportunity to provide a shape which will satisfy all artistic tenets. It must also be realised that aesthetic considerations will sometimes conflict with functional limitations. Part of the education of a product designer should be concerned with methods of achieving an acceptable compromise.

1.7 Ergonomics

Ergonomics is defined as the relation between man and his occupation, equipment and environment, particularly the application of anatomical, physiological and psychological knowledge to the problems arising therefrom. The growing emphasis given to considering the effectiveness of the combination of the man and the machinery creates the demand for more ergonomics attention to be given to the design and selection of equipment.

Whilst, in general, sound ergonomics practice is unlikely to add to the cost of items of equipment (provided consideration is not left to a late stage in the design), the application of ergonomics in the design process will not cost less than any other specialist service, such as electrical, mechanical or pneumatic engineering. However, the real difference comes when the whole life costs are examined, for shortcomings in ergonomics can often lead to quality problems, absenteeism, labour turnover, safety costs and low output figures for the whole of the working life of the equipment.

It is clearly necessary therefore for managers responsible for others' working conditions, to consider carefully ergonomic requirements during design, selection and layout of equipment.

The five special senses of man are often highly developed over a wide range and are usually more effective than mechanical sensing devices. The aim is to facilitate optimum reception by the operator with efficient processing and appropriate action. Any physical or mental condition which interrupts this flow must be eliminated or reduced.

Factors which can interrupt the flow are:

(1) Design anomalies which result in a physical inability to reach controls — often there is failure in standardisation of controls which results in uncertainty, with an operator becoming confused;
(2) difficulty in manipulation and control causes an unnecessary demand for physical effort;
(3) poor presentation, and distribution, of visual data as, for example, may occur in a road vehicle with wide pillars or badly positioned driving mirrors;
(4) environmental factors which affect the operator — these include noise, heat, cold, fumes and gases, and discomfort, headache and fatigue are frequent effects which produce a consequent loss of efficiency.

The workspace is frequently a source of problems, at one extreme introducing hazards and at the other unnecessarily interfering with the well-being and performance of the individual. Problems arise when equipment has not been designed with consideration for the dimensions of the human operator.

A more common problem is the poor workspace which results when several pieces of equipment are combined into a single work station. Frequently items are selected and assessed separately and are only considered as a single interface during installation.

The most important source of data for good workspace design is the science of anthropometry, or body dimensions. An example of anthropometric data is shown in Figure 1.3.

Often average dimensions are utilised in equipment design, but designs must reflect the range of human dimensions and an average is too big for half the population and too small for the other half. The data shown in Table 1.1 allow for the range by using the statistical measure of percentiles. This means that for example only 5 per cent of men are shorter than 1630 mm (the 5th percentile) and only 5 per cent are taller than 1880 mm (the 95th percentile).

The average is the 50th percentile, which will be a value rarely used in design. The rule for selecting the appropriate percentile is: for clearances use the 95th percentile and for reaches use the 5th. This rule will ensure that at least nine out of ten people will be able to fit comfortably at the work station. Table 1.2 indicates the average values attained by the human frame in various postures.

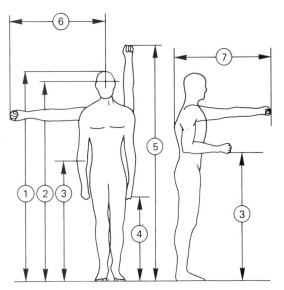

Figure 1.3 Human body dimensions (Table 1.1 provides definitions of each of dimensions 1 to 7)

There are two aspects to ergonomics:

(a) to design equipment to meet physical standards of the operator — by considering the 5–95th percentile group, most problems of a physical nature can be overcome;
(b) to understand and plan for mental capacity and the problems of human behaviour and reaction which are often unpredictable but, in emergencies, are those of habit. This second problem is a contributory factor to many accidents.

A person has a limited mental capacity which can be overloaded with extraneous worries. The strain of modern living together with the need to perform a complex operation can produce a state in which an

Table 1.1 Standing dimensions

Dimensions	Male Percentiles			Female Percentiles		
	5	50	95	5	50	95
Body weight (kg)	56.5	75.5	95.0	47.5	64.5	81.5
1 Height (mm)	1630	1750	1880	1520	1630	1740
2 Eye height	1550	1660	1770	1450	1550	1650
3 Elbow height	970	1040	1110	890	950	1010
4 Knuckle height	730	790	850	650	710	770
5 Upward reach	1950	2110	2270	1870	2020	2170
6 Sideways reach	760	825	890	650	710	770
7 Forward reach	735	800	865	650	710	770

Table 1.2 Average available arm force

Workspace	Posture	Push (N)	Pull (N)
Restricted footroom and buttock space		3.8	4
Restricted footroom		4	14
No restriction		10	13
Hand support available		26.5	23.6
Buttock support		22.5	8
Thigh support		9.4	24

operator will no longer respond to warning information. The so-called inexplicable failure of a routine operation is often found on further investigation to be due to mental overload. We all experience the 'Now look what you have made me do!' syndrome. When a person suffers from mental overload he becomes worried and distracted and in consequence commits actions which he would not normally do. In other words, he becomes what is described as 'accident prone'. Such a case is usually treated with amusement. However, it is a very real condition and is likely to produce consequences far more serious than dropping china in the kitchen.

It is necessary to have more intelligent operators for the more complicated modern equipment. It follows that a person of low intelligence, or one who has been accustomed to a simple machine for many years, will not be capable of operating the more complex and costly machines of today. The saying 'it is difficult to teach an old dog new tricks' remains a truism. If it is attempted, failure of the operator and damage to the costly machines will often result.

The operation of modern equipment is no longer simply a question of moving knobs and levers. It is essential for the operator to understand the machine and its functions and for him to play his part in the system. There are optimum hours of work and rest and there is legislation in most countries to ensure that these are adhered to. There is a personal limit to the attention anyone can offer, after which his concentration fails. It is, therefore, essential that rest is taken before reaching this particular condition. Operating comfort is an ideal which most people seek. Man is adaptable and able to cope with many awkward and uncomfortable situations; he will make his own adaptations to equipment to serve his own particular needs. It is, however, because of his very adaptability that he may become a hindrance to the work of the designer since the latter is frequently not made aware of the difficulties being experienced by the operator.

The work study expert employs the techniques devised and evaluated by the ergonomists. The British Standards Institution has defined work study as a generic term for those techniques, particularly Method Study and Work Measurement, which are used in the examination of human work in all its contexts and which lead systematically to the investigation of all factors which affect the efficiency and economy of the situation being reviewed in order to effect improvement. It helps to produce the best from both men and material engaged on a working programme, and being concerned with the efficient use of manpower and machine it also promotes safe working.

It is necessary, when engaged in work study, to break down an operation into its component parts and to examine each part carefully. It is a combined study of how best? and how quick? What is the best way of doing a particular job and what is the optimum time? With regard to the latter it must be remembered that rest periods are essential, and higher production can often be obtained by ensuring that these rest periods are of the right length. These periods are physiological in requirement and are advised as a result of long experience in these matters by work study experts.

It is important to remember that the rate of recovery from fatigue is greatest in the first few minutes of rest. Therefore, frequent short rests are better than fewer longer breaks.

A purpose of ergonomics is to facilitate the immediate and correct comprehension of information and the identification and manipulation of controls.

All efforts must be made to ensure that displays are clear and positive. Colour can provide a most useful contribution to a visual display. The best presentation of scaled measurement comes from rotational indicators against well spaced marking on a well contrasted background plus adequate illumination of scale. When undue physical effort is demanded of an operator, servo mechanisms should be incorporated in the machine. This has happened with steering and braking in heavy vehicles in which automatic gear change is now also commonplace.

Vision is the special sense which is most easily overloaded, and this problem is best illustrated by the presentation of display on the flight deck of a large aircraft. It is impossible for the flight crew to check simultaneously every visual signal and dial. Sometimes it is necessary to reinforce the visual display, say of a variation which goes past a limiting condition, by means of an alarm to attract the attention of the operator through another of his senses. Most frequently an audible signal is used, such as a buzzer. Dials should be arranged so that the indicators fall into pattern when at normal to enable an operator to scan a bank of dials without undue strain. Whenever the abnormal occurs the indicator of the relevant dial will change and so alter the pattern, a fact which is relatively easy to observe.

There are three types of indicator.

(1) A check reading indicator which, when demanded, gives information as to the state of equipment. It can also confirm the functioning of a mechanism when in use. This is demonstrated by the direction flasher indicator in a motor car.

(2) A qualitative indicator will demonstrate a dynamic measurement without exact precision. The ideal example is that of a temperature gauge which records: cold – normal – hot. The exact temperature is not required.

(3) A quantitative indicator will require precision. A car's speedometer is an example of such an indicator. A quantitative indicator requires more frequent attention than the other two do.

A quantitative indicator should never be used if a lower-order one will do. The use of check reading and qualitative indicators presents little problem in design. However, there are several varieties of dial in quantitative indicators. These include the vertical and horizontal linear types, and the semicircular, round and open-window rotational types. In the last the pointer is fixed and the scale moves. In the remainder the pointer moves. Experiment has shown that the open-window dial is the one which produces least errors in reading, although the round dial has probably as much merit. It is shown that 1 cm spacing markings on a dial are best suited to accurate reading.

1.8 Design of controls relative to indicator types

A check reading indicator has a single action control, e.g. on-off, as in an electric light switch. A qualitative indicator can have a multiple-choice action control, e.g. push-button station selection, as with radio or TV channel control. A quantitative indicator can also have continuous control within parameters, e.g. a car steering wheel during vehicle movement. In every case the control which is most suited to the operation must be used.

One must consider the degree of expectancy which is inherent in most people. By employing a customary movement an operator expects a certain result. For example, if a steering wheel is turned in a clockwise fashion one expects to turn to the right. With a clockwise turn of a knob one might expect increased output or vice versa for an anticlockwise turn. When a switch is pressed down one expects lights to go on and vice versa. This is normal expectation. Often, however, the expected outcome is not what actually happens and an accident results.

In these circumstances the operator does exactly the opposite to what is required.

Take the case of the two-car family. Unless the cars are identical in make, model and fitted extras it is certain that indicator and control layout will be different. Hence, the family member occasionally taking over the less familiar vehicle may find himself confused in the event of an emergency and thereby temporarily not in total control. Although the confusion may last for only a second or two the outcome is an accident. Thus a fan is switched on instead of lights, an incorrect gear shift is attempted, or perhaps through tiredness the loss of oil pressure is overlooked and the engine seizes. In the latter situation a combination of visual and audio signals could avoid some nasty consequences.

Ergonomics may contribute to vehicle design and thus lead to standard controls and a more rational array of indicators. Also, it may lead to the introduction of devices to offset the consequence of a sheer habit, such as attempting to drive on the left of the road in right-hand-side traffic flows.

Conflicts can also arise from confusion over different national conventions. For example in Europe a switch moves down for 'on', while in America the opposite is true.

Finally, the force needed for operation must be within the capacity of the operator. Data are available on this question (see bibliography) but can be complicated by the biomechanics of the work station, in particular by the way the operator can create the reaction. The significance of this is shown in Table 1.3.

Table 1.3 Selection of types of display

Use of information	Display	
	Counter	Moving pointer
Reading specific numbers	Very good	Fair
Observing rates of change of a value	Very poor	Very good
Setting in a specific value	Fair	Very good

The influence of these considerations on product design, particularly in a competitive field where manufacturing efficiency is a basic requirement, seems obvious and the designer needs data on the optimisation of human activity if he is to reach meaningful conclusions as to the most appropriate relationships between form and process.

Bibliography

BESANT, C. B. (1983) *Computer Aided Design and Manufacture*, Ellis Horwood.

CONTACT WORK RESEARCH UNIT, *Quality of Working Life*.

DAMAN, STROUDT and McFARLAND (1966) *Anthropometry: The Human Body in Equipment Design*, Harvard University Press, Cambridge, Mass.

DUGGAN, T. V. (1971) *Power Transmission and Vibration Considerations in Design*, Butterworths.

EDHOLM, O. G. (1967) *The Biology of Work*, World University Library.

FANGAR, P. O. (1972) *Thermal Environments: Thermal Comfort*, McGraw-Hill.

FLURSCHEIM, C. (1977) *Engineering Design Interfaces*, Design Council.

GALER, I. (1987) *Applied Ergonomics Handbook*, Butterworths, 2nd edn.

GRANDJEAN, E. (1980) *General Ergonomics: Fitting the Task to the Man*, Taylor and Francis, London.

GRATTAN, E. and JEFFCOATE, G. O. (1968) 'Medical factors and road accidents', *British Medical Journal*, **1**, pp. 75–79.

GREGORY, S. A. (1972) *Creativity and Innovation in Engineering*, Butterworths.

HANDLEY, W. (ed.) (1977) *Industrial Safety Handbook*, McGraw-Hill.

HUBKA, V. (1982) *Principles of Engineering Design*, Butterworths.

JONES, J. C. (1980) *Design Methods*, Wiley.

JONES, S. W. (1973) *Product Design and Process Selection*, Butterworths.

KROUSE, J. K. (1982) *Computer Aided Design and Computer Aided Manufacture*, Marcel Dekker.

MAYALL, W. H. (1967) *Industrial Design for Engineers*, Iliffe.

McCORMICK, E. J. (1970) *Human Factors Engineering*, McGraw-Hill, 3rd edn.

McGOWAN, J. (1967) *Commercial Vehicles – Engineering and Operation*, Institution of Mechanical Engineers.

MORGAN, C. T. (1975) *Introduction to Psychology*, McGraw-Hill, 5th edn.

MURRELL, K. F. H. (1965) *Ergonomics*, Chapman and Hall, London.

PITTS, G. (1973) *Techniques in Engineering Design*, Butterworths.

PRONIKOV, A. S. (1973) *Dependability and Durability of Engineering Products*, Butterworths.

RIDLEY, J. (1986) *Safety at Work*, Butterworths, 2nd edn.

SHERWIN, K. (1982) *Engineering Design and Performance*, Ellis Horwood.

TJALVE, E. (1979) *A Short Course in Industrial Design*, Butterworths.

TJALVE, E., ANDREASEN, M. M. and FRACKMANN SCHMIDT, F. (1979) *Engineering Graphic Modelling*, Butterworths.

TOWN, H. C. (1971) *The Design and Construction of Machine Tools*, Butterworths.

2

Engineering materials

In engineering design, the choice of a material is a culmination of the consideration of the objective of the design exercise, the method of manufacture and economic viability. Material choice is not made in isolation.

Engineering materials can be conveniently grouped into:

Ferrous metals

Non-ferrous metals

Plastics and rubbers.

To arrive at a sensible choice of material for a given application, the way in which a material behaves and the terms used should be studied. The glossary at the end of this chapter indicates those terms likely to confront the designer, particularly in respect of metals, although some of the terms arise in a modified context when referring to plastics.

Each manufacturing company should have its own internal design policy laying down both company standards and national and international standards. If this has been done, then to some extent the basis for a design philosophy in respect of materials has been laid down.

2.1 Factors of safety

Factors of safety are sometimes specified by government departments or their agencies and this is certainly true in respect of aircraft designs where safety has to be balanced against weight penalties as well as the more general aspects of compromise. In general engineering, safety factors are often developed as the result of long experience. The factor of safety is sometimes a factor of ignorance used to cover misuse, transport hazards and erection errors.

Commonly used factors range from 1.25 to 4 depending on the uncertainties involved, and can be applied to the yield stress for ductile materials and to the ultimate tensile strength for brittle materials and to the fatigue strength for parts subjected to fatigue loadings.

It is in this context that the designer must consider whether he uses the ultimate tensile strength of the material or keep his stress to under the yield point, which is defined as the stress magnitude which corresponds to a definite amount of permanent set when the load is removed, usually 0.1 or 0.2 per cent of the original gauge length. This is referred to as the 0.1 or 0.2% proof stress.

2.2 Choice of material

The most difficult exercise for a designer is the intelligent choice of a material having regard to a manufacturing process and his own company's facilities. In the case of metals the manufacturing process will only marginally affect the mechanical properties but with plastics the process can have a profound effect on the properties of the moulded or otherwise processed item.

Jones (1973) puts forward an evaluation plan in which a broad classification of properties might be made in terms of physical, mechanical, technological and chemical considerations, characterised by the performance of a given material in respect of conductivity, tensile strength, forgeability and resistance to corrosion. A wide outlook is provided by an evaluation plan on the lines given in Table 2.1, from which steel would appear to be the optimum choice for this set of parameters.

Alternatively, a graphical evaluation representing the ranking of a customer's requirements can be

Table 2.1 Ranking a client's requirements

Important parameters	Ideal rating	Choose from	
		CI	Steel
Strength	10	9	10
Life	8	7	8
Cost	8	4	5
Appearance	5	4	3
Total		24	26

provided. One such typical graph is shown in Figure 2.1. The performance of alternative materials can be compared by inspection.

Within such broad outlines it is difficult to classify materials in order of their importance in the general field of industrial design, but few would quarrel with the placings of metals first on the list. If material is supplied in bulk form, the various casting and forming processes have pre-eminence — sand, permanent mould and die casting, extrusion and forging spring readily to mind. The conversion of sheet metal into desired shapes may be achieved by stamping or pressing, while structural shapes are most readily produced by rolling. The latter process is also responsible for producing much rod and bar stock, although many cylindrical profiles are also produced by forging because of the improved properties which result.

Whatever type of material is to be designated, the real problem is the intelligent use of test data.

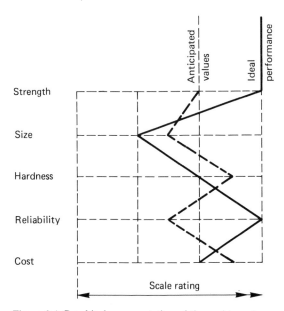

Figure 2.1 Graphical representation of the ranking of a customer's requirements

Evaluation of a working stress from ultimate or proof stress values implies knowledge of the test procedure which is not always available. Quite apart from the test loading cycle, the size, shape and finish of test pieces exercise a profound influence when a simulation of their behaviour is the basis of a prediction of a component performance.

Most currently available materials in Britain are made to conform to relevant British Standards which sometimes have a direct relationship with American and European standards. If goods are being designed for export an examination of these standards is important.* The standards lay down minimum physical properties and chemical compositions. In practice it will be found that the material manufacturers usually exceed the minimum properties in one or more aspects and the designer is advised to work in the final analysis to the manufacturer's figures if he has the freedom to quote proprietary materials and that stocks of such materials are available in the sizes required.

2.3   Ferrous materials

A ferrous material is one in which the major constituent is iron. The vast majority of engineering metals are ferrous, because ferrous metals are comparatively cheap and have high elastic moduli. Steel is basically an alloy of iron with up to 1.7% carbon. It may also contain other elements, some as impurities, but carbon is the master element even if in percentage terms it is a smaller proportion than other elements deliberately added for specific purposes. For example BS 970 (050 A10), 'Free cutting steel', has 0.07–0.15% C; 0.1% Si; 0.8–1.2% Mn; 0.2–0.3% S; and 0.07% P maximum.

The most popular and comprehensive range of steels for general usage is found within BS 970. Aircraft steels have their own designation such as the S range and steels to DTD specifications. These are listed in subsequent tables.

Ruling sections are important, and are well documented in BS 971 for steels and indicate that the basic properties listed in BS 970 are available only when the relationship between section size and heat treatment procedure has been fully established. If physical properties, such as conductivity, are ignored it is the rate of cooling that determines final material properties. Thus the mass effect must be considered, and how size and shape influence material properties obtained after heat treatment processes.

It is not always possible to choose a steel from a known stress system. For example, it is possible for

* THE (Technical Help to Exporters), British Standards Institution, Maylands Avenue, Hemel Hempstead, Herts.

two steels to have the same strength and hardness, yet one of these may have a superior ability to absorb a shock load or an overload because it has ductility (see Glossary). The same analysis can be applied to resilience, toughness and impact resistance. If one considers high temperatures, then creep becomes important.

Some desirable properties may be imparted by heat treatment. For example in the case of a simple tool like a chisel, the working end is hardened and tempered to provide a lasting cutting edge while the shaft is left normal to absorb hammer blows without chipping. It is also possible to case harden a product such that the outer skin is hard while the inner core retains a certain ductility. It can often be more economical to use a case hardening steel even with the extra operation of hardening, than to specify, for example, a high vanadium steel.

If appearance is important then a decision may have to be made between a material which could be regarded as self-finished, such as Stelvetite,* Colorcoat,* galvanised, stainless steel, etc., and one that requires additional and subsequent operations such as chromium plating.

2.3.1 Impurities

In any steel there are minor amounts of impurities, and these may modify the properties of the steel unless their quantities are controlled as laid down in relevant material specifications. These residual elements are described below.

2.3.1.1 Silicon

Silicon is present in ferrite in the solid solution and exerts a stiffening effect. Large quantities may cause embrittlement. It is used to deoxidise steels and lower the temperature at which gases are liberated to below melting point.

2.3.1.2 Phosphorus

Large amounts (above 0.05%) of phosphorus produce an embrittling precipitate and it is an undesirable element in steel.

2.3.1.3 Sulphur

Sulphur exists in steel as a precipitate, and as FeS it takes up a position on the grain boundaries and can have an embrittling effect. As MnS it is not so objectionable, and forms in preference to FeS provided the sulphur content is low enough. Sulphur up to 0.2% is sometimes deliberately added to give free machining steel.

* Products of the British Steel Corporation.

2.3.1.4 Manganese

Manganese exists as MnS or as Mn_3C in association with pearlite. It combines readily with sulphur to reduce embrittlement and produces a fine lamellar pearlite. It produces a higher tensile steel than plain carbon, as well as providing improvements in elastic limit and toughness. Steel with manganese is used for crusher jaws, caterpillar tracks, etc.

2.3.2 Heat treatment

The heat treatment of steel consists of heating and cooling the solid at controlled rates in order to vary its microstructure and hence its mechanical properties. The changes are diffusion controlled, and so time is needed for them to occur.

Before the properties of the steel can be altered by heat treatment, it is necessary to obtain the steel in the austenitic condition by preliminary heating. The treatment may then be designed to homogenise the material and to harden it. Manufacturers supply the necessary data relating to a specific steel and the designer, if he chooses such a steel, need only repeat the instructions for the shop floor.

The alloying elements affect the size of the component that can be fully hardened, and the ruling section indicates whether the core of a material will have the desired properties. Also of considerable importance is the direction of subsequent forming work, many quoted test values relate to the longitudinal direction and a lower rating is applicable to other directions. Thus for certain applications it is not possible to ignore the effect of subsequent working on the theoretical properties suggested by the molecular structure of an ingot. A fruitful method of attack when trying to instigate cost effectiveness exercises for basic materials is to ask the question: 'Why not use mild steel?'

Many young designers, not appreciating the versatility of treatments which can be applied to low-carbon steels, are prone to specify unnecessarily sophisticated materials which, quite apart from their increased cost, impose problems when subsequently worked. Accepting that the performance of mild steel on a stiffness basis is more or less equivalent to that of highly alloyed varieties, it can be considered as the starting-point of stronger materials whose improved properties are the result of:

(1) increasing carbon content (carburising is typical);
(2) cold working (drawing is typical);
(3) careful alloying followed by hardening and tempering.

A cost penalty must of course be incurred for additional working or an improved specification.

It is conventional to regard strength and ductility as alternatives and alloying does not necessarily affect this compromise providing the most effective heat treatment has been used. Tensile value improvements of about 77 MN m^{-2} for steels are indicated by the addition of suffixes N to Z on type designations, although the full range of letters is not applicable to all materials. Such improvements are linked with a decrease in percentage elongation and an increase in penetration hardness. Figure 2.2 is typical of ductility variation for alternative materials.

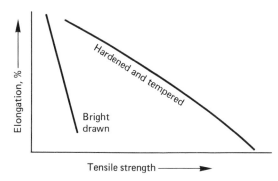

Figure 2.2 Variation in ductility for different materials

A useful table can be drawn up in terms of strength/weight ratios, since in many cases the optimisation is in terms of carrying a particular load at a minimum cost.

2.3.3 Ruling sections

It is assumed that ruling section requirements for cylindrical bars are satisfied and that cost is calculated on the basis of raw material being processed as cheaply as possible to meet the specifications. Cost will fluctuate slightly with quantity and with alternative forming methods. In certain situations alloyed steels may be cheaper as raw material, and this may be the most effective criterion if the machining programme is small.

It is of interest to compare material cost characteristics on a weight and a volumetric basis, preferably on logarithmic axes. The relative order of cost will not be the same, e.g. the material cost of an aluminium alloy may be 30% cheaper than the same dimensional design in mild steel (although 13% dearer in terms of equivalent strengths). In practice of course dimensions would be changed to take advantage of the best features of alternative processes, and factors allowing for different scales of processing charges would be taken into account. The real design technique is of lightweight form rather than the direct application of lightweight materials to a particular shape. Particular attention should be paid to stiffness when designing in light alloys, and similar precautions need to be taken with

high grade alloyed steels whose full strength utilisation theoretically permits very thin sections.

2.3.4 Common steels

When carbon is alloyed with iron, steel is formed. Carbon steels contain, in addition to carbon, small amounts of manganese, phosphorus, sulphur and silicon. Alloy steels have certain other alloying elements added to produce the end properties. In most steel making, the principal reaction is the combination of carbon and oxygen to form a gas. Controlling the amount of gas evolved during solidification determines the type of steel. If practically no gas is evolved the steel is said to be killed because it lies quietly in the ingot moulds. Increasing degrees of gas evolution results in four types of steel, namely semi-killed, capped and rimmed steels. These are defined in the Glossary.

Some carbon steels and high-strength low-alloy steels can be supplied in all four types; alloy steels and stainless and heat resisting steels are normally manufactured only as killed steel.

2.3.4.1 Low-carbon steels

Low-carbon steels have relatively low tensile values and are selected where cold formability is the primary requirement. Within the carbon range of this group, strength and hardness will increase with increase in carbon and with cold working, but such increases in strength are at the expense of ductility. Steels in this category do not freely machine. Free-cutting steels are however available in this category, usually with an addition of selenium and/or sulphur.

2.3.4.2 Medium-carbon steels

Medium-carbon steels are selected for use where their higher strength properties are needed and are frequently further hardened and strengthened by heat treatment or cold working. Small forgings are often made from this type of steel which, in bar form, is used for machined components.

2.3.4.3 High-carbon steels

High-carbon steels are used principally where wear is a consideration, for example in cutting edges, springs, etc. Cold forming methods are not always practical with this group of steels which are usually limited to flat stampings.

2.3.4.4 Surface hardening

Surface hardening the above steels is attainable after quenching and is largely a function of the carbon content of the steel. The depth to which the hardness will penetrate depends not only on the carbon content but also on the total content of the alloys present and the grain size. Through hardening is not always desirable because a ductile core is often essential in applications where shock loads are present.

2.3.5 Alloy steels

Alloy steels are the most expensive of the ferrous range because of the additional elements they contain and the accuracy with which they are added. In addition to the residue elements, the principal effects of the most common additives are given below.

2.3.5.1 Manganese

This element contributes to strength and is of major importance in increasing the depth of hardness penetration after quenching.

2.3.5.2 Silicon

Increasing the silicon content increases the resilience of steel for spring applications. Silicon also raises the critical temperature for heat treatment. Increasing the silicon content promotes the susceptibility of steel to decarburisation.

2.3.5.3 Aluminium

When this element is present in alloy steels in amounts approximating to 1%, it promotes nitriding properties (surface hardening by means of nitrogen-bearing gases at high temperatures).

2.3.5.4 Nickel

When nickel is present in appreciable amounts, it results in higher strength steels with improved shock resistance. It counteracts the brittleness which develops in most pearlite steels at subnormal temperatures. Nickel lowers the critical temperature of steel and widens the temperature range for successful heat treatment. Nickel is used to promote resistance to corrosion. In larger amounts, nickel is present in stainless and heat-resisting steels for resistance to heat and corrosion.

2.3.5.5 Chromium

Chromium is used in constructional steels primarily to increase hardness, improve hardenability, and promote the formation of carbides. Chromium steels are relatively stable at elevated temperatures and have exceptional wear resistance. Chromium enhances corrosion resistance and heat resistance, and it is the essential element in stainless and heat-resisting steels.

2.3.5.6 Molybdenum

Molybdenum has, in common with manganese and chromium, a major effect on increasing hardenability. This element has a strong effect in increasing the high-temperature tensile and creep strengths of alloy steels. Molybdenum additions to high-chromium or chromium-nickel corrosion-resisting steels promote resistance to many forms of corrosive attack. Steels containing molybdenum are considered to be less susceptible to temper brittleness.

2.3.5.7 Vanadium

Vanadium is a strong deoxidising element and it promotes a fine austenitic grain size. Hardenability of medium-carbon steels is increased with a minimum effect upon grain size with vanadium additions of about 0.04 to 0.05%; above this content, the hardenability decreases with normal quenching temperatures. However, the hardenability can be increased with the higher vanadium contents by increasing the austenitizing temperatures.

2.3.5.8 Titanium

In pearlite steels titanium acts as a deoxidiser. When present in amounts of 0.02 to 0.05%, it increases the yield point of plain-carbon steels. Weldability is promoted without the necessity for normalising. In austenitic stainless steels the element is utilised to retard intergranular corrosion.

2.3.5.9 Boron

Boron is added to steel to increase hardenability. It is effective only when added to fully killed steels. Boron intensifies the hardenability characteristics of elements which are already present in the steel and makes possible a large degree of alloy conservation when employed with steels containing small amounts of alloying elements. Boron is very effective when used with low-carbon alloy steels, but the effect diminishes as the carbon increases.

2.3.6 Multiple alloying elements

A combination of two or more of the above alloying elements usually imparts some of the characteristic properties of each. Constructional chromium-nickel alloy steels, for example, develop good hardening properties, with excellent ductility, while chromium-molybdenum combinations develop excellent hardenability with satisfactory ductility and a certain amount of heat resistance.

The combined effect of two or more alloying elements on the hardenability of a steel is considerably greater than the sum of the effects of the same alloying elements used separately. The general effectiveness of the nickel-chromium-molybdenum steels, both with and without boron, is accounted for in this way.

2.3.7 *Steels to BS 970*

In the latest revision of BS 970, six parts are enumerated thus:

Part 1   Carbon and carbon manganese steels (including free cutting steels);

Part 2   Direct hardening alloy steels (including alloy steels capable of surface hardening);

Part 3   Steels for case hardening;

Part 4   Stainless, heat resisting and valve steels;

Part 5   Carbon and alloy spring steels for the manufacture of hot formed springs;

Part 6   SI Metric equivalents for use with BS 970 (Parts 1 to 5 inclusive).

In preparing the revision it was found necessary to abandon the En designation system previously used. A new six figure digit designation system, described fully in PD 6423, has now been introduced. The units are for the most case metric values.

Prior to the introduction of the new numbering system with BS 970 steels were defined by an En classification which has been in existence for many years. It will be a long time before the new system is fully operational, particularly as most senior engineers are very familiar with the En series.

Not all the specifications require the steels to meet specific mechanical test values but are ordered on composition. For those steels which are specified and ordered on composition, reference should be made to the appropriate specification.

Where a range of UTS values is given a letter is appropriate to each particular band as shown in Table 2.2.

2.3.8 *Steels for use at above ambient temperature*

A further important series of steel specifications issued by the British Standards Institution are BS 1501 and 1506. As these steels are commonly used where temperatures other than room temperatures are involved, strengths at various temperatures are given in the specifications.

BS 1501 Part 1: Carbon and carbon manganese steels.

BS 1501 Part 2: Steel for fired and unfired pressure vessels — Plates alloy steels.

BS 1501 Part 3: Steels for fired and unfired pressure vessels — Plates corrosion and heat resisting steels.

BS 1502 Steels for fired and unfired pressure vessels — Sections and bard.

BS 1503 Steels for fired and unfired vessels — Forgings.

BS 1504 Steel castings for pressure purposes.

BS 1510 Steel for use in the chemical, petroleum and allied industries. Low temperature supplementary requirements to BS 1501/1506.

2.3.9 *Special steels*

Over a period of time many new materials appear on the market and the designer should keep up to date with their properties. New materials do not usually fulfil a standard specification, but are developed to meet a particular need. For example, there are various coated steels which enable the designer to select a material which requires no additional finishing after being formed. In another direction, materials have been developed to meet either particular processes (such as superplastic materials for deep drawing) or to meet particular environmental conditions.

Table 2.2 Code letters for steel to BS 970

Condition	tonf in^{-2}	N mm^{-2} (MPa)	Condition	tonf in^{-2}	N mm^{-2} (MPa)
P	35–45	550–700	V	65–75	1000–1150
Q	40–50	620–770	W	70–80	1080–1240
R	45–55	700–850	X	75–85	1150–1300
S	50–60	770–930	Y	80–90	1240–1400
T	55–65	850–1000	Z	100 minimum	1540 minimum
U	60–70	930–1080			

2.3.10 Steels for high temperatures and corrosion resistance

The method of making steel exerts a profound influence on the creep resistance of carbon steel and is affected by the deoxidising process and by the complex interaction between the main constituents, i.e. carbon, manganese, silicon, aluminium and nitrogen. The ferritic alloy steels offer an attractive combination of strength and cost for high temperature work. These are basically steels containing chromium, vanadium, molybdenum, nickel and tungsten. Simple austenitic steels, such as the 18/8 composition (18 chromium, 8 nickel), represent the optimum combination of alloying elements which give good corrosion resistance and ease of fabrication. The complex austenitic steels have many more additives to improve the mechanical and physical properties.

Carbon steels for high-temperature purposes can be considered to be those containing 0.05–0.25% carbon, 0.5–1.5% manganese and small amounts of silicon, sulphur, phosphorus, aluminium and nitrogen. In practice, high-temperature carbon steels use a carbon range of 0.05–0.20%, the lower limit being set by the need for minimum tensile properties and the upper limit by fabrication and welding considerations. Five elements are known to affect the high-temperature mechanical properties of carbon steel. Carbon, manganese and nitrogen exert a direct influence while aluminium and silicon act indirectly through their affinity for nitrogen. Normalising at around 650°C is generally recommended for plain carbon steels. A high normalising temperature may coarsen the grain and dissolve precipitated carbides. Variation in the normalising temperature can also have an effect on creep behaviour. Working the steel or stress relieving after normalising also has an affect on the properties.

Ferritic alloy steels offer an attractive combination of strength and cost, their most important characteristic in high temperature applications being their creep strength. The metallurgical interaction of the constituents is complex and it is often more practical to consider steels under such arbitrary headings such as carbon/molybdenum; chromium/molybdenum; chromium/molybdenum/vanadium; martensitic 12% chromium steels. Additions of titanium and niobium are used as stabilisers and in some cases to prevent subsequent weld decay. Of the simple austenitic steels the 18 chromium, 8 nickel represents the optimum combination of alloying elements which gives good corrosion resistance and ease of fabrication in a fully austenitic structure. Other steels in the same category can have between 18 and 25% chromium and 8 to 25% nickel with possible additions of niobium, titanium, molybdenum and tungsten in addition to small amounts of carbon, manganese and silicon. The more complex austenitic alloys have a predominance of molybdenum, niobium, titanium and vanadium and it has been found that the addition of boron can have important effects on high-temperature strength and ductility. The austenitic steels can be roughly divided into three classes (a) those based on the classic 18 chromium, 8 nickel, (b) increased chromium to improve oxidation resistance, and (c) addition of other elements to obtain further improvements in high temperature mechanical properties generally by heat treatment and/or warm working. Warm working is generally accepted as a form of prestressing at around service temperatures which, for example in a turbine disc, provides high stress resistance at the hub, where creep is not important, and good creep resistance at the rim.

2.3.11 Inco Alloys International Ltd

Most designers will find the current range of nickel alloys sufficient to meet their high temperature requirements and those in more general use are listed in Table 2.3. There are, in addition, several grades developed for specific conditions such as that

Table 2.3 Nickel steel alloys

Alloy	Description	Sand casting	Shell casting	Bar	Forging	Drop forging	Plate and sheet	Pipe or tube
Langalloy	S3S heat resisting steels and nickel alloy	●	●					
Ferralium	Super stainless steel	●	●	●	●		●	●
Hastelloy	Corrosion resistant high nickel alloys	●	●	●	●		●	●
Monel	Corrosion resistant nickel/copper alloys	●	●	Wrought forms available from Inco Alloys International Ltd				
Nickel		●	●					

Table 2.4 Inconel and Nimonic alloys for heat resistance (courtesy Inco Alloys International Ltd)

Alloy number	Type, annealed condition	0.2% proof stress (MPa or lb in^{-2} × 1000)		Tensile strength (MPa or lb in^{-2} × 1000)		Elongation (%)	
		700°C	1000°C	700°C	1000°C	700°C	1000°C
Inconel 600	Good oxidation resistance at high temperatures. Used for furnace and heat treating equipment	175 (25.36)	40 (5.80)	365 (52.90)	74 (10.72)	51	61
Inconel 601	High temperature alloy resistant to oxidising and carburising environments	280 (40.58)	45 (6.52)	360 (52.17)	50 (7.25)	53	–
Inconel 617	An alloy with an exceptional combination of high temperature strength and oxidation resistance	170 (24.64)	120 (17.40)	525 (76.09)	150 (21.74)	80	120
Inconel 706	Precipitation hardenable variant of 718 with significantly impaired machining characteristics	780 (113.05)	–	860 (124.64)	–	24	–
Inconel 718	High strength alloy with slow response to precipitation hardening that enables welding and annealing with no spontaneous hardening	920 (133.33)	–	1150 (166.67)	–	20	–
Inconel X-750	Precipitation hardening non-magnetic alloy used for its corrosion resistance and strength up to 815°C	830 (120.29)	–	965 (139.86)	–	5	–
Inconel MA754	Mechanically alloyed dispersion hardened alloy for gas turbine blades (Bar)	–	–	440 (63.77)	190 (27.54)	45	25
Incoloy 800	Ni, Fe, Cr alloy that resists oxidation, carburisation and other harmful effects of high temperature exposure	180 (26.08)	–	300 (43.48)	–	70	–
Incoloy 800H	A variant of 800 giving impaired high temperature creep ruptive properties						
Incoclad 671/800H	A composite tubing offering the high temperature strength of 800H with resistance to high temperature corrosion						
Incoloy DS	General purpose heat resisting alloy	210 (30.44)	35 (5.07)	335 (48.55)	65 (9.42)	49	75
Incoloy MA956	Mechanically alloyed dispersion strengthened alloy available as sheet (Sheet)	–	–	330 (47.83)	110 (15.94)	15	8
Nimonic 75	High temperature alloy with good mechanical properties and outstanding resistance to oxidation at high temperatures	200 (28.99)	50 (7.25)	420 (50.87)	80 (11.59)	57	58
Nimonic 80A	Precipitation hardening creep resisting alloy for service at temperatures up to about 815°C	650 (94.20)	40 (5.79)	850 (123.19)	75 (10.87)	24	82
Nimonic 81	Similar to 80A, but with high resistance to corrosion by NaCl, Na$_2$SO$_4$ and V$_2$O$_5$	500 (72.47)	–	790 (114.50)	–	25	–
Nimonic 86	Sheet alloy with good ductility, high creep strength and exceptional resistance to cyclic oxidation at 1050°C (Sheet)	260 (37.68)	45 (6.52)	500 (72.46)	100 (14.49)	74	50

Alloy number	Type, annealed condition	0.2% proof stress (MPa *or* lb in^{-2} × 1000)		Tensile strength (MPa *or* lb in^{-2} × 1000)		Elongation (%)	
		700°C	*1000°C*	*700°C*	*1000°C*	*700°C*	*1000°C*
Nimonic 90	Precipitation hardening creep resisting alloy for service at temperatures up to about 920°C	680 (98.55)	40 (5.79)	970 (140.58)	80 (11.59)	12	77
Nimonic 91	Modified alloy 90 with increased chromium to improve corrosion resistance to salt and sulphur contaminates	580 (84.06)	60 (8.69)	945 (136.96)	95 (13.77)	28	138
Nimonic 101	Modified alloy 105 with increased chromium to improve corrosion resistance to salt and sulphur contaminates	600 (86.96)	150 (21.74)	990 (143.48)	160 (23.18)	30	67
Nimonic 105	Precipitation hardening creep resisting alloy for temperatures up to about 940°C	775 (112.32)	125 (18.12)	1050 (152.17)	200 (28.98)	–	–
Nimonic 115	Precipitation hardening creep resisting alloy for service at temperatures up to about 980°C	770 (111.59)	225 (32.61)	1060 (153.62)	370 (53.62)	16	19
Nimonic 263	Precipitation hardening creep resisting alloy for temperatures up to about 850°C	460 (66.67)	75 (10.87)	750 (108.69)	100 (14.49)	23	68
Nimonic 901	Precipitation hardening alloy with maximum service temperature of about 600°C	810 (117.39)	75 (10.87)	910 (131.89)	90 (13.04)	12	–
Nimonic DE13	High temperature matrix hardened sheet alloy similar to alloy 75, but with higher mechanical properties	300 (43.48)	80 (11.59)	550 (79.71)	150 (21.74)	44	52
Nimonic PE16	Precipitation hardening creep resisting alloy for service at temperatures up to 750°C	400 (57.97)	60 (8.69)	500 (72.46)	75 (10.87)	27	–
Nimonic PK33	Vacuum processed alloy providing sheet material with high ductility in welded assemblies and high creep strength (Sheet)	710 (102.90)	80 (11.59)	1000 (144.93)	110 (15.94)	18	56
Nimocast 80	Casting alloy for service at temperatures up to about 815°C						
APK1	Powder alloy consolidated by hot isostatic pressing. Supplied either as HIP or forged	930 (134.78) 960 (139.13)	160 (23.18) 200 (28.98)	1260 (182.61) 1240 (179.71)	300 (43.48) 400 (57.97)	18 28	8* –†

* Hot isostatic pressed
† Forged properties depend on method of forging

Engineering materials

Table 2.5 Langalloy cast stainless steels

Number/name	Composition	Specifications		1.0% proof stress	Tensile (N mm^{-2})	% 5.65 So	Brinell
15V	18Cr, 8Ni	BS 3100 302C25 BS 3100 304C15 BS 1504 304C15	ASTM A296 CF-8 AISI Type 304 DIN No 1.4312	240	480	26	140–160
1V	18Cr, 8.5Ni, Nb. Stabilised niobium also prevents weld decay	BS 3100 347C17 BS 1504 347C17	ASTM A296 CF-8C AISI Type 347 DIN No 1.4553	240	480	22	160–180
3V	18Cr, 10Ni, 3Mo	BS 3100 316C16 BS 1504 316C16	ASTM A296 CF-8M AISI Type 316 DIN No 1.4410	240	480	26	150–170
33V	18Cr, 10Ni, 3Mo	BS 3100 316C12 BS 1504 316C12	ASTM A296 CF-3M AISI Type 316L DIN No 1.4404	215	430	26	150–170
7V	18Cr, 8Ni, 3Mo	BS 1504 844	AISI Type 316 DIN No 1.4410	240	480	26	150–170
8V	18Cr, 8Ni, 3Mo. Free machining	BS 1504 844	AISI Type 316	240	480	12	150–170
16V	18Cr, 8Ni, 3Mo	BS 3100 316C71 BS 1504 316C71		260	510	26	140–160
18V	18Cr, 8Ni, 3Mo. Free machining	BS 3100 316C71F		260	510	12	140–160
13V	18Cr, 12Ni, 3.5Mo	BS 3100 317C16 BS 1504 317C16	ASTM A296 CG-8M AISI Type 317 DIN No 1.4436	240	480	22	150–170
12V	18Cr, 12Ni, 3.5Mo	BS 3100 317C16F		240	480	12	150–170
22V	18Cr, 10Ni, 3Mo, 1Nb	BS 3100 318C17 BS 1504 318C17	DIN No 1.4581	240	480	18	150–180
14V	18Cr, 10Ni, 3Mo, 1Nb	BS 3100 318C17F		240	460	12	150–180
5V	18Cr, 15Ni, 3Mo. For non-magnetic applications	BS 3100 316C16F		240	480	20	140–160
20V	20Cr, 29Ni, 3.2Mo, 3.2Cu. Outstanding resistance to sulphuric, phosphoric, nitric, chromic acid, etc.		ASTM A296 CN-7M	200	430	20	130–150
25V	25Cr, 12Ni. Heat resisting	BS 3100 309C30	ASTM A297, Grade HH DIN No 1.4837				
4V	23Cr, 11.5Ni, 3W. Heat resisting		AISI Type 309				
8R	15Cr, 60Ni. Heat resisting	BS 3100 334C11	ASTM A297, Grade HW				
9R	18Cr, 37Ni. Heat resisting	BS 3100 331C60	DIN No 1.4865 ASTM A297, Grade HT				

Hastelloy
  Alloy B
  Alloy C
				343
				324
					490
					490
						6
						4
							200–280
							200–280

Nirolium Alloy 130	Cast molybdenum/nickel alloy weldable		ASTM A743, A744 N12M	262 yield stress	525	25 (% on 2 in)	

Table 2.6 Selection of corrosion-resisting alloys; ranges of properties are for common section sizes (courtesy Inco Alloys International Ltd)

Annealed material at 20°C		*0.2% yield* (MPa *or* lb in^{-2} × 1000)	*Tensile strength* (MPa *or* lb in^{-2} × 1000)	*Elongation* (%)	*Hardness* (*Brinell*)
Nickel 200	Commercially pure wrought nickel	103–207 (15–30)	379–552 (55–80)	55–40	90–120
Nickel 201	Similar to Nickel 200 but with carbon content controlled to a maximum 0.02%. Suitable for temperatures above 315°C.				
Monel 400	Strong weldable NiCu alloy resistant to corrosion by sea water and various acids	172–276 (25–40)	483–586 (70–85)	60–35	110–149
Monel K500	Age-hardenable alloy combining corrosion resistance of Monel 400 with increased strength and hardness	586–827 (85–120)	896–1138 (130–165)	35–20	250–315
Inconel 600	Excellent high-temperature properties and resistant to corrosion	207–345 (30–50)	552–690 (80–100)	55–35	120–170
Inconel 625	Low-carbon high-Mo alloy with high strength from cryogenic temperatures to 980°C and with exceptional fatigue strength	517 (75)	930 (135)	45	180
Inconel 825	Developed for aggressive corrosive environments	241–448 (35–65)	586–724 (85–105)	50–30	120–180

used for the electrode for a sparking plug. In addition to those tabulated other alloys have been developed for specific applications, for example, transformer laminations, constant modulus alloys, for springs operating at elevated temperatures and low expansion alloys.

With special applications in mind it cannot be too strongly emphasised that early consultation with the material suppliers may save many wasted hours.

With complex alloys properties tend to vary with manipulation and, as an example, the curves in Figures 2.3 to 2.6 are indicative of the behaviour of Inconel 625.

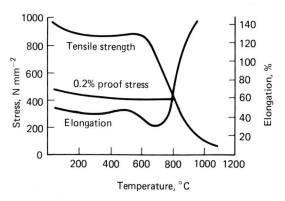

Figure 2.3 Tensile properties of annealed bar (heat treatment 930–1040°C)

2.3.12 *Stainless steel*

The generic term 'stainless steel' covers many standard compositions as well as variations bearing company trade names and special alloys made for particular applications. Stainless steels vary in their composition from a fairly simple alloy of iron with around 11% chromium, to complex alloys that include up to 25% chromium, with substantial quanti-

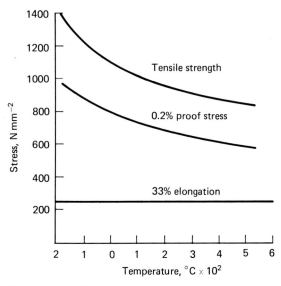

Figure 2.4 Tensile properties of cold rolled sheet (20% reduction, as rolled)

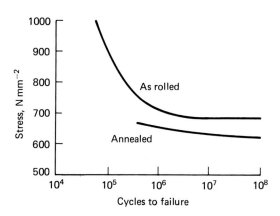

Figure 2.5 Fatigue strength of hot-rolled bar at room temperature

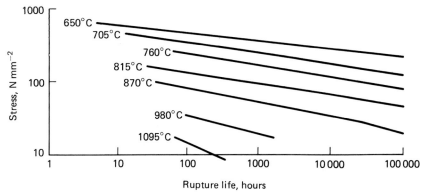

Figure 2.6 Rupture life of solution treated material

ties of nickel, molybdenum and several other effective elements. At the high-chromium, high nickel end of the range, the steels merge into other groups of heat-resisting alloys. The term 'stainless steel' implies a resistance to staining, rusting, and pitting and the materials have room-temperature yield strengths that range from 200 N mm^{-2} to more than 1700 N mm^{-2}. All have good oxidation resistance up to operating temperatures of 700°C and, in some applications temperatures as high as 1200°C can be tolerated. At the other extreme of temperature the austenitic stainless steels maintain their toughness down to temperatures approaching absolute zero.

Stainless steels can be shaped and fabricated in conventional ways; shapes can be produced by powder metallurgy techniques; cast ingots can be rolled or forged and the rolled products can be drawn, pressed, bent, extruded, or spun. Stainless steel can be further shaped by machining, and can be joined by soldering, brazing and welding. It can also be used as an integral cladding on plain carbon or low-alloy steels.

Stainless steels are regulated by various international specifications, for example British Standards, DTD specifications for aircraft and military purposes, AISI (American Iron & Steel Institute), ASME, DIN, IDO etc.

Outside these specifications, individual steel makers supply grades which are suited to special applications and which do not confirm to any national or international specifications.

All the stainless steels, however, irrespective of specifications, can be conveniently classified into five major classes that represent three distinct types of alloy structure. These classes are ferritic, martensitic, austenitic, duplex and precipitation-hardening.

2.3.12.1 Austenitic stainless steels

These are the most commonly used stainless steels. The high-temperature form of iron is known as austenite. The structure is non-magnetic and can be retained at room temperature by appropriate alloying. The most common austenite retainer is nickel. Hence, the traditional and familiar austenitic stainless steels have a composition that contains sufficient chromium to offer corrosion resistance, together with nickel to ensure austenite at room temperature and below. The basic austenitic composition is the familiar 18:8 alloy (18% chromium, 8% nickel alloy). Both chromium and nickel contents can be increased to improve corrosion resistance, and additional elements (most commonly molybdenum) can be added to further enhance corrosion resistance.

The austenitic structure can be encouraged by elements other than nickel, e.g. manganese and nitrogen. The most important difference lies in the higher strength of these alloys.

If a metal or alloy is plastically deformed by bending, squeezing, hammering, or any means that takes it beyond its yield point, it becomes harder and stronger. This effect is particularly pronounced in the austenitic stainless steels. Its ductility, however, is simultaneously reduced.

Austenitic stainless steels of the 200 and 300 series, when heated in the range 430 to 870°C and slowly cooled, can become susceptible to intergranular corrosion often termed welding decay, although this is rarely experienced with today's modern steelmaking practices which allow very low carbon levels to be reached as standard. The commonly held theory of chromium impoverishment arises from the slow cooling from the sensitising temperature range permitting the precipitation of a chromium-rich carbide at the grain boundaries. The adjacent areas, decreased in chromium, became anodic sites in an electrochemical corrosion cell in acidic environments. Intergranular corrosion of ferritic stainless steels is also known.

2.3.12.2 Ferritic stainless steels

This class is so named because the crystal structure of the steel is the same as that of iron at room temperature. The alloys in the class are magnetic at room temperature and up to their Curie temperature of about 760°C. Common alloys in the ferritic class contain between 11 and 27% chromium, no nickel, and carbon levels below 0.2% in the wrought condition. The low-chromium alloys are among the cheapest stainless steels, and therefore, where strength requirements can be met and the corrosion problem demands are not exacting, they have an economic appeal. BSC's Hyform 409, used extensively for car exhaust systems, is a typical example of a stainless steel with compatibility with other ferrous materials and, relative to other stainless steels, is of low cost.

The mechanical properties of ferritic stainless steels compared with those of low-carbon steels give the clue to the differences in cold forming methods for these materials. The higher yield strength of stainless implies that more power must be supplied to the forming equipment for a given amount of deformation; the higher ultimate tensile strength indicates that a higher load can be applied before rupture; the lower ductility measured in simple tension suggests less plastic deformation prior to fracture.

The rapid drop in ductility with cold working usually necessitates the use of fully annealed sheet and suggests intermediate annealing.

2.3.12.3 Martensitic stainless steels

Just as iron-carbon alloys are heat treatable, so alloys of iron, chromium, carbon and other elements

Table 2.7 Austenitic stainless steels (courtesy BSC Stainless Steels)

BS 1449	AISI	Forms	Main characteristics	Major constituents (%)		Tensile strength (N mm^{-2})	Service temperature (°C)
301 S12	301	Plate. Precision strip	High cold work hardening rate, moderate formability	C CR Ni	0.15 max. 16–18 6–8	540 (softened) to 1240 (full hand)	800
302 S17	302	Precision strip	Weldable with good formability and general corrosion resistance	C Cr Ni	0.08 max. 17–19 8–11	510 (softened)	800
304 S15	304	Plate	Good weldability, formability and general corrosion resistance	C Cr Ni	0.06 max. 17.5–19 9–11	510 (softened)	800
304 S16	304	Precision strip	Excellent drawability, good weldability and general corrosion resistance	C Cr Ni	0.06 max. 17.5–19 9–11	510 (softened)	800
304 S12	304L	Plate. Precision strip	Weldable and resistant to sensitisation. Good corrosion and oxidation resistance.	C Cr Ni	0.03 max. 17.5–19 9–12	490 (softened)	800
305 S19	305	Precision strip	Good formability and general corrosion resistance	C Cr Ni	0.1 max 17–19 11–13	460 (softened)	800
309 S24	309	Plate	Excellent oxidation resistance, weldable	C Cr Ni	0.15 max. 22–25 13–16	540 (softened)	1050
310 S24	310	Plate	Excellent oxidation resistance, low magnetic permeability, weldable	C Cr Ni	0.15 max. 23–26 19–22	540 (softened)	1100
315 S16	–	Precision strip	Highly corrosion resistant. Weldable	C Cr Ni Mo	0.07 max. 16.5–18.5 10–13 1.25–1.75	540 (softened)	800
316 S16	316	Plate. Precision strip	Highly corrosion resistant. Weldable	C Cr Ni Mo	0.07 max. 16.5–18.5 9–11 1.25–1.75	540 (softened)	800
316 S12	316L	Plate. Precision strip	Highly corrosion resistant, weldable and resistant to sensitisation	C Cr Ni Mo	0.03 max. 16.5–18.5 11–14 2.25–3.0	480 (softened)	800
317 S16	317	Plate	Extremely highly corrosion resistant. Weldable	C Cr Ni Mo	0.06 max. 17.5–19.5 12–15 3–4	540 (standard)	800
317 S12	317L	Plate	Extremely highly corrosion resistant. Weldable. Resistant to sensitisation	C Cr Ni Mo	0.03 max. 17.5–19.5 14–17 3–4	490 (standard)	800
320 S17	–	Plate. Precision strip	Highly corrosion resistant. Weldable. Resistant to sensitisation	C Cr Ni Ti Mo	0.08 max. 16.5–18.5 11–14 4 × C-0.6 2.25–3.0	540 (softened)	800
321 S12	321	Plate. Precision strip	Weldable and resistant to sensitisation. Good corrosion and oxidation resistance	C Cr Ni Ti	0.08 max. 17–19 9–12 5 × C-0.70	510 (softened)	800
347 S17	347	Plate. Precision strip	Weldable and resistant to sensitisation. Highly resistant to hot concentrated nitric acid	C Cr Ni	0.08 max. 17–19 9–12	510 (softened)	800

Table 2.8 Ferritic stainless steels (courtesy BSC Stainless Steels)

BS 1449	AISI	Forms	Main characteristics	Major constituents (%)		Tensile strength (N mm^{-2})	Service temperature (°C)
403 S17	403	Plate. Precision strip	Weldable. Heat resistance and moderate corrosion resistance	C Cr Ni	0.08 max. 12–14 0.5 max.	420 (softened)	750
405 S17	405	Plate. Precision strip	Weldable. Heat resistance and moderate corrosion resistance	C Cr Ni Al	0.08 max. 12–14 0.5 max. −0.3	420 (softened)	750
409 S17	409	Precision strip	Weldable. Heat resistance and moderate corrosion resistance	C Cr Ni Ti	0.09 max. 10.5–12.5 0.7 max. 5 × C min. 0.7 max.	420 (softened)	750
430 S15	430	Plate. Precision strip	Fairly good general corrosion resistance. Formable	C Cr Ni	0.1 max. 16–18 0.5 max.	430 (softened)	800
434 S19	434	Precision strip	Good resistance to atmospheric corrosion. Formable	C Cr Ni Mo	0.1 max. 16–18 0.5 max. 0.9–1.3	430 (softened)	800

can be quenched for maximum hardness and subsequently tempered to improve ductility.

Martensitic stainless steels, which contain 11% or more of chromium, have great hardenability; substantial thicknesses will harden during air cooling and oil quenching. The hardness of the as-quenched martensitic stainless steel depends upon its carbon content but in developing its mechanical properties through quenching and tempering, there is a slight reduction in its corrosion resistance.

The martensitic alloys are hard and have low ductility, particularly if the carbon content is much above 0.2%. To improve the ductility (and simultaneously reduce the strength) the steel is tempered: it is heated so that the martensite begins to decom-

pose, when some of the carbon atoms have the opportunity of forming carbides, hence relieving the structural distortion.

2.3.12.4 Precipitation-hardening stainless steels

Just as the familiar aluminium age-hardening alloys can be heat treated to improve their strength through a process that is associated with the formation of a precipitate, so stainless steels can be designed so that their composition is amenable to precipitation hardening. However there is very little application for this type.

Table 2.9 Martensitic stainless steels (courtesy BSC Stainless Steels)

BS 1449	AISI	Forms	Main characteristics	Major constituents (%)		Tensile strength (N mm^{-2})	Service temperature (°C)
410 S21	410	Precision strip	Hardenable. Heat resistant and moderate corrosion resistance	C Cr Ni	0.09–0.15 11.5–12.3 1.0 max.	H and T 550/700	750
420 S45	420	Precision strip	Hardenable. Heat resistant and moderate corrosion resistance	C Cr Ni	0.28–0.36 12.0–14.0 1.0 max.	H 540	–

2.3.12.5 Duplex stainless steel

This type has tended to take over from the precipitation hardening steels. For example, BSC's highly alloyed ferritic/austenitic to Werkstoff 1.4462 is a mixture of different phases giving high strength and resistance to corrosion through the development of a fine grain structure. It is thus well suited to the oil industry particularly for down-hole applications where highly corrosive mixtures of liquids and gases are encountered.

2.3.12.6 Properties

Properties are substantially influenced by chemical composition. Hence specifications include chemical composition, together with trace elements.

Mechanical properties — strength, ductility, hardness, creep resistance, fatigue — of various wrought and cast stainless steels are discussed later and the accompanying tables indicate typical properties for several of the most popular stainless steel specifications.

2.3.12.7 Strengthening mechanisms

There are many effects of alloy additions: chromium, already mentioned, imparts properties of corrosion resistance and also brings about changes in the physical, mechanical and chemical properties. Among other things, the strength of iron is increased by alloy additions.

There are however three pertinent methods of strengthening stainless steel: (a) work hardening of austenitic steel, (b) hardening by martensitic formation and (c) precipitation hardening.

2.3.12.8 Annealing

The purpose of annealing is to put a material in its soft condition to enable subsequent forming operations to be achieved. It should not be confused with tempering, which is an integral second part of the double treatment of quenching and tempering and is used to obtain a desirable combination of strength and ductility in hardenable steels.

Obviously, annealing means different processes to different materials. For example, martensitic stainless steels can be annealed by heating them above their critical temperature (into the austenite range) and cooling them so slowly that ferrite rather than martensite forms. Or they can be annealed by heating them to a subcritical temperature, at which the martensite formed during a prior cooling will decompose. The purpose of annealing is not to obtain a satisfactory combination of strength and ductility such as in quenching and tempering, but simply to soften to permit joining processes to be made. The high-temperature anneal induces the more complete softening and is known as a full anneal.

2.3.12.9 Stress relieving

While the heat treatment known as stress-relieving may in fact involve annealing, the intention of the process is not to soften the steel (although that may, of course, occur) but to reduce residual stresses built into the structure during shaping and welding.

2.3.12.10 Corrosion

All grades of stainless steel are resistant to staining, rusting, pitting, scaling or other surface deterioration even in environments approaching 100% relative humidity or completely immersed. They are also resistant to heavily polluted industrial atmospheres which do not contain chlorides. The passivating film is not however impervious to chloride ions, and thus in sea water and atmospheres containing chloride ions the lower-alloy stainless steels may exhibit some staining and random pitting. In terms of resistance, AISI type 316 (18:8 austenitic) is best of the common stainless steels.

In high-temperature oxidising atmospheres, the resistance of stainless steel to scaling depends on the chromium content. In this respect the austenitic range of 22–26% chromium and 8–20% nickel show the best resistance. Silicon and aluminium are often added to improve oxidation resistance.

Stainless steels are susceptible to nitriding and for this reason have limitations in ammonia processing equipment.

2.3.12.11 Stress corrosion cracking

Since stress-corrosion cracking was first recognised, interest and intensity of investigation have continued due to the potentially catastrophic nature of the failure.

Stress-corrosion cracking is the brittle fracture of an alloy, exposed to a specific corroding medium, at low tensile stress levels with respect to the design strength of the alloy. Although a tensile stress must be present, it may be residual or applied, or a combination of these. The time to failure in each environment is unpredictable: it depends upon the total stress, the temperature and the effective concentration of the aggressive ionic species. Only pure metals are immune to stress-corrosion cracking, and for all other metals and alloys there exists a set of conditions for which failure may occur by stress-corrosion cracking. The fracture is generally at right angles to the direction of stress. It is characteristic of this failure mechanism that a specific aggressive anion can be identified with a particular class of alloys.

2.3.12.12 Mechanical properties

Stainless steel materials conform in the main to standard specifications. For example, plate is usually supplied to BS 1449 Part 2 and BS 1501 Part 3. In many cases these are directly related to the AISI, Werkstoff and other international standards. In addition, individual manufacturers produce special grades to meet particular requirements. BSC for example produce Red Fox 34, Hi-proof variants of standard austenitic steels. Esshete 800 and 18% Ni maraging steels.

As well as sheet and plate, stainless steel can be obtained in bar form, as castings and forgings. Bars of varying cross sections are usually drawn by users from stockholders, for example Barpoint in the West Midlands and Alloy and Metal Stockholders with depots covering the British Isles. Bar specifications encompass those designated below:

302 S25	320 S17	420 S29
303 S21	321 S12	S37
S41	S20	S45
304 S12	325 S21	430 S15
S15	326 S36	431 S29
310 S24	347 S17	441 S29
315 S16	403 S17	S49
316 S12	410 S21	
S16	416 S21	
317 S12	S29	
S16	S37	
	S41	

2.3.12.13 Soldering stainless steel

Soldering is a method of joining metals using a filler with a lower melting point than those of the metals being joined. What normally happens is that the filler metal (solder) penetrates a capillary gap between the components and bonding takes place by partial solution or the formation of intermetallic compounds. The strength of any given joint is usually governed by that of the solder. But where, for any particular reason, a specific type of solder must be used, the optimum strength will be influenced by the design of the joint and soldering technique used.

A successfully soldered joint relies initially upon the ability of the solder to 'wet' the surface of the stainless steel and to this end the area must be completely free from any dirt, grease or resistant metal oxides. Solvents will get rid of the grease and dirt whilst suitable selected fluxes will remove the oxides, both before and during the soldering operation. The method and manner of heating are also very important aspects of the soldering operation, especially with the austenitic grades of stainless steel which have a low thermal conductivity and high coefficients of expansion.

In the context of soldering, 'soft' refers to very low melting point solders, usually those based on tin lead compositions with melting points as low as 183°C. Hard soldering, or silver soldering as it is often called, covers compositions which are rich in silver and have melting points from about 630°C to 720°C; in both strength and corrosion resistance these alloys are markedly superior to soft solders. They also present better properties at elevated temperatures.

All grades of stainless steel can be joined to each other and to many other metals and alloys by soldering with but few notable exceptions which include aluminium and magnesium.

Because soldering relies largely upon capillary action for its effectiveness, it follows that careful attention must be paid to the joint design. Since most soldering alloys have lower mechanical properties than those of stainless steels, it is logical to employ lap type rather than butt joints, in order to achieve optimum strengths. For the same reason, the joint area should be as large as possible and the joint clearance designed to provide the best capillary action for the solder.

For many years, the most common and readily available fluxes for the soft soldering of stainless steels have been those based on acidified zinc and ammonium chlorides. They are obtainable in liquid or paste form under many proprietary brand names.

2.3.12.14 Brazing

Brazing alloys are usually composed of copper, silver, and zinc, and their action is to flow onto and partially into the metals that are being joined, forming a permanent bond between the pieces.

All stainless steels can be brazed. Joints must be clean, but no fluxes are required. The disadvantages of brazing arise mainly through two inevitable occurrences:

(1) The brazing metal must, if the joint is to be effective, diffuse into the stainless steel. Hence there may be a loss of corrosion resistance in the area of the joint, which may be exaggerated through the galvanic effect of the two dissimilar materials. High-temperature brazing alloys may penetrate grain boundaries and cause severe weakening, and brazing stressed parts may lead to subsequent stress-corrosion cracking.

(2) The flow temperature of copper-base brazing alloys is above 1000°C. At such temperatures the austenitic grades (unless they are stabilised) are sensitive, and the martensitic grades will, if they are not slowly cooled, harden in a region immediately adjacent to the joint. The regions further from the joint will have effectively become tempered, with a consequent loss of strength.

2.3.12.15 Welding

In resistance welding, metal is heated by the passage of electric current (directly applied or induced) to a temperature below its melting point and the joint is made by the application of pressure. In seam welding the workpieces are continuously fed beneath a rotating electrode, which supplies the power, or beneath an electrical induction coil, which induces a current in the steel. In spot welding two electrodes supply both the heating current and the pressure. Resistance welding is generally used on production items: it is not economically employed where a variety of short-run items are involved.

The good forgeability of most of the stainless grades, coupled with their high electrical resistance and low thermal conductibility, favours resistance welding methods.

In fusion welding, parent metal is actually melted and filler metal is usually (though not always) added. In fusion arc welding, heat is supplied by the arc struck between an electrode and the job. This method of welding is most commonly used in fabricating shops and in the field where the variety of work is wide.

The structure that results from a fusion weld contains a small casting (the weld bead) and a heat-affected zone adjacent to it. Thus the properties of the weldment are determined by these two regions.

Austenitic grades are by far the most easily weldable of the three principal grades. They are often referred to as the 300 series, on the basis of the specification numbers allocated to them in the BS and AISI classification systems. Although alloyed principally with chromium and nickel they may also contain appreciable amounts of molybdenum, and small amounts of niobium and titanium.

These alloys will retain an austenitic face centred cubic crystal structure from their solidification temperatures right through to sub-zero conditions, and do not suffer from excessive grain coarsening at elevated temperatures.

These two factors are largely responsible for their excellent weldability, since there is no danger of them hardening due to the weld thermal cycle, the joints remaining ductile and tough in the as-welded condition. Exceptions are the free-machining types 303 and 303Se which contain added sulphur and selenium respectively. Because of this, they are prone to hot-cracking of the weld metal, unless precautionary measures are taken against this happening.

If austenitic stainless steels are held for prolonged periods in the 450/870°C temperature range, chromium-rich carbides will begin to precipitate at the grain boundaries. This reduces the effective chromium content of the boundaries and the corrosion resistance is thereby impaired. The length of time the steel can remain at elevated temperatures

before the formation of carbides varies according to the temperature.

Precipitation occurs more rapidly, the higher the carbon content of the steel.

Arc welding results in an appreciable temperature rise in the area of the joint. The peak temperature attained and the length of time spent in the elevated range are determined by the heat input and the thickness of the materials being joined. Since most modern welding techniques are designed to produce low heat inputs, they are unlikely to cause unacceptable carbide precipitation in present day steels, except in extreme cases such as the multi-pass welding of thick sections.

When thick sections are being welded, or if the corrosion conditions or working temperature are critical, either an extra low carbon content grade or a stabilised grade may be the best choice. In the stabilised grades, which contain titanium or niobium, the carbides of these elements form in preference to chromium carbide, thus helping to retain the corrosion resistance of the material.

When designing welded structures in austenitic stainless steels, the allowable reduction in corrosion resistance of the joint compared with the parent material should be clearly specified. Once this has been established, the material composition and the electrode type can be chosen. From a metallurgical viewpoint, it may be necessary to specify the low carbon or stabilised grades for many applications, since improvements in steelmaking practices ensure that the typical carbon content of standard grades usually fall well below the permissible specification maximum. In practice, however, the extra low carbon or stabilised grades are more often than not specified for welding applications.

Designing joints in austenitic stainless steels is generally straightforward except for a number of points which should be borne in mind. For example, if small tight crevices are present in welds which will be in contact with liquids, a form of selective attack, known as crevice corrosion, can occur. Sensible design, using fully penetrated welds, wherever possible, and taking precautions to avoid weld metal solidification cracking, will help to prevent this occurrence.

Perhaps one of the biggest problems in welding these steels is the control of distortion. Austenitic steels have a coefficient of thermal expansion some 50% greater than that of carbon steel and a thermal conductivity of only one third. Therefore, temperature gradients can build up more rapidly, causing unequal expansion and distortion. This can be minimised by a properly planned approach to the welding of each joint. Low heat input, balanced welding, symmetrical joints, good fit and well designed jigs will all help.

Although *ferritic grades* do not possess the excellent all-round weldability of the austenitic grades, they nevertheless come in for extensive welding, especially in thicknesses up to 2mm, for which the TIF and Resistance processes are widely used.

The standard '400' series of ferritic stainless steels contain 11% to 27% chromium and up to 0.2% carbon. They are magnetic, do not harden on quenching and have coefficients of thermal expansion similar to mild steel.

In some cases the welding process will impair both joint toughness and corrosion resistance. The loss of toughness is due to the formation of coarse grains in the weld and heat-affected zone together with the possibility of some martensite formation in certain grades, this effect being more noticeable in the higher chromium materials.

The coarse heat-affected zone structure is extremely notch sensitive at temperatures below approx 200°C and can lead to fabrication difficulties, especially in thicker sections or complicated structures. The loss of toughness after welding becomes less pronounced as the carbon content is reduced. For example, the BSC stainless grades 430, 434, and HYform 409, all have better welding performances than grades containing the maximum allowable carbon and chromium levels.

Martensitic stainless steels are more difficult to weld than either the austenitic or ferritic grades but a carefully designed welding procedure will generally ensure satisfactory results.

The more common grades have chromium contents of from 11.5% to 18% and carbon contents of from 0.08% to 0.75%. They can be hardened from approximately 1000°C and tempered between 300°C and 750°C to produce a wide range of mechanical properties. They are magnetic and have coefficients of thermal conduction and expansion similar to mild steel. But, because these grades possess air-hardening tendencies, a hard and often brittle heat-affected zone can be produced during welding. This hardness depends on the carbon content of the material which for most welding applications is usually held to below 0.25%.

2.3.12.16 Machinability

Production economy founded on material, tool and machine parameters has to be considered in tandem with operating characteristics in the choice of stainless steels. While material characteristics have been the poor relation in recent years, current cost cutting exercises now demand that machinability is fully taken into consideration.

To take a case in point, stainless hollow bar made by conventional methods can vary in its physical properties. As a consequence, cutting speeds have to be matched to the poorest rather than the best batches to avoid frequent disruption of production due to varying cutting parameters. This applies particularly when NC machines are used.

Where stainless steels can be manufactured to improve tolerances to provide more consistent materials, faster cutting speeds can be employed. This results in shorter machining times and significant cost savings. A research programme carried out by Sandvik with the objective of improving machining characteristics of stainless steel hollow bar has resulted in greater uniformity of properties in their steels and a significant improvement in machinability. The improved hollow bar is available off the shelf in the UK in austenitic grades and over 130 different sizes as part of Sandvik's commitment to customer service. The bar may be cut to length or of random length, as required.

Sandvik's research showed that the trace elements present in all steels but not included within the specifications, have a marked effect on machinability for good or bad. Efforts were made to establish an optimum balance of these constituents while retaining other essential properties. The result has been an improvement that has enabled cutting speeds to be increased by up to 25% when using cemented carbide cutting tools.

2.4 Cast iron

Iron castings play a vital role in all branches of engineering and are second only to wrought steel in terms of annual tonnage produced by the metal industries. Compositions are produced in the foundry melting shop which allow production of components ranging from a few grams to many tonnes in weight. They include the easily machinable grey irons, wear resistant irons and corrosion and heat resistant types. The malleable and spheroidal graphite iron, synonymous with nodular iron (also known as ductile iron) offers in addition toughness and ductility, thereby combining the inherent advantages of the cast irons with some of the strength and toughness of steel. The main advantage of cast irons is that they are extremely versatile.

The basic structure of all the cast irons depends on the chemical composition of the iron and the rate of cooling from the molten to the solid state. The mechanical properties of each type and grade of iron are governed by its metallurgical structure. For this reason an elementary understanding of the principal influencing factors is desirable.

The Council of Ironfoundry Associations has produced an excellent publication, *An Introduction to the Cast Irons*, which presents in simple terms the basic metallurgy and, with descriptions, the choice of irons.

Cast iron is usually defined as an alloy of iron and more than 1.7% carbon although the usual carbon content is between 2.4 and 4.0%. It is still a relatively inexpensive material, although the price climbs when one comes to consider high duty cast irons, alloy irons and spheroidal graphite irons. In ordinary slowly cooled cast iron, carbon may be present in the following forms:

(1) with a small quantity of carbon to form the solid solution ferrite;
(2) combined with the iron to form cementite which will combine with some ferrite to form pearlite — excess cementite will however be present in a free form;
(3) as free carbon or graphite.

These forms of carbon can exist together and their properties will control the mechanical properties of the cast iron. When all the carbon is combined the structure will be hard and brittle and is known as white iron. When the proportion of free carbon is high the structure is grey and the iron is known as grey iron. It is weak in tension due to the graphite flake, and heat treatment can improve the mechanical properties by changing the form of the graphite. Mottled irons are grades between the white and grey. By controlling the rate of cooling when casting, the properties of the casting can be varied, and chilling is part of this control operation.

2.4.1 Grey iron

Grey cast iron is essentially an iron/silicon/carbon alloy containing other important elements that modify the structure and properties of the resulting alloy. It is characterised by the formation of graphite as flakes in a steel-like matrix. Before a particular grade of cast iron is specified it should be remembered that machinability can be expected to fall as tensile strength increases and the casting becomes more susceptible to hard spots. A designer should not therefore be tempted to specify a grade of iron with a higher tensile strength than is necessary since this frequently results in increased machine shop costs. The majority of grey iron produced is of a predominantly pearlitic matrix, which is the main requirement when strength is desired. A grade having a ferritic matrix is necessary when good machinability is the main requirement.

2.4.2 Malleable iron

Iron that solidifies without free graphite in the matrix is known as white iron. Malleable cast irons are essentially white irons which have been suitably heat treated to convert the combined carbon present into graphite nodules, which results in improved strength and ductility. British Standards provide for three forms of malleable iron:
Whiteheart (BS 309): which is easy to cast in thin section and has ductile skin with a tough core;
Blackheart (BS 310): which is very ductile with excellent machinability;
Pearlitic (BS 3333): which has high strength with good machinability.

2.4.3 Spheroidal graphite irons

The spheroidal graphite or nodular irons (BS 2789) are used where high strength, good ductility and shock resistance are the main requirements. These irons are of closely controlled composition, and the controlled treatment causes the graphite to form into nodules instead of flakes, resulting in an increase in strength and ductility. The best known spheroidal graphite irons are those marketed under the trade name of Meehanite.

A recent development in SG irons has been austempering, which is a controlled process of heating and quenching which improves tensile strength, ductility and toughness. BCIRA is currently undertaking a development programme to provide designers with the necessary data in order to promote the use of these austempered SG irons, particularly for gears and pinions.

2.4.4 Austenitic iron

The special purpose irons manufactured to BS 3468 have an austenitic matrix produced by alloying. They may have either a flake or spheroidal graphite structure and are used where corrosion resistance is the main requirement.

2.4.5 White and martensitic cast iron

White irons solidify white without graphite formation. Their characteristics are a completely white fracture and high hardness which makes them suitable for abrasion resistant components. By alloying with nickel and chromium the hardness is further increased by the formation of stable martensite. These high chromium/high carbon irons also offer high resistance to corrosion. They may be conveniently divided into three groups:

(1) Unalloyed and low alloy white irons;
(2) Martensitic white irons;
(3) High chromium/high carbon white irons.

Table 2.10 summarises the cast irons covered by British Standards specifications.

Table 2.10 British Standards specifications for cast iron

BS 1452	Grey iron castings
BS 1591	Corrosion resisting high silicon iron castings
BS 310	Blackheart malleable iron castings
BS 3333	Pearlitic malleable iron castings
BS 309	Whiteheart malleable iron castings
BS 2789	Iron castings with spheroidal or nodular graphite
BS 3468	Austenitic cast iron

2.4.6 Design stresses

It is the view of BCIRA that the tensile design stress of the malleable irons should not exceed the limit of proportionality, and as a general rule a maximum design stress of 0.75 times the limit of proportionality is suggested. Since the limit of proportionality is approximately 0.75 and 0.6 of the 0.1% proof stress value for ferritic blackheart malleable irons and other malleable irons, respectively, this limits the design stress to 0.56 × 0.1% proof stress value in blackheart malleable irons and 0.45 × 0.1% proof stress in other malleable irons.

It is suggested that for a number of applications the design stress in fatigue should be one third of the value quoted unless personal knowledge of specific tests otherwise dictates.

2.5 Aluminium and its alloys

The outstanding qualities of these metals are their high strength/weight ratios and their ease of formation and fabrication to meet the requirements of almost any design. A very high degree of resistance to atmospheric and chemical attack is provided by the natural oxide film which forms as a result of a chemical reaction with oxygen in the air. Prolonged exposure to the atmosphere tends to thicken the oxide film producing a protective patina. This protective film, unlike applied finishes such as paint or lacquer, is integral with the metal and will reform spontaneously when penetrated or damaged.

Aluminium is also an excellent conductor of heat and electricity and has high heat reflectivity and low heat emissivity values. It is non-combustible, non-toxic, easily cleaned and, although attractive in its natural state, an extensive variety of decorative surface treatments can be applied to give a wide range of finishes and colours.

Pure aluminium is light, ductile and durable. It is available commercially in purities ranging from 99% to 99.99% (super purity).

Alloying pure aluminium with other metals increases its strength and hardness, but this generally involves some sacrifice in ductility and the modification of some other characteristics. The principal alloying elements are copper, magnesium, silicon, manganese and zinc which, either singly or in combination, are added to produce properties suitable for a wide range of applications.

Pure aluminium may be used as a cladding for alloys, e.g. the high strength materials containing copper or zinc, thereby affording protection to the alloys against atmospheric or chemical attack.

Pure aluminium and its alloys are divided into two broad groups; the work-hardening materials, which include pure metal, deriving their strength (i.e. temper) from the amount of cold work applied, and heat-treatable alloys in which the strength depends upon controlled heat-treatment.

2.5.1 Work hardening and annealing

All purities and alloys of aluminium work-harden to varying degrees according to their compositions. Work hardening occurs by any deformation (e.g. rolling, pressing, drawing, etc.) carried out at temperatures lower than that at which recrystallisation commences. This results in an increase in strength but a decrease in ductility, which is demonstrated by the difference in properties between the various tempers of the non-heat-treatable materials. Annealing removes the effects of cold working and restores the metal to its fully soft condition. Partial annealing may be carried out to relieve internal stresses or to soften the metal, either for further working or to achieve a required level of properties. Annealing conditions depend in practice upon the equipment employed, type of load etc. and can generally only be determined by trial.

2.5.2 Heat treatment

The following notes are a brief outline of the purposes and methods of heat treatment as applied to rolled aluminium alloys. The advice of the supplier should always be sought, as the exact combinations of time and temperature are determined by the compositions of the alloys, dimensions of the pieces, the load and type of furnace used.

The two most common heat treatments applied to rolled products are:

(1) *Solution treatment*: The uniform heating to a prescribed accurately controlled temperature within the range of 450°C–540°C depending on the alloy, for the requisite period. Rapid cooling from this temperature, usually by quenching, and subsequent spontaneous ageing at room temperature (natural ageing), usually for up to five days, produces a stable level of

properties. Any severe cold forming must be completed within thirty minutes to two hours of quenching.

(2) *Precipitation treatment (artificial ageing)*: Heating the solution treated alloy uniformly to an accurately controlled temperature up to 200°C for the requisite period, to obtain the highest level of mechanical strength.

In common with other European countries and America, Australia and Japan, the United Kingdom uses the international four-digit system of designations for aluminium alloy compositions. This permits the ready identification of compositions, both nationally and internationally, and supersedes other designations formerly in use.

In the four-digit system the first digit indicates the main alloying constituent as follows:

1	Pure Metal	5	Magnesium
2	Copper	6	Magnesium/Silicon
3	Manganese	7	Zinc
4	Silicon	8	Others

The second digit, if it is other than '0', indicates a compositional modification of the basic alloy.

In the case of pure aluminium, the third and fourth digits indicate the minimum aluminium content, e.g. 1050 = 99.50% Al; 1080 = 99.80% Al.

In the case of alloys, the third and fourth digits have no special significance and merely serve to identify a particular alloy, e.g. 5052 — formerly 52S; 2014 — formerly 14S.

In due time the British Standard General Engineering Specifications will be revised to incorporate the system, which will also be developed to include internationally standardised methods of designating material tempers and conditions.

The temper or heat treatment condition is designated by a suffix to the purity or alloy designation. The suffix symbols are given in Table 2.11.

2.5.3 *Material specifications*

Table 2.12 gives an outline of the range of aluminium and aluminium alloys specified by British Standards for aerospace and general engineering applications. Manufacturers of these materials often exceed the minimum values given in the specifications and it is therefore prudent for the designer to seek the manufacturer's values when finalising a design.

Table 2.11 Heat treated condition of aluminium alloys

Temper or heat treatment designation	Definition
	Non-heat-treatable or heat-treatable materials
M	As manufactured. Materials which acquire some temper from shaping processes in which there is no special control over the thermal treatment or amount of strain hardening.
O	Annealed. Material which is fully annealed to obtain the lowest strength condition.
	Non-heat-treatable materials
H2	Strain hardened. Material subjected to the application of cold work
H4	after annealing (or hot forming) or to a combination of cold work
H6	and partial annealing/stabilising in order to secure the specified
H8	mechanical properties. The designation is in ascending order of tensile strength.
	Heat-treatable alloys
TB	Solution heat-treated and naturally aged. Materials which receive no cold work after solution heat treatment except as may be required to flatten or straighten it. Properties of some alloys in this temper are unstable.
TE	Cooled from an elevated-temperature shaping process and precipitation-treated.
TF	Solution heat-treated and precipitation-treated.
TD	Solution heat-treated, cold worked and naturally aged.

Table 2.12 Range of British Standard aluminium and aluminium alloys

BS 1161	Specification for aluminium alloy sections for structural purposes
BS 1470*	Wrought aluminium and aluminium alloys for general engineering purposes — plate, sheet and strip
BS 1471*	Wrought aluminium and aluminium alloys for general engineering purposes — drawn tube
BS 1472*	Wrought aluminium and aluminium alloys for general engineering purposes — forging stock and forgings
BS 1473	Wrought aluminium and aluminium alloy for general engineering purposes — rivet, bolt and screw stock
BS 1474*	Wrought aluminium and aluminium alloys for general engineering purposes — bars, extruded round tubes and sections
BS 1475	Wrought aluminium and aluminium alloys for general engineering purposes — wire
BS 1490	Aluminium and aluminium alloy ingots and castings
BS 1615	Anodic coatings on aluminium
BS 1683	Coated aluminium foil for wrapping processed cheese
BS 2627	Wrought aluminium for electrical purposes — wire
BS 2758	Vegetable parchment/aluminium foil laminates for wrapping dairy and other food products
BS 2897	Wrought aluminium for electrical purposes — strip with drawn or rolled edges
BS 2898	Wrought aluminium and aluminium alloys for electrical purposes — bars, extruded round tube and sections
BS 3313	Part 1 Aluminium capping foil for glass containers
	Part 2 Aluminium capping foil for skirted closures for plastics containers
BS 3660	Glossary of terms used in the wrought aluminium industry
BS 3987	Anodic oxide coatings on wrought aluminium for external architectural applications
BS 4300	Specifications (supplementary series) for wrought aluminium and aluminium alloys for general engineering purposes
	Part 1 Aluminium alloy longitudinally welded tube
	Part 4 BTR E6 Solid extruded bars and sections suitable for bright trim reflector applications
	Part 5 FC 1 Freecutting bar and wire alloy
	Part 6 NS 31 Sheet and strip
	Part 7 NS 41 Sheet and strip
	Part 8 NS 51 Plate sheet and strip
	Part 10 NT 51 Drawn tube
	Part 11 NF 51 Forging stock and forgings
	Part 12 NE 51 Bar, extruded round tubes and sections
	Part 13 NG 52 Welding wire
	Part 14 HS 17 Plate sheet and strip
	Part 15 HE 17 Bar extruded round tube and sections
BS 4842	Stoving organic finishes on aluminium extrusions and preformed sections for external architectural application
BS 4868	Profiled aluminium sheeting for building
BS 5313	Aluminium catering containers and lids
BS 5439	Specification for aluminium foil catering containers
CP 118	The structural use of aluminium
AU 89	Anodized aluminium for automobile use

* Aerospace Series L aluminium and aluminium alloys

2.5.4 *Mechanical and physical properties*

Young's modulus, torsion modulus and Poisson's ratio are given below for all purities of aluminium and its alloys:

Young's modulus	$69 \times 10^3 \text{ N mm}^{-2}$
Torsion modulus	$26 \times 10^3 \text{ N mm}^{-2}$
Poisson's ratio	0.33

The fatigue strength of aluminium and its alloys, as with other structural metals, is reduced by the presence of stress raisers such as rough surfaces,

Table 2.13 Available forms of aluminium and its alloys (courtesy Aluminium Federation)

Alloy designation	Plate	Sheet and strip	Drawn strip	Drawn tube	Longit-udinally welded tube	Forging stock and tube	Bolt and screw stock	Rivet stock	Bar, etc.	Solid con-ductor	Wire
1080A	•	•									•
1050A	•	•		•		•		•	•		•
1200	•	•		•					•	•	•
1350			•						•	•	•
2011									•		•
2014A	•	•		•		•	•	•	•		•
2024	•	•									
2031						•					
2117								•			
2618A	•					•			•		
3103	•	•									•
3105		•									
4043A											•
4047A											•
5005		•									•
5056A							•	•			•
5083	•	•		•		•			•		
5154A	•	•		•		•		•	•		•
5251	•	•		•	•	•			•		•
5454	•	•		•		•			•		
5554											•
5556A											•
6061				•					•		•
6063				•		•			•		•
6063A									•		
6082	•	•		•		•	•	•	•		
6101A									•		
6463									•		
7010	•										
7020	•	•							•		
7075	•	•				•			•		

abrupt changes of sections, joints and corrosive environments. The intrinsic fatigue strength for aluminium alloys after 50 million reversals of stress has a value of between 25 to 50% of the ultimate tensile strength depending upon the alloy and its temper and heat treated condition.

Above 100°C the strength of aluminium and its alloys tends to decrease with increasing temperature. Because of the original heat treatment not all the strength will be recovered when the temperature drops back to room value. For this reason applications at temperatures above 100°C should be considered jointly with the manufacturing company.

In low-temperature applications the proof stress, tensile stress elongation and hardness is progressively raised as the temperature falls. As it does not produce brittle characteristics like steel, aluminium is highly suitable for cryogenic applications.

Aluminium and its alloys can be cold formed without difficulty except that with the heat-treatable materials, the harder the material the more difficult it will be to form. For example, for the same material the forming characteristics may vary from excellent for the M condition to fair for the H8 condition.

Welding by inert gas shielding techniques (TIG, MIG. . .) and resistance welding is very successful. Metal arc welding poses difficulties while oxy-acetylene should not be used with heat treatable alloys. These alloys should also avoid the use of inert gas shielding. Resistance welding however gives excellent results.

2.6 Magnesium

Magnesium is the world's lightest structural metal. Aluminium is one and one-half times as heavy, iron and steel are four times as heavy, and copper and nickel alloys are five times as heavy.

The fields of usefulness for magnesium alloys can be divided into two types: structural and nonstructural. Structural magnesium are best known for its applications in the aircraft industry. The light weight and durability of magnesium are also desirable for hand trucks, portable tools, e.g. magnesium castings for drills, chain saws, impact hammers, sanders and similar equipment. Industrial machinery provides opportunities to use magnesium's lightness and durability; household goods, office equipment, instruments of many types, and sporting goods are examples of further applications.

Nonstructural uses of magnesium include its use as an alloying agent in non-ferrous alloys as an oxygen scavenger and desulphuriser for nickel and copper alloys, and as a reducing agent in the production of titanium and zirconium and in the Grignard reaction of organic chemistry. In finely divided form, magnesium also finds a use in pyrotechnics.

2.6.1 Magnesium alloys

Magnesium, when alloyed with aluminium, manganese, zirconium, zinc, rare-earth metals, and thorium, yields alloys with high ratios of strength to weight. The magnesium-alloy systems of commercial importance are the magnesium/aluminium/zinc, magnesium/rare-earth/zirconium, and magnesium/zinc/zirconium.

The average specific gravity of the magnesium alloys is 1.8. The metal has the lowest density of all structural metals and possesses excellent strength-to-weight ratio, fatigue and damping capacity. It is non-magnetic, has relatively high electrical conductivity, and exhibits good dimensional stability in service.

Magnesium can be shaped and worked by practically all methods known to the metalworker. It can be cast by sand, die and permanent-mould methods; extruded into a variety of shapes; and rolled into sheet and plate. Magnesium is readily forged and can be formed by drawing, bending, spinning, impact extrusion and other methods. Joining is accomplished by arc, electric-resistance, and gas-welding methods and by adhesive bonding, riveting, bolting and brazing.

Magnesium has good stability in atmospheric exposure and resistance to attack by many chemicals including alkalies, chromic and hydrofluoric acids, and such organic chemicals as hydrocarbons, most alcohols, phenols, amines, esters and most oils.

Magnesium has useful electrochemical characteristics as a result of its high position in the electromotive force series of metals. Magnesium alloys present no toxicity hazard.

Magnesium members with thickened sections are often more efficient under compressive loads than other metals because the thicker sections minimise secondary failure of flanges. Magnesium provides a combination of rigidity, serviceability, and design efficiency because it is possible to use thick sections and still attain a weight saving.

Magnesium alloys exhibit good dimensional stability in service at temperatures up to 90°C. Some cast magnesium alloys are subject to slight permanent growth at temperatures exceeding 90°C.

The general S-curve trends noted in all age-hardening alloy systems are also noted in the curves for magnesium alloys. Magnesium castings may be considered to have achieved their full hardening in the solution-heat-treated and artificially aged condition.

Strength tends to increase as hardness increases, but the use of hardness tests as a definite index to ultimate strengths is not feasible for magnesium alloys. A graph of strength values determined from hardness values against actual strength values from the same samples shows a very large scatter.

2.6.2 Castings

Magnesium alloy sand castings range from those weighing only a few ounces to those over many thousands of pounds. Magnesium-alloy sand castings are of normally uniform quality with good structural soundness. Intricate castings with thin walls which do not meet pressure requirements can be impregnated to secure soundness.

Molten magnesium does not react with iron and therefore permanent-mould dies for magnesium work are usually made of cast iron, although in certain cases low-alloy die steel has been used. A minimum of die surface treatment is required, which permits rapid production from the machine. Because magnesium does not solder to the die, it is possible to cast small-diameter cored holes with little or no taper and to employ complicated coring.

The preferred section thickness for magnesium die castings ranges from 1.5 mm to 5 mm with a minimum thickness of 1.2 mm being recommended. The maximum mechanical properties of magnesium die castings are achieved in this thickness range. Both external and internal threads can be die-cast in magnesium. Magnesium parts are also cast in production by foundries using the precision investment (lost wax) process, AM100A and AZ92A obtaining small, very intricate parts with controlled surface textures and extremely close tolerances.

2.6.3 Wrought forms

Wrought forms of magnesium include sheet, plate, tube extrusions and forgings.

Chemical treatments on magnesium provide good paint adhesion. In manufacture and assembly these chemical coatings may be difficult to keep intact and unscratched, so primers must adhere well to both chemically treated and bare magnesium surfaces. Such primers may be used clear or pigmented with zinc chromate or titanium dioxide and may be air-dried or baked.

Conventional primers for other metals are usually not suitable for magnesium and hence should not be used unless adequate tests, preferably under actual service conditions, have indicated their suitability. In most cases primers designed for magnesium adhere well to steel and aluminium. Finish coats are chosen on the same basis as for other metals.

The baking of finishes on magnesium alloys may be in ovens or by means of infrared lamps. Consideration must be given to the effect of baking times and temperatures upon the mechanical properties of certain magnesium alloys. Except for AZ31A-H24 sheet, which should not be heated above 150°C, all alloys may be heated to 175°C.

Magnesium in contact with dissimilar metal surfaces provides a potential source of corrosion unless adequately protected. The protection required varies with the severity of the corrosion environment and the metal with which the magnesium is coupled. The metal-to-metal contacts are probably most important. For interior use where condensation is unlikely to occur, paint coatings provide protection against bimetallic couples.

Another way of reducing galvanic corrosion is to electroplate the magnesium. A copper/nickel/chromium system eliminates the potential difference between magnesium and the dissimilar metal.

2.7 Brass

The brasses are copper-based alloys in which the major alloying addition is zinc. The generic term 'brass' covers a wide range of materials with quite different properties and fields of application. Correct choice of brass is therefore important if manufacturing and operating requirements are to be met in the best possible way.

The most popular alloys have copper contents ranging from 58% to 95%. Apart from the major alloying element, zinc, small additions (less than 5%) of other alloying elements are made to modify the properties so that the resulting material is more suitable for a given application.

The higher copper containing materials (copper more than 63%) can be extensively deformed at room temperature, and are widely used for the manufacture of complex components by pressing, deep drawing, spinning and other cold forming processes. If the copper content is below 63% in binary brasses, the room temperature ductility is reduced. Such alloys can be extensively hot worked by rolling, extrusion, forging and stamping; their ability to be cold formed is limited.

Whilst intrinsically easy to machine, the addition of small amounts of lead to brasses improves this property even more and gives rise to the well known 'free machining brass'.

Brasses have good electrical and thermal conductivities and are markedly superior in this respect to ferrous alloys, nickel based alloys and titanium. Their relatively high conductivity, combined with corrosion resistance, makes them an ideal choice for the manufacture of electrical equipment, both domestic and industrial. Condenser and heat exchanger tubing also require the good thermal conductivity of copper and its alloys.

In the softened or annealed condition, the plain brasses are soft and ductile, but when cold worked, e.g. by rolling or drawing, their strength increases markedly. Strong stiff structures can be assembled from extruded-and-drawn sections and bars; and rolled sheet and plate can be fabricated into containers and other items of plant which work under pressure. Specific alloying elements improve the strength and give a range of materials termed 'high tensile brasses'.

Brasses can be broadly divided into two distinct groupings: alpha brass and duplex brass.

2.7.1 Alpha brasses

This range of cold working brasses contain upwards of 63% copper. They are characterised by their ductility at room temperature, and can be extensively deformed by bending, spinning, deep drawing, cold heading and thread rolling. The best known material in this group contains 30% zinc and is commonly known as '70/30' or 'cartridge' brass — due to its use in the manufacture of cartridge cases. '70/30' brass possesses the optimum combination of properties, being capable of being severely cold drawn. Its ductility allows cold manipulation and the alloy has better corrosion resistance than the higher zinc brasses. Tubes for heat exchangers are frequently manufactured from the alpha brasses, normally of 70/30 composition, often containing minor alloying additions which enhance corrosion resistance.

For less demanding fabrication, such as spring contacts in a domestic electrical socket, an alloy with a higher zinc content (and hence lower price) can be used, such as '67/33' (2/1 brass) or '63/37' (common brass). These alloys are not as ductile as the '70/30' alloy, although their other mechanical properties are similar. They are perfectly adequate for all but the most severe cold working operations.

Alloys with higher copper contents (80 to 95%), which closely match gold in their colour, are known as 'gilding metals', and are used for the manufacture of costume jewellery, badges, buttons, etc., as well as decorative metalware and roll-formed sections for architectural applications.

2.7.2 Duplex brasses

These alloys, termed 'alpha-beta brasses', 'duplex brasses' or 'hot working brasses', contain between 38% and 42% zinc. In contrast to the alloys of the first group, their ability to be deformed at room temperature is more limited. They are, however, significantly more workable than the alpha brasses at elevated temperatures and can be extruded into bars of complex section, either solid or hollow, and hot forged in closed dies ('hot stamped') to complex shapes.

The alloys are available as extruded rods, bars and sections, which in turn are the starting point for

the manufacture of a vast range of engineering components and accessories.

The British Standards Institution provides a complete coverage of wrought and cast copper base alloys in the following specifications:

BS 1400   Cast copper and copper alloys
BS 2870   Rolled copper and copper alloys — sheet, strip and foil
BS 2871   Copper and copper alloy tubes
           Part 1:   Copper tubes for water, gas and sanitation
           Part 2:   Tubes for general purposes
           Part 3:   Tubes for heat exchangers
BS 2872   Copper and copper alloys — forging stock and forgings
BS 2873   Copper and copper alloy wire
BS 2874   Copper and copper alloy rods and sections other than forging stock
BS 2875   Rolled copper and copper alloy plate

2.8 Thermoplastics

A vast amount of information has been published in technical papers and in trade literature in an attempt to describe various aspects of the behaviour of plastics. The results of standard tests, such as those described in BS 2782 or the ASTM equivalent, are widely quoted in manufacturers' data sheets and elsewhere but this type of information needs to be treated with caution. Tests which determine various conventional measures of strength, rigidity, etc. commonly applied to metals should also be treated with reserve.

When a thermoplastic is subjected to a tensile test, its stress/strain characteristic is different from that of say steel in three respects. The yield stress is lower, the yield strain is higher and below the yield point there is no region of constant slope. The modulus of a thermoplastic depends on the prevailing strain and also on time under load and on temperature.

The basic mechanical properties may be split conveniently into three groups, creep and long-term deformation up to but not including fracture, long-term strength and fatigue, and short-term strength mainly associated with impact behaviour. It should also be noted that properties of thermoplastics can be affected by the process of producing a component; for example, the temperature of injection moulding can increase impact resistance up to a certain point after which the value will decrease.

For each plastics material, special grades exist which have been tailored both to create certain enhanced properties and to aid processability. Chemical additives help to achieve these. In addition there are morphologically tailor-made plastics, such as high density polyethylene, and ultra high molecular weight versions. Other additives can effect flame retardancy and lubricity.

Process selection depends on the nature of the polymer, the type and size of finished product, production quantity, service conditions and cost. A broad classification for thermoplastics processing is as follows:

Casting
Extrusion
    Profile extrusion
    Coating and laminating
Moulding
    Injection
    Rotational
    Blow
    Vacuum
    Compression
Others
    Dip coating

Plastics can be machined, drilled and stamped; they can be decorated by hot foil stamping, electroplated, offset printing, metallising, etc. Assembly can be carried out by heat welding, ultrasonic welding and common fastening techniques. Solvent welding can be used on some plastics. It is also common for metal parts to be inserted during processing.

Many different companies manufacture a wide range of plastics material and a major problem for the designer is that on published data it is practically impossible to compare the properties of one manufacturer's material with an identical or similar material from another manufacturer. Not only do they often use different test methods and sometimes different units, but the chemical additives make further differences. Additional complications arise from the many different grades of the same material. The only sure way of comparing properties is for the designer to carry out his own comparative test under controlled conditions. In the following pages no attempt has been made to show comparisons although typical values for specific materials are given for some plastics to indicate the approximate values.

Plastics materials fall broadly into two groups: thermoplastics and thermosetting materials. The former are characterised by their ability to flow under heat and pressure, while the latter undergo a chemical change at specified temperatures and pressures and subsequently any attempted deformation results in destruction. This section deals only with thermoplastics.

A principal advantage of plastics is the ease with which they can be formed into complicated shapes while their compositions may be varied to emphasise certain characteristics such as electrical properties, specific chemical resistance, flow properties, etc.

Nevertheless it must be noted that an improvement in one specific characteristic usually results in a loss in other characteristics.

2.8.1 Acetals

One of the strongest and stiffest thermoplastics, acetal is also characterised by excellent fatigue life and dimensional stability. Other outstanding properties include low friction coefficients, exceptional solvent resistance and high heat resistance for extended use up to 104°C. At present there are two basic types of acetal: a homopolymer and a copolymer.

Acetals are highly crystalline thermoplastics which accounts for their excellent properties and predictable long-range performance under load. In creep resistance, acetal is one of the best thermoplastics; however, apparent modulus falls off consistently with long-term loading. Acetals have a strength of around 67 MPa and a flexural modulus of 2830 MPa.

For practical design purposes, yield point and ultimate tensile strength for acetal homopolymer are the same at room temperature; however, a well defined yield point with considerable elongation is exhibited by the copolymer at room temperature and by both types at elevated temperature.

Acetals have an excellent fatigue endurance limit; at 100% RH it is 35 MPa at 25°C and is 21 MPa at 65°C. Furthermore, lubricants and water have little effect on the fatigue life. Although the effects of frequency appear negligible in the 60 to 800 cycles per second range, higher frequencies affect properties due to the generation of heat.

The impact strength of an acetal does not fall off abruptly at subzero temperature as does that of many other thermoplastics. Hardness of acetals is only slightly reduced by moisture absorption or temperature below 100°C.

While not as good as that of nylons, abrasion resistance of acetals is better than that of many thermoplastics. Like nylons, acetals have a slippery feel. Acetals are especially notable among thermoplastics because of their resistance to organic solvents. However, in contact with strong acids, acetals will craze.

Combined with the good mechanical properties of an acetal are its good electrical properties. Its dielectric constant and dissipation factor are uniform over a wide frequency range and up to temperatures of 120°C. Ageing also has little effect on its electrical properties.

Acetals are available as compounds for injection moulding, blow moulding, and extrusion. Grades reinforced with glass fibres (higher stiffness, lower creep, improved dimensional stability) or PTFE-

Table 2.14 Common thermoplastics for engineering applications

Material	Injection moulding	Rotational moulding	Blow moulding	Vacuum moulding	Compression moulding	Extrusion	Casting	Dip coating	Sintered	Sheet	Film	Foam
Acetal	•		•			•						
Acrylic	•		•	•		•	•			•	•	
Acrylonitrile butadiene styrene (ABS)	•		•	•		•				•		
Cellulosics	•	•	•	•						•	•	
Chlorinated polyether	•					•		•		•		
Ethylene vinyl acetate (EVA)	•		•			•						
Fluorocarbons (FEB, PTFE, PCTFE, ETFE)	•							•	•			
Polyamides (Nylon)	•	•	•			•	•			•	•	
Thermoplastic polyester	•		•			•						
Polycarbonates	•	•	•			•				•	•	
Polyethylene	•	•	•			•				•	•	•
Polyimide									•	•	•	
Polypropylene	•	•	•			•				•	•	•
Polyphenylene oxide PPO	•					•						
Polystyrene	•		•		•	•				•	•	•
Polyurethane (also as elastomer)									•			•
Polysulphone	•					•				•		
Vinyl	•	•	•			•	•			•	•	•

fluorocarbon fibres (improved frictional and wear properties) are also on the market.

Many applications involve replacement of metals where the higher strength of metals is not required and costly finishing and assembly operations can be eliminated. Typical parts include pump impellers; gears; appliance cases and housings; motor car turn signals and carburettors; conveyor belt sections; bearings; plumbing components; pipe and fittings; machinery parts; and aerosol containers.

2.8.2 Acrylics

Acrylics have outstanding resistance to long-term exposure to sunlight and weathering. Polymethyl methacrylate (PMMA), a hard, rigid and transparent material, is the most widely used member of the acrylic family. Cast PMMA sheet has excellent optical properties (it transmits about 92 per cent total light) and is more resistant to impact than glass. It is not as resistant to surface scratching as glass, however, although new surface coatings are being made available to overcome this limitation.

In addition to excellent optical properties, acrylics have low water absorption, good electrical resistivity, and fair tensile strength. The heat resistance of acrylics is on the order of 93°C.

More recently, modified acrylics and acrylic multipolymers that offer high impact strength and toughness in addition to the standard acrylic properties have been made available. These grades incorporate elastomeric or alloying constituents that impart the added strength (up to 10 to 20 times as much as general-purpose acrylic crystal). Acrylics are available as compounds for extrusion, injection moulding, blow moulding, and casting. Extruded or cast sheet, and film are also marketed.

Typical applications include: outdoor signs, glazing, aircraft canopies, washbasins (formed from sheet and backed up with spray-on reinforced plastics), lighting applications, knobs, handles, escutcheons, safety shields, and machine covers. Some of the transparent acrylic multipolymers have found application in the drug and food packaging industry.

Special types of acrylic sheet are available for specific applications. For example, ultra-violet transmitting acrylic sheet provides increased transmission of ultra-violet light in the wavelengths between 280 and 360 mm. Ultra-violet filtering acrylics can absorb radiation just below the visible spectrum at about 375 mm. Heat deflection temperatures range from 74 to 100°C but continous service temperatures should not exceed 82°C.

2.8.3 Acrylonitrile butadiene styrene (ABS)

This material is basically a copolymer based on styrene in order to improve the poor impact resistance of styrene. ABS materials have superior strength stiffness and toughness compared with many plastics and have major applications in the engineering sector, typical applications being housing for TV sets, telephone, fascia panels, luggage, etc. ABS materials are however susceptible to chemical attacks by chlorinated solvents, esters, ketines, acids and alkalis.

The use of ABS polymers outdoors is limited by the ageing process but stabilisation by atmospheric oxygen ensures mouldings remain serviceable for many years when used indoors. Typical yield values of ABS range from 40 to 50 MPa and impact values, Izod 1.0 mm notch to BS 2782 Method 306A, can be as high as 305 J/m.

2.8.4 Cellulosics

The family of cellulosics includes acetate, cellulose acetate butyrate (CAB), cellulose propionate, and ethyl cellulose. There are other cellulosics, but these are the most widely used. Cellulosics are characterised by good strength, toughness and transparency, and high surface gloss. In addition, they have good chemical resistance. Generally, these thermoplastics should not be used at temperatures much above 76–104°C.

Cellulose acetate is the lowest cost cellulosic material. It has good toughness and rigidity. (Typical Izod impact strength: 200–300 J m^{-1}). This easily moulded material is available in a variety of grades ranging from soft to hard.

Cellulose acetate butyrate (CAB), although a little more expensive than the straight acetate, is somewhat tougher, with a horn-like quality, and has lower moisture absorption (0.9–2.2 per cent in 24 hours against 1.9–7 per cent for acetate). It has relatively good weatherability and excellent transparency.

Cellulose propionate is similar to cellulose acetate butyrate in both cost and properties, but it has somewhat higher tensile strength, modulus and impact strength (500–600 J m^{-1} Izod).

Ethyl cellulose is what might be called the impact grade of the cellulosics. The excellent toughness of this material is maintained over a wide temperature range. Ethyl cellulose also has moderately low moisture absorption. In addition, this cellulosic is available in self-lubricating grades and is often used in the production of film and hot dip protective coating materials.

Nearly all cellulosics are noted for their toughness, but none of these materials is generally recommended for applications involving anything more than relatively low loads. The main feature of cellulosics is their excellent mouldability which results in a brilliant, high-gloss finish.

Cellulose acetate is subject to dimensional changes due to cold flow, extreme heat, and moisture absorption. Cellulose acetate butyrate is a slightly more stable material, but still not outstanding in comparison to some other thermoplastics. This material, however, is one of the few thermoplastics that resists weathering. This property, combined with its good optical properties, makes cellulose acetate butyrate an excellent material for outdoor signs. Cellulose propionate is similar in properties to butyrate. Ethyl cellulose has several outstanding properties. It withstands heavy abuse and has good environmental resistance: heat distortion point at 1.8 MPa is up to 90°C; water absorption is 1.8 per cent in 24 hours; weathering resistance is excellent. Like other cellulosics, however, it is not primarily a load-bearing material.

Cellulosic compounds are available for extrusion, injection moulding, blow moulding, and rotational moulding. Cellulosics are also widely used in the form of film and sheet.

Typical applications include *cellulose acetate* — knobs, appliance housings and handles; *cellulose acetate butyrate* — tool handles, knobs, dials, appliance housings, steering wheels, signs, light globes; *cellulose propionate* — automobile arm rests, pen and pencil barrels, appliance housings and toys; *ethyl cellulose* — flashlight housings, tool handles, roller wheels, and refrigerator breaker strips.

2.8.5 Chlorinated polyether

This thermoplastic has good dimensional stability and abrasion resistance. It is readily fabricated and may be used as a corrosion resistant coating material. It has a specific gravity of 1.4 with 0.01 per cent water absorption over 24 hours. Its tensile strength ranges around 41 MPa and it has a heat distortion temperature of 150°C at 0.45 MPa. Chlorinated polyether has excellent resistance to both organic and inorganic chemicals.

2.8.6 Fluorocarbons

Outstanding properties of fluorocarbons include inertness to most chemicals and resistance to high temperatures. Fluorocarbons have a rather waxy feel, extremely low coefficients of friction, and excellent dielectric properties which are relatively insensitive to temperature and power frequency. Mechanical properties are normally low, but this changes dramatically when the fluorocarbons are reinforced with glass fibres or molybdenum disulphide fillers.

There are numerous fluorocarbons available, but the two most widely used types are polytetrafluoroethylene (PTFE) and polychlorotrifluoroethylene (PCTFE).

PTFE is extremely heat resistant (up to 260°C) and has outstanding chemical resistance, being inert to most chemicals. Its coefficient of friction is lower than that of any other plastic and it can be used unlubricated. PTFE has a tensile strength on the order of 10.3 to 34 MPa and an impact strength of 133 to 160 J m^{-1}. PTFE also has outstanding low temperature characteristics and will remain flexible at even very low temperatures.

PCTFE has a heat resistance of up to 200°C, a tensile strength of 31 to 41 MPa, and an impact strength of 133–144 J m^{-1}. It is chemically resistant to all inorganic corrosive liquids, including oxidising acids and is resistant to most organic solvents except certain halogenated materials and oxygen-containing compounds (which cause a slight swelling).

In terms of processability, however, PCTFE can be moulded and extruded by conventional thermoplastic processing techniques while PTFE (since it does not soften like other thermoplastics do) must be formed by processes similar to powder metallurgy (i.e. powders are compacted to the desired shape and sintered). More recently, a copolymer of PTFE and hexafluoropropylene known as FEP (fluorinated ethylene-propylene) has been made available. FEP shows essentially some of the same properties as PTFE (i.e. toughness, excellent dimensional stability, and outstanding electrical insulating characteristics over a wide range of temperatures and humidities), but it exhibits a melt viscosity low enough to permit it to be moulded by conventional thermoplastic processing techniques.

Other members of the family of fluoroplastics include: vinylidene fluoride, a high-molecular weight material which has a high tensile strength (44.8 to 46.9 MPa), low cold flow characteristics, and is thermally stable (343°C for short periods of time, 150°C for longer durations); ethylene tetrafluoroethylene (ETFE), a melt-processable fluorocarbon with good high temperature and chemical resistance characteristics; and ethylene-chlorotrifluoroethylene (E-CTFE), a strong, highly impact resistant material that can also be moulded or extruded on conventional thermoplastics equipment.

In the unfilled condition, fluorocarbons, in general, have only fair resistance to deformation under load. When reinforced with such materials as molybdenum disulphide, graphite, asbestos or glass, the fluorocarbons show increased stiffness, hardness and compressive strength, and reduced elongation and deformation under load.

Of all fluoroplastics, PTFE has the lowest friction coefficient and adhesiveness which make it ideal for self-lubricating bearings, gliding pads and coatings, where non-stick and release properties are prominent. Both PTFE and PFA offer maximum continuous service temperatures of 260°C as compared to 205°C for FEP and 155°C for ETFE, so the former two would naturally be chosen where heat requirements are stringent. On the other hand, if heat requirements are not so severe, FEP or EFTE may be quite satisfactory and may be processed and used more economically. Again, PTFE, FEP, PFA would be chosen to withstand extremely corrosive fluids such as pure sulphuric or nitric acids.

While FEP has better mechanical properties such as elastic modulus at low temperatures than PTFE, PFA retains greater stiffness at high temperatures. PFA has also a better flex life, while ETFE is the toughest fluoroplastic when mechanical requirements are greatest. Mechanical properties like rigidity, dimensional stability, mechanical strength, stress-crack and wear resistance can be enhanced by fillers.

For the insulation of wires and cables of great lengths, the melt-processible copolymers (FEP, PFA and ETFE) will be preferred to PTFE, since coating with the latter can only be done in batches instead of continuously. In particular, ETFE will be favoured where toughness and impact strength are required. A PTFE part generally requires several finishing operations before a rough-cast is obtained which must then be machined further in order to obtain a finished part. On the other hand, a FEP, PFA or ETFE resin part can be injection moulded in a one-stage operation. Although the cost of PTFE resin is lower than that of FEP, or ETFE, finished PTFE parts often prove to be more expensive because of additional finishing operations and resulting material losses. Simple parts which require little or no finishing are easily produced from PTFE, while parts must be made in thousands before injection moulding becomes economical.

Complex parts requiring several finishing operations when made from PTFE can be manufactured at a lower cost with FEP or ETFE at an output of only a few thousand pieces. For PFA, the break-even point will be at higher outputs because of higher resin price.

When choosing the type of fluoroplastic for the manufacture of a given part, the design engineer must decide which resin combines the characteristics in processing and in use best suited to the mechanical, thermal, chemical and electrical requirements of the particular application he has in mind, including such factors as form, dimension, number of parts, dimensional tolerance and price.

2.8.7 *Polyamides (Nylon)*

Nylons have high tensile strengths (up to 55 to 76 MPa in some grades), high modulus (in flexure: 1448 to 3448 MPa), and good impact strength. Abrasion resistance is high, resistance to heat can go to 121°C and electrical properties and chemical resistance are good. Nylons resist non-polar solvents, including aromatic hydrocarbons, esters, and essential oils. They are softened by and absorb polar materials such as alcohols, glycols, and water.

Several different types of nylon are on the market, but the two most widely used types of nylon 6/6 (hexamethylene diamine adipic acid) and nylon 6 (polycaprolactam).

Nylon 6/6 is the most common polyamide moulding material. Special grades of nylon 6/6 include: (1) heat-stabilised grades for moulding electrical parts, (2) hydrolysis-stabilised grades for parts to be used in contact with water, (3) light-stabilised grades for weather-resistant mouldings, and (4) higher-melt-viscosity grades for moulding of heavy sections and for better extrudability.

Special grades of nylon 6 include: (1) grades with higher flexibility and impact strength, (2) heat and light-stabilised grades for resistance to outdoor weathering, (3) grades for incorporating nucleating agents to promote consistent crystallinity throughout sections, thereby providing better load-bearing characteristics, and (4) higher viscosity grades for extrusion of rod, film, pipe, large shapes, and blown bottles.

Other types of nylon include: nylon 8, an alcohol-soluble type used for impregnating and coating synthetic and natural fabrics, rubber goods, paper, leather, metal, etc; and nylon 6/10, similar to type 6/6 but with lower moisture absorption, lower heat resistance, lower yield strength, and greater flexibility; and types 12 and 11 which have substantially lower moisture absorption and high strength.

Creep rates for nylons at various stress levels under both tension and compression show only a small deformation within the initial 24-hour period and increase from this point in a linear manner. This means that long-term deformation can usually be predicted accurately on the basis of short-term tests.

Stress-strain data on nylon show that the material reacts in a linear manner up to loads of about 2 MPa. At higher stresses, elongation becomes proportionately greater until a yield point of 58.6 MPa is reached at 25% elongation. In spite of the reduction in area, the further drawing of nylon strengthens it so that the ultimate tensile strength is as high as 76 MPa (at 300% elongation).

The high moisture absorption of nylons causes dimensional change with increasing moisture content. While Type 6 absorbs moisture more rapidly than Type 6/6, both eventually reach equilibrium at about 2.7% moisture content in 50% RH air, and about 9 to 10% in water.

Other key engineering characteristics of nylons are excellent wear, abrasion and chemical resistance. Nylons are resistant to most solvents and are especially resistant to petroleum oils and greases, alkalis, lactic acids, and photographic solutions. They are generally soluble in molten phenol and hot formic acid and are attacked by concentrated solutions of mineral acids.

The dielectric strength of nylon is on the order of 385 to 470 V per mil, volume resistivity is 45×10^{13} ohm-cm, and the dissipation factor is 0.01 to 0.09. However, in many of the electrical applications in which it is used, its mechanical strength and resistance to oils and greases are also important factors.

General-purpose nylon moulding materials are available for extrusion, injection moulding, blow moulding, rotational moulding, and (for the nylon 6 materials) casting or anionic polymerisation. Nylon sheet and film are also marketed.

For specific engineering applications, a number of speciality nylons have been developed, including:

molybdenum-disulphide filled nylons (to improve wear and abrasion resistance, frictional characteristics, flexural strength, stiffness, and heat resistance); glass fibre-filled nylons (to improve tensile strength, heat distortion temperatures, and, in some cases, impact strength), and sintered nylons. Sintered nylons are fabricated by processes similar to powder metallurgy (the same as used for TFE fluorocarbons).

2.8.8 Polycarbonates

Polycarbonates are among the stronger, tougher and more rigid thermoplastics. In addition, they have a ductility normally associated with the softer, lower modulus thermoplastics. These properties, together with excellent electrical insulating characteristics, are maintained over a wide range of temperatures (−51 to 138°C) and loading rates. Although there may be a loss of toughness with heat aging, the material still remains stronger than many thermoplastics.

Polycarbonates are transparent materials and resistant to a variety of chemicals. They are, however, attacked by solvents. The creep resistance of these materials is one of the best for thermoplastics. With polycarbonates, as with other thermoplastics, creep at a given stress level increases with increasing temperature. Yet, even at temperatures as high as 121°C, creep resistance is good.

Tensile yield strength at room temperature is about 60–76 MPa. Yield occurs at a strain of about 5%. Elongation is in the range of 50 to 100%, with ultimate tensile strength falling in the same range as tensile yield strength.

The characteristic ductility of polycarbonate provides it with very high impact strength. Typical notched Izod values are about 700 J m^{-1} on a $\frac{1}{8}$ in thick specimen. Unnotched specimens show much greater impact resistance. Fatigue resistance is also very good.

Moisture absorption for polycarbonates is low and equilibrium is reached rapidly. The materials, however, are adversely affected by weathering; slight colour change and slight embrittlement can occur on exposure to ultra-violet rays.

Polycarbonate moulding compounds are available for extrusion, injection moulding, blow moulding, and rotational moulding. Film and sheeting with excellent optical and electrical properties are also available. Among the speciality grades, glass-reinforced polycarbonates have proved especially popular by virtue of their improved ultimate tensile strength, flexural modulus, tensile modulus, and chemical resistance. In comparison with unfilled polycarbonates yield stress is around 90 MPa.

Typical applications include: safety shields, lenses, glazing, gears, electrical relay covers, helmets, pump impellers, sight gauges, cams and gears, aircraft components, automative bumper extensions, bezels, telephone switchgear, snow-mobile components, boat propellors, water bottles, and housings for hand-held power tools and small appliances.

2.8.9 Polyethylenes

Polyethylenes are characterised by toughness, near-zero moisture absorption, excellent chemical resistance, excellent electrical insulating properties, low coefficient of friction, and ease of processing.

Polyethylenes are classified by density as follows: Type 1 — 0.910–0.925 g cm^{-3} (called low density), Type 2 — 0.926–0.940 g cm^{-3} (medium density), and Type 3 — 0.941–0.965 g cm^{-3} (high density, also called linear polyethylene). The primary differences among the three types are in rigidity, heat resistance, chemical resistance, and ability to sustain loads. In general, as density increases, hardness, heat resistance, stiffness, and resistance to permeability increase. As density decreases, tensile strength and impact strength increase.

Low density polyethylene is quite flexible (stiffness modulus: 89.6 to 207 MPa), with high impact strength and relatively low heat resistance (maximum recommended service temperature is 60 to 80°C, although grades are available with heat resistance up to 93°C).

Medium density polyethylene has a stiffness modulus of 214 to 1034 MPa and maximum continuous service temperature of about 82 to 121°C. Although the low and medium density polyethylenes are so flexible that they do not completely break in Izod impact tests, the high density types have values up to 1068 J m^{-1} of notch, depending on the resin.

Other interesting types of polyethylenes include: cross-linked (chemically or by irradiation) polyethylene, an infusible thermosetting material which has high heat resistance; olefin copolymers, consisting of ethylene and materials like vinyl acetate or ethyl acrylate, which offer a combination of low temperature flexibility with non-migratory ingredients, toughness, good stress-crack resistance, and ease of processing; and high-molecular weight polyethylene (72 000 and over molecular weight) which has extremely high impact strength, excellent low temperature properties, and outstanding wear and abrasion resistance.

Polyethylenes, in general, are not outstanding load-bearing materials, but high density polyethylene can be used for some short-term light loads.

Since a polyethylene part under load can deform a great deal, it is usually considered to have failed before the actual breaking point is reached; yield strength is much more meaningful for design purposes. Although high density polyethylene has a good low temperature yield strength (76 MPa at −40°C), it does not perform as well as some other thermoplastics as temperature is raised (25.5 MPa at 23°C, 7.6 MPa at 93°C).

The fatigue endurance limit of high density polyethylene is 12.4 MPa (50 to 100% RH, 21°C); low and medium density materials are better. This is also true for impact strength.

Few thermoplastics have the excellent chemical resistance and dielectric properties of polyethylenes. Soluble in some organic solvents above 60°C, polyethylenes resist bases and acids at room temperature. Resistivity (both volume and surface) and dielectric strength are high.

Forms available include polyethylene compounds that can be extruded, injection moulded, blow moulded, rotational moulded, etc. Film and sheet are available, as are systems filled with carbon black (for ultraviolet stability), asbestos (for improved high temperature performance), and glass fibre (for improved mechanical properties). Cellular polyethylene, a foam-like material, has improved mechanical and electrical properties, which make it an excellent electrical insulator. Rigid polyethylene foam is also available.

Typical applications include: housings, pipe, heater ducts, housewares, toys, automobile side panels, battery parts, containers, wire and cable insulation, bottles, film and other packaging products, and materials handling.

2.8.10 Polyimides

Generally, this class of materials is based on an aromatic dianhydride and an aromatic diamine. However, although they share the general linear structure of a thermoplastic, melting points are so high that conventional processing techniques cannot be used. Thus polyimides are available as fabricated parts (by machining, punching, or specialised direct forming techniques), coatings for wire and fabrics, and as a binder for diamond abrasive wheels. It should be noted, however, that in the early 1970s, polyimides were introduced that could be moulded using conventional thermoset conditions and moulding equipment, as well as thermoplastic conditions and moulding equipment.

The outstanding physical properties of polyimides make them valuable in applications involving severe environments such as high temperature and radiation, heavy load, and high rubbing velocities. In terms of heat resistance, the continuous service of polyimides in air is on the order of 260°C. At elevated temperatures, polyimide parts retain an unusually high degree of strength and stiffness. However, prolonged exposure at high temperatures can cause a gradual reduction in tensile strength. In common with most plastics, polyimides show aniso-

tropy or differences in properties depending on the direction of force used in fabrication.

Polyimides are resistant to most dilute or weak acids and organic solvents. They are not attacked by aliphatic or aromatic solvents, ethers, esters, alcohols, and most hydraulic fluids. But they are attacked by bases such as strong alkali and aqueous ammonia solutions. The resin is also not suitable for prolonged exposure to hydrazine, nitrogen dioxide, or to primary or secondary amine components.

The minimum tensile strength for polyimides at 23°C is 72 MPa. In tension, ultimate elongation at ambient temperatures is 7–9%. In compression, parts fabricated from polyimide resin can be permanently distorted, but will not break until a strain level of over 50% is reached. The parts are stiff, with a modulus of elasticity at 23°C of 3100 MPa. Parts fabricated from unfilled polyimide resin have unusual resistance to ionising radiation and good electrical properties and will continue to operate up to around 400°C.

Typical applications include components such as gears, covers, bushings, turbo-fan engine backing rings, insulators, washers, piston rings, valve seats, etc, for such industries as aircraft and aerospace, nuclear power, office equipment, and electrical/electronic.

2.8.11 Polypropylene

Interest in polypropylenes lies in a balance of many desirable characteristics. Fairly rigid materials (flexural modulus: 1034 to 1655 MPa), polypropylenes have better resistance to heat (heat distortion temperature at 0.45 MPa: 93 to 121°C) and to more chemicals than do other thermoplastic materials at the same cost level. Polypropylenes have negligible water absorption, excellent electrical properties, and they are easy to process.

In much the same manner as density is important in determining the mechanical properties of polyethylenes, the isotactic index (related to the repeated units in the stereo-regular molecular chain) of a polypropylene very often determines the characteristics of the material. An increase in the isotactic index of a polypropylene will sharply increase the yield strength of the material. Hardness, stiffness, and tensile strength also increase. On the other hand, as the isotactic index decreases, elongation and impact strength increase.

The ability to carry light loads for long periods and over wide temperature ranges is one of the properties that make polypropylenes valuable in engineering applications. For example, tensile yield strength (38 MPa at 23°C) and tensile modulus (an average of 1172 MPa at 23°C) are still quite good at 100°C, 12.4 and 276 MPa respectively. In addition, polypropylenes tested at 60°C react in a linear manner to stresses up to about 7 MPa in this range there should be no permanent deformation.

Polypropylenes do not have outstanding long-term creep resistance, but fatigue endurance limit is excellent. It is often used for integral hinges.

One of the limitations most often mentioned for polypropylenes is their low temperature brittleness ($-20°C$). However, polypropylene copolymers have been developed with brittleness points of about $-29°C$.

Like all other polyolefins, polypropylenes have excellent resistance to water and to water solutions, such as salt and acid solutions that are destructive to metals. They are also resistant to organic solvents and alkalis. Above 80°C, polypropylene is soluble in aromatic substances such as toluene and xylene, and chlorinated hydrocarbons such as trichloroethylene.

Polypropylenes have excellent electrical resistivity (both volume and surface) and their dielectric strength is high.

Polypropylenes are available as moulding compounds for extrusion, injection moulding, blow moulding, and rotational moulding. Film and sheet are on the market, as are several different types of filled and reinforced moulding compounds. Polypropylene foams are also available.

For the most part, the filled polypropylenes use asbestos. These materials offer excellent impact strength and stiffness at temperatures up to 121°C. Other favourable properties include: low coefficient of friction, low heat absorption, excellent chemical resistance, and good dielectric properties.

Typical applications include portable radio and television cabinets, pipe and fittings, automative interior parts, housewares, bottles, carrying cases with integral hinges, pump impellers, fibres, coil formers, luggage, electrical connectors, and packaging.

2.8.12 Polysulphone

Polysulphone is a rigid, strong thermoplastic that is both stable and self-extinguishing. It can be moulded, extruded, or thermoformed in sheets into a wide variety of shapes. Characteristics of special significance to the design engineer are its heat-deflection temperature of 175°C at 1.8 MPa and long-term use temperature of 14% to 175°C. Adding glass fibres in 5 to 10% concentration greatly improves its environmental stress-crack resistance.

Polysulphone has high tensile strength — 70 MPa at yield — and stress-strain behaviour typical for rigid, ductile materials.

Flexural modulus of elasticity is high — nearly 2760 MPa at room temperature. With increases in temperature, flexural modulus stays above 2068 MPa to about 160°C.

Polysulphone is highly resistant to mineral acid, alkali, and salt solutions. Its resistance to detergents, oils, and alcohols is good even at elevated temperatures under moderate levels of stress. For example, specimens have withstood 500 hours in 2% detergent solution at 60°C and 10.3 MPa stress.

Polysulphone will be attacked by such polar organic solvents as ketones, chlorinated hydrocarbons, and aromatic hydrocarbons.

Its electrical properties are retained over a wide temperature range up to 177°C and after immersion in water or exposure to high humidity. Tests of electrical properties of polysulphone, polycarbonates, and polyacetals indicate two areas of significant difference. First, the dissipation factor of polyacetals is higher by a factor of 10, compared to polysulphone and polycarbonates. Second, good electrical properties are retained up to 177 to 190°C for polysulphone, 135 to 149°C for polycarbonates, and 99 to 121°C for polyacetals.

The value of polysulphone as an engineering material is best measured by studying creep or elongation under load. At room temperature for 10 000 hours (over a year) at 20.7 MPa, polysulphone shows about 1% total strain after a year. At 99°C, the creep of polysulphone at 20.7 MPa is higher than at room temperature, but total strain is still well under 2% after nearly a full year of such exposure.

Typical applications include integrated circuit carriers, connectors, coil bobbins, housings for meters, switches and electronic components, light-fixture sockets and shades, under-the-boot switch and relay bases, domelight bezels.

2.8.13 Polystyrene

The name polystyrene designates a large family of thermoplastics derived from the basic styrene monomer. In general, polystyrenes are characterised by low cost, ease of processing, hardness, and excellent dielectric properties. An important characteristic of polystyrene is that within this family of materials there are many types specifically tailored to provide good mechanical, thermal, and chemical properties.

General-purpose polystyrene is the low cost member of the family. Properties include: hardness, rigidity, optical clarity, dimensional stability and excellent processability.

Modified or impact polystyrene (rubber reinforced) extends the uses of polystyrenes into those areas where high impact strength and good elongation are required. Most products of this type have the rubber molecularly grafted to the polystyrenes; however, some are produced by mechanical mixing.

Styrene-acrylonitrile (SAN) is the most chemical resistant polystyrene. It has excellent resistance to acids, bases, salts, and some solvents. It also has a high heat distortion point (90°C at 1.8 MPa) and a higher tensile modulus (2760–4140 MPa) than most other thermoplastics. Another type of polystyrene commercially available is a low-temperature grade.

High impact polystyrene is generally recognised in the field as the best styrene material for load-bearing applications. The other types of polystyrene offer various improvements in chemical, thermal, and optical performance, usually at the sacrifice of mechanical properties.

High impact polystyrene is a very rigid material (modulus of elasticity in tension: 2070 MPa); however, it does not withstand long-term tensile loads as well as some other thermoplastics.

When loads are to be held longer than 500 hours, most high impact polystyrenes have design strengths between 5.5 and 10.5 MPa. Stress-strain data show high impact polystyrene to be very stable at low loads (15% strain at 2.0 MPa for 1000 hours). However, strain is as much as 35% for great loads (7 MPa) and for less time (100 hours).

Extra-high impact polystyrene is available with a notched impact strength as high as 250 J m^{-1} (Izod). Extrusion, injection moulding, compression moulding, and blow moulding polystyrene compounds are available, as are polystyrene film, sheet, and foam. Glass-fibre-reinforced polystyrenes have improved mechanical and thermal properties.

Typical applications include pipe and fittings, refrigerator parts, automobile interior parts, appliance housings, battery cases, TV picture masks, dials and knobs, washing machine filters, packaging, toys, and housewares.

2.8.14 Polyurethane

The thermoplastic material is available in three forms, (a) as a rigid foam, (b) as a flexible foam and (c) as an elastomer. They are characterised by high strength and good chemical and abrasion resistance. The rigid foam is widely used as a thermal insulation material while the flexible foam makes an excellent cushion material. The elastomeric material is used in solid tyres and shock absorbers.

2.8.15 Polymethyl methacrylate (PMMA)

This material has exceptional optical clarity and resistance to outdoor exposure. It is resistant to alkalis, detergents, oils and dilute acids but is attacked by most solvents. Its unique property of internal reflection is useful in advertising signs and in some medical applications (see also Acrylics).

2.8.16 Thermoplastic polyester

These linear polyesters are highly crystalline, with a melting point near 225°C. They are hard, strong, and extremely tough. Other characteristics include: high resistance to abrasion, a low coefficient of friction, high resistance to cold flow, good chemical resistance, good dielectric properties, and low moisture absorption. Thermoplastic polyesters can be extruded, injection moulded, or blow moulded.

Reinforced compounds (with glass, talc, or asbestos) are available. The reinforced compounds retain most of the easy processing characteristics of the unmodified resin.

Applications include gears, bearings, housings for pumps and appliances, impellers, pulleys, switch parts, furniture bumper extensions, and other products in competition with metals or high-performance plastics. The resin is also recommended for packaging applications, especially for products (i.e. food and medical goods) that are to be sterilised by radiation. It is also being used for blow moulded carbonated beverage bottles.

The development and introduction of polybutylene terephthalate or PBT resulted in a marked increase in the capabilities of thermoplastic polyesters for injection moulding since it offered significant processing improvements over previously available PET.

Thermoplastic polyesters are lightweight, versatile engineering materials which exhibit stable physical properties over a wide range of temperatures and humidity conditions. With their combination of high heat distortion temperatures, excellent chemical resistance, and low water absorption, thermoplastic polyesters offer long-term dimensional stability unmatched among crystalline polymers, as well as low deformation under load.

In addition to its surface properties, it is a dimensionally stable gear material. Because the resins have very low water absorption, gears, cams and other load bearing parts resist swelling when subjected to high moisture environments. They keep their original size and properties, without binding or changing critical contact areas.

Thermoplastic polyesters show outstanding thermal resistance. Heat deflection temperatures, ranging from 155°C at 0.45 N mm^{-2} in unreinforced grades to 215°C at 0.45 N mm^{-2} in glass reinforced grades. In addition to high temperature resistance, glass-reinforced grades of VALOX resin have very low mean coefficients of thermal expansion — in the area of 5.6 to 7.2 × 10^5/°C. Because of this property, these grades can be used in many metal replacement applications under conditions of thermal cycling.

All thermoplastic polyesters are characterised by their excellent resistance to a variety of chemicals, including aliphatic hydrocarbons, petrol, oils and fats, alcohols, glycols, ethers, high molecular weight esters and ketones, dilute acids and bases, detergents, and most aqueous salt solutions.

2.8.17 *Vinyl*

Vinyls are very versatile, ranging from extremely flexible, plasticised grades to very rigid vinyls (e.g. a modulus in flexure of about 440 MPa). Chemical resistance of the rigid material is excellent. In addition, vinyls are easy to process by a number of different techniques.

Vinyls are used mainly for their chemical and weathering resistance, high dielectric properties or abrasion resistance. The most widely used vinyls are polyvinyl chloride (PVC) and PVC copolymers (e.g. vinyl chloride-vinyl acetate).

PVC and PVC acetate copolymers are formulated to provide such a wide and diverse range of properties that characterisation by performance is difficult. In general, PVC materials are tough, with high strength and abrasion resistance, exceptional resistance to a wide variety of chemicals, and excellent dielectric characteristics. The recommended temperature range for PVC is −54 to 80°C.

Rigid PVC is essentially unplasticised, has a hardness similar to that of hard rubber, an impact strength of 13 to 64 J m^{-1} notch (Izod), and modulus in flexure of 2600 to 4500 MPa.

Flexible PVC is a plasticised material which often contains, in addition to plasticisers, other ingredients such as stabilisers and pigments in various proportions. Typical property data include: tensile strength 8.2 to 24 MPa; elongation 200 to 450%; 100% modulus 8.3 MPa to 19.3 MPa. A cold flexure temperature of about −57°C is obtainable.

Other types of vinyls include: polyvinyl acetate, a widely used thermoplastic adhesive; polyvinyl alcohol, a water-soluble film; polyvinyl acetals (formals and butyrals), widely used as additives to improve adhesion and mechanical properties of other plastics; and polyvinylidene chloride, a tough, abrasion resistant vinyl with better than ordinary heat resistance (100°C maximum service temperature).

Vinyls can be extruded, cast, injection moulded, blow moulded, rotationally moulded, and calendered. Film and sheet are available, as are both rigid and flexible foams.

Typical applications include pipe and fittings, electrical wire insulation, valve seats, chemical storage tanks, adhesives, packaging, upholstery, shoe components, flooring, and outerwear.

2.8.18 *Processes*

A major factor in the design of any component is the manner in which it is made. The form and dimensions (especially the thickness) of a plastics item are often decided by the technological dictates of the processing machinery (extruder, injection machine, etc.) and the ancillary equipment (die or mould) which will make it. For instance, an injection moulded form specified as cylindrical may require a slight taper to allow its removal from the mould. On a blow moulding, a large part of the wall may have to be much thicker than is necessary to carry the stress in order to provide sufficient thickness in other parts of the moulding which are subject to thinning during the operation. In other words when an engineer considers a plastics material for the production of a part or a component, it is essential for him to have at his disposal details which will enable him to arrive at an accurate assessment of performance in practice. These details include a knowledge of:

(1) the fundamental properties of the material — taking into account the effects of time and environment;
(2) the design of the component in relation to the function it has to perform.

It is however equally important for the engineer to have available data which relate the design of the component to the possibilities of, and the limitation imposed by, the processing techniques employed.

Unlike many traditional materials where fabrication techniques are few and well understood for historical reasons, plastics suffer from two major disadvantages; first, the materials themselves have no lengthy history and secondly, several of the processes are either completely novel or much modified versions of traditional techniques. Mitigating these factors, however, is the technical advantage which make plastics materials indispensable in a wide range of work.

Plastics are no longer the cheaper substitutes. Parts can fail, not because the material or fabricating method is at fault but because, for example, the position of a feed point has led to a weak weld line. The result of this situation has led, in fact, to a demand from industry in general, and design engineers in particular, for more data on what might lossely be called plastics design criteria.

2.8.18.1 Semi-finished plastics

The annual consumption of plastics materials used for machining is over £10m. These materials are mainly in the form of rod, tube and block nylon (polyamide), acetal in their various grades, and PVC with smaller amounts of polyolefines (polypropylene, UHMW, HMW and HD and LDPE) and very small quantities of PPO, PES, ABS, PC. In addition there is a huge sheet market which, whilst not strictly engineering, involves production of guards, screens, visors and safety glazing generally, which is as large again. Finally industry which can be considered as corrosion resistant plant involves plating barrels, corrosive fume ducting, acid tanks and similar, and here the products are primarily PVC and polypropylene in sheets, blocks, tubing and pipes.

The growth in the use of plastics has to be matched by technical service from the manufacturers of the polymers, the bulk of which are used for injection moulding. However a substantial industry has developed in the supply of semi-finished shapes, e.g. in rods, tubes, blocks and sheets, and the use of these is expanding rapidly for three main reasons:

(1)   The most obvious area is for prototype work and to prove component design prior to substantial expenditure on injection moulding tools. This is absolutely essential and naturally is common practice.
(2)   The growth in automatic tooling and NC machines has proved invaluable in the production of high precision machined parts. Dependent entirely on the complexity of the piece, it can now be advantageous to produce by machining rather than by injection moulding.
(3)   The other ingredient that plays a greater part in industry than ever before is the interest rate. Injection moulding is cost effective when producing parts. However the rate at which parts may be produced is likely to be much greater than the rate of consumption within the production unit itself. There is then a Catch 22 situation. Is the machine run to produce low cost parts which will inevitably mean carrying substantial stocks, or is it run for two hours a day which is obviously uneconomic from the production angle, but does avoid stock finance costs? Stock of raw material is required before the event as well as stock of finished mouldings, whereas on an almost daily basis semi-finished rods/tubes, etc. are available for supply in virtually all thermoplastic materials.

2.8.18.2   Injection moulding

Injection moulding is the basic method for the production of close-tolerance three-dimensional components in thermoplastics. The process consists basically of heating a charge of thermoplastic material to a constant plastic state and then transferring that charge under pressure into a closed mould. Before removal from the mould, the part is cooled to produce a component with the greatest possible degree of homogeneity.

From the point of view of component design the scope of the technique is very wide, the only major limitation being that associated with deep under-cuts. It is possible by the judicious use of sliding cores and moving mould components to produce both internally and externally threaded mouldings and parts containing deep bores and/or holes. The technique can be extended even further by the use of loose mould inserts, but here the question of economic production rates must be considered.

Injection moulding offers the following major advantages:

(1)   Mouldings can be produced in a completed finished state, no post-moulding operations being necessary.
(2)   Very close tolerances can be maintained on all dimensions provided due allowance is made for mould shrinkage.
(3)   Very accurate consistency of wall thickness.
(4)   High output rates — these can be significantly increased in many instances by the use of multi-impression moulds.
(5)   Very wide range of application — injection machines currently available allow the manufacture of components from a few grams up to tens of kilograms and in size up to 3 m or more in diameter and length.
(6)   Possibility of producing parts incorporating metal inserts.

Limitations of the technique include:

(1)   High initial machine costs.
(2)   In many cases high mould costs — these arise from the necessity for very high quality and strength in injection moulds.
(3)   Difficulties associated with the production of mouldings where there are wide variations in section — these can lead to sink marks and other moulding faults.

2.8.18.3   Compression moulding

This is the basic technique for the production of mouldings from thermosetting materials, and is based on the fact that when subjected to heat, thermosetting materials pass through a plastic phase before chemically cross linking. If, therefore, pressure is applied during that phase, the material flows and takes any particular shape as defined by mould contours.

In practice the process consists of placing a predetermined amount (weight or volume) of moulding powder or pellets into the mould cavity, which is heated, and exerting pressure on the charge by closing the mould and applying an external force. The moulding pressure is maintained for a preset period to enable the moulding to cure (chemically cross link), after which the mould is opened and the moulding ejected.

In general the factors governing mould design in injection moulding apply, the major limiting factor again being that associated with deep under-cuts. Parts containing internal and external threads as well as deep bores and/or holes can be produced and loose inserts may be employed. Limitations of the process include:

(1) Mouldings as produced can contain a flash and this must be removed by a second operation, in certain cases by hand.

(2) Initial mould costs are high, these arising as with injection moulding from the requirement for very high quality and strength.

(3) Outputs are usually lower than for injection moulding, this being due to the fact that the moulding cycle must include the time necessary for cross linking to be effected. Production rates can be increased by the use of multi-cavity moulds.

(4) Due to the fact that there is some movement of material at low temperatures, i.e. during its non-plastic state, inserts (especially fine pins or wire) may be displaced.

2.8.18.4   Low pressure moulding

An extension of the compression moulding system, low pressure moulding is applied mainly to large area products using liquid resin systems coupled with fibrous (glass fibre) reinforcements. The development of low pressure systems, and with it the ability to produce very large area parts, stems from the fact that there is no requirement for a high pressure system to effect resin flow or to consolidate the moulding. Although low pressure moulding of glass reinforced plastics offers many of the advantages associated with the high pressure compression system, it has the disadvantage, compared with the hand lay-up systems, of high machine and mould costs. In effect, these two factors preclude the use of the technique for all applications other than those produced in very large numbers, e.g. components for consumer durables, motor cars, etc.

2.8.18.5   Transfer moulding

The transfer moulding system was evolved to overcome some of the limitations associated with compression moulding, and in particular the difficulty of moulding components incorporating metal inserts. It may be considered as a process intermediate between compression moulding and injection moulding.

In essence, the transfer moulding system is based on the use of a cylinder from which material in the plastic state is transferred into a closed mould via an enclosed runner system. This means that pressure is applied to material of relatively low viscosity and therefore exhibiting very good flow characteristics.

Apart from the elimination of insert displacement, transfer moulding tends to reduce flash. Further, due to the fact that frictional heat is generated as the material enters the mould, cure times can be reduced as compared with conventional compression moulding systems. As powder loading of a mould cavity is eliminated, there is an added advantage stemming from the fact that the technique is more adaptable in many respects to fully automatic systems.

2.8.18.6   Blow moulding

The blow moulding technique is based on the use of a hot plastics tube, blown, after being sealed at one end, to form hollow shapes as defined by the mould into which the tube is passed. The tube (parison) is normally produced by the extrusion technique although a process variant using an injection moulded 'gob' can be employed. The technique was developed initially for the production of bottles and similar hollow plastics containers from thermoplastics materials, in particular those having good melt strength characteristics such as low and high density polythene. Developments of the basic principle allow the production of completely closed parts such as balls.

In the main the technique is still used for the production of bottles and containers, but more recently there has been a growing trend for its use in the manufacture of technical mouldings. In all cases the technique is restricted to components in which only the outside dimensions of the parts are critical — it is not possible to maintain engineering tolerances on internal dimensions or the wall thickness of the moulding, despite improvements in the control of the tube production technique.

Essentially, therefore, in the engineering field the process has been restricted to the manufacture of container-like products. However, with secondary operations, it is possible to manufacture open ended tubular components. An extension of the latter is the production of a closed symmetrical component which after extraction is split to give two identical open-ended parts. The latter system is sometimes employed for the production of domestic cold water cisterns. It is not easy to produce parts incorporating large lugs or bosses on the container wall and at the same time maintain a constant wall thickness.

In most cases the blow moulding system offers the advantage of using relatively low cost moulds. Moulding pressures are low compared with injection moulding, allowing cast aluminium or fabricated sheet steel to be employed as mould-making materials. Multi-impression moulds are possible in many cases, again leading to cost reductions. To some extent, however, lower mould costs are offset by slower cooling times. In many instances wall thicknesses are greater than those used in injection moulding which, coupled with the fact that cooling can be applied on the outer surface only, leads to longer cooling times. In general the initial costs of blow moulding machinery are lower than those for injection machines although running costs are in many cases similar.

As well as being limited to components where close tolerances can be maintained on outside dimensions only, the blow moulding process does not allow the manufacture of parts with wide variations in wall thickness. Further, major changes in direction, e.g. corners, tend to lead to thinning, although up to a point the latter disadvantage can be eliminated by parison wall thickness control systems. It is not possible to make components with holes in the body walls and therefore these must be produced as a secondary post-moulding operation. Externally threaded parts can be made.

2.8.18.7 Thermoforming

This is the basic technique for processing plastics in sheet and film form and is restricted in the main to box-like components, i.e. parts in which one end is open. In many cases where thin walled, large area parts are required, the thermoforming technique is the only method technically feasible. There are, however, two major drawbacks which restrict the application of the techniques in engineering applications: non-uniform wall thickness due to thinning on corners, etc., and uni-directional orientation. In brief the technique consists of heating a thermoplastic sheet to its softening point and forming that sheet against the contours of a mould by the application of pressure. The system, whichever of the variants is employed, suffers from the fact that the cost of plastics sheet materials is high compared with basic raw material due to the additional processing costs.

Another cost disadvantage arises from the fact that there is usually a trimming operation and where holes are required there is again a secondary operation. From a design standpoint it is not possible to mould components incorporating bosses or lugs, although ribs are easily produced.

There are three basic forming methods: (1) mechanical, (2) vacuum and (3) pressure (compressed air).

Set against these limitations are the following:

(1) Basic simplicity of the processing method.
(2) The ability to maintain very consistent properties and product dimensions.

2.8.18.8 Mechanical or matched mould forming

This system uses matching male and female mould halves between which the sheet is pressed. The sheet can be pre-heated or, depending on product contour, the moulds can be heated. In certain cases trimming can be eliminated by the use of pre-cut blanks.

Moulds are normally of steel or aluminium and are made to high accuracy. This, coupled in many cases with low output rates, makes it the most expensive of the forming methods and has led to its being superseded by alternative systems. Matched metal moulding is still used, however, in many applications where internal and external dimensions are critical. By careful mould design and process control it is possible to maintain close tolerances on wall thickness when component shape is symmetrical.

2.8.18.9 Vacuum forming

Vacuum forming as the title suggests is a method of fixing a plastic sheet above a mould, heating it, and then drawing it by vacuum from below via vents in the mould. After cooling, the part is set to the shape of the mould and is then removed for trimming. The mould may be male or female to suit component design and material. The system has the advantage of basic machine simplicity and, more important, low cost moulds can be employed. Mould making materials include plaster of Paris, wood, epoxy resins and metal alloys which make the process economic even when requirements are very small.

Despite considerable process improvements, the technique is limited by the fact that it is very difficult to maintain wall thickness tolerances on all but a few parts. Sharp corners and parts of very high draw ratios should be avoided. On thick sections there is invariably a trimming operation as well as secondary operations such as piercing and drilling if holes are required.

2.8.18.10 Pressure forming

Air blowing can be likened to vacuum forming, the essential differences being that the hot sheet is formed by compressed air from above and that female moulds are used in most cases. It has the major advantage of allowing much higher pressures to be employed. The technique is the one most widely used with acrylic sheet due to the fact that properties of this material at processing temperatures make it difficult to manipulate by vacuum forming. (A variant of the technique, free-air blowing, is used extensively for parts requiring high clarity such as aircraft canopies.) In many respects pressure forming allows much greater process control than vacuum forming and is capable of being developed, as it has been, to give very high forming rates. In particular the technique has been adapted, in combination with mechanical forming, for the production of thin-walled packaging parts on a continuous basis and at very high speeds. On thick sections the greater degree of control of drawing rates allows closer tolerances to be maintained on wall thickness. In general, however, the basic limitations of 'thinning' and orientation apply.

2.8.19 Properties of some thermoplastics

Figure 2.7 is intended as a guide to the selection of an appropriate engineering plastic. It is important to appreciate that the properties of the final component depend not only on the choice of plastics material, but also on the process involved in producing the component, tools and temperature, etc. It is therefore important that early consultation with suppliers, toolmakers and processors is made.

The values given are average properties based on published data, and it may be found that specific brands have either superior or inferior properties as compared with the values given. Reinforcements are based on the use of glass fibres. Figure 2.7 has been based on the information provided by GKN Kings Norton Ltd. of Birmingham to whom acknowledgements are given.

Glossary of metallurgy

Ageing
Ageing is a change in a metal by which its structure recovers from an unstable condition produced by quenching or cold working. Ageing which takes place at room temperature may be accelerated by slight increases in temperature. In the aged condition, the material has improved mechanical properties. See also *Precipitation, hardening, Quench ageing, Strain ageing, Stress relieving*.

Alloy
A substance consisting of two or more elements of which at least one is metal. Most pure metals can be strengthened by small additions of other metals or non-metals.

Austempering
Austempering is a heat treatment process for steel that has been heated above the transformation range and thereby converted to austenite. It is performed in a bath held at a temperature of

between 250 and 450°C (i.e. at a temperature at which a bausitic structure is formed). The fine grain structure tends to give great ductility for a given strength. See also *Stainless steel*.

Annealing
Annealing is a heat treatment process used to soften a metal. It is also used to promote homogeneity by diffusion, and to relieve residual stresses arising from cold working and welding operations. It usually involves very slow cooling after having been raised to the annealing temperature.

Brinell hardness
The Brinell hardness (BHN) test for determining the hardness of metallic materials consists of applying a known load to the surface through a hardened steel ball of known diameter. The size of the impression is used in determining the hardness number thus:

$$\text{BHN} = \frac{P}{\frac{1}{2}\pi D \left[D - \sqrt{(D^2 - d^2)} \right]}$$

where P is the applied load (kg), D is the diameter of the steel ball (mm), and d is the diameter of the impression (mm).

Tabulated values of BHN against diameter, d, are given in BS 240: Part 1. Because there is some deformation of the ball it is standard practice to use a 10 mm diameter ball with an applied load of 3000 kg for 30 seconds for hard materials and 500 kg for 60 seconds for soft materials. The thickness of the materials tested should be not less than ten times the depth of the indentation. See also *Rockwell hardness, Vickers hardness, Knoop hardness, Scleroscope hardness, Mohs' hardness*.

Brittle fracture
Brittle fracture is a failure of structural steels, of both plain carbon and those of low alloy content, usually at low temperature, 0°C or lower. The fractures always start from a notch of some kind and are associated with a lack of ductility. These failures can be catastrophic, since little energy is absorbed into the material.

Case hardening
Case hardening is a process of surface hardening involving a change in the composition of the outer layer of an iron based alloy followed by appropriate thermal treatment. Typical processes are carburising, cyaniding, carbonitriding and nitriding. Depths up to 1.3 mm can be achieved. Plain carbon steels with carbon content below 0.2% can be used or 3% nickel alloy steels.

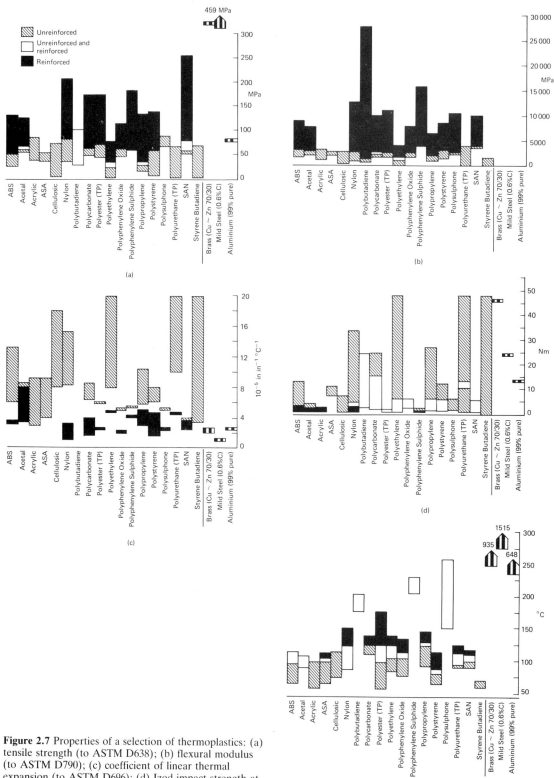

Figure 2.7 Properties of a selection of thermoplastics: (a) tensile strength (to ASTM D638); (b) flexural modulus (to ASTM D790); (c) coefficient of linear thermal expansion (to ASTM D696); (d) Izod impact strength at 23°C; (e) resistance to heat (continuous — no load)

Table 2.15 Comparison of hardness values

Brinell 3000 kg load 10 mm ball		Diamond pyramid number (Vickers) (HV)	Rockwell number		Scleroscope number	Equivalent tensile strength for steel (N mm^{-2})
Diameter of impression (mm)	Hardness number (HB)		C Scale 150 kg diamond cone (HRC)	B Scale 100 kg 1.6 mm ball (HRB)		
2.05	899	–	–	–	–	3027
2.10	856	–	–	–	–	2890
2.15	817	–	–	–	–	2749
2.20	780	1150	70	–	106	2640
2.25	745	1050	68	–	100	2517
2.30	712	960	66	–	95	2409
2.35	682	885	64	–	91	2286
2.40	653	820	62	–	87	2193
2.45	627	765	60	–	84	2116
2.50	601	717	58	–	81	2023
2.55	578	675	57	–	78	1946
2.60	555	633	55	120	75	1869
2.65	534	598	53	119	72	1792
2.70	514	567	52	119	70	1730
2.75	495	540	50	117	67	1670
2.80	477	515	49	117	65	1606
2.85	461	494	47	116	63	1544
2.90	444	472	46	115	61	1498
2.95	429	454	45	115	59	1452
3.00	415	437	44	114	57	1405
3.05	401	420	42	113	55	1359
3.10	388	404	41	112	54	1297
3.15	375	389	40	112	52	1266
3.20	363	375	38	110	51	1220
3.25	352	363	37	110	49	1174
3.30	341	350	36	109	48	1143
3.35	331	339	35	109	46	1112
3.40	321	327	34	108	45	1081
3.45	311	316	33	108	44	1050
3.50	302	305	32	107	43	1019
3.55	293	296	31	106	42	988
3.60	285	287	30	105	40	958
3.65	277	279	29	104	39	927
3.70	269	270	28	104	38	911
3.75	262	263	26	103	37	880
3.80	255	256	25	102	37	849
3.85	248	248	24	102	36	834
3.90	241	241	23	100	35	803
3.95	235	235	22	99	34	788
4.00	229	229	21	98	33	772
4.05	223	223	20	97	32	757
4.10	217	217	18	96	31	726
4.15	212	212	17	96	31	710
4.20	207	207	16	95	30	695
4.25	201	202	15	94	30	680
4.30	197	197	13	93	29	664
4.35	192	192	12	92	28	649
4.40	187	187	10	91	28	633
4.45	183	183	9	90	27	618
4.50	179	179	8	89	27	610

Table 2.15 *continued*

| Brinell 3000 kg load 10 mm ball | | Diamond pyramid number (Vickers) (HV) | Rockwell number | | Scleroscope number | Equivalent tensile strength for steel (N mm^{-2}) |
Diameter of impression (mm)	Hardness number (HB)		C Scale 150 kg diamond cone (HRC)	B Scale 100 kg 1.6 mm ball (HRB)		
4.55	174	174	7	88	26	602
4.60	170	170	6	87	26	595
4.65	167	166	4	86	25	587
4.70	163	163	3	85	25	579
4.75	159	159	2	84	24	564
4.80	156	156	1	83	24	556
4.85	153	153	0	82	23	541
4.90	149	149	−1	81	23	525
4.95	146	146	−2	80	22	517
5.00	143	143	−3	79	22	510
5.05	140	140	−4	78	21	494
5.10	137	137	−6	77	21	486
5.15	134	134	−7	76	21	479
5.20	131	131	−9	74	20	463
5.25	128	128	−11	73	20	456
5.30	126	126	−12	72	19	448
5.35	123	124	−14	71	19	440
5.40	121	121	−16	70	19	432
5.45	118	118	−17	69	19	417
5.50	116	116	−19	68	19	409
5.55	114	114	−20	67	19	402
5.60	111	112	–	66	19	394
5.65	109	109	–	65	18	386
5.70	107	107	–	64	18	378
5.75	105	105	–	62	18	371
5.80	103	103	–	61	18	363
5.85	101	101	–	60	18	355
5.90	99.2	99	–	59	18	351
5.95	97.3	97	–	57	17	347
6.00	95.5	95	–	56	17	355

Coherency

The continuation of a lattice structure between a matrix and a precipitate. As the precipitate grows in size, if its lattice spacing or form is different to that of the matrix the lattice may be deformed giving coherency strains.

Creep

Creep is a continuous or semi-continuous deformation with time under constant stress at constant temperature taking place at stress intensities below the yield point (proportional limit).

Damping capacity

Damping capacity is the ability of a material to internally dissipate mechanical strain energy. Materials of high damping capacity sound dead when struck. Vibrations are caused to die out owing to the plastic strain converting the energy of vibration into heat.

Diamond pyramid hardness

Diamond pyramid hardness (DPH) is determined by forcing a square based diamond pyramid having an apex angle of 136° into the specimen under loads usually of 5 to 50 kg. The hardness is defined as the load per unit area of surface contact in kg mm^{-2}. DPH is synonymous with DPN (diamond pyramid number) and VPN (Vickers pyramid number).

$$DPH = \frac{1.8544P}{d^2}$$

where d is the length of the average diagonal (mm), and P is the load (kg).

Values are tabulated in BS 427, Part 1.

Dispersion strengthening

This is the strengthening of a metal due to the presence of a dispersion of fine particles of a material which is not soluble in the lattice. It therefore differs from precipitation hardening in which the particles are rejected from solution in the parent material, strengthened by their development of coherency strains, and redissolve at high temperatures. The materials used for dispersion strengthening must be chemically inert in the lattice, hard, of sub-micron size and uniformly dispersed for the optimum effect.

Ductility

Ductility is the property that permits permanent deformation in length before fracture. Ductility is usually determined by cupping tests such as the Erichsen and Olsen tests.

Elastic limit

Elastic limit is the greatest stress that a material is capable of developing without a permanent deformation remaining upon complete release of the stress. In many materials the elastic limit and limit of proportionality are the same.

The stress-strain diagrams of certain metals are practically straight lines up to the point where marked plastic flow begins. The stress at which the straight line graph changes to a curve is called the proportional limit. When plastic flow proceeds readily with a small increase in the load applied, the metal is said to have a yield point, which is taken as the stress at which this marked increase in strain begins. However, many metals, including some steels, do not have a well defined yield point. In such cases a value for what is termed the yield strength is found by determining the stress at which a stated amount of plastic flow, usually 0.2% permanent set, has occurred. In the determination of the elastic limit, the yield point, etc., a standard size test piece is subjected to increasing loads and the corresponding extensions are noted. The greatest value of the stress, calculated on the original cross-section, that the material withstands before fracture is called the ultimate strength (see Figure 2.8). The elongation of the specimen at fracture and the reduction in the area of the section at the place of fracture are also calculated, since these values are some indication of the ductility and formability of the material.

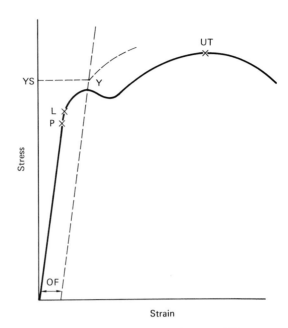

Figure 2.8 A generalised stress-strain curve: UT, ultimate tensile strength; P, proportional limit; L, elastic limit; Y, yield point; YS, yield stress; OF, offset 0.2%

Elastic constants

(1) The longitudinal modulus of elasticity (Young's modulus, E) is defined by stress divided by strain. Since

$$\text{stress} = P/\text{area}$$
and
$$\text{strain} = \text{extension/original length},$$

$$E = \frac{P \times \text{original length}}{\text{cross-sectional area} \times \text{extension}}$$

(2) Compression modulus,

$$K = \frac{\text{volumetric stress}}{\text{volumetric strain}} = \frac{PV}{wA}$$

(3) Shear modulus (Coulomb's or torsion modulus or modulus of rigidity),

$$G = \frac{\text{shear stress}}{\text{shear strain}} = \frac{P}{A\Theta}$$

(4) Poisson's ratio $(\sigma) = \dfrac{\text{lateral strain}}{\text{longitudinal strain}}$

For the elastic load of metals it varies between 0.25 and 0.5.

Related by $E = 3K (1 - 2\sigma)$

$1 + \sigma = E/2G$

Θ is the angle of shear (radians); P is the load; A is the area of cross section; w is the reduction in volume; and V is the uncompressed volume.

Fatigue

Fatigue is a phenomenon that causes failure which takes place under conditions involving repeated flexure or fluctuating stress below the ultimate stress of the material. Fatigue strength is the highest value of stress which can be withstood for a given number of cycles without failure. Endurance, N, is the number of stress cycles, S, that can be endured before fracture. This is usually shown graphically (Figure 2.9) and is referred to as the *S-N* curves.

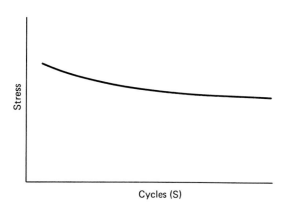

Cycles (S)

Figure 2.9 A generalised *S-N* curve

Factor of safety

Factor of safety is used in design to allow for errors, intangibles and anticipated deterioration in service. It is defined by

$$\text{Factor of safety} = \frac{\text{yield or proof stress}}{\text{working stress}}$$

If the material has little elasticity (i.e. it is brittle as glass, ceramic, etc.) then

$$\text{Factor of safety} = \frac{\text{ultimate strength}}{\text{working stress}}$$

Impact testing

Impact testing compares the brittleness and notch sensitivity of materials. The usual test consists of the determination of the energy absorbed in breaking a notched specimen by a single blow. The two accepted tests are the Charpy and the Izod tests.

Knoop hardness

The knoop diamond indenter has a rhombic base with diagonals in the ratio 1:7 and included apical angles of 130° and 172° 30′.

$$\text{Knoop hardness number} = \frac{14.23P}{d}$$

where d is the length of longer diagonal (mm).

Mohs' hardness

A scale used in mineralogy for classifying the hardness of materials. It is quite arbitrary and is merely comparative. See Table 2.16.

Table 2.16 Mohs' hardness number

Mohs' hardness number	Mineral
10	Diamond
9	Carborundum
8	Topaz
7	Quartz
6	Feldspar
5	Apatite
4	Fluorite
3	Calcite
2	Gypsum
1	Talc

Precipitation hardening

Precipitation hardening is the hardening of a metal by the rejection of a fine dispersion of rejected solute from a supersaturated solid solution. Most precipitation hardening systems operate in a similar way, peak hardness usually being attained in the later stages of coherency or at the onset of incoherency. In some systems there is no evidence of coherency strains and the fine precipitates appear to act alone as impediments to dislocation movements. See also *Dispersion strengthening*.

Quench ageing

Changes in the mechanical properties of a material as a result of ageing at room temperature or moderately elevated temperatures after quenching from a high temperature.

Rockwell hardness

The Rockwell hardness test uses an indenter applied to the surface under a minor load of 10 kg. When this ceases to penetrate, a major load is applied for 4–5 seconds and is removed as soon as the indenter ceases to penetrate further into the material, leaving the minor load still applied. The hardness is determined from the depth of penetration resulting from the application of the major load (the original effect of the minor load is ignored). Several scales (A–V) are used although the scales most commonly used are A, B and C. Equivalents are given in BS 891: Part 1 for A to K inclusive and BS 4175 for N to T scales.

Scleroscope hardness

Scleroscope hardness is based on the height of rebound of a diamond tipped hammer weighing 1/12 oz (2.36 g) falling from a fixed height. The height of rebound is a measure of the hardness.

Stainless steel

A term used to describe a very wide range of materials of which the only common feature is that they all contain chromium to enhance corrosion resistance. They can be divided into three main groups.

(1) Ferritic and hardenable chromium steels
(2) Austenitic and substantially austenitic steels
(3) Precipitation hardening steels, which includes martensitic steels, and fully and semi-austenitic steels.

Steel types

Killed steels are characterised by a more uniform chemical composition and thorough deoxidation. The latter is achieved by adding silicon, manganese and aluminium. Killed steels are used in forging, carburising, heat treating and for applications such as plates for pressure vessels, tanks, ships' hulls, bridge trusses, etc.

Semi-killed steels have characteristics intermediate between those of killed and rimmed steel.

Capped steel is cast in a mould to which a capping is added to solidify the top and enforce internal pressure build-up which gives a surface condition similar to that of rimmed steels.

Rimming steels, because of their characteristics, can be advantageously adapted to cold bending, forming and heading applications, deep drawing and pressing. They are made by partially deoxidising before casting into a mould. The skin is almost free of carbon and other impurities.

Strain ageing

Changes in the mechanical properties of metals as a result of ageing at room temperature or moderately elevated temperatures after plastic deformation.

Stress relieving

Stress relieving is a process of reducing internal residual stresses in a metal by heating to a suitable temperature and holding for a suitable period. It is sometimes simply referred to as ageing.

Superplasticity

Superplasticity is a marked increase in ductility observed when a metal is strained at a temperature at which structural changes are simultaneously occurring in the material.

Vickers hardness

The Vickers standard indenter diamond is a square-based pyramid of 136° included angle. Usually applied under 30 kg load it produces much smaller indentations than the Brinell and has the advantage that irrespective of load, the indentation is always of the same shape. The hardness number is determined as the load/area of impression in kg mm^{-2}.

$$H_D = \frac{1.8544P}{d^2}$$

where P is the load (kg), and d is the average diagonal of impression (mm).

Values are tabulated in BS 427. See also *Knoop hardness*.

Bibliography and addresses

Literature

ANGUS, H. T. (1987). *Cast iron: physical and engineering properties*, Butterworths, 3rd edn revised by R. Elliott.
BCIRA. *Engineering data on nodular cast irons* (SI units), BCIRA, Alvechurch, Birmingham.
BCIRA. *Engineering data on grey cast irons* (SI units), BCIRA, Alvechurch, Birmingham.
BCIRA. *Engineering data on malleable cast irons* (SI units), BCIRA, Alvechurch, Birmingham.
CDA. *The brasses — properties and applications*, Copper Development Association.
CDA. *The brasses — technical data*, Copper Development Association.
CIA. *A practical guide to the design of grey iron castings for engineering purposes*, Council of Ironfoundry Associations, 14 Pall Mall, London.
CIA. *Guide to the engineering properties of iron castings*, Council of Ironfoundry Associations, 14 Pall Mall, London.
CIA. *An introduction to the cast irons*, Council of Ironfoundry Associations, 14 Pall Mall, London.
CIA . *Introduction to casting design*, Council of Ironfoundry Associations, 14 Pall Mall, London.
CRAWFORD, R. J. (1981) *Plastics Engineering*, Pergamon Press, Oxford.
CRAWFORD, R. J. (1985). *Plastics and Rubber, Engineering Design and Applications*, MEP Ltd, London.
INCO. *Ni-resists and ductile Ni-resists — Engineering properties*, Ref. 2574, Inco Europe Ltd, Millbank, London.
INCO. *SG Ni-resist iron type D-2 M for cryogenic castings*, Ref. 2961, Inco Europe Ltd, Millbank, London.

INCO. *Ni-resist News* (summarises ISO specifications), Ref. 4381, Inco Europe Ltd, Millbank, London.

INCO. *Nickel SG iron — Engineering properties*, Ref. 4077, Inco Europe Ltd, Millbank, London.

JONES, S. W. (1973) *Product design and process selection*, Butterworths.

MILLER, E. (ed.). *Plastics Products Design Handbook: Part A*, Marcel Dekker Inc. for the Society of Plastics Engineers (USA).

Manufacturers and suppliers of plastics

AMARI PLASTICS LTD, 52 High Street, Kingston-on-Thames, Surrey.

AMCELL LTD (UK), 70–80 St Albans Road, Watford, Herts.

BASF (UK) LTD, Earl Road, Cheadle Hulme, Cheshire.

BAYER (UK) LTD, Bayer House, Strawberry Hill, Newbury, Berkshire.

BRITISH INDUSTRIAL PLASTICS LTD, Popes Lane, Oldbury, W. Midlands.

BRITISH PLASTICS FEDERATION, 5 Belgrave Square, London.

DU PONT (UK) LTD, Wedgewood Way, Stevenage, Herts.

ENGINEERING POLYMERS LTD, Birchwood Road Park, Risley, Cheshire.

GENERAL ELECTRICS PLASTICS EUROPE, Box 117, Bergen op Zoom, Holland.

ICI PLASTICS DIVISION, Welwyn Garden City, Herts.

MONSANTO LTD, 10–18 Victoria Street, London.

3

Stress analysis

3.1 Experimental stress analysis

The analysis of stress can be undertaken by experimental methods. These methods almost invariably involve a general technique, whereby loads are applied to a physical representation of the structure or component under analysis and the resulting strains then measured. Exceptions to this general technique such as Prandtl's membrane analogy, which compares the stresses in a torsion member with the gradients on a pressurised membrane, are rarely used in practice.

The most direct method of determining experimentally the stresses in a structure or component is to build and test a full-scale prototype. The strains can be measured during the test with, for example, strain gauges and the stresses calculated from them. Such a test specimens will not only have all the prescribed nominal geometric detail of the production item, but it should also contain actual features, such as welding distortion, resulting from the manufacturing process involved. On completion of the stress analysis the specimen can, if required, be subjected to tests from which static strength or fatigue endurance can be directly determined.

From a technical viewpoint, therefore, a full-scale test specimen has much to recommend it: such specimens are widely used in both the aircraft industry, where a high degree of structural integrity is vital, and in the car industry, where the cost can be offset against a long production run.

However, in many instances, the physical dimensions involved make full-scale testing economically unacceptable; not only does the test specimen have to be provided but a substantial rig for applying the loads is also required. The testing of a small-scale model or replica under reduced loading may then be an acceptable alternative. This is probably the oldest method of structural design. It was frequently advo-

cated in the nineteenth century, and three centuries earlier Michelangelo recommended it as a method of increasing the understanding of the behaviour of structures. It can be cheap and rapid and the results are directly applicable to full-scale structures.

In addition to reducing the model/prototype scale, it is also frequently advantageous to use a different material for the model from that used on the prototype. The advantages of such a substitution are that a model material may be selected from which a test specimen can be manufactured more cheaply than it could be from the prototype material. Also, a model material can be chosen which has a low elastic modulus so that only small loads are necessary to produce measurable strains and deflections. Both model and prototype material must, however, have a similar stress/strain relationship over the relevant stress range and this usually restricts the use of substitute materials to investigations within the elastic range.

The principles of structural similarity described elsewhere (Hetenyi, 1950) yield the following equations, which can be used to relate the elastic strains, stresses and deflections measured on models to those of their prototype equivalents:

$$\epsilon_p = \epsilon_m \frac{W_p}{W_m} \times \left(\frac{l_m}{l_p}\right)^2 \times \frac{E_m}{E_p}$$

$$\delta_p = \delta_m \frac{W_p}{W_m} \times \frac{l_m}{l_p} \times \frac{E_m}{E_p}$$

$$f_p = f_m \frac{W_p}{W_m} \times \left(\frac{l_m}{l_p}\right)^2$$

where ϵ is the strain at a particular point in the structure, δ is the linear deflection at a particular point in the structure, f is the stress at a particular point in the structure, W is the applied load, l is a particular linear dimension, and E is the elastic modulus. Suffixes p and q refer to prototype and model, respectively.

3.1.1 Model material

A variety of model materials are available, each with its own particular advantages and disadvantages. A material should be selected for each investigation, bearing in mind that it should have the following characteristics.

(1) A stress/strain curve of a form appropriate to the investigation.
(2) An elastic modulus low enough to avoid the need for heavy and expensive test rigs, but not so low that strain gauges produce significant reinforcing, or that strains due to the self weight of the specimens become significant.
(3) Where prototypes are constructed from two different materials, e.g. steel and concrete, they must be represented by model materials whose elastic moduli are in the same ratio to each other as are those of the prototype materials.
(4) Theoretically the Poisson's ratios of the prototype and model materials should be identical. In practice these ratios may vary by as much as 0.28 (steel) to 0.49 (stress frozen epoxy). Even with these extreme differences, the resulting discrepancies between prototype stresses and those indicated by the models are usually less than 10%.
(5) The material should exhibit an appropriate creep behaviour, the requirement for elastic investigations being that at any time after load application the strain must be proportional to the stress regardless of the stress level, i.e. the material's elastic modulus may vary with time but not with stress.
(6) It should be available in suitable forms for the construction of the model, e.g. resin for casting, sheet, bar or tube.
(7) It should be amenable to manufacturing processes such as machining, moulding and gluing or welding.
(8) It should be available at low cost.

The following materials, listed with their characteristics, are quoted as examples of some that have been used for model investigations.

3.1.1.1 Steel

The feature of steel that commends it as a model material is that the unique form of its stress/strain curve defines it as the only suitable model material that can be used to reproduce accurately the post yield behaviour of steel prototypes (TRRL, 1977). However, where components of a small-scale steel model are to be welded, the avoidance of excessive distortions and unrepresentative residual stresses requires specific skills. Substantial loading rigs are also required to withstand the relatively high loads involved in testing steel models.

3.1.1.2 Acrylic (such as Perspex and Plexiglass)

This material is available in the form of sheet, bar, block or tube and is suitable for the analysis of elastic stresses. It is easily cut, and components may be glued together to produce homogeneous structures using one of the proprietary adhesives, such as Tensol No. 70 cement. If residual stresses exist in the acrylic, the vapour from the adhesive can cause crazing, but this can be avoided by either annealing the acrylic at 70°C to remove the residual stresses or by using a jet of air to disperse the vapour. Acrylic softens at a temperature of 135°C and may then be moulded if required.

Under load the deflection of acrylic increases with time, the rate of creep one minute after load application being about 3% min^{-1} and after two minutes virtually zero.

The elastic modulus is about 3300 N mm^{-2}.

3.1.1.3 Rigid PVC (such as Cobex, Darvic and Vybak)

These materials are also available in sheet form but in a greater range of thicknesses than acrylic. Their stress/strain behaviour is similar to that of acrylic, but they do not normally suffer from crazing.

3.1.1.4 Epoxy resins (such as Araldite CT200 (100 parts) – HT 907 (60 parts))

Epoxies are often a more suitable material than acrylic for producing models of cast or forged components. They are supplied in the form of a resin and hardener which can be mixed and cast into the required form, the final models being made by either machining pre-cast blocks, precision casting to the required shape or cementing together machined or cast components. The elastic modulus of typically 3100 N mm^{-2} may be varied by either adjusting the resin/hardener ratio or by adding a filler material.

Epoxies tend to creep at room temperature in a similar manner to acrylic, although to a lesser extent. They are noteworthy in that, unlike acrylic, they are significantly birefringent, a property which enables them to be used for photoelastic analysis.

3.1.1.5 Silicone rubber

Rubber models can be valuable for qualitative analysis since their very low elastic modulus enables modes of distortion to be examined visually under manual loading.

The models may be cast in wood, metal, plaster or sand moulds (Monaghan, 1970).

3.1.1.6 Copper

Models with extremely thin (0.1 mm) shells can be made by electroplating copper onto a wax surface of the required shape. The wax surface is coated with a conducting paint and the wax subsequently melted away. Models produced in this way have been used in studies of buckling of spheres (Thompson, 1960).

3.1.1.7 Lead/Antimony/Arsenic alloys

These alloys have been developed for producing models which will, at room temperature, reproduce the creep strain and creep rupture characteristics of steels at high temperature. The difficulties and expense involved in making precision strain measurements at high temperatures and over long periods of time are thus avoided. The proportion of the alloying elements can be adjusted to achieve various required characteristics (Fessler and Belamy, 1973).

3.1.1.8 Polythene

Polythene has a typical elastic modulus of $200 \, N \, mm^{-2}$. This enables it to be used in conjunction with acrylic to represent composite concrete and steel structures. The use of conventional resistance strain gauges on polythene is precluded by its low modulus.

3.1.2 Loading

Loads may be applied to full-scale test specimens either by dead weights acting via strings running over pulleys as required or by the 'deflection' method, using a jack. The deflection method has two advantages:

(1) If failure of the specimen occurs during loading, the loads are automatically reduced due to the resulting increase in flexibility of the specimen. This tends to limit the damage and allows repairs and modifications to be carried out before further testing is done. Under similar circumstances, dead weight loading would be likely to destroy the specimen completely.

(2) If the specimen material is subject to creep, the effects of this may be offset by using a measuring device such as a ring gauge, made from the specimen material, for determining the 'apparent' applied load. As creep occurs in both the specimen and the ring, the strains in both remain the same, but the 'actual' applied load is relaxed. The load/deflection calibration of the ring can be calculated using an assumed elastic modulus and the same modulus then used for 'E' when converting test specimen strains to protctype strains. Alternatively, accurate theoretical calculation of the strain at some point in the specimen may be possible and in that case, strains measured at that point may be used for determining the 'apparent' applied load.

Combinations of axial load, bending moments and shears at specified positions in a loaded member can, if required, be simply applied as a single load which is offset and inclined from the neutral axis of the member by the appropriate amounts.

Where there are a number of loading points on a test specimen, the use of a single jack or dead weight acting through a whiffle tree composed of a series of interlinked beams will ensure that the loads at each point remain 'in step' throughout the tests.

3.1.3 Stress measurement

The most common method of determining the stresses in a test specimen is by the use of resistance strain gauges (Holister, 1979). These versatile tools exist in a variety of different configurations and types. For example:

(1) Single element gauges for use where the *strain* alone is required in one direction.
(2) Rosettes of two elements for use where the direct *stresses* in two specified directions are required.
(3) Rosettes of three elements for use where the directions and magnitudes of the *principal stresses* or strains are required.
(4) Micro strip gauges, each consisting of a series of up to ten elements with small gauge lengths (minimum 0.5 mm) arranged in a line. These are used to resolve the strain distributions at positions of high strain gradient, i.e. at strain concentrations.

The gauges, as their name implies, measure strains, and these may be converted to stresses using the following equations:

$$f_x = \frac{E}{1 - \mu^2} \; \left(\epsilon_x + \mu\epsilon_y \right)$$

$$f_y = \frac{E}{1 - \mu^2} \; \left(\epsilon_y + \mu\epsilon_x \right)$$

where f is stress, ϵ is strain, E is the elastic modulus, and μ is Poisson's ratio. Suffices x and y indicate two mutually perpendicular directions.

The gauges are normally connected to an automatic data logger which records the strains.

When used on plastics materials, the gauge current should not exceed 5 mA, preferably with pulsed energisation to avoid errors due to heating. Furthermore, when used on specimens made from a material with a low elastic modulus such as acrylics, subsidiary tests should be done with each type of gauge to ensure that their reinforcing effects, which result in underpredictions of the strains, are small.

While strain gauges can be used to determine the stresses at specified points, brittle lacquers serve a complementary role in that they will indicate the strain distribution over a wide area (Hearn, 1971). The lacquer is sprayed on to the test specimen and allowed to dry. On loading, visible cracks develop in the lacquer at a particular threshold strain level (typically about 500 μ strain) and, as load is increased, the spread of these cracks, which run normal to the maximum stress, gives a vivid indication of the overall strain distribution. The accuracy of the lacquer does not compare with that of resistance strain gauges, but these gauges may be fitted subsequently to determine accurately the strains at the positions of interest indicated by the lacquer tests. The combination of brittle lacquer and resistance strain gauges therefore represents a powerful analysis technique.

3.2 Photoelastic stress analysis*

Photoelastic stress analysis is an extremely powerful technique which enables a complete stress analysis to be carried out on engineering components or structures even at the design stage. It is capable of supplying solutions to both two-dimensional and three-dimensional stress problems and, for the purpose of introducing the technique, two-dimensional stress systems will be considered.

---

* The text of this section first appeared in *Chartered Mechanical Engineer* (CME) and is reproduced here by permission.

The technique of photoelastic stress analysis involves the making of a scale model in a suitable transparent plastics and placing the model in a beam of polarised light using an instrument called a polariscope. If loads are applied to the model in a similar direction to those applied in service to the actual component, then an interference pattern will be visible in the model. The interference pattern will consist of coloured fringes called isochromatics if white light is used as the illuminant or black fringes on a self-coloured background if monochromatic light is employed. These fringe patterns can be interpreted to give information on the magnitudes of the principal stresses which are present in the model and then, by using a simple formula, the stresses in the actual component can be determined even though the component material may be steel, aluminium, cast iron, glass, ceramic or even plastics itself. For the model to be compatible it is essential, of course, that the plastics from which the model is made should be elastic and stressed within its elastic limit and that the prototype material should also be elastic and stressed within its elastic limit.

A second set of interference fringes is also visible under certain conditions, which are dealt with later, and these fringes are termed isoclinics. Isoclinics enable the directions of the principal stresses at any point in the model to be determined and, from these, stress trajectories or stress flow lines can be drawn for the actual component under similar loading conditions.

For a more complete understanding of what happens when polarised light is passed through a loaded plastics model, reference should be made to Figure 3.1. This diagram shows a loaded plastics model placed between two polarising filters, respectively called a polariser and an analyser, through which a single ray of monochromatic light (that is, light of a single wavelength) is passing. At the point where the ray passes through the model the two principal stresses, σ_1 and σ_2, are inclined as indicated. It will be useful to trace the path of the single ray of light commencing from the light source.

A ray of ordinary monochromatic light can be imagined to consist of a series of transverse wave vibrations in random planes and some of these planes are represented by the direction vectors. As this ray passes through the polarising filter, which has its optical axis in the vertical plane, then only the vertical vibration of the ray will pass through. This vibration is known as a plane polarised light wave and it is sinusoidal in character. As this plane polarised light wave passes through the thickness of the model two remarkable things happen: first, the wave splits up into two separate components, one of which vibrates in the direction of the algebraic maximum principal stress σ_1 and the other vibrates in the direction of the algebraic minimum principal stress σ_2. This is because the plastics becomes

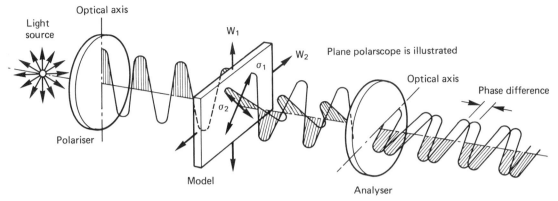

Figure 3.1 The passage of polarised light through a loaded plastics model. $\sigma_1 - \sigma_2 = nf/t$, where n is the phase difference, f is the material fringe value and t is the model thickness

birefringent or double refracting under strain. Secondly, each component wave will pass through the thickness of the plastics at a velocity which will depend upon the magnitude of the particular principal stress along whose axis each component passes and upon the optical properties of the plastics itself. (This effect is produced by the fact that the refractive indices are proportional to stress levels in the plastics.) If σ_1 has a larger magnitude than σ_2, then there will be a phase difference in the emerging component waves which can be used as a measure of the magnitude of $\sigma_1 - \sigma_2$. When these two component waves arrive at the analyser position their horizontal components will pass through and the effect will be to produce two component waves of similar amplitude and retaining the phase difference. Here are the essential ingredients for optical interference which gives rise to the fringe pattern already mentioned. The method of interpreting these fringe patterns will be presented a little later.

Another optical effect will be observed if one of the principal stresses is parallel with the optical axis

of the polariser and reference should be made to Figure 3.2. In this case, the emerging plane polarised light wave enters the model in a direction parallel to a principal stress — say, σ_1. Since there is no horizontal component in the σ_2 direction, the plane polarised light wave passes through unchanged and, in meeting the analyser, it is vibrating perpendicularly to the horizontal polarising axis of this filter. Consequently, no light can pass through and, to an observer looking into the polariscope, a black spot would be present at the point under consideration. This black spot would tend to lie with other black spots to form a continuous fringe which is termed an isoclinic. The definition of an isoclinic is that it is the locus of points at which there is a constant inclination of principal stress directions.

A synchronous rotation of the polariser and analyser to, say, 20° from the horizontal position would produce other isoclinic lines on which principal stress directions would be 20° to the former case. It will be realised that these isoclinic lines cannot give any information on the magnitudes of the principal

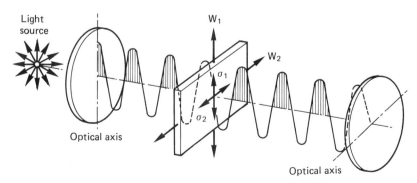

Figure 3.2 Having one of the principal stresses parallel with the optical axis of the polariser gives rise to an isoclinic fringe

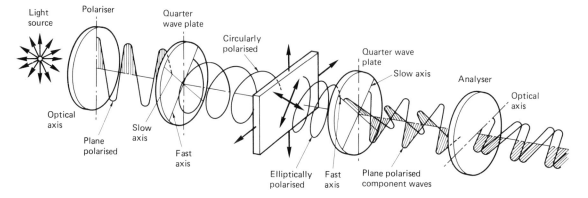

Figure 3.3 Passage of polarised light using quarter-wave plates

stress differences but in fact give valuable information on principal stress directions.

In using a plane polariscope, similar to the one illustrated in both Figures 3.1 and 3.2, the isoclinic lines will be superimposed upon the fringe pattern and this can be very confusing when information on stress magnitudes is required. Extremely rapid rotation of the polariser and analyser synchronously would eliminate the isoclinic lines from the fringe pattern but a more practical arrangement is to place what are termed quarter wave plates into the optical system, as illustrated in Figure 3.3.

It has already been seen that the light emerging from the polariser will be plane polarised light but, on passing through the first quarter wave plate (Q_1), it will be changed into circularly polarised light which does not have any directional property. The circularly polarised light entering the model will eventually emerge as elliptically polarised light and the second quarter wave plate (Q_2) will convert it back into two plane polarised component waves. Because of the non-directional character of circularly polarised light, the isoclinic fringes will not be produced in the model and all the observer will see under these conditions are the isochromatic fringes which give information on the stress magnitudes.

A model of a disc in diametral compression is shown in Figure 3.4. The illustration shows the isochromatic fringes only, as the isoclinic fringes have been eliminated by the use of circularly polarised light.

3.2.1 Interpretation of isochromatic fringe patterns

The fundamental formula for obtaining quantitative stress determinations from isochromatic fringe patterns is as follows:

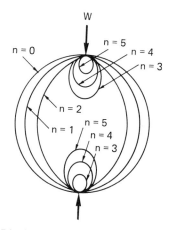

Figure 3.4 Disc in diametral compression

$$\sigma_1 - \sigma_2 = \frac{nf}{t}$$

where σ_1 is the algebraic maximum principal stress, σ_2 is the algebraic minimum principal stress, n is the fringe order, f is the material fringe value (an optical property of the plastics material), and t is the model thickness.

It is useful to compare isochromatic fringe patterns in two-dimensional models with contour maps. For example, Figure 3.5 shows a fringe pattern of a disc in diametral compression together with a plot indicating fringe orders across the horizontal diameter. Fringe orders are counted from points where $\sigma_1 - \sigma_2$ is equal to zero in a similar manner to the way in which contour lines on a map are counted from sea level datum. As the maximum shear stress τ_{max} is equal to $\frac{1}{2}(\sigma_1 + \sigma_2)$ it will be seen that the individual fringes may be considered as being lines of constant maximum shear stress. Close spacing of fringes indicates steep stress gradients.

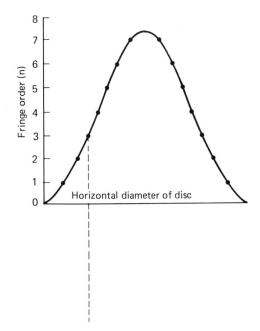

Figure 3.5 Fringe pattern of a disc in diametral compression

3.2.2 Stress determinations on free boundaries

At any point on a free boundary there can be only one principal stress and it will be tangential to the boundary. If the tangential stress is tensile then it will be the algebraic maximum principal stress σ_1 whilst if it is compressive it will be the algebraic minimum principal stress σ_2.

Consider the example in Figure 3.6 of a ring in diametral compression and, in particular, points A and B on the outer and inner boundaries, respectively. From a consideration of the geometry of the model and its loading it can be inferred that at point A the tangential stress will be tensile and will thus be σ_1. At point B the tangential stress will be compressive and will, therefore, be σ_2.

On a free boundary, therefore:

$$\sigma_1 = \frac{nf}{t}, \text{ where } \sigma_2 = 0$$

$$\sigma_2 = -\frac{nf}{t}, \text{ where } \sigma_1 = 0$$

(The negative sign indicates a compressive stress.) As $f/t = F$ (model fringe value) the above equations can be simplified to:

$$\sigma_1 = nF$$

$$\sigma_2 = -nF$$

Figure 3.7 shows the fringe pattern in the right hand half of a ring under diametral compression and at point A the fringe order 'n' can be counted as four commencing from the zero point which is indicated. The fringe order at point B will be twelve. If we assume that the model is made from Araldite CT-200 the material fringe value in sodium light is 10 kN m^{-2} per fringe and its thickness is 0.005 m; then the following calculations can be carried out to determine the boundary stresses at points A and B:

Model fringe value

$$F = \frac{f}{t} = \frac{10}{0.005} = 2000 \text{ kN m}^{-2} \text{ per fringe}$$

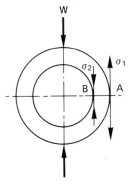

Figure 3.6 At point A the relevant equation is $\sigma_1 = nf/t$; at point B the relevant equation is $\sigma_2 = -nf/t$

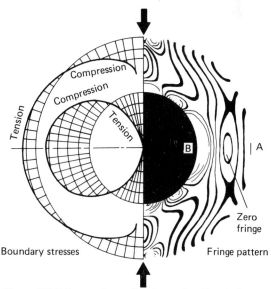

Figure 3.7 Fringe pattern of a ring under diametral compression

At point A

$$\sigma_1 = \frac{nf}{t} = nF$$

$$= 4 \times 2000$$

$$= 8000 \text{ kN m}^{-2}$$

At point B

$$\sigma_2 = -\frac{nf}{t} = -nF$$

$$= -12 \times 2000$$

$$= -24\,000 \text{ kN m}^{-2}$$

By counting fringe orders at other points on the outer and inner boundaries complete stress plots can be obtained as shown in the left hand half of Figure 3.7.

It may appear difficult to isolate the $(\sigma_1 - \sigma_2) = 0$ positions from which to start counting fringe orders, but if the model is viewed in white light then these positions will show up as lines or points which are black in colour. Reverting to monochromatic light would then allow the fringe orders to be counted from these points.

The signs of the boundary stresses can be determined by several methods but the photoflex urethane compensator will be described. If a small square of photoflex is squeezed between the finger and thumb, as shown in Figure 3.8, with its diagonal tangential to point A in the ring then increasing pressure on the compensator will eventually produce blackness at point A. The compressive stress in the compensator has thus been cancelled out by a tensile tangential stress in the model. If a similar

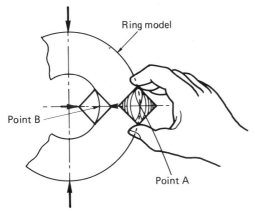

Figure 3.8 Photoflex urethane compensator

procedure is followed for point B then pressure on the compensator will increase the fringe order at point B as the compressive stresses in the compensator will be added to the compressive stresses at point B. However, as a double check, if the compensator is turned through 90° with its axis normal to the boundary at point B then blackness will result as the pressure is increased. The above procedure assumes that the model material has positive birefringence which is the case for most photoelastic materials (Hilborne and Sharples, 1970).

3.2.3 Stresses at points within boundaries

In a two-dimensional model, the maximum shear stress or, alternatively, the difference of the two principal stresses $(\sigma_1 - \sigma_2)$ can be obtained by using the fundamental formula already referred to.

Although it is not often required to separate individual principal stresses within a model boundary, as in the great majority of engineering examples it is the boundary stresses which are the most important, the individual principal stresses can nevertheless be separated using oblique incidence, shear difference or other methods and the references (Drucker, 1951; Stokey and Hughes, 1954; Hiltscher, 1961; Allison and Blackmore, 1968) may be followed.

Directions of principal stresses at any point can be determined by passing plane polarised light through a model and rotating the polariser and analyser synchronously until an isoclinic line passes through the point. The angle of rotation of the polariser and the analyser will then give the direction of one of the principal stresses at that point with reference to the polarising axis of the polariscope. Tracing a family of isoclinic lines for different degrees of rotation of the polariser and analyser enables stress trajectories to be subsequently plotted, as shown in Figure 3.9.

3.2.4 Transference of stresses from model to prototype

Having obtained the stresses in the model, it is a simple matter to relate them to the stresses in the actual prototype by use of the following equation:

$$\sigma_p = \sigma_m \times \frac{W_p}{W_m} \times \frac{l_m}{l_p} \times \frac{t_m}{t_p}$$

where suffixes p and m refer to prototype and model, respectively, and where σ is the stress, W is the load, l is the length, and t is the thickness. This

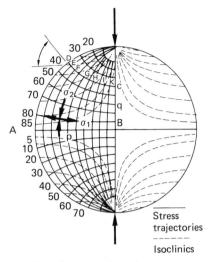

Figure 3.9 Plot of stress trajectories

equation is used for two-dimensional, or plain stress, problems only and a slightly modified version is used for three-dimensional analyses.

3.2.5 Calibration of model materials

One of the most convenient methods of calibrating model materials is to load a small disc, say of about 40 mm diameter, in diametral compression and to measure the fringe order at the centre of the disc. Using the Tardy method of compensation, which is later described, the fringe order can be measured to an accuracy of 0.02 fringe.

In Figure 3.10 the stress situation at the centre of a disc under this loading condition is shown. At the centre of the disc

$$(\sigma_1 - \sigma_2) = \frac{8W}{\pi dt}$$

where W is the diametral force, d is the diameter, and t is the thickness.

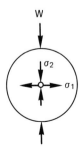

Figure 3.10 Disc loading conditions

The fundamental equation of photoelasticity was seen to be:

$$(\sigma_1 - \sigma_2) = \frac{nf}{t}$$

Therefore:

$$f = \frac{8W}{\pi dn}$$

With, for example, Araldite CT200 epoxy resin material, it is advisable, because of optical creep, to leave the load on the disc for about 45 minutes and then to take the fringe order reading. By this time, the optical creep will have stabilised. Similarly, the load on an actual model would also require to be left on for the same time before readings are taken. Optical creep, which is manifested by an increase of fringe order with time, varies with different model materials but some typical examples are shown in Figure 3.11.

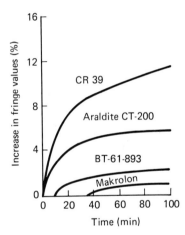

Figure 3.11 Graph showing optical creep

3.2.6 Measurement of fractional fringe orders

Various methods of compensation are available for the measurement of fractional fringe orders but one of the most popular, which is termed the Tardy Method of Compensation, is described below.

When polariscope elements are set up to give dark field conditions, as in Figure 3.12, the fringes are integral orders (e.g., 1, 2, 3, 4 . . .). It is frequently necessary to measure fringe orders accurately at points which may lie between two integral order fringes and the Tardy method is a convenient means of determining fringe orders to an accuracy of 0.02

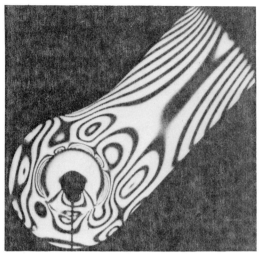

(a)

(b)

Figure 3.12 (a) Stress pattern of loaded lug; (b) typical stress on gear tooth

fringe. The procedure in using this method is as follows:

(1) Remove the quarter wave plates so as to observe the model in plane polarised light.
(2) Rotate the polariser and analyser synchronously until an isoclinic line passes through the point of interest.
(3) Replace the quarter wave plates into the system and rotate each by the same amount that the polariser and analyser has been rotated (in the same direction, of course).
(4) Rotate the analyser in such a direction that the lowest order of fringe next to the point is moved to the point and maximum extinction obtained.

(5) Divide the angle of rotation of the analyser by 180° and this will give the fractional part of the lower order fringe relating to the point under consideration.

Most polariscopes have a fractional fringe order scale on the analyser from which the fractional fringe can be read directly.

3.2.7 *Photoelastic model-making materials*

The correct choice of plastics material for model-making has an important bearing on the success of a photoelastic analysis.

Details of the materials in common use are given below and in Table 3.1 will be found some of their more important mechanical and optical properties. Please note that these are properties at room temperature and that the quoted fringe values relate to the use of sodium light with a wavelength of 589.3 nm. If mercury green light, having a wavelength of 546.1 nm, is used then the relevant fringe values may be found from the following equation:

Material fringe value (Hg) = Material fringe value (Na) × 546.1/589.3.

3.2.71 **Araldite CT200 epoxy resin**

This resin is the most widely used photoelastic material in UK applications. In the cast state, it exhibits good mechanical properties and strength, with little creep or time-edge effect. To avoid time-edge effect, which is caused by either absorption or loss of moisture from the surfaces of models, giving rise to compressive or tensile edge stresses, the models made from this material can be stored in an oven at a temperature of around 75°C (Strannigan, 1964).

Araldite CT200 is cast with hardener HT901 (phthalic anhydride) in the following resin/hardener proportions:

Araldite CT200   100 parts by weight
Hardener HT901   25–30 parts by weight

Machining of Araldite CT200 materials does not usually present any problems. It is performed with sharp tools, using low rates of feed and a copious supply of coolant.

3.2.7.2 **Columbia resin CR39**

Being colourless and of good clarity, this material is a popular choice for two-dimensional photoelastic demonstrations models. It has moderate mechanical strength, displays a moderate amount of creep, but exhibits minimal time-edge effect. Owing to the

Table 3.1 Properties of some photoelastic model materials at room temperature

Material	Tensile strength (MN m^{-2})	(lb in^{-2})	Modulus of elasticity (MN m^{-2})	(lb in^{-2})	Poisson's ratio	Fringe value of material at 589.3 nm (kN m^{-1} fr^{-1})	(lb in^{-1} fr^{-1})
Araldite CT200/HT901	70–90	10000 13000	2700–3400	0.4–0.5×10^6	0.36	9.6–10.5	55–60
Araldite CT200/HT907	70–90	10000 13000	2700–3400	0.4–0.5×10^6	0.34	14.7–15.8	84–90
Columbia Resin CR39	48	7000	1700–2400	0.25–0.35×10^6	0.44	14.9–17.5	85–100
Photoflex	–	–	0.7–4.1	100–600	0.48	0.14–0.17	0.8–1.0

presence of initial stresses in the plane of the sheet, the material is only suitable for normal incidence work. At oblique incidence, it will exhibit pronounced birefringence. With conventional machining, CR39 is prone to chipping. This condition can be avoided by the use of hand filing or high-speed routing.

3.2.7.3 Photoflex polyurethane

This is used as the photoelastic material for certain dynamic applications, where problems of self-weight are involved, or simply for ease of demonstration. The material has a very high stress-optic sensitivity, quite low modulus of elasticity and does not suffer from creep or time-edge. Machining of Photoflex is carried out at high cutting speeds. In the case of sheet material for two-dimensional analysis, shape cutting can be achieved with a high speed router.

Bibliography

ALLISON, J. M. and BLAKEMORE, R. H. (1968) 'Analysis of photoelastic data for stress separations', *JBCSA*, Recent advances in stress analysis, **4**, pp. 4–7.

DRUCKER, D. C. (1951) 'The method of oblique incidence in photoelasticity', *Proc. of the Society for Experimental Stress Analysis*, **VIII**, 1, pp. 51–66.

DURELLI, A. J. and RILEY, W. F. (1965) *Introduction to Photomechanics*, Prentice-Hall.

FESSLER, H. and BELAMY, R. A. (1973) *Use of models for the prediction of creep behaviour of components*, I. Mech. E. Conf. Publication 13, pp. 170.1–170.10.

FROCHT, M. M. (1941 and 1948) *Photoelasticity*, Vols. I and II.

HEARN, E. J. (1971) *Brittle Lacquers for Strain Measurement*, Merrow Publishing.

HENDRY, A. W. (1966) *Photoelastic Stress Analysis*, Pergamon Press, Oxford.

HETENYI, M. (ed.) (1950) *Handbook of Experimental Stress Analysis*, John Wiley, New York.

HEYWOOD, R. B. (1969) *Photoelasticity for Designers*, Pergamon Press, Oxford.

HILBORNE, G. L. and SHARPLES, K. (1970) 'A cheap and easily used photoelastic compensator', *Strain*, **6**, 4.

HILTSCHER, R. (1961) 'Development of the lateral extensometer in two-dimensional photoelasticity', *Proceedings of the 1st International Symposium on Photoelasticity*, pp. 43–56.

HOLISTER, G. S. (ed.) (1979) *Developments in Stress Analysis — 1*, Applied Science Publishers, London.

KUSKE, A. and ROBERTSON, G. (1974) *Photoelastic Stress Analysis*, John Wiley.

MONAGHAN, M. L. (1970) 'A quantitative rubber model analysis technique', Conf. on Experimental Stress Analysis, Cambridge.

STOKEY, W. F. and HUGHES, W. F. (1954) 'Tests on the conducting paper analogy for determining isopachic lines', *Proc. of the Society for Experimental Stress Analysis*, **XII**, 2, pp. 77–82.

STRANNIGAN, J. S. (1964) *Variation of edge stress during storage of an epoxy resin*, National Engineering Laboratory Report No. 127.

THOMPSON, J. M. T. (1960) 'Making of thin metal shells for model stress analysis', *J. Mech. Eng. Sci.*, **2**, 2.

TRRL (1977) *Recommended Standard Practices for Structural Testing of Steel Models*, Transport and Road Research Laboratory, Suppl. Report No. 254.

4

Bearings

In the last half-century, habits and customs have undergone a dramatic transformation. Man has grown wings and flies faster than sound; he can explore the ocean bed and carry out tasks at depths hitherto uncontemplated; he travels hundreds of miles over smooth ribbons of concrete; he can live in one town and work in another. The domestic kitchen, once a room of drudgery, has been transformed into a centre of efficiency with electrical servants summoned by the push of a button. The home contains an endless variety of entertainments awaiting the turn of a dial. Man can select his own brand of climate regardless of the weather.

All this progress has been the result of invention and discovery and, although electronics, as distinct from mechanics, plays an increasingly large part in our daily lives, in the final analysis there is nearly always something that has to move or be moved within every technological product. And wherever there is movement there are bearings.

Bearings are viewed differently by different people:

> 'Now in mutual glee the bearings glint
> In oil rinsed circles of blind ecstasy'

(Quoted from the late Sir George Dowty's opening address to the 1972 Cheltenham Bearing Conference.)

Engineers do not describe their bearings in so colourful or poetic a manner, but all engineers, whether as design draughtsmen or as technical executives, are faced at some time with the task of selecting and fitting bearings.

Bearings cut across specialist frontiers in that they are to be found in widely diverse applications, ranging from instruments to large marine propeller shafts, yet they all face the same parameters and constraints to a greater or lesser degree.

The purpose of this chapter is to provide a backcloth against which the reader can view his own problems and hopefully recognise the direction in which he should pursue his quest for answers to his specific problems.

There are existing, and no doubt will continue to exist, designers who choose a bearing type either intuitively or from personal preference. While this approach might be condemned, quite frequently the designer is unwittingly using a selection process of considerable merit.

It is easy to adopt a parochial attitude in considering bearing design and application and the turbine designer might be forgiven for not allowing that the instrument designer has bearing problems of similar magnitude although not of similar size. There are, however, two prime requirements common to all bearings. These are:

(1) to support the load,
(2) to permit motion.

These may be regarded as obvious, but they provide the starting point to develop further headings, e.g.

Load	Environment
Motion	Life span
Location	Maintenance
Accuracy	Cost—initial
Quality	Cost—in service
Repeatability	

Other headings will undoubtedly be conceived and to these it will be necessary to add detail to cover a particular requirement for a specific application. The objective is to lay down the basic functional requirements before looking for the bearing.

The material in this chapter first appeared in *Engineers' Digest*, and is reproduced here by permission.

While an ideal bearing might be described as that providing no redundant function and using existing features to the maximum advantage, it is inevitable that the final selection of a bearing will be a compromise, as indeed are most selection processes in engineering.

There is a wealth of information available concerning the characteristics and capabilities of all types of bearings. Full use of this information will not, however, be made if the right questions are not asked by the designer. And the earlier the bearing manufacturers are asked the questions, the greater the chance of making an optimum choice. Although a particular bearing may, from bearing design data, appear to be the best answer, it may well mean a housing which is not readily integrated into the basic design or, in overall terms, is expensive. It is therefore essential to study outside factors because these too govern the selection of an ideal bearing.

The far-reaching effects on overall weight can be all too easily overlooked. Apart from the basic bearing weight/cost relationship, there are often more important additional and attendant effects on the overall machine design brought about by:

(1) basic bearing dimensions,
(2) the need or otherwise for a lubrication system,
(3) the provision to replace a bearing,
(4) the effects of shaft and/or housing flexure.

Similarly a look at bearing cost can be wholly misleading. The true cost is the overall equipment cost and, frequently, operating and maintenance costs not forgetting lubrication and/or cooling costs.

The foregoing generalities warn the engineer that the selection of a bearing is far from a simple task. Nevertheless, these facets must be kept in mind when considering the next step which is to observe the characteristics of the envelope generated by speed and load parameters for each type of bearing. Generalised shapes are shown in Figure 4.1, and these can aid bearing selection, since the best bearing is likely to be the one that has an envelope similar to that of the intended application.

So far no mention has been made of materials. The material for the shaft is usually dictated by outside considerations, but where a shaft runs directly in its bearing the material of the shaft must be compatible (in for example wear characteristics) with the material used for the bearing. In general, the bearing material will be softer than that of the shaft, but subsequent paragraphs will detail the importance of material compatibility.

Another important consideration is whether or not a lubrication supply is possible or even desirable, since this will affect the initial choice of bearing. For example, in a water pump it may be preferable to specify a water-lubricated bearing or one that has inherent lubricity. To a degree this latter parameter superimposes a heat dissipation problem which in many applications provides the prime reason for a lubrication system.

An even more hostile environment is found in a turbine exhaust diverter valve flap isolater designed to rotate through 90 degrees, switching the 535°C gas between a heat exchanger and a by-pass/blast stack. The stub shaft of the flap is of 130 mm diameter stainless steel and exerts a torque of 25 000 N m. At a peak temperature of 350°C the shafts expand axially 12 mm. Deva metal was selected for the shaft bearings because of its ability to operate in temperatures of up to 1000°C in corrosive, abrasive and hostile environments while retaining its self-lubricating properties (Figure 4.2 and 4.3).

A not unimportant aspect is the installation of bearings, whatever the type. The best and most suitable bearing is doomed to an early failure if it is incorrectly fitted. Today's economics in a mass market preclude the individual fitting of bearings. Therefore the bearing not only has to be made from the right material with appropriate clearances, etc., but must also be designed to ensure that it cannot be incorrectly fitted or distorted. There is a whole new specialisation developed in bearings and their specific applications, particularly plain bearings. The most important of these are those concerned with shell bearings for diesel engines of all sizes and petrol engines for cars.

For this reason alone, it is highly desirable that early discussions with the bearing manufacturers be held when these types of applications are under consideration.

4.1 Plain bearings

Plain metal bearings have moved a long way from a cast iron housing into which white metal was poured and subsequently machined. Yet the basic concepts still exist and white metal (Babbitt metal) is still poured into cast iron housings for certain applications. Emphasis has, however, moved from the direct-lined housing to prefinished thin-wall shell bearings. The basic concept is simple — a steel backing, either half or full circle — is lined with the appropriate bearing material pressed or machined to size so that it can be placed in the housing ready to receive the shaft.

The current production of these trouble-free shell bearings (although simple in concept there have been many problems to overcome) is a tribute to the perseverance and skill of the bearing manufacturers. They are relatively cheap and the steel backing takes the load; the actual bearing material is thin which improves its fatigue resistance, and the whole bear-

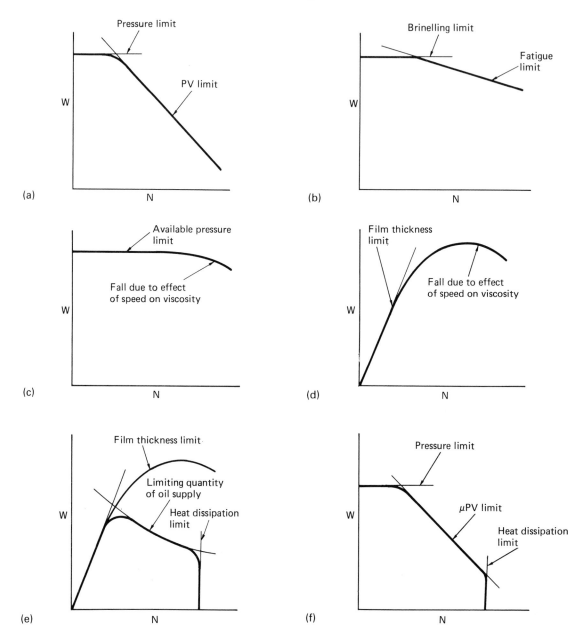

Figure 4.1 Performance envelopes for different bearing types plotted on a log scale. (a) Rubber bearings; (b) rolling bearings; (c) externally pressurised film bearings (hydrostatic); (d) pressure-fed film bearings (hydrodynamic); (e) self-contained film bearings; (f) porous metal bearings

ing can be easily altered to meet the changing power developments of the application. The thin-walled concept readily lends itself to high-volume production in a variety of bearing materials. As may be obvious, this type of bearing predominates in car engines.

4.1.1 *Metallic bearings*

Developments in bearing materials have been slow but thorough, each improvement being fully consolidated. The number of different material groups is relatively small, typically:

Figure 4.2 Valve flap isolator: close-up of Deva metal bearing

(1)   Copper-based alloys
(2)   Aluminium-based alloys
(3)   White metals with tin base
(4)   White metals with lead base

These have been listed above in descending order of material hardness and fatigue strength.

Metal bearings are synonymous with the term lubricated bearings, since a metal shaft rubbing directly in a metal bearing without a separating oil film will ultimately seize. The requirement to operate without a separating oil film can, however, be met in other ways, as will be discussed.

At this stage in considering metal bearings it is as well to distinguish between (a) the hydrodynamic bearing, and (b) the hydrostatic bearing.

In a hydrostatic bearing, the surfaces are separated by a film of lubricant forced between them under pressure from an external source pump. Since the film is not generated by the relative movement of the bearing surfaces (as in a hydrodynamic bearing), full film conditions exist at zero speeds. With hydrostatic bearings, the bearing characteristics and the stiffness of the bearing are usually controlled by an external controller of which there are many variations. A widely used control device is the simple orifice or capillary which has the advantage of making the bearing system independent of bulk and ambient temperature changes. Slot restrictors are simple to manufacture and offer similar characteristics as capillaries.

The load capacity of a hydrostatic bearing is primarily dependent on the available supply pressure of the lubricant. Running speed has little effect on load, although, with liquid lubricants, a slight fall in capacity may occur due to a reduction in viscosity caused by an increase in temperature, as shown in Figure 4.1. The principle of operation is shown in Figure 4.4, from which it will be seen that the bearing has recesses over which the pressure acts uniformly. The recess pressure is dependent on bearing load and area, while the flow rate depends on the difference between the supply pressure and the recess pressure and also on the characteristics of the control device.

With the hydrodynamic type of fluid film bearing, the load capacity increases with speed provided that the oil film is maintained. The basic mechanism for this is the natural occurrence wherever two surfaces in relative motion have a liquid present to act as a lubricant. The wedge formation is shown in Figure

Figure 4.3 Valve flap isolator: position of one of the bearings

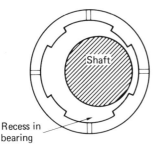

Figure 4.4 Eccentricity of shaft exaggerated in diagram of hydrostatic bearing

4.5 and, initially, as the shaft starts to rotate, the point of contact moves in an opposite direction but, in so doing, squeezes out the lubricant. This action causes a pressure which lifts the shaft away from the bearing surface and the shaft eventually finds a position of equilibrium. The natural wedge shape is achieved with a circular shaft in a circular bearing, and this simple geometry will meet the majority of normal applications. However, more complex bore shapes can be made, e.g., lemon bores, lobe bores etc., necessary in some applications to give shaft stability and acceptable stiffness and damping characteristics.

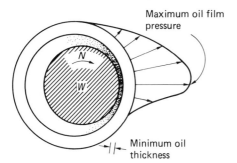

Figure 4.5 Pressure distribution in hydrodynamic bearing

The oil film to ensure the hydrodynamic effect is usually maintained by an external pressurised lubrication system, although oil thrower discs and rings can be used as can wick-fed lubricators. However, for other than pressure-fed systems, the difficulties of maintaining a continuous film result in a lower load capacity and lower safe operating speeds. In addition to this effect, the absence of a flow of lubricant means that the heat generated has to be dissipated directly into the main body of the assembly.

All bearings have a friction torque loss and, with the exception of hydrostatic bearings, this torque will be a maximum on starting. Hydrostatic bearings have a friction torque proportional to speed with zero torque at zero speed. Figure 4.6 compares the

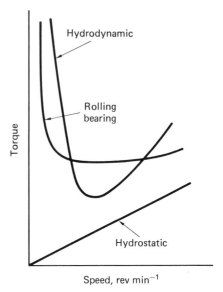

Figure 4.6 Torque/speed characteristics of rolling and fluid film bearings

torque/speed characteristics of rolling and fluid film bearings.

With all forms of hydrodynamic bearings the performance is very sensitive to the establishment of a full converging film in the region where the pressure has to be generated to carry the applied load. It is therefore important to feed an adequate amount of lubricant in the right place, and it is in this context that the size and geometry of oil grooves are important (ESDU Data Sheet 66023). The design of the groove should ensure that the lubricant is adequately fed into the bearing, while at the same time allowing maximum bearing surface area in highly loaded regions. Additionally it is known that grooves can affect the onset of cavitation erosion within a bearing, and this is instrumental in the bearing surface breaking up. Cavitation in this context is only just beginning to be understood, and bearing manufacturers are earnestly studying these problems.

For the user, the point has arrived when a design decision has to be made and, depending on the type of application, calculations carried out. There are many ways in which a detailed design analysis can be made, and accepted ways can be found in advanced text books, the ESDU Data Sheets, literature and data produced by bearing manufacturers, and the many specialised papers published by professional institutions. A paper of particular interest is 'Designing a plain bearing' by D. R. Garner of The Glacier Metal Company, which was presented at an International Conference at Leeds University in 1975.

A significant advance in the design methodology of plain bearings has been developed by The Glacier Metal Co. Ltd. with the use of charts. These are based on setting multi-variable data into two-dimensional design charts developed by F. A. Martin of The Glacier Metal Co. and are fully reported and discussed in the 1977 Proceedings of Information Systems for Designers. A specific application of these charts for plain journal bearings operating under a steady load was presented by Martin and Garner at the First European Tribology Congress and published by the Institution of Mechanical Engineers.

To complement these aids for designing bearings for safe operation, Glacier has developed computer programs for specific bearings and applications, and these enable many variables to be fed into the computer. The results can then be analysed and an optimum bearing designed. Typical computer programs include:

(1) engine bearings—main and big ends,
(2) plain steadily loaded journal bearings,
(3) thrust bearings,
(4) non-circular bearings,
(5) tilting-pad bearings.

Figure 4.7 provides a useful guide to bearing selection. It can be seen from these curves that the rubbing type of bearing is suitable for relatively low speeds or for oscillatory motion, and that rolling bearings have their main field of application for shafts below about 50 mm in diameter. It will also be seen that fluid film bearings are the best type for use at high speeds.

It has already been said that the design of a single part of an assembly requires knowledge of other components in that assembly. This knowledge covers the restrictions placed on the design of the other part by other components and the influence of all the parts on the performance of the end product. An example is the design of plain hydrodynamic bearings for reciprocating engines in which the fundamental dimensions of the bearings are largely influenced by crankshaft parameters. It is a subject which has grown in importance, since the size of engines for a given power has shrunk to a point where it is all too easy to underdesign the crankshaft bearings in planning the engine layout. Vickery *et al.* (1974) considered these aspects in some depth, with particular emphasis on the surface finish of the crankshaft. The importance of the material and surface finish cannot be overestimated and information obtained from practice by the use of the scanning electron microscope has produced valuable data.

The remarks on plain bearings have so far been confined to metallic types needing a full oil supply system. There are, of course, many applications where this is either inconvenient or impossible and

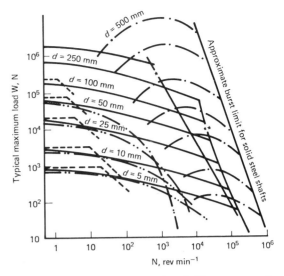

Figure 4.7 Maximum load capacity of different types of bearing at various speeds:

– – – – – Plain bearings in which the surfaces rub together;
— · — Hydrodynamic plain bearings;
———— Rolling bearings;
– – – – Porous bearings impregnated with lubricant. Externally pressurised bearings can be used over the whole range of loads and speeds.

** Approximate maximum speeds for gas turbine special ball bearings.
* Approximate maximum speeds for commercial rolling bearings

therefore a range of materials to meet these demands has been developed.

4.1.2 *Composite bearings*

Fatigue strength, conformability and compatibility of certain plastics make them ideal as bearing materials except where very high temperatures are present. The Glacier Metal Company, for example, has developed a range of bearings based on an acetal copolymer bonded onto a steel backing via a porous sintered interlayer. The thickness of the plastics above the sinter is 0.254 mm and this, where necessary, can be bored or reamed to a minimum of 0.127 mm. The sinter between the plastics and steel plays an important part in providing a high capacity loading.

The particular virtue of this type of bearing is, however, the capability of the acetal copolymer whose characteristics can be further enhanced by (a) the incorporation in the polymer of a small percentage of solid lubricant and (b) imposing on the surface of the plastics lining a pattern of indents that act as a grease reservoir.

This composite material, known as DX, is not recommended for use without a lubricant, but in the presence of a trace of oil or grease its performance is superior to that of other known marginally lubricated materials. Full details for selecting the appropriate bearing dimensions, wear rates and lubrication requirements are given in Glacier's Designer's Handbook.

Glacier Metal's DU range of bearings requires no lubrication and can be used at all temperatures between −200 and +280°C and is resistant to most solvents, industrial liquids and gases. DU composite material (Figure 4.12) consists of three bonded layers, a steel backing strip and a porous bronze matrix impregnated and overlaid with a PTFE/lead bearing material. During normal operation a thin film from the PTFE lining is transferred to the opposing surface (e.g., the shaft) and maintained there throughout the working life of the bearing.

The benefit gained by the addition of the lead or lead oxide to PTFE is associated with an exothermic chemical reaction which takes place locally at the rubbing interfaces and results in a chemically bonded film of PTFE on the mating surface.

Complementary to the DU range is Glacier's DQ grade, which is supplied in bar or tube form or which can be supplied as moulded parts.

More recently Glacier introduced Hi-eX bearing material, one of a range of composite plain bearing materials which offer feasible solutions to dry, marginally and hydrodynamically lubricated bearing problems. It is particularly suited to oscillating, frequent stop/start and high-load/low-speed conditions. Hi-eX is a composite material in which a porous bronze sinter is bonded to a steel backing and impregnated and lined with a polymer surface of PEEK containing various fillers including PTFE and graphite.

Also of interest to the designer will be Glacier's DEVA bearing materials as a range of standard blanks and machined components. DEVA metal is a high performance self-lubricating bearing material produced by advanced powder metallurgy techniques, its metallic matrix incorporating a fine graphite powder. It can operate at temperatures up to 600°C in hostile environments and can be water-lubricated.

A more recent innovation to the plain bearing scene is that developed by Ampep plc. Known as Fiberslip bearings, they have been successfully used in aircraft, where considerable performance data have been amassed. Fiberslip is constructed from a top cloth consisting of glass fibres interwoven with PTFE yarns. This top cloth is then laminated under heat and pressure with a backing glass cloth containing phenolic resin. During the lamination process the phenolic resin in the backing cloth bleeds through the top bearing layer and sets to produce a hard plastics-like sheet. Fiberslip laminates provide a bearing surface consisting of approximately 50% PTFE and 50% resin and a reverse side consisting of approximately 50% resin and 50% glass. The material is then bonded to various bearing configurations such as cylindrical bushes and spherical bearings.

4.1.3 *Carbon bearings*

A particularly important material for bearings is carbon. It has long been known that the coefficient of friction of carbon is low, particularly when it occurs in the form of graphite. Although by nature it is ideally suited for dry friction applications, it can be used under non-lubricating fluid conditions. Perfect hydrodynamic conditions are not often met in practice, and solid-solid contacts are often formed. The use of carbon in these applications does not eliminate the contacts so formed but avoids the risk of seizure. In addition, non-impregnated graphites have the advantage, by reason of their porosity, that they are able to hold lubricants within their pores and this maintains a permanent liquid film. When impermeable materials must be used, carbon may be impregnated with resins or metals.

Carbon is primarily used where lubrication is either impossible, undesirable, difficult or costly; suitable environments include:

(1) high temperatures (up to 600°C),
(2) corrosive fluids and atmospheres,
(3) avoidance of contamination by lubricants (e.g. textiles, food, etc.).

Two factors which limit the load and speed for a carbon bearing are the wear rate and the temperature. Although carbon will withstand very high temperatures in a reducing atmosphere, oxidation starts at about 400 to 500°C in normal atmospheres. Carbon bearings should be as simple as possible in

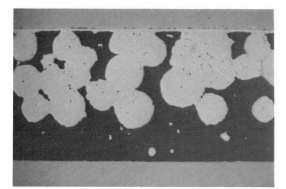

Figure 4.8 Microsection through Glacier Metal's DU bearing material

shape and, since carbon is a ceramic, care should be taken to avoid chipping at the edges. For this reason, cylindrical forms are recommended with a well defined chamfer on the bore and on the outside diameter. The housing should also be chamfered to ensure an easy lead-in, and the manufacturer's instructions should be adhered to in considering interference fits. Lubricant grooves can be machined on the bore, but care should be taken to ensure that they are not introduced at the maximum loading points. The wall thickness of a carbon bush without lubrication grooves can be based on the formula.

$$\text{thickness} = 3 + 0.10D$$

where D is the journal diameter in millimetres.

Shafts running in carbon bearings should be made of steel or cast iron, although care should be taken to ensure that the surface is free from rust as this will cause very rapid wear. Non-ferrous shafts should be avoided. For minimum wear the shafts should be machined; too smooth a finish can also give rise to abnormal wear. Clearances between shaft and bore are usually taken as proportional to diameter of the shaft, i.e. for a dry-running bearing $0.003\ D$ and for a lubricated bearing $0.001\ D$.

As with a plain metal bearing or metal composite bearing, the advice of the bearing manufacturer should be sought in the early stages, since they can advise on the right grade of carbon to use. Carbons can be adjusted to meet almost every condition and, as an example, Le Carbone (GB) Ltd. of Portslade, Sussex have some seventeen standard grades.

4.1.4 *Porous metal bearings*

Porous metal bearings are produced by the powder metallurgy process in which fine metal powders are partially compressed in precision tools to the required shape and the compacts sintered at high temperatures in a reducing atmosphere. The rigid metal sponge thus created contains myriads of interconnecting reservoirs which are then impregnated with a lubricant. Porosity depends upon the degree of compaction and varies between 20 and 40%. Low porosity gives high mechanical properties and thermal conductivity, but low oil-holding capacity, whereas with high-porosity bearings the opposite is true.

The advantage of porous metal bearings is their availability in a wide range of stock sizes at low cost and the elimination of an external oil supply. The oil supply from the porous walls is self-regulating, and thus the hazards of oil drip are reduced. The majority of porous bearings operate under marginal lubrication conditions, where a thin film separates the rubbing surfaces. The load is insufficient to rupture the oil film and the speed is low enough to avoid its decomposition. Over a long period the film will, however, oxidise and become progressively charged with fine wear particles. For these reasons the oil has a finite life and needs to be replaced if the bearing is to continue to function efficiently. It is therefore important to be able to estimate the life of the bearing and its relation to the life of the machine.

A porous metal bearing contains a quantity of oil equal to the product of the bearing volume, the porosity and the degree of impregnation. The requirement of the bearing for oil is, among other things, a function of the surface area of the bore. Thus, the effective quantity of oil varies as the wall thickness and the porosity. As the rate of oil circulation within the pores from the pressure region to the unloaded region also depends on wall thickness and permeability, it is necessary to find a compromise in designing for a particular application. Although the thickest wall and the greatest porosity provide the largest oil-holding capacity, they do not necessarily give the longest life or the most efficient running.

The loss of oil from a porous metal bearing is approximately proportional to the logarithm of the running time; thus, the rate of oil loss is high to start with and decreases with running time. This is useful for the initial running-in period. Figure 4.9 indicates typical oil loss curves and, as a general recommendation, the bearing should be re-impregnated before the content has fallen to about 70%.

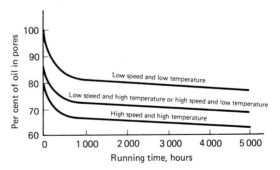

Figure 4.9 Oil loss in porous bearings

Experience confirms that if the PV value is less than 3.5 (calculated with P measured in kg cm^{-2} and V measured in m s^{-1}), there is unlikely to be any difficulty in keeping the running temperature low enough for an acceptable life. If the PV value is between 3.5 and 35, the design should be checked to confirm the rise in temperature is acceptable and that the predicted life is sufficient. With a PV value of over 35, there is a likelihood of running into a heat-dissipation problem which could give rise to an unacceptably short life.

78   *Bearings*

If imperial units are used, i.e. if P is measured in lbf in^{-2} and V in ft min^{-1}, then the PV values referred to above can be taken as 10 000; between 10 000 and 100 000; and over 100 000.

The factors which control successful operation of any type of journal bearing apply equally to sintered and solid metal bearings, and the prime considerations of load, speed and operating temperature can be the most immediate indications of the suitability of a sintered metal bearing in specific applications. A basic rule-of-thumb method of assessing suitability is first of all to apply a pressure velocity factor of 18 maximum using metric units, and 50 000 using imperial units. At the extremes of pressure in the one case and speed in the other case, the PV factor of 18 (or 50 000) will not apply, but a general guide can be given to establish the limits within which the factor can be applied for any specific set of circumstances.

Apart from pressure and velocity, the biggest influence on bearing performance is the temperature obtained at the bearing surface during operation. This can be more critical for a self-lubricating bearing, as the stability of the lubricant at an elevated temperature could be responsible for determining the ultimate performance in the absence of a recirculating system. The majority of lubricants used in engineering are based on mineral oils and, whilst many of the highly refined oils have anti-oxidation additives, these have a finite life, based on time and temperature after which the oil will rapidly form gummy deposits.

The basic difference between self-lubricating bearings and other types of journal bearings is the fact that a limited amount of oil is being used continuously, as the bearing is not usually designed for applications where frequent maintenance or oil-circulating systems are used; consequently, the stability of the lubricant is of prime importance in estimating bearing life, as shown in Figure 4.10.

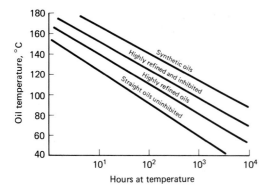

Figure 4.10 Relative oxidation life of oils as a function of temperature

Lubricants other than mineral oils are available for high-temperature work, and earlier objections of poor film strength and lubricating properties have largely been overcome, but even with these newer lubricants there is a life factor, depending on time and temperature. As yet, there is insufficient practical knowledge of the use of these lubricants to enable any accurate assessment of performance to be made where long running periods are involved.

The present limitation of temperature dictated by the use of mineral oil can be taken for practical purposes as 90°C at the bearing surface. Some indication of the time/temperature parameters can be obtained by an experimentally established figure of 1000 hours at 125°C before serious deterioration of a fully inhibited highly refined mineral oil used continuously within a self-lubricating sintered metal bearing takes place. A further variable in any bearing calculation is the viscosity index of the lubricant and, where an application can become critical because of temperature rise, this factor must also be considered, because of a lowering of the load-carrying capacity of the oil film.

It is possible, by using available formulae, to determine in theory a bearing performance and to design a suitable bearing for a given application, but there are always a number of imponderables which are introduced in the practical application of such a theoretical design.

As previously indicated, the limiting factor in the design of porous metal bearings is the running temperature, because this controls the rate of oil deterioration and the change in running clearance through differential thermal expansion. The rate at which heat is generated per unit of bearing surface area is proportional to the product of the pressure, the velocity and the coefficient of friction. Thus, an increase in duty assessed in PV terms can readily be achieved by a reduction in the coefficient of friction. As in the case of plain bearings, the coefficient of friction can be reduced by keeping the bearing pressure high and the shaft velocity low consistent with maintaining hydrodynamic lubrication. With porous metal bearings the limit of hydrodynamic lubrication is reached when the rate of oil leakage into the pores (owing to the oil film pressure) is greater than the rate at which the oil film is created. At this critical point hydrodynamic lubrication is lost and the coefficient of friction rises rapidly as metal-to-metal contact is made (Marshall and Morgan, 1965/66; Cameron *et al.*, 1962). Figure 4.11 indicates practical design limitations for hydrodynamic lubrication.

As in the case of other types of bearings, bearing manufacturers should always be asked for their advice if it is suspected that the application may be in excess of the general capabilities of a ready-made porous bearing.

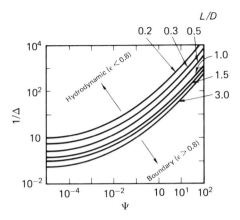

Figure 4.11 Practical design limitation to ensure hydrodynamic lubrication. ϵ, eccentricity; l/Δ, load factor (Sommerfeld reciprocal); ψ, design parameter $\Phi H/c^3$, where Φ is the viscous permeability (cm^3), H is wall thickness of bearing (cm), c is radial clearance (cm); L/D is bearing length/shaft diameter

Some applications taking advantage of the self-lubricating properties of the bearings may run at excessive speeds, but are used for such short and infrequent periods. that the temperature rise is not significant. In this type of application some practical work is advisable to establish that the rate of heat dissipation of the bearing assembly is more than adequate for the longest duration of continuous running for which the bearing is designed.

At the other end of the scale, heavily loaded slow-moving applications are acceptable if a progressive wear rate (on shaft, bearing, or both) can be accepted. When boundary friction conditions exist, it is not possible to calculate with any degree of accuracy the rate of wear, and some practical background is more desirable than pure calculation.

For slow and intermittent use (less than 0.13 m s^{-1}) the load should not exceed 280 kg cm^{-2} and care should be exercised in the design of the housing so that full support is given to the bearing, and also the shaft should be rigid enough to prevent excessive deflection, which would lead to binding. At slow speeds, if the operation is continuous and heat dissipation poor, seizure conditions can be reached under adverse conditions with catastrophic failure of shaft and bearing being possible. A more usual failure, however, is that of a very high wear rate which could be accelerated by poor shaft finish or abrasive contamination.

The most predictable performance for self-lubricating bearings lies in the region where the speed is sufficient to provide fully fluid conditions of lubrication and yet is not excessive from the point of view of heat generation. Working up to a maximum calculated PV factor of 18, the minimum surface speed would be between 0.76 and 1.4 m s^{-1} depending on lubricant, operating temperature and running clearance.

Typical of an available range of porous bearings are those manufactured by GKN Bound Brook Ltd. under the name of Lubrook and Ferrocite. These bushes are supplied finished to close limits of dimensional accuracy by forming and sizing in high-precision dies. They should be fitted into rigid housings, a suggested interference fit for medium-sized bearings being around 0.05 to 0.1 mm. Shaft clearances can be based on a linear relationship with shaft diameter, e.g. 0.03 mm for a 13 mm diameter shaft and 0.1 mm for a 130 mm diameter shaft. Lubrook is a material of high copper content and Ferrocite has iron and copper in roughly equal amounts. A stronger grade is Ferrocite J, which is basically a porous iron bearing. All three grades provide for a PV factor of 18, while the maximum static bearing pressure for Lubrook is 527 kg cm^{-2} and Ferrocite J, 1406 kg cm^{-2}. A selection of typical porous metal bearings made by Manganese Bronze Ltd is shown in Figure 4.12.

Figure 4.12 Selection of typical porous bearings. (Courtesy Manganese Bronze Powder Metal Group)

4.1.5 Thermosetting bearing materials

This chapter so far has dealt in some detail with plain metal bearings, composite metal/plastics bearings and porous metal bearings. A further group of considerable importance is the plastics group which may conveniently be divided into thermosets and thermoplastics, with or without reinforcements.

Thermosetting resins are cross-linked polymers whose basic characteristic is that they char rather than melt on being overheated. They are harder and generally have better temperature resistance than other plastics. To overcome their brittleness they are usually reinforced with fibres or fabric, or used bonded to a metal backing. In many materials a resin is used for bonding together other components of the bearing, as well as for its own bearing properties.

Reinforced thermosets are particularly suitable for use running immersed in water. Under suitable conditions they have the ability of taking a high polish and of running with low friction. The major drawback is the large and variable degree of swelling resulting from the adsorption of water.

In the thermosets there is a range of bearing materials using phenolic resins with cotton or asbestos reinforcements, with the addition, in some cases, of other additives such as molybdenum disulphide. For example, the Railko range is grouped under five principal headings. Firstly, the AL grade which is a phenolic impregnated asbestos cloth cured under heat and pressure to produce the strongest of the Railko asbestos grades. Their outstanding strength makes them ideally suited for heavy-duty bushings in trains, ships, etc. The AL grades are also available impregnated with graphite with or without oil impregnation.

The WA grades consist of an asbestos yarn wound on a mandrel and impregnated with phenolic and cured under heat and pressure. Although it does not have the high compression strength of the AL grades, it does possess high hoop strength and is ideally suited for large bearings up to 1.5 m in diameter. The WA grade may also be oil-impregnated. A particular grade, WA80H, has been developed by Railko for the third generation of oil-lubricated stern tube bearings for large ships, the largest to be made so far being of 1500 mm inside diameter by 1500 mm long.

The CL 40 grade consists of a phenolic impregnated cotton cloth, while the fourth grade AF are asbestos-filled thermosetting resins for moulding into specific shapes. The fifth, grade PX, has a PTFE surface layer backed onto material similar to the AL grades.

Wear rates are approximately as shown in Figure 4.13 and these are compared with other bearing

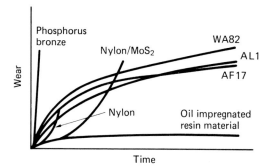

Figure 4.13 Wear rates of phenolic resin based bearings compared with other bearing material

materials. It will be seen that greatly improved characteristics of the phenolic resins can be obtained by additional oil impregnation.

The frictional heat build-up is the principal limiting factor controlling the speed at which the bearing can operate. The rate of temperature rise depends on the pressure applied, the coefficient of friction and the rate of heat dissipation and surface roughness of the shaft. It has been shown from experience, however, that the simple *PV* relationship provides a reliable guide to bearing design until a hydrodynamic lubrication condition pertains, when new criteria will apply as discussed for plain metal bearings.

In the dry conditions, the maximum *PV* value for these materials is 110 (metric units) and 330 for PX grades, but up to six times these values can be obtained with oil-impregnated materials and regular relubrication, ensuring that the heat generated is effectively removed. It should be noted that an even greater improvement can be achieved if the bearing is run under hydrodynamic conditions.

As with most bearings, the running clearances are important, and 0.05 mm would be a typical mean clearance for a 12 mm diameter shaft. Again, if hydrodynamic conditions exist, these clearances can be reduced. Optimum wall thickness has been shown to be a function of shaft diameter and takes into account the closure effect when an interference fit is applied. The optimum wall thickness is given by the formula

$$1.75 + 0.05d$$

where *d* is the shaft diameter in millimetres.

It should be borne in mind that these materials are hygroscopic and allowances must be made for the effect of liquids with which they are to be associated. As with other types of bearings, it is important to consult with the bearing manufacturers to ensure that the most effective design criteria are applied for a specific application.

A typical application for Grade ALIS is for slide strips in a range of fork lift attachments made by H. Cameron Gardner Ltd. They also use ALIIS bushes. An example of the use of WA82S is to be found in the bottom steady bush in the Rydry range of sump pumps manufactured by Ryaland Pumps Ltd.

4.1.6 Thermoplastic bearing materials

Whilst there is a great variety of bearing types operating in circumstances ranging from oil immersion to the ultra-high vacuum in space, there is an equally wide range of materials which might be useful in bearing applications. The selection of materials, together with their manufacture and fabrication, is a complex process, usually heavily influenced by the availability of certain machinery and the compliance of the customers.

It is important to explore potential benefits of new materials, for these will influence not only the climate of thinking about their properties, but also about the means of production and the integration of the product into an engineered article. Thus, if the bearings were an integral part of the structural members of a device, many savings in costs and labour could be envisaged. It might be worth doing this even though the performance was not as good.

Some hindsight is valuable, particularly over the choice of metals as bearing materials. When the oil film breaks down, friction and wear problems become serious; in many user applications oil is not tolerable, and new types of bearing are necessary. Work with oil additives has progressed to the point where they lie empathetically with bearing materials. Such complex technologies cannot sensibly proceed independently and, whilst problems of fundamental incompatibility of oil additives and bearing materials are rare, separate development is unlikely to achieve an optimum design for the best performance.

Exploration of other types of materials has a variety of roles and potential benefits; one would want to choose types of materials that can be formed and fabricated conveniently and whose properties can be adjusted over wide limits. Polymers can fulfil many of these aims and fillers can act as reinforcement agents; they may confer other desirable properties as well; for instance, they may have a chemical activity which acts as an extreme temperature antiseize component. Their shapes may include fibres, flakes or irregular lumps, and their dispersion and arrangement in a polymer medium is in general not easy to control.

In considering the specification for a bearing it is generally expected that friction will be low, the load-bearing capacity adequate, the wear rate sufficiently small, and the debris harmless. It is also necessary to withstand the environment, be it oil, water or air, and that it should possess and maintain the correct shape and dimensions. Perhaps the greatest limitation is that it should not overheat.

In order to secure low friction one must either choose a polymer which has this property — PTFE (polytetrafluoroethylene) is the prime representative of this class — or one which includes quantities of easily sheared fillers (graphite, molybdenum disulphide, etc.) or one ensures that a fluid layer of gas or liquid is maintained between shaft and bearing. If liquids are to be used, they must not only have the correct rheological properties, but they will need to wet the polymer without penetrating its structure or attacking it in any way. There are a number of thermoplastics which are softened by the oil compounds and are easily softened and distorted by heat or by incorporation of soluble liquids into their structure. Some thermoplastics are also liable to crack when exposed to traces of some chemicals; this environmental stress cracking, somewhat similar to the stress corrosion of metals, is not readily predictable.

To achieve load-bearing capability and dimensional stability, one must ensure that the structure is rigid enough. This is helped by using crystallisable polymers, but more permanently and effectively by a degree of curing and crosslinking. Fillers, too, play an important role, but they need to be carefully chosen in case they have abrasive properties. The wear rate is affected by the degree of abrasion and of polymer degradation.

Most plastics are processed in the melt, and while this appears a simple solution there are problems. Thermoplastics may be melted and extruded into moulds, etc., but when they cool they may crystallise and therefore shrink. The rate of cooling is of great importance. The orientation of fillers is also very variable within a moulded shape. Thus, bearings made in this manner can lead to unsuspected inhomogeneities. Nevertheless, substantial progress has been made by manufacturers, and a well defined range of plastics materials has been developed for bearings; these materials, provided that due consideration has been given to their choice, will answer many problems.

One such material is PTFE, which has several very attractive properties as a dry bearing material and, in an unlubricated condition, can be used up to temperatures of about 280°C. It has a low coefficient of friction and a high resistance to chemical attack. In its pure bulk form, however, it has two major disadvantages: its compressive strength is low, and its wear rate high. However, by adding finely divided filler particles of various materials and shapes, the wear rate can be greatly reduced and the compressive strength can be approximately doubled. These materials then give lower wear rates than any other plastics-based material.

One of the fundamental processes in the wear of PTFE (and, indeed, of most polymer-based materials) is the formation of a film of PTFE on the counterface, by transfer of particles from the parent material. This transferred film effectively reduces the wear rate of the bearing material. Fillers may assist in forming an adherent transfer film, and the more abrasive ones may act by polishing the counterface to a smoother finish. Many different fillers have been tried, singly and in combination, to enhance particular properties, such as wear resistance, strength, or thermal conductivity. One of the best from the point of view of wear resistance is a lead/bronze/graphite filled material, in which it is claimed that the lead reacts with the PTFE at the rubbing surface, and chemically bonds the transfer film to the counterface (I. Mech. E., 1967).

The wear factor of these materials shows a considerable increase at high pressures, and life is further reduced at these pressures because the useful wear depth, before escalating damage commences, is reduced. At pressures above 50 MN m^{-2}, materials using PTFE in fibre form are outstanding, and several types are available. One uses PTFE fibre interwoven with glass fibres in such a way that PTFE is largely present at the rubbing surface, while the opposite surface is largely glass, and is cemented with a phenolic resin to a metal backing. This material has exceptional load capacity — up to at least 400 MN m^{-2} — and, in fact, the static load is normally limited by bulk deformation of the steel supporting ring. At low speeds the wear resistance is also exceptionally good. Performance falls off rapidly at speeds above about 0.25 m s^{-1}, probably largely due to the high thermal resistance of the bearing layer.

A second material of this type consists simply of chopped PTFE fibres bonded together and to a backing fabric with a modified phenolic resin. A bearing surface of mixed PTFE and carbon fibres also shows promise for the future.

Other widely used thermoplastics are the nylons, polycarbonates and acetals, for which the dry wear performance is not particularly good. The materials are relatively cheap, however, and, particularly when filled with PTFE, provide adequate wear performance for a variety of non-critical dry applications. Nylon also performs well in abrasive conditions. However, the performance of nylon, and especially acetal, is greatly enhanced by operation with even very small amounts of conventional lubricants. The main problem, particularly with nylons, is their moisture absorption and hence swelling.

Polyimide is a relatively new material having exceptional thermal stability, and consequently a very high PV capability. Graphite-filled grades give reasonable wear resistance and the material should have application for use at temperatures around 300°C, or for PVs above about 1.5 MN m^{-2}, m s^{-1}, particularly if its current cost can be reduced. For best performance at high PV it needs to be in the form of a relatively thin bonded liner, in which form it will also have a substantially increased load capacity.

In common with other bearing materials the efficiency of thermoplastics bearings will be greatly improved if enough lubricant is present to fill a good part of the bearing clearance by supporting part of the load hydrodynamically, leaving a smaller load to be carried by solid contact between the surfaces. The amount of load carried hydrodynamically increases with the factor ZN/P where Z is the fluid viscosity, N is the rotational speed and P is the nominal bearing pressure. Light loads, high speeds

and viscous fluids all encourage hydrodynamic operation.

A good example of an acetal resin impregnated with a lubricant is Railko Pv80, in which the oil is impregnated by a patented process. It is claimed that Pv80 can operate for considerable periods of time under useful PV conditions without additional lubricant, because acetal resin requires only trace amounts of oil at the bearing interface.

4.2 Rolling element bearings

The simple advantage of rolling element bearings over plain bearings is that rubbing friction is changed to rolling friction. This means that (a) there is less loss of power on account of the lower coefficient of friction; (b) frictional resistance on starting from rest is less than in a sliding bearing; and (c) rolling element bearings are more compact in relation to the load carried. Disadvantages could be higher initial costs, noise and low tolerance to contaminants, but these are often outweighed by the advantages.

Most of today's requirements are met by bearings having rolling elements in the form of spheres, cylinders, truncated cones or barrels. During the 80 years of growth and development in the industry a large variety of shapes of rolling elements have been used in bearings, but the difficulties in accurately producing some of the more complicated ones have led to their virtual abandonment.

The UK bearing industry has also felt the effect of foreign competition, and rationalisation has taken place with heavy investments in new plant and techniques to ensure that the most popular ranges of bearings can be produced accurately and consistently at a competitive price.

The rolling element shape which is most easily and accurately generated is the sphere, and this is one of the reasons why ball bearings are the most popular of all rolling element bearings. They are made in a variety of types, but the single-row radial ball bearing is the most widely used. Designed primarily for radial loading, this bearing is also capable of carrying axial loads in either direction with or without a radial load. An increase in radial loading can sometimes be achieved by increasing the complement of balls, but this also places a limit on the axial load that can safely be applied. Because of its construction, this type of bearing is more accommodating of misalignment than other types of rigid bearing and also has good speed capability. Variations of this type include shielded and sealed versions supplied prelubricated. A selection of bearing types is shown in Figures 4.14 to 4.19.

The single-row angular contact ball bearing is similar in construction to the radial ball bearing, except that the inner and/or outer race is cut away

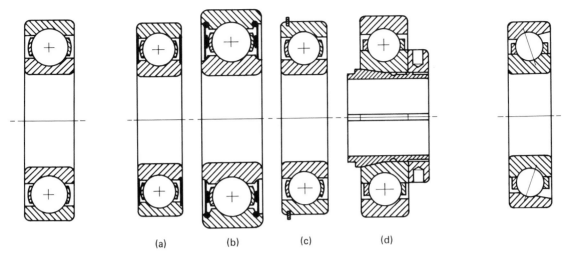

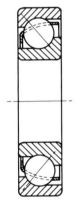

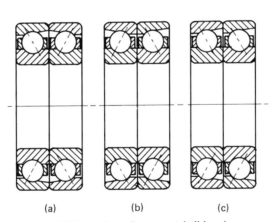

Figure 4.14 Single-row radial bearing

Figure 4.15 Variations on the single-row radial ball bearing

Figure 4.16 20° single-row angular contact ball bearing

Figure 4.17 40° single-row angular contact ball bearing

Figure 4.18 Paired angular contact ball bearing

Figure 4.19 Double-row self-aligning ball bearing

on one side to enable a larger number of balls to be inserted without the use of filling slots. Nominal contact angles range from 12 to 40 degrees depending on application, and these are built into the race during manufacture.

When used singly, angular contact ball bearings can carry axial load in one direction only and, if a radial load is to be applied, this must be substantially less than the axial load to ensure correct tracking of the balls. It is usual to employ angular contact bearings in pairs and in this arrangement they are suitable for radial loads with axial loads in either direction. The magnitude of the radial and axial loads can then be in any proportion.

The need to relieve a nominally rigid bearing from the effect of shaft and housing deflections led to the introduction of self-aligning bearings. These have a lower load-carrying capacity due to the spherical form of the outer raceway which gives little support to the balls. Only small angles of contact between the balls and raceways are possible, and therefore these bearings are suitable for only a light axial load.

Roller bearings are more expensive to produce than ball bearings, but for a given size they have appreciably higher capacity for radial loads. In simple terms, a ball bearing gives a point contact while a roller bearing provides a line contact. Cylindrical roller bearings are more susceptible to the effects of misalignment than ball bearings and attention has been given to the blending of the ends of the rollers into the cylindrical portion in order to eliminate the stress concentrations that would otherwise occur.

Roller bearings can be divided into three main categories, plain cylindrical, taper roller and needle roller. These are dealt with in subsequent paragraphs and are illustrated in Figures 4.20 to 4.23. A fourth category is the spherical roller bearing which contains two rows of barrel-shaped rollers and is similar in principle to the double-row self-aligning ball bearing. Such bearings are capable of appreciably higher radial loading owing to the improved contact conditions between raceways and rollers. They are also more suitable for axial loading than ball bearings, but in general this should be limited to

Figure 4.23 Spherical roller bearing

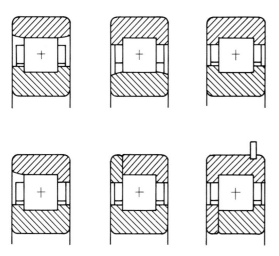

Figure 4.20 Variations on cylindrical roller bearings

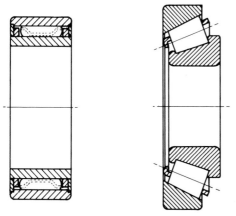

Figure 4.21 Needle roller bearing

Figure 4.22 Tapered roller bearing

avoid imposing the entire bearing load onto one row of rollers. The speed capabilities of these bearings are not high, but they have proved to be very successful under heavy load conditions where accurate alignment cannot be obtained. A fifth category concerns split roller bearings.

4.2.1 Bearing life

When a stationary bearing is loaded, the rolling elements indent the track and, although such deformation is primarily elastic, permanent deformation does occur and should not be so great as to cause vibration and noise. A correctly mounted ball bearing usually fails through fatigue. As the bearing rotates, the load produces a cyclic load on each bearing element. Engineering materials, although identical, do not always fail at the same time, and therefore it is usual to express bearing life in terms of a period in which a certain percentage of the population will have failed under a given loading condition.

This period is expressed as the number of revolutions in which 10% of the bearings will have failed and is referred to as the L_{10} life (sometimes called the B_{10} life). Thus, if the design life is equal to the L_{10} life, 10% of the bearings will fail in less than the design life but 50% will last more than five times the design life. In critical applications where the 10% failure rate cannot be tolerated, it may be necessary to make the design life shorter than the L_{10} life. Major manufacturers have tables and charts which will indicate the life span for any bearing under specified conditions but, as emphasised in the section on plain bearings, it is well worth while contacting a manufacturer for advice at the earliest possible stage.

Rolling element bearings have an ultimate speed limitation above which such effects as the centrifugal action of the rolling elements and the cage, heat dissipation problems, supply of lubricants, etc. play a critical role. Figure 4.24 illustrates a typical pattern of operating limits arising from the static load capacity, fatigue life and speed limitation.

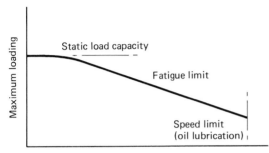

Figure 4.24 Typical operating limits for ball bearings

4.2.2 Load ratings

It has been found that the design life can be related to the dynamic load capacity and to the actual equivalent load on ball and roller bearings. From these equations the dynamic load capacity may be defined as the equivalent load which can be applied for an L_{10} life of 10^6 revolutions. On this basis, the dynamic load capacity may be greater than the static load capacity and it will be necessary to check that the latter capacity is not exceeded at very slow speeds.

In the late 1950s an ISO technical committee on rolling bearings prepared a recommendation covering methods of evaluating dynamic load ratings of rolling bearings and this was published in 1962 as ISO/R 281. This recommendation was not, however, implemented as a British Standard. Since 1962, experience in the application of ISO/R 281 indicated that the recommendation should be improved and updated as an International Standard and the United Kingdom played an active part in the work involved. This culminated in the issue of ISO/R 281/1 *Rolling bearings — Dynamic load ratings and rating life*, Part 1 *Calculation methods*, which has been adopted completely as BS 5512, Part 1.

The standard sets out methods of calculating the basic dynamic load ratings and rating life of rolling bearings manufactured from good-quality hardened steel in accordance with good manufacturing practice and basically of conventional design as regards the shape of rolling contact surfaces. It also specifies methods of calculating adjusted rating life to take into account various reliabilities, materials and op-erating conditions. Relevant definitions and symbols are included, together with calculation methods covering basic dynamic radial load ratings, dynamic equivalent radial load and basic rating life for radial ball bearings, thrust ball bearings, radial roller bearings and thrust roller bearings and also life adjustment factors for reliability, materials and operating conditions for these types of bearings. Limitations on the application of the calculation methods are fully described in the scope and field of application, and any additional limitations relevant to particular types of bearing are included in the relevant clauses.

It is intended to issue a further part of BS 5512 in due course to provide supplementary background information regarding the derivation of formulae and factors given in Part 1. This further part will implement the corresponding ISO publication.

If fatigue is taken as the performance limit, it may be assumed that the life of a rolling element bearing in terms of number of revolutions, N, is proportional to the cube of the reciprocal of bearing load, i.e. $N = (1/W)^3$. Thus, for a given life, W is proportional to $N^{1/3}$. The actual maximum load is also limited by the capacity of the bearing to carry static load which in this case is limited by the resistance of the races to Brinelling.

4.2.3 Service conditions

Premature failure in service is more often than not the result of one, or a combination of the following faults rather than a statistical casualty:

(1) incorrect bearing selection,
(2) unsatisfactory design features of bearing assembly,
(3) inadequate lubrication,
(4) unsuitable mounting technique,
(5) inadequate maintenance facilities.

The designer should have practical knowledge of the service conditions of the application in order to achieve a sensible bearing selection. Important factors which will influence this selection can be identified as:

(1) normal and overload conditions,
(2) direction of load,
(3) speed range,
(4) alignment requirements,
(5) type of lubrication to be employed,
(6) environmental conditions,
(7) bearing protection required,
(8) bearing control features.

Sufficient information is made available from bearing manufacturers to allow the designer to make initial selection against known loads and speeds although, on many occasions, the effect of the duty cycle and fluctuating load are completely overlooked with the result that larger bearings than necessary are employed. The designer can usually obtain information regarding lubrication and bearing protection, although these are interdependent on the speed range and environmental conditions.

Often, however, fundamental control features which should be stipulated in order to obtain satisfactory service performance, such as diametric internal clearance, limiting inner and outer ring eccentricities, silent running and special cage requirements, to name a few, are entirely ignored.

Bearings which do not rotate or move only fractionally are not subject to normal fatigue; nevertheless, there is a limit to the static load which they can carry. This limit is determined by the permanent deformations which develop in the load-carrying surfaces. Experience shows that, providing the total permanent deformations in raceways or rolling elements of the most heavily loaded element do not exceed 0.0001 times the rolling element diameter, the resulting fatigue life will not be greatly influenced in the event of the bearing operating under rotating conditions.

4.2.4 Bearing assemblies

An increasing number of major bearing manufacturers are now providing not only the bearing itself, but also the housing as a complete subassembly. As a unit, it enables the bearing manufacturer to ensure that some of the problems that could arise from inadequate housing are eliminated at source. For example, SKF (UK) Ltd. have produced a second generation front wheel drive hub unit (see Figure 4.25) for a Volvo experimental taxi in Sweden. The factors which led to this were the need for a simple mounting and high operational reliability. The risk of bearing failure arising through faulty clearance adjustments has also been eliminated by this design. The unit is lubricated for life and is equipped with integral seals.

A further example of this philosophy can be found in the INA special self-centring clutch release bearing, shown in Figure 4.26, designed to overcome the problem of 'sticky' clutch movements. Self-centring of this bearing is achieved by the relative motion of the non-rotating (either inner or outer) bearing ring in relation to a fixed backplate and location hub. As the rotating ring is physically connected to the non-rotating ring, the complete bearing element is free to move. To dampen this movement and hold the bearing element in place when its required off-centre position is achieved, a conical spring is employed. The resulting friction between the inner ring and the backplate is sufficient to hold and control the bearing element radially. Self-centring of the bearing by the clutch is achieved by the clutch diaphragm spring fingers centrifugally pulling the

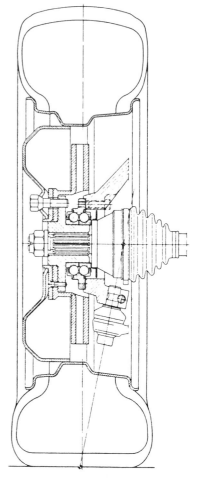

Figure 4.25 Bearing arrangement for a driven front wheel incorporating a second-generation hub unit

outer ring of the bearing element into line until there is no relative movement between the two surfaces.

Additionally the INA Bearing Co. Ltd. also market a very wide range of power transmission units consisting of bearings of various types and sizes set into a wide range of housings, e.g. pillow or plummer blocks, flanges, etc. to suit all possible applications ranging from the primitive to the highly sophisticated. These all use rolling bearings from INA's extensive range.

Berron-Marvis Industrial Ltd. claim to be the largest manufacturer in the UK of SN type plummer blocks. These will accept either self-aligning ball bearings or spherical roller bearings for shafts of from 76 to 140 mm in diameter. The company also market type GPK plummer blocks as originally supplied by RHP. These are suitable for shafts of from 63 to 178 mm in diameter.

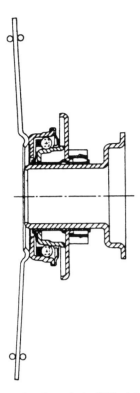

Figure 4.26 Section through the INA clutch release bearing assembly

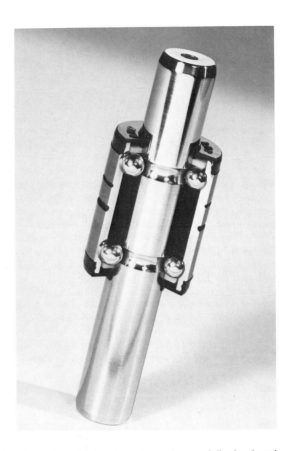

Figure 4.27 Section through bearing specially developed for automotive applications. One end drives the fan, the other end powers the water pump impeller. (Courtesy RHP)

An example of a bearing specially developed for an automotive application is RHP's fan and pump spindle (FPS) bearing, shown in Figure 4.27. This bearing carries the fan-belt load and transmits the drive forward to the fan and rearward to the water pump impeller. It has two rolling-element raceways integral with the drive shaft and a wide outer race giving an extremely compact and rigid assembly. The rolling elements are usually balls, but in the case of extreme belt loads one row may be of rollers. The cages are injection moulded, heat stabilised nylon, which is quiet running and wear resistant. The FPS bearings are greased and sealed for life with high-temperature nitrile seals bonded on to spring steel retainers.

These bearings are available in a range of standard diameters, usually determined by the load they are required to carry. The spindle lengths are specified to suit individual applications.

A special conveyor roller bearing introducing a completely new concept will also help to dispel the idea that rolling bearings are only for sophisticated precision mechanical assemblies. The bearing, manufactured by SKF (UK) Ltd., has been in use for some years with highly successful results and has been accepted as a standard by the National Coal Board (now British Coal).

SKF designed the bearing specifically for use in maintenance-free conveyor idlers, knowing that bearings installed in belt conveyors must operate in unfavourable surroundings. Currently, the bearing's main application is in coal conveyors, where the material normally conveyed contains a high degree of finely divided coal dust, which can penetrate the bearings causing serious damage. The idler bearing was therefore designed to offer several distinct design advantages, the main one being a seize-resistant property under hostile environmental conditions.

Designated 415705, the new bearing is a single-row deep-groove ball bearing type, with metric boundary dimensions $25 \times 52 \times 12$ mm. The seize-resistant property of the bearing was achieved by increased ball size, a flexible nylon cage and changes to the track conformity, enabling the bearing to tolerate dirt particles with less risk of seizure.

Seize resistance is an important factor when considering safety, because bearings near to seizure will run hot, which can be lethal where there is a risk of explosion. A further consequence of the new bearing's large ball size is a significant increase in its load-carrying capacity which can be effectively utilised to increase its range of duties. Additional features of the idler bearing are its greater tolerance to misalignment and its small corner radii.

4.2.5 Lubrication

The choice of lubricant for a rolling bearing lies between grease and oil and, essentially, is determined by the type of bearing used and the rotational speed of the application. Other factors, such as environmental conditions and maintenance facilities, must influence this selection. Oil undoubtedly is the more efficient lubricant and is essential for very high speeds or for extended running at temperatures appreciably in excess of 100°C. It is also commonly used where the bearings are enclosed in a casing containing other components for which oil is essential. On the other hand, grease has many natural advantages and, where the operating conditions permit, the tendency is to use grease wherever possible.

The advantages of grease over oil are:

(1) it is easier to retain in the bearing housing,
(2) it has greater cleanliness in operation,
(3) it combines effective lubrication with permanent coating qualities giving protection against corrosion,
(4) it adds to the effectiveness of closures for excluding dirt and moisture,
(5) it is easy to handle, and
(6) replenishment can be done quickly and conveniently.

Grease-lubricated bearings operating at high speed require frequent relubrication but, unless the quantity of lubricant supplied at each regreasing interval is very closely controlled, churning and unacceptable temperatures will result. The period during which a grease-lubricated bearing will function without relubrication is dependent on bearing type and size, speed and operating temperature, plus the type of grease being used. The relubrication interval is also related to the service life of the grease, and most bearing manufacturers can provide a guide for the frequency of grease replenishment. Environmental conditions naturally influence the regreasing interval.

For small deep-groove ball bearings the service life of the lubricant often exceeds that of the bearing application and regreasing is not normally required. In general, however, relubrication must be shorter than grease service life if satisfactory lubrication is to be assured. If bearings have been correctly selected, fitted and adequately protected, the main extent of maintenance work is to replenish the grease from time to time. The frequency of this attention depends on the nature of the application, the bearing size, speed and temperature. It is important to avoid too frequent attention which may lead to over-filling.

The amount of oil required merely to lubricate a bearing, as distinct from cooling it, is very small and, unless the combination of load and speed is severe, a few drops per minute are sufficient. Selected oils should contain oxidisation and corrosion inhibitors and, when required to operate over a wide range of temperatures, should have a high viscosity index. The most fundamental requirement for a rolling bearing is that the oil should have a sufficiently high viscosity at operating temperature to provide effective lubrication. Again, most manufacturers can provide a guide to the selection of suitable oils.

In small gearboxes it is common practice to rely on splash from the gears, but in larger industrial gearboxes the bearings and gears may be lubricated by oil jets or sprays. In some cases oil flung off from the gears is led to the bearings by galleries specially formed in the casing. Bearings are frequently run with oil bath lubrication; in such cases the depth of oil must be such that it extends approximately half way up the lowest ball or roller in the bearing. On some small, high-speed spindles the oil may be fed to the bearings from an oil bath by means of wick feed.

Drip feed systems are commonly used, but are on a total loss basis unless provision can be made for recirculating the oil. A number of ingenious recirculating devices for providing continuous and drip feeds for bearings on vertical shafts are in use. Of the many methods of oil lubrication, the static oil bath is the simplest. In addition to the normal design features associated with this type of housing the designer must make allowance for oil level equalisation within the housing by cross-porting. Experience has indicated than when double-row bearings are employed there is a strong possibility that one row will become partially starved of oil with subsequent unfortunate results unless the oil equalisation features are incorporated.

Increased bearing speed raises the operating temperature and accelerates oxidisation of the oil. To maintain acceptable bearing temperatures and also avoid frequent oil changes, an oil force feed circulating system must be employed. It is, however, possible in some applications to use the inherent pumping action of the bearing (e.g. taper roller and spherical roller thrust bearing) to create a self-induced circulating system.

Other oil systems include oil mist which is extensively used for machine tool and rolling mill applications involving high-speed operation. Free-fog is a problem on large installations due to the possible toxic effect, but oils having a low free-fog rating are available.

In many modern applications bearings are required to carry relatively heavy loads at extremely high speeds and, in such cases, oil in excess of the lubrication requirements of the bearings must be added for cooling purposes. Typical examples are mainline bearings on jet engines, and it is common practice to pump oil to the bearings individually through jets.

4.2.6 Future developments

With regard to future developments in rolling bearings, the main field would appear to be in the use of new and improved materials and methods of manufacture. Considerable investigation is in hand in this area and improvements have already been made in the cleanliness of steels for rings and rolling elements. As a result, vacuum-remelted steels and electroflux remelted steels, while too expensive for general use, have been adopted for the bearings in the mainline positions on jet engines where a high degree of reliability is essential. Vacuum-degassed steel is also widely employed on many of the standard bearings used in general engineering, giving improvements in fatigue life and assisting in the general tendency towards the use of smaller bearings for conditions of increased severity.

The possibilities of moulded plastics components for bearings are not being overlooked. Moulded cages are quite widely used in ball bearings and in certain applications their flexibility gives them a definite technical advantage over the more conventional pressed steel cages. At the same time, there is a need for plastics of improved dimensional stability and the ability to resist high temperatures. If these can be obtained at a cost comparable with that of conventional materials, the field of application would undoubtedly expand.

The exploitation of the specific properties of plastics, particularly their low density, high elasticity and their adaptability for special geometric forms, as well as their very modest requirements with regard to lubrication, provides considerable functional advantages. A prerequisite is, however, that consideration is paid to the behaviour of the plastics in the presence of the lubricant to be used and at the operating temperatures, etc. The maximum operating temperature limits the use to which plastic cages can be put, but the continuous development of new more durable plastics will certainly lead to an increasing number of rolling bearings being equipped with this type of cage in future.

4.2.7 Tapered roller bearings

Tapered roller bearings which were once considered mainly for slow speed, heavily loaded applications are now found to be very cost-effective in more lightly loaded applications. One of the main features of a tapered roller bearing is that it is able to take both radial and thrust loads in any combination and therefore eliminates the need for separate thrust races if heavy thrust loads are involved. Another important aspect is that, compared with other types of roller bearing, the ratio of its load-carrying capacity to bearing size is very advantageous. This means that if bearing size can be kept to a minimum, the overall size of bearing housing and associated parts can be kept correspondingly small, with consequent savings in material and costs.

A tapered roller bearing has four main components, as shown in Figure 4.28. These are the cone or inner race, the tapered rollers, the cage which is used to space the rollers and the cup or outer race. The angle that the centre line of the rollers makes with the centre line of the bearing can vary (Figure 4.29) and will affect the ratio of the thrust to radial capacity ratings, i.e. the greater the angle the greater the ratio of the thrust to radial rating. Also, if the lines from the tapered rollers are projected they meet on a common point along the centre line of the bearing, thus ensuring true rolling motion of the rollers around the track.

As mentioned earlier, the cage is used to space the rollers and does not have the function of guiding them as in the case of cylindrical roller bearings. Correct alignment of the rollers is obtained by the roller against the rib contact. The force diagram (Figure 4.30) illustrates how the resultant forces on the cup and cone produce a small seating force of the roller against the rib, ensuring full line contact along the roller, and therefore maximum capacity.

The basic type of tapered roller bearing is the single-row (TS type). These bearings are usually mounted in pairs, as shown in the following two typical applications.

Figure 4.31 shows a 'direct mounting', that is with the large ends of the rollers facing inwards, and Figure 4.32 illustrates an 'indirect mounting', where the large ends of the roller point outwards. Direct mountings are normally used where the bearings are spaced fairly widely apart and the loads on the shaft are between the bearings. The indirect mounting is normally used to increase the stability of a shaft when a cantilevered load is involved.

Multi-row bearings, i.e. 2- and 4-row tapered roller bearings, are used for heavy-duty applications where high radial loads are involved (Figures 4.33 and 4.34).

The tapered roller bearing relative to most other types of bearing has a higher load-carrying capacity

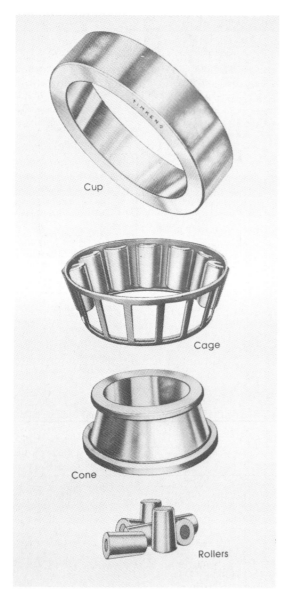

Figure 4.28 Component parts of a Timken taper roller bearing

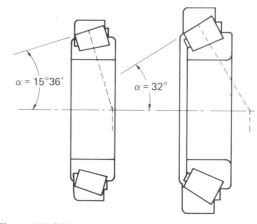

Figure 4.29 Effect of varying the taper of the rollers

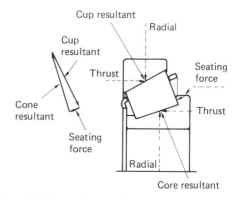

Figure 4.30 Force diagram for a taper roller bearing

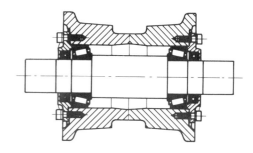

Figure 4.31 Diagram showing 'direct mounting' of taper roller bearing

within a given section height. This is illustrated in Figure 4.35. This diagram shows the life of a tapered roller bearing compared with ball and cylindrical roller bearings of the same bore size (35 mm) under a radial load of 950 daN. Even though the section height of the tapered roller bearing is smaller, a much better calculated life is achieved. The much smaller tapered roller bearing of 19 mm bore on the right of the diagram gives a similar life to that of the larger ball bearing.

The significance of this is of great importance to engineers and designers. Designers of gearboxes that are not equipped with tapered roller bearings are finding that if they want to uprate their box without increasing the overall size they can do so by simply redesigning to incorporate tapered roller

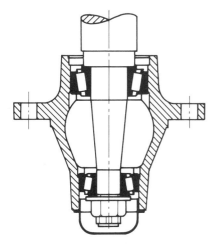

Figure 4.32 Diagram showing 'indirect mounting'

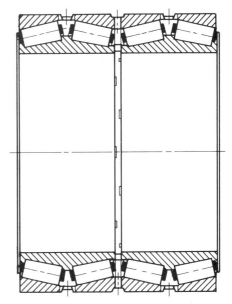

Figure 4.34 Four-row taper roller bearing for heavy duties

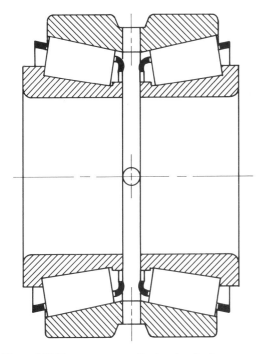

Figure 4.33 Two-row taper roller bearing for heavy duties

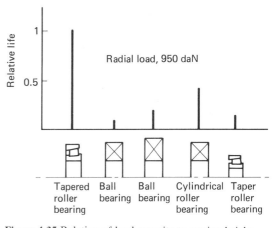

Figure 4.35 Relation of load capacity to section height

bearings. Manufacturers of washing machines who want to increase spin speeds, again without increasing the bearing size, can do so by using tapered roller bearings.

Because of their construction, tapered roller bearings can be adjusted, and this therefore allows the bearings to be set to their optimum running condition. Bearing setting can be carried out by adjusting either the inner or outer race. In some cases, especially in high volume usage, there is a need for

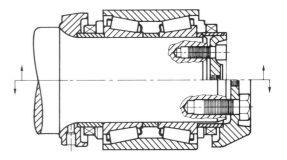

Figure 4.36 Two views of the Timken AP bearing

manual adjustment to be eliminated. New techniques have been developed which enable the bearings to be set with close accuracy requiring a minimum of operator skill. Three such techniques are now being widely used in industry with good results. These are Set-Right, Acro-Set and Clamp-Set. For each of these methods very little skill is needed, but discussion with the bearing manufacturer is advisable before employing them. Some manufacturers, such as The Timken Company, have published brochures describing each of these techniques in depth.

The setting up of a metric standard has been under discussion for a number of years in the roller bearing industry and has now been finalised. A new standard for metric tapered roller bearings, ISO 355, has been published and will form the future guidelines for both manufacturers and users alike. This does not mean an overnight change to totally metric-dimensioned bearings will take place. Owing to the large use of inch-sized bearings throughout the world the change-over will, of necessity, be gradual.

Over the years, a number of variations on the standard type of tapered roller bearing have been produced to meet specific application requirements. These 'specials' have now become part of the general range of tapered roller bearings and have found widespread usage.

The Timken 'AP' bearing was originally developed for railway applications and has proved successful on railways by rolling millions of trouble-free car-miles. This self-contained tapered roller bearing is increasingly used in industrial applications, particularly in rolling mill equipment.

The main characteristics of the 'AP' bearing (Figure 4.36) is that the self-contained cartridge provides substantial cost savings in design and installation, separate fabrication of most auxiliary parts is eliminated, the pre-assembled and pregreased units reduce installation costs, and high-quality thoroughly tested radial lip seals provide exceptional protection, minimum relubrication and low maintenance.

The 'AP' bearing is particularly suitable for mill table rolls, continuous casters, crane bridge and trolley wheels, and all types of steelworks cars.

The crossed roller bearing is a form of tapered roller bearing which has been evolved for a special purpose, that is to give as near as possible the advantages of a two-row bearing in the space of one. Although the bearing was developed with this specific purpose in mind, it has been found to have a great number of other advantages which make it particularly suitable for certain types of application. Its main applications are in the machine tool industry — for vertical boring mills and rotary tables of all descriptions. Figure 4.37 shows a typical mounting in a vertical boring mill.

A major factor in the cutting performance of a machine tool is the dynamic stiffness of its spindle. Experimental analysis has shown that dynamic stiffness is greatly influenced by the adjustment of the bearings supporting the spindle. A slight preload on the bearings is found to give the best combination of damping characteristics and radial stiffness which, in turn, gives optimum accuracy and allows the greatest rate of metal removal.

Maintaining the correct bearing setting over a wide speed range is very important, and this can

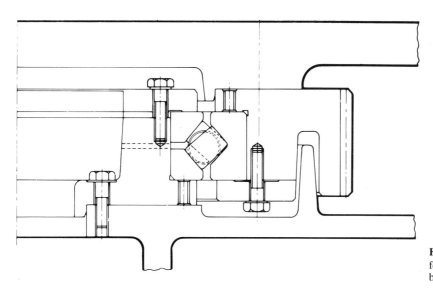

Figure 4.37 Typical mounting for Timken crossed roller bearing

now be achieved by a recently developed bearing known as the Hydra-Rib bearing (Figure 4.38). The Hydra-Rib bearing has a floating rib on the outer race which is held against the rollers under pressure, using an oil or pneumatic system. It is used with a conventional tapered roller bearing at the spindle nose and allows the preload to be set to give the optimum dynamic stiffness for any particular conditions; it then remains constant for that setting, even if the thermal conditions change.

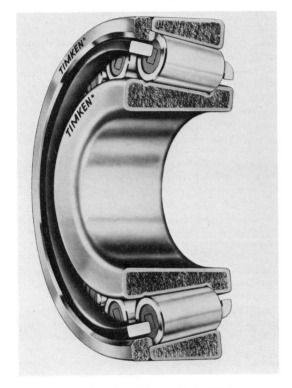

Figure 4.38 Section of the Timken Hydra-Rib bearing

Several British and US companies are now using the Hydra-Rib bearing in their latest designs of sophisticated machine tools.

The Timken Unit Bearing is a tapered roller bearing which is able to take thrust loads in both directions, although it has great thrust capacity in one particular direction. The main application of this type of bearing is on passenger car axles, although there is growing interest in the industrial field for the fork lift and agricultural tractor industries.

4.2.8 Needle roller bearings

Needle roller bearings derive their name from the fact that their rollers have a high length/diameter ratio. Another important difference between cylindrical rollers and needle rollers is in the principles of rolling element guiding method. Of the two basic needle roller bearing types the full complement bearings rely upon a suitably controlled circumferential clearance between the needle rollers for optimum operation. In caged bearings, the guidance of needle rollers is realised by accurately designed and produced cages whose bars guide the rolling elements parallel to one another, as well as provide their retention in one or both radial directions. Because the needle roller bearings have, in general, relatively small cross-sections, they are capable of carrying loads equal to or greater than most other types of rolling elements of comparable outside diameter, permitting larger shaft diameters.

The large number of contact lines in the full-complement bearings makes them well suited to static, slow-rotating or oscillating conditions, whereas the cage function in the caged bearings makes them better suited for higher speeds and shaft deflections.

It is very common to run needle roller bearings on an adequately hardened shaft, since the construction generally does not include the inner ring as an essential part of the bearing unit. The small bearing cross-sections enable an equipment designer to reduce its size and thus obtain a cost saving.

The most noticeable limitation inherently possessed by radial needle roller bearings is their inability to absorb axial loads. This is primarily because the needle rollers are of relatively small diameters and unsuitable for axial guidance; coupled with this, the inner rings, when used, are entirely separable. The most commonly used types of needle roller journal bearings to be found today are:

(1) needle roller complements,
(2) full complement and caged drawn-cup bearings,
(3) cage and needle roller assemblies,
(4) machined ring bearings, and
(5) cam followers and cam rollers.

Other less frequently used types are also generally available. Each type of bearing is able to meet a wide range of operating conditions, although the designer is strongly advised to study manufacturers' catalogues, or better still seek their advice by personal contact. Discussions of designs for optimum roller paths, formulae for evaluation of load ratings and limiting speeds, as well as method of evaluation for theoretical bearing lives, can be obtained from bearing manufacturers.

One of the most economical and basic methods of resolving a needle roller bearing problem is to use a path of needle rollers assembled directly between a suitably hardened and ground housing and shaft and axially located between hardened end washers. When these requirements can be met and where needler roller assembly is not difficult or production rate is sufficiently high to make use of special assembly equipment, such assemblies constitute a bearing that is small in section and high in load-carrying capacity, as well as being usually financially economical. Different end forms of needle rollers are available to suit various applications, the main types being shown in Figure 4.39.

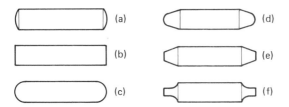

Figure 4.39 Different end forms for needle rollers: (a) spherical end — widely used and economical; (b) flat end — maximum effective contact length; (c) ball end — allows generous fillet between raceway and locating shoulder; (d) crankpin end — allows largest practical fillet; (e) conical end — used where lip retention of rollers is required; (f) trunnion end — allows easier lip retention of rollers

Needle rollers can be made available with a controlled contour — a refinement where the central portion is cylindrical with the diameter gradually reducing towards the ends of the roller's effective length. This feature enables (a) equalised distribution of stresses along the entire length of contact of roller and raceway under conditions of uniform loading and (b) reduced concentrations of stress at the ends of the rollers under conditions of slight misalignment that causes non-uniform loading. In general, needle roller complements used for rotating motion should employ a smaller number of larger diameter needle rollers, but when required for oscillating motion a larger number of small diameter needle rollers should be employed. When considering the use of needler rollers, their selection for specific application requirements should always take into account the desirable circumferential and radial clearances, in order to prevent non-uniform loading of the needle rollers and even ultimate lock-up of the complement. The minimum end clearance per path should generally be 0.25 mm. In applications where a couple is imposed on the shaft, two rows of needler rollers should be used to provide stability and a more uniform load distribution on the shaft and outer raceway.

Fitting of loose needler rollers can be a problem and thought should be given to the most economical method of assembly. When comparatively small numbers of assemblies are to be fitted with needle rollers, it may be sufficient to coat the housing bore and the needler rollers thinly with grease to hold

them in position. For volume production loading devices are useful.

The drawn-cup needle roller bearing using a full complement path of needle rollers was introduced in 1934, and this breakthrough in design opened up a wide field for needle roller bearings in applications where comparatively high rotational speeds occur.

When bearing housing design requirements dictate the use of materials of low rigidity, such as aluminium alloy, and also where it is not practical to harden and grind the housing bore, drawn-cup needle roller bearings provide an economical solution. Rolling characteristics are thus realised, yet their cross-sections are equivalent to or a little greater than those of plain sliding bearings.

The bearing cup is produced from low-carbon, bearing-quality steel deep-drawn and case-hardened, and the needle rollers are of high-carbon steel, through-hardened, ground and lapped to provide the accuracy required for minimum friction in operation. In the caged variant the cup is identical and dimensionally interchangeable with the equivalent full complement bearing. Whereas in the former type the needle rollers are retained inwardly by a hardened cage, in the latter they are retained by the turned-in lips of the cup.

Another type of full complement drawn-cup bearing comprises an unlipped precision-drawn cup and a full complement of grease-retained needle rollers. The cage used in drawn-cup bearings is of continuous construction, designed to provide rigidity and minimise wear. The cage contacts the rollers only near their ends (Figure 4.40) and at the roller pitch line, whereas the portions of the cage that retain the rollers inwardly cannot contact the rollers while the bearing is operating. Thus, there is no wear which might affect roller retention. Caged drawn-cup bearings are better for applications where high speeds and shaft misalignments or deflections under load are present although, due to having fewer needle rollers, their load-carrying capacity is reduced. Drawn-cup bearings are also manufactured with one end closed, the closed end providing a useful seal in constructions where the shaft is not required to extend beyond the bearing. These bearings may also

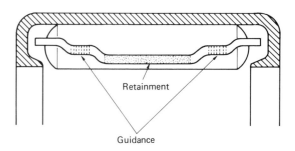

Figure 4.40 Arrangement of cage for needle rollers

be obtained with a centrally located oil hole in the cup to facilitate relubrication of the bearing.

In order to accomplish the small bearing cross-section the walls of the cups are made as thin as manufacturing procedures permit. Therefore, the cups in most instances tend to go out of round due to heat treatment effects, and it is important to note that only after the drawn-cup is pressed into a housing of proper dimensions does it form an accurate hardened outer raceway for the needle rollers.

When contemplating the design of equipment of compact design expected to perform at high speeds, cage and needle roller assemblies may provide the desired solution. Such a design would often dictate the use of relatively small shaft diameters subject to high deflections, thus requiring good-quality materials to meet these needs. The advantage provided by the use of cage and needle roller assemblies is in the ability of the cage to guide the needle rollers parallel to each other during operation.

A typical cage and needle would be of one-piece construction, providing both inward and outward retention of the needle rollers. The design gives maximum cage strength consistent with the inherent high load ratings of needle roller bearings. The cage is piloted from the outer raceway, where lubrication is better, and is often made from a plastics material. The controlled contour needle rollers used in these assemblies are of high carbon chrome steel, through-hardened, ground and lapped to close tolerances for diameter and roundness.

Since the cage and needle roller assembly uses a housing as its outer ring and the shaft as its inner ring, virtually the only limit to the precision possible is the capability of the end user's equipment to hold the tolerances of the housing and the shaft.

End locating surfaces for cage and needle roller assemblies should be hardened to minimise wear. For satisfactory operation, the minimum axial clearance should be 0.2 mm. Shaft and housing fillets adjacent to the assemblies must not exceed 0.8 mm. Housings must be of sufficient cross-section to maintain adequate roundness and running clearance under load.

Cage and needle roller assemblies are particularly suited to application involving high speeds at no appreciable load on the bearing. Such situations often arise in high-speed constant-mesh gears and planetary pinions. Whereas the centrifugal forces would tend to lock a full complement of needle rollers to the outer race, the lower frictional characteristics of the assembly allow satisfactory operation under these conditions. Premature failures of cage and needle roller assemblies occur when loads are exceptionally high, causing spalling of the needle rollers and/or the raceway surfaces in contact. When failures are attributable to lack of lubrication be-tween the cage and the outer race, success can sometimes be achieved by plating the cage. Generally, spalling commences at the ends of the line of contact due to excessive shaft or housing deflection.

The raceways against which the rollers operate or the surface against which the washers bear must be square with the axis of the shaft to within one in one-thousand. Equally important is the dish or cone effect of the raceway or the surface backing the thrust washer. This must also be within one in one-thousand as measured radially from the shaft centre-line.

Since the bearing design allows for high-speed operation and substantial load distribution over the many needle rollers contained in each bearing, departures from the specified squareness and the dish or cone effect are often the major cause of bearing failures. This is especially true of heavily loaded applications.

Where applications are more demanding, involving heavy dynamic, static or even shock loads, the machined ring type of needle roller bearing may be found to give best results. The bearing outer ring is of channel-shaped construction, of bearing-quality steel, heat-treated to provide maximum load rating. Common with other cages, the design of the cage used in this type of bearing separates the guiding and the retaining functions. That portion of the cage which prevents the needle rollers from dropping inward does not contact the rollers while the bearing is operating. The cage is radially located by the outer ring flanges and contacts the rollers only near their ends and at the roller pitch diameter. The design leaves the central area of the cage open to enhance circulation of lubricant. The quality built into the needle rollers with controlled contours assures even load distribution in the bearing and introduces unsurpassed control upon the operating clearances in the bearing.

4.2.9 Split roller bearings

At first sight the concept of the split roller bearing would appear to contravene all the established practices designed to ensure a long trouble-free rolling bearing life. Yet experience over a 70 year span has proved otherwise, and the split roller bearing has an enviable record of performance plus the advantage of being able to provide a greater degree of freedom for the designer.

Their chief advantage lies in the economics of the design and construction of the plant in which the bearings are incorporated. As the bearings are assembled radially, i.e. not threaded along the shaft, shafts can be designed solely to resist torque and bending moments and, by the elimination of shoulders and threaded portions, the risk of shaft fatigue is greatly reduced. Since little consideration has to be given to the problem of assembling and dismantling the bearings in place, the design can be simpler and more compact with no loss of bearing accessibility.

The success of the split roller bearing has been built upon a painstaking examination of the mode of failures associated with rolling element bearings in general. With rigidily mounted roller bearings, edge loading can be one of the reasons for reduction in bearing life. As edge loading continues, the inevitable rolling fatigue sets in, resulting in spalling and ultimate failure. Edge loading arises from:

(1) shaft and/or housing taper,
(2) misalignment, and
(3) excessive shaft deflection.

The extent to which races are made convex in shape and rollers are relieved does not eliminate the problem, but modifies the load at which it starts and the subsequent life of the bearing.

Fretting corrosion can occur between fitted surfaces when there is relative movement of the order of 2.5 μm and can occur under heavily loaded inner ring shaft and outer ring housing contact. One possible way of overcoming this particular problem is by the use of cyanoacrylate type adhesives. The most common cause of all failures is that of corrosion; it is also the most difficult to detect in its early stages. Another common cause of failure is through insufficient or incorrect lubrication. All these aspects have been thoroughly researched and the use by manufacturers of cleaner steels goes some way towards reducing the incidence of failures in any type of bearing, but designers must take note of factors such as:

(1) the correct initial bearing selection, taking into account the required statistical life;
(2) that not only the maximum load is considered but also the duration and direction of every load;
(3) the speed and cycle of speed corresponding to the load;
(4) that all running temperatures over 100°C need careful selection of lubricants and at temperatures over 150°C the dynamic rating of the bearing may be lowered;
(5) the use of rubbing seals and the possible substitution by non-rubbing seals; and
(6) the arrangement of shafts so that expansion is taken into account (by temperature rise and the effect of differential temperatures).

Attention to these points and discussion with the bearing manufacturer will lead to a choice of bearing where the split roller type (Figure 4.41) is in no way inferior to solid raceways and offers greater design freedom and operational economy. Cooper Roller Bearings' technical department and team of district

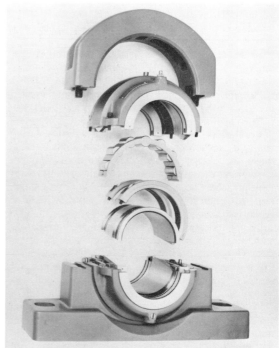

Figure 4.41 (a) Typical split roller bearing, showing angle of split to ensure smooth transfer of load; (b) exploded view of a split roller bearing on a plummer block. (Courtesy Cooper Roller Bearing Co. Ltd.)

engineers are available to assist in bearing selection as required.

It is sometimes assumed that the construction of a split roller bearing prevents it being run at high speed. This is not so. Provided the basic accuracy of the bearing and its mounting is maintained, speeds up to $dn = 1\ 000\ 000$ can be achieved, where d is the shaft diameter in millimetres and n is speed in rpm. These high-speed split bearings are often made in large diameters as encircling bearings for wire stranding machines in sizes from 150 to 1550 mm. Split roller bearings, as manufactured by Cooper Roller Bearing Co. Ltd., are classified for each size as Series 01, 02, 03 and 04, which in effect refers to their duty, i.e. medium, heavy and extra heavy and special light duty, and involve a change in the diameter of the roller and thickness of raceways. The 'standard range of mountings covers pedestal, flange, take-up, rod-end and hanger outer casings, plus the standard bearing and cartridge assembly. Bore sizes start at 40 mm, and a full range of inch sizes is manufactured. Comprehensive details are available from the company.

4.2.10 The life of restored bearings

The high cost of new rolling-element bearings for aircraft turbine engines and other high-speed applications has led to proposals for ball and roller bearings being removed at routine overhauls to be re-used after refurbishing or restoring. A theoretical analysis of the life of such bearings has been performed by NASA to determine how their use might affect existing maintenance and replacement policies. It was shown that the mean time between failures was 90–100% of that of a new bearing.

Refurbishing consists of dismantling, cleaning and visually and dimensionally inspecting removed bearings. If no major imperfections are found, the bearings are reassembled, lubricated and packaged for further use. Restoration is a logical extension and includes grinding the races and other critical surfaces to their original characteristics and dimensions. Where necessary the bearing faces, bores and outer diameters are ground and nickel or chrome plated to a thickness that will allow the surfaces to be reground to the original specified dimensions. Both inner and outer raceways are ground to a depth of at least 0.05 mm, but not more than 0.15 mm. This removes all superficial damage and a large portion of the fatigue-damaged stressed volume. The bearings are then fitted with new over-size balls or rollers.

The analysis of restored bearing life is based on the Lunberg-Palmgren theory for rolling-element bearings, modified to show the effect of removing a portion of the fatigue-damaged stressed volume. In predicting the reliability of restored and refurbished bearings it is assumed that the probability of survival of the bearing is equal to the product of the individual probabilities of survival of the newly stressed and previously stressed materials. The stressed volume removed by grinding and the number of stress cycles accumulated before grinding are therefore variables affecting the reliability of the restored bearings.

It is shown that there is a small bias towards earlier failures of restored and refurbished bearings. Depending both on the amount of material removed by grinding and on the time the bearing was in service before being restored, the 10% life of the restored bearings ranges from 74% to 100% of the 10% life of brand new bearings. Renewal theory shows that the mean time between failures for restored and refurbished bearings ranges from 90% to 100% of that of new bearings. Since this is not a significant difference, existing maintenance and replacement policies should not be adversely affected by using restored and refurbished bearings as replacements at overhaul.

Further information is contained in NASA Technical Note D-8486 by Coy *et al.*, available from Microinfo Ltd, Alton, Hampshire.

4.3 Magnetic bearings

Magnetic levitation of a shaft unsupported by any visible means has an aura of science fiction; however, magnetic bearings are not only possible, but are in use today. There is little published literature — considerably less than on gas bearings — but two sources of field force, magnetic in origin, can produce mechanical force without physical contact. These are the forces associated with permanent magnets and those associated with electromagnetic effects.

Bearings working on an electromagnetic principle can be in two forms. Either the force of attraction between a magnetic material and an electromagnet may be used, or the interaction between the magnetic fields of two current-carrying conductors. In these two areas, the discovery of superconducting materials and the use to which this can be put can be superimposed, and considerable work has been done at the University of Warwick on magnetic levitation particularly in respect of high-speed tracked vehicles.

Reverting to straightforward magnetic shaft/bearing combinations, a major problem arising from a shaft freely supported in a magnetic field is one of stability.

To ensure stability, a servo system can be applied, but this absorbs power and is an undesirable complication; hence work is being done to find practical and less complicated ways of achieving stability.

A more common approach that can often be adopted where the load acts in one direction only is by using the magnetic field to support the load and mechanical or other constraints to provide stability. A little wear may result from the constraints, but it would be considerably less than that caused by the main load. It is this type of approach that has been used in the bearings of some electric supply meters.

The use of cryogenic materials offers advantages in that, as the electric resistivity approaches zero at close to absolute zero temperature, currents set up inductively in the materials will persist and create a mechanical force by interaction of two flux fields. Instability does not arise with the use of a magnet, permanent or otherwise, and a diamagnetic material such as a superconductor.

The use of superconductive materials has been investigated for use in frictionless cryogenic gyroscopes which find applications in navigation for space vehicles, missiles and in the more conventional areas such as ships and aircraft.

It is interesting to note that instability does not occur with time-variable magnet fields, and this principle can be used to levitate objects to float in an alternating magnetic field.

More recently the company Société de Mécanique Magnétique (S2M), formed in June 1976 and jointly owned by the Société Européenne de Propulsion (SEP) and SKF France, was created to manufacture and market internationally magnetic suspensions for all types of industry. S2M has developed a completely new type of bearing — an active electromagnetic bearing — and has thus made a significant contribution to bearing technology. The new bearing, which essentially consists of a moving component (the rotor) and a stationary component (the stator) has the following properties:

(1)   loads are accommodated without mechanical contact between the moving and stationary components;
(2)   The position of the rotor is continuously controlled by equipment which causes it to maintain its nominal position, i.e. displacements are immediately corrected; and
(3)   the bearing provides mechanical damping which can be controlled and has a stiffness which can be adapted to the particular application.

Development of this new bearing technology originally directed at military and space projects. Today the active magnetic bearing is quickly gaining favour in general engineering, since its special characteristics and operating properties meet technical demands which could otherwise only be partially fulfilled by conventional technological means.

The electromagnetic bearing principle can most simply be described by a mechanical model. Figure 4.42 shows a rotor suspended in a system of springs

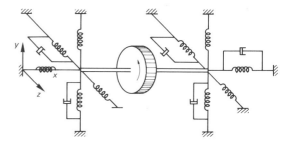

Figure 4.42 Mechanical model of an electromagnetic bearing arrangement where a rotor is suspended in a system of springs and dampers

and damping devices. The rotor is driven at speed and is controlled with respect to the other five degrees of freedom by the viscoelastic suspension. This therefore determines:

(1)   the radial movement along the y axis;
(2)   the radial movement along the z axis;
(3)   the axial movement along the x axis;
(4)   rotation about the z axis; and
(5)   rotation about the y axis.

Figure 4.43 shows the principle of the design of a radial active magnetic bearing incorporating four electromagnets. A cylindrical ferromagnetic rotor 'floats' in magnetic fields produced by the electromagnets which are positioned in pairs diametrically opposed. The current to the windings of the electromagnets is delivered via amplifiers. For a complete magnetic suspension with both radial and axial guidance a total of ten amplifiers is needed.

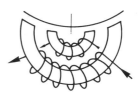

Figure 4.43 Diagram showing the principle of an active magnetic radial bearing. The four electromagnets control the position of the rotor through signals generated in the sensors

The rotor is in equilibrium under the influence of the electromagnetic forces. Its position is determined by four sensors which register any displacements; one and the same displacement is measured by one or more of the sensors. Generally these are of the induction type which produce an electric tension when the rotor is displaced. The position signals from the sensors automatically correct the current passing through the electromagnets and therefore the strength of the magnetic fields, by means of an electronic control system. The differences in strength of the various magnetic fields produces a force which strives to return the rotor to its nominal position. Adjustment takes only milliseconds.

The electronic system incorporated in the control equipment comprises a number of circuits for the treatment of the position signals from the sensors. These circuits have to:

(1) perform a signal integration to achieve stiffness in the system at low frequencies (the signal frequency of external sources of interference is approximately 10 Hz);
(2) produce a phase turning giving the maximum value centred on the inherent frequency of the system to achieve the requisite damping and thus stability; and
(3) produce a linearisation, making it possible to obtain an electromagentic force which is proportional to the displacement of the rotor.

A bearing arrangement with active magnetic bearings is usually designed to include two radial and one thrust bearing (single or double direction). Figure 4.44 shows a complete bearing arrangement incorporating the design where the rotor is outside the stator. Alternatively, the rotor may be positioned inside. The stator section, which is carried by two supports, comprises the following components: at the centre an asynchronous motor which drives the rotor, at each side of the motor a sensor and a radial bearing with eight poles, and at the far end a double-direction thrust bearing with two windings. The rotor is equipped on the inside with rings of ferromagnetic sheet, without grooves or windings, which correspond to each of the bearing components of the stator.

The active magnetic bearing differs from established bearing types in a number of respects. The most important is the load-carrying capacity. The load-carrying capacity of an active magnetic bearing is dependent on the ferromagnetic material employed, the rotor diameter and the width of the magnetic field. The relationship can, for a radial bearing, be expressed as

$$C_r = p_r D B$$

where C_r is the radial load-carrying capacity (N), p_r is the material constant (N cm^{-2}) = 25 for silicon sheet (97% iron, 3% silicon) = 50 for cobalt sheet (53% iron, 45% cobalt, 2% vanadium), D is the rotor diameter at air gap (cm), and B is the width of magnetic field (cm).

For an axial bearing the load-carrying capacity can be determined from the equation

$$C_a = 2\pi p_a D_e h$$

where C_a is the axial load carrying capacity (N), p_a is the material constant (N cm^{-2}) = 50 for silicon sheet = 100 for cobalt sheet, D_e is the external rotor diameter (cm), and h is the width of magnetic field (cm).

Conventional bearing types (rolling, hydrodynamic and hydrostatic bearings) have a constant stiffness which is determined by the bearing geometry and the material used and is independent of other factors. The active magnetic bearing has completely different elastic properties. Here, the stiffness is a function of the inherent frequency of the control equipment and also proportional to the mass suspended.

Generally, the stiffness of an active magnetic bearing is less than that of a rolling bearing but, on the other hand, it can be adapted to the operating conditions of a specific bearing arrangement. This adaptibility is unique to the magnetic bearing, since the stiffness of all other bearing types is determined by the design.

The active electromagnetic bearing offers a considerable number of advantages, some of which have already been mentioned. They can be referred to certain design conditions, namely the complete absence of mechanical contact between the rotor and the stator, the special properties of the control equipment and also the new possibilities with regard to the machine design. It can therefore be considered appropriate to divide the advantages into three groups.

(1) Advantages due to absence of mechanical contact imply:
  (a) no wear;
  (b) very high rotational speeds (a peripheral speed of up to 200 m s^{-1} can be permitted in the air gap, see the comparison with other bearing types);
  (c) noiseless operation;
  (d) virtually unlimited life of the electromechanical components, as the moving parts are not equipped with windings;

Figure 4.44 Complete active magnetic bearing arrangement. The rotor is dismounted to show the design of the stator with electromagnets and sensors

(e) very small temperature rise during operation;

(f) no need for lubrication or seals;

(g) ability to function in a vacuum and also in a corrosive atmosphere;

(h) virtually independent of the ambient temperature, the temperature range at which the bearings may be used being $-150°C$ to $+450°C$;

(i) very small rotor power losses, solely resulting from magnetic losses by hysteresis and Foucault currents.

(2) Advantages resulting from the control equipment enable the magnitude and phase of the electromagnetic force to be modified and this means that it is possible to produce special properties as required in the bearing arrangement. Above all it is possible to achieve:

(a) a stable equilibrium characterised by rotation of the moving component about its principal axis of inertia and not about the bearing axis;

(b) a damping in the suspension arrangement so that the critical speeds of the rotor can be passed without difficulty;

(c) a very high stiffness providing the greatest accuracy in the equilibrium position of the rotor.

(3) Advantages with regard to the machine design. The active magnetic bearing cannot replace established bearing designs without special adaptation. When developing a bearing arrangement – not just improving the performance of an existing machine – the properties of the magnetic bearing may be exploited, e.g.:

(a) the possibility of magnetic alignment of a number of bearings;

(b) the ability to carry out micrometric displacements of the rotor in the air gap during rotation;

(c) very high reliability;

(d) no maintenance requirements.

When the first American communication satellites intended for operation in a geostationary orbit, i.e. stationary relative to earth, were designed, a problem was encountered with the momentum wheel for the steering function. This mechanical component is vital in that it determines the life of the satellite. Ways of achieving the following primary goals were therefore sought:

(1) to have a bearing arrangement life of at least 10 years; the use of ball bearings would hardly permit more than 5 to 7 years;

(2) to reduce friction in the bearing arrangement to conserve the energy produced by the solar cells in the satellites;

(3) to correct minor deviations from orbit (in the order of $\pm 1°$) without requiring a cardan suspension;

(4) to be able eventually to use a momentum wheel to store energy, in which case its mass would have to be less than that of the solar cells.

In 1971, tests were carried out with a model equipped with passive magnetic bearings (equipped with permanent magnets), but these gave poor results. An invitation was then extended to specialists throughout the world to submit bearing arrangement proposals. As a result of this, SEP, together with the West German firm Teldix, were commissioned to design a momentum wheel completely suspended by magnetic means in active bearings. The work was divided into two stages. The first stage resulted in a model which was only intended to control rotation. Its electronic equipment was not miniaturised but consisted of a number of printed-circuit cards for the different functions. After the model had been completed, work on the actual components for installation in the satellites was started, the comprehensive electronic equipment this time being based on integrated circuits.

Figures 4.45 and 4.46 show the design of the mechanical components of the momentum wheel. The electromagnets of the thrust bearings AL1 and AL2 are controlled by the position sensors AS1 and AS2 and hold the rotor suspended axially. Similarly, radial support for the rotor is provided by two bearing pairs RL1 to RL4 in the upper position and corresponding bearings RL5 to RL8 in the lower. The radial position sensors are indicated by RS1 to RS8.

Figure 4.45 Satellite momentum wheel

This satellite momentum wheel constitutes the first ever operational application for active magnetic bearings. The technical data quoted above would not have been possible if this type of bearing had not been used, and the results achieved are completely in accordance with the goals.

Meteorological satellites make it possible to investigate the atmosphere and heat balance and are thus singularly useful for weather forecasting. As satellites can collect information which is superior in

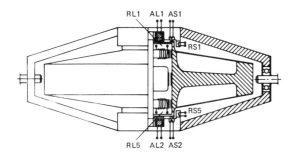

Figure 4.46 Active magnetic bearing arrangement for momentum wheel

quality to that obtained by conventional means, use is now being made of them for 'teledetection' in other fields. They are used, for example, in prospecting for minerals and oil, documenting resources in agriculture and forestry and also marine resource charting.

Ground stations have been established around the world to receive signals emitted by various satellites, which are stationary and moving relative to earth. For example, continuous photography with light and also infra-red light is undertaken in space. Images are transmitted by short wave to the ground stations, where the impulses are transformed into photographs by special image display units. SEP, the company which developed the momentum wheel with active magnetic bearings, was given a contract by the French National Meteorological Institute to develop an image display unit in co-operation with the Centre of Meteorological Space Studies (CEMS) at Lannion, France.

An image display unit, known as Vizir, is based on modulated laser beam techniques, using coded impulses received from the satellite. Very accurate reproductions are carried out of the observations made by the satellite. Images are obtained on negative photographic film measuring 400 × 400 mm and are composed of 15 000 lines, each of 15 000 points. Each point has a diameter of only 27 μm. The speed of reproduction is 1000 lines per minute, so that each separate picture takes 15 minutes to transmit.

The high quality of the image produced depends primarily on the fact that the drum on which the film is rolled is supported by active magnetic bearings. These provide a minimum constant friction and high rotation accuracy. The constant value of the friction makes it possible to obtain a smooth regulation of the film drum speed, which can be varied from 60 to 1800 rpm. An asynchronous motor placed adjacent to the drum provides the drive, with the stator internal to the rotor.

The combination of two sophisticated techniques — electro-optical modulation and active magnetic bearings — has made it possible to deve-

lop an apparatus to give very accurate reproduction of space photography.

4.4 Bearing life

Bearings, like most other products, end their life through one of three modes or by a combination of modes:

(1) failure either sudden or progressive,
(2) obsolescence, or
(3) duty cycle completion.

The design process usually attempts to ensure that failure does not occur before the end of a specified design life, and a situation when all three modes occur at the same time can be considered ideal. Design life is usually dictated by cost considerations; where a high degree of reliability and safety is required, a higher cost will undoubtedly be involved since tighter limits in manufacturing would be imposed, thus leading to higher rejects. With lower costs almost certainly the risk of failure will be higher.

A number of techniques are available for analysing failures in bearings in order to determine causes and to predict future and possible trends. A number of these have been discussed at the symposia, *Information Systems for Designers*, hosted by Southampton University. Another technique where a number of failures is being recorded is to plot failure rate against life and see if the relationship is rising or falling. A mathematical approach is to use the Weibull distribution for the statistical analysis of failure.

Sudden failures are more likely to be easier to understand than slow progressive failures, although the former usually involve several causes which have a synergistic effect.

This chapter has no pretensions to providing design information in order to achieve a defined life. It hopes to provide an indication of the large number of factors which must be considered when specifying and fitting bearings. This process is complicated by the necessity of deciding what type of bearing needs to be considered.

In broad terms these types are:

(1) rolling bearings — ball, roller, needle, or taper roller,
(2) plain metallic bearings,
(3) plain non-metallic bearings — plastics, carbons, ceramics, etc.,
(4) combinations of (2) and (3),
(5) air bearings, and
(6) magnetic bearings.

Neither air nor magnetic bearings are considered here, since their applications form a very small proportion of the total.

Useful pointers to the selection of bearings are given in the *Tribology Handbook* and ESDU data sheets where it will be seen that a fluid film is essential in hydrodynamic bearings which effectively means metallic bearings. With dry rubbing bearings, i.e. (3) and (4) above, the important factor is the choice of material. Factors important in the life of a bearing can be enumerated as:

(1) geometry, i.e. the shape, size and loading of the bearing, clearance, etc. This also includes correct fitting;
(2) temperature — high, low, cycle, intermittent, etc.;
(3) surface finish;
(4) lubrication;
(5) materials used;
(6) contamination; and
(7) vibration.

The design of hydrodynamic bearings can be a daunting task for any designer. With roller element bearings a selection process is usually sufficient since manufacturers' catalogues give tabulated information on size, load, speed and life, etc., although these should be carefully studied and understood before applying.

With plain hydrodynamic bearings such classified information is not always easy to come by and, with the continual up-dating of machinery, it is difficult to obtain detailed information in a readily digestible form. In the very early stages of design of a new piece of machinery or plant, the basic envelope into which the bearings must fit is decided, this being dictated by shaft size and overall dimensions of the machine. It is not appropriate to make detailed studies at this stage since inevitably changes will have to be made to both dimensions and operating conditions. Therefore information is required which enables non-specialists in bearings to produce realistic preliminary designs which, at the later detail stage, do not prove restrictive to the bearing designer.

Fundamental performance data for hydrodynamic bearings are fairly common, but the emphasis should be placed on the interpretation of calculated results so that the designer can appreciate more fully the limitations of hydrodynamic bearings. Particularly convenient and well documented procedure for cylindrical ball bearings is given in appropriate ESDU data sheets. Whilst there is still a considerable amount of calculation to be carried out, the process is quite straightforward but, after performance estimates have been obtained for a particular design of bearing under specific operating conditions, judgements must be made on results as to whether the design is practical, i.e. will operate satisfactorily without damage or distress, and whether it is an optimum design, e.g. would a

smaller bearing with a lower loss power be acceptable?

The limiting conditions of load and speed which a bearing can successfully accept are indicated in Figures 4.47 and 4.48. The breakdown of the oil film can rapidly lead to severe wear, overheating and ultimately to bearing failure. There is evidence to show that the initial film breakdown occurs at a predictable film thickness which is a function of surface roughness which in turn is dependent upon machining process and bearing size. The importance of surface finish has been dealt with in some depth in a paper by researchers at Vandervell Products (see Bibliography).

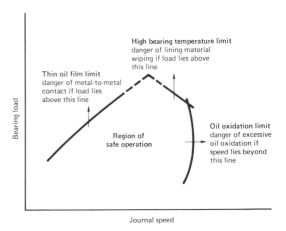

Figure 4.47 Limits of safe operation for hydrodynamic journal bearings

To increase the operating oil-film thickness for given conditions of load and speed, the bearing size must be increased or a thicker lubricant and/or a reduced inlet temperature used. Changes in oil supply pressure usually have little effect. Any increase in clearance may either increase or reduce the film thickness, depending on the precise operating conditions.

The limiting acceptable temperature obviously depends on the lining material, but, whatever the material used, the temperature must always be kept well below its theoretical melting point. The bearing material temperature is controlled by the amount of lubricant passing through the active part of the oil film and this is insensitive to feeding conditions, providing the bearing is not starved. The bearing temperature may also generally be decreased by increasing the bearing size or clearance or by using a thinner grade of oil.

A further point that should be noted is the influence of machine temperatures on the bearing. If there can be an appreciable heat soak along the shaft or through the bearing housing then the design

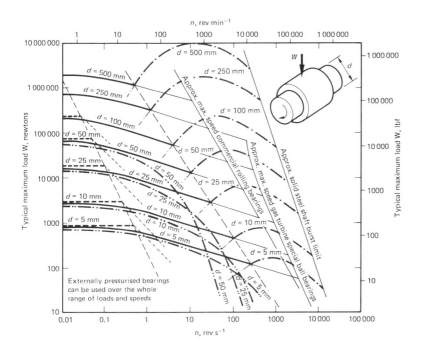

Figure 4.48 Selection chart for journal bearings. (Courtesy Michael Neale and Associates)

must allow for adequate oil flow to deal with it. In some machinery the worst temperature conditions at the bearing can occur after shutdown when heat soak raises temperatures above peak running values. Oxidisation of the lubricating oils is another consideration that must be carefully looked at.

An important point, which has not been indicated on Figure 4.47, is the instability of a shaft within the oil film. Under certain conditions, often normally at low load and/or high shaft speeds, a self-excitation and self-sustaining motion can be set up where the shaft centre presses around the bearing centre at something slightly less than half shaft speed. Under these conditions the hydrodynamic action of the bearing is practically lost, and metal-to-metal contact can occur. If left for long periods fatigue type damage is produced due to the high temperatures generated. There can also be large and unacceptable vibrations transmitted through the machine. If normal cylindrical bore bearings cannot be designed to avoid the instability limit, then some form of bore profiling may be the answer. Figure 4.49 shows the more commonly used type of bearings in order of their resistance to half speed whirl, (e) being better than (a).

Rolling bearings have been known for centuries although it was not until the end of the nineteenth century that they came into common use. Experience showed, however, that even the best cared for rolling bearing eventually failed by fatigue in the highly stressed region under the balls and rollers.

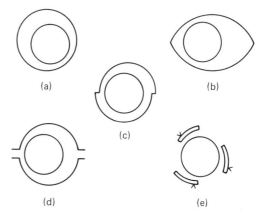

Figure 4.49 Five common ways of relieving half speed whirl in journal bearings: (a) plain journal; (b) lemon bore; (c) displaced halves; (d) partial arcs; (e) tilting pads

From that observation grew the mainly empirical science of life prediction. The life expectation of a rolling bearing, provided it is not subject to abuse, is set by the fatigue limit. Life therefore depends on the number of stress cycles and is directly proportional to the number of revolutions. It also depends markedly on the intensity of stress and therefore on the load.

Empirically it is found that life is proportional to load. Because fatigue failures occur randomly, there is no certain value for the life expectancy of rolling bearings. The standard practice is for manufacturers to quote the load which 90% of all bearings they manufacture will sustain for one million revolutions without failing, with the assumption that 10% of the bearings will fail.

The idea of designing for a 10% failure rate is difficult to accept, although it can be argued that the philosophy is well founded in the random nature of fatigue in metals. The situation becomes worse when more than one bearing is in a system. Fortunately for engineers, quite modest reduction in load increases the life of a rolling bearing dramatically on the basis of life being proportional to $load^{-3}$. This means that halving the load gives eight times the life.

The static load-carrying capacity of the rolling bearing can be taken as equal to that for a dry or marginally lubricated plain bearing with the same shaft diameter. If the static capacity is exceeded, and this sometimes happens during shock loads, the races can be damaged by indentation from the balls or rollers. Sometimes light loads can be detrimental because the rolling elements skid between the races instead of being forced to roll. Rolling bearings will accept either oil or grease, and the greatest danger is over lubrication, since too much oil or grease impedes the bearing and excessive churning leads to dangerous overheating. The fitting of bearings and shafts is of considerable importance and the axial growth of a shaft due to temperature changes can throw excessive load onto bearings if this is not taken into consideration. Too tight a fit of the inner race on the shaft or the outer race in its housing will reduce and may even destroy clearances. There are bearings which are specially designed to expect mal-alignment, but it is not always possible to fit these and therefore careful consideration of housing and shaft dimension and limits must be undertaken.

Factors influencing metal fatigue are well known, and a general definition of failure by fatigue is that a component subjected to a repeated or fluctuating stress will ultimately fail at a mean stress lower than that determined for the material in a normal tensile test. Fatigue failure under conditions of rolling contact is a special case and, as explained earlier, is not usually expressed in the same manner as for structural components.

Three main metallurgical factors affecting fatigue life are: the cleanness of the steel; the structure and distribution of the free carbides in the hardened steel; and the quality of the heat treatment carried out to produce the hardened structure. This is usually within the province of the bearing manufacturers and is not a prime worry for the designer who is fitting the bearings.

The Leeds Tribology Unit has produced a concise and academically independent note about the L_{10} life which says that it needs to be understood at the outset that a perfectly made, properly lubricated ball or roller bearing run under any given load/speed condition will have a finite life. It will eventually fail even without abuse, not (unlike most engineering components) by slowly wearing out, but suddenly due to material fatigue. Usually this starts as a small pit in the running tracks and quickly develops to produce flaking and destruction of the smooth surfaces. British Standard BS 5512 also provides for adjusting rating life and contains a table, the use of which can improve the reliability of rolling bearings.

End load or preload conditions in bearings play an important part in the life of a bearing. The typical curve shown in Figure 4.50 demonstrates that every bearing in every application has an optimum setting. If one considers the system life based on catalogue predictions represented by a straight line, it can be seen that significantly more life is obtained at the optimum setting which is usually a small amount of preload.

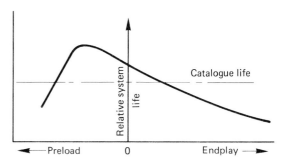

Figure 4.50 Effects of preload on rolling bearing life

Porous metal bearings are in contrast to solid metal bearings which, if properly designed and supplied with clean oil, have in theory an infinite life. A porous metal bearing has a finite life unless steps are taken to rejuvenate it. This arises from two factors connected only with the oil which is responsible for bearing life in terms of quantity and quality. A porous metal bearing initially contains a quantity of oil equal to the product of the bearing volume, the porosity and the degree of impregnation. On the other hand the bearing oil requirements are, amongst other things, a function of the surface area of the bore; thus, the effective quantity of oil varies as the wall thickness and the porosity. In short, although the thickest wall and the greatest porosity give the greatest oil holding capacity, they do not necessarily give the longest life or the most satisfactory running.

Unlike in a solid bearing, the lubricating oil does not flow in and out of the system and the quantity of oil circulating in the pores is maintained continuously at near the running temperature. Cooling is by conduction along the shaft and through the housing, while the rate of circulation of oil in the pores can be estimated for a given set of conditions.

The majority of true dry bearings, that is bearings requiring no lubricant, are based on PTFE, although for less arduous applications composites such as molybdenum disulphide, graphite-filled nylon or PTFE-filled polyacetal are available. The same fillers in polyimide provide a thermally stable bearing with useful dry wear resistance, although the polymer is expensive. The most important point to realise is that, in operation, dry bearing materials wear continuously. In this respect they are different from conventionally lubricated plain bearings which, in general, wear only during start-up and shut-down or when the lubricant becomes seriously contaminated. They are also different from rolling element bearings which normally fail by fatigue.

For any given set of operating conditions the rate of wear is primarily determined by the intrinsic wear resistance of the material and the way in which the sliding surface and the surface of the dry bearing material itself become modified during the action of sliding. In most cases wear-limited life rather than friction determines the suitability of a dry bearing for an application. When considering dry bearings based on polymers other than PTFE, two points should be appreciated:

(1) In order to reduce friction, solid lubricants are invariably added to the polymer to increase strength, dimensional stability and improve the thermal properties, while the polymers are often filled or reinforced.

(2) When filled and reinforced, most of the materials are suitable only for low duty applications, because running temperature is restricted by low softening points of the plastics materials.

The temperature limit for materials based on organic materials is effectively around 300°C and for higher temperatures inorganic materials must be used. One such group of materials is based on carbon. With this type of bearing there are basically three major factors affecting bearing life, i.e. a high temperature causing break-down of lubrication; ingress of dirt into the system; and incorrect selection of bearing for the application.

The contribution of lubricant to bearing life is difficult to quantify as it is dependent upon the bearing and application. In the case of a poor lubricant, life can be reduced dramatically until one is able to use a material such as carbon which can operate with marginal lubrication providing loads and speeds are not too onerous.

The effects of incorrect bearing assembly on bearing life can be quite dramatic and a major problem is that of alignment. In addition to the thermoplastics materials there are a number of proprietary materials, particularly reinforced thermosets. These have been developed to overcome many of the problems associated with thermoplastic bearings and to some extent the problems associated with metal bearings. They have a high load-carrying capacity and there are grades that can be used within a temperature range of −160 to over 200°C, while the fatigue resistance is often very much better than that associated with pure metal bearings. A further advantage with thermoset materials is their ability to accommodate a considerable amount of wear debris and foreign matter within their relatively soft matrix.

A major development with this type of bearing has been their application to stern tubes and propeller shafts of very large ships. These have been approved by the various classification societies, such as the Lloyd's Register of Shipping. In this application they also have the considerable advantage that, in an emergency, the shafts can be lubricated with the seawater with which they are in contact.

Although little has been said on the subject of lubrication as such, it has been implicit in all that has been said that lubrication plays an extremely important part and, in this connection, the correct choice of lubricant, its viscosity, the method in which it is applied and the rate at which it flows around the system are all vitally important aspects to be considered in the life of a bearing.

A study (3rd Cheltenham Bearing Conference, 1978) as shown by Figure 4.51 has revealed that trace amounts of water in the lubricant — of the order of 100 to 400 ppm — can reduce bearing life. Condensed water in the system or even the humidity of air can be detrimental. Additives capable of negating the effects of moisture are volatile and therefore not practicable in real service.

In summing up failure in plain bearings it may be said that foreign matter such as dirt particles in the lubricant exceeding the minimum oil film thickness will leave fine score marks or scratches. Inadequate clearance or overheating, or insufficient oil supply and possibly excessive load, will also create superficial melting and flow of bearing material. Fatigue

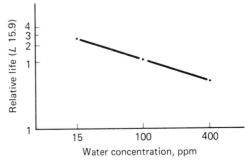

Figure 4.51 Effect of water concentration in lubricant on bearing life

failure in plain bearings results in cracking, often in a mosaic pattern, with a loss of area of lining. Excessive interference fits between shaft and bearing will distort a bearing, causing overheating and fatigue.

Fretting, which has not previously been mentioned, occurs where two contacting surfaces, often normally at rest, undergo minute oscillatory tangential relative motions and may manifest itself by debris oozing from the contact, particularly if it is lubricated with oil. On inspection the fretted surfaces show shallow pits filled and surrounded with debris. The movement may be caused by vibration or can often arise from one of the members undergoing cyclic stressing. It often occurs in rolling bearings when stationary under external vibrations. Malalignment of shafts is a quick way to a short life in bearings; often, with heavy shafts, the weights and the deflections are not sufficiently considered. All this will lead to very short life.

Cavitation erosion is created by changes of pressure in the oil film associated with interrupted flow and tends to remove metal from the bearing in regions near joint faces or grooves. Failures in rolling bearings are almost always those of fatigue, although Brinelling or bruising of the grooves of the bearing track can be caused by the rolling element being brought into violent contact with the race, often during assembly. It can also be created under fretting conditions, i.e. vibration while the bearing is stationary. The effects of malalignment are equally applicable to rolling bearings.

While the designer can take all the necessary precautions in the early stages of design to ensure that the life of a bearing is optimised, it is always wise to consult with bearing manufacturers whether it be in respect of plain, rolling, plastics or other bearings. Major reputable companies have a vast store of knowledge and in many cases have computerised programs which will enable them to feed in very quickly all the operating information which the designer has at his disposal and can then confirm or predict the life of a bearing or come up with some alternative scheme which will improve the designer's original concept.

Bibliography

BSI (1977) BS 5512, Part 1, *Roller bearings, dynamic ratings and rating life: Calculation methods*, British Standards Institution.

CAMERON, MORGAN and STAINSBY (1962) 'Critical conditions for hydrodynamic lubrication of porous metal bearings', *Proc. I. Mech. E.*

CHELTENHAM BEARING CONFERENCE (1974) 'Know your bearings', 1st Cheltenham Bearing Conference, Publication Services, Worthing.

CHELTENHAM BEARING CONFERENCE (1978a) 'Looking beyond the catalogue ratings', 3rd Cheltenham Bearing Conference, Publication Services, Worthing.

CHELTENHAM BEARING CONFERENCE (1978b) 'Preloading rolling bearings', 3rd Cheltenham Bearing Conference, Publication Services, Worthing.

COY et al. 'Life analysis of restored and refurbished bearings', NASA Technical Note D-8486, available from Microinfo Ltd, Alton, Hampshire.

ESDU Data Sheet No. 66023, Engineering Science Data Unit, 251–259 Regent Street, London.

GLACIER METAL, *Designer's Handbook*, The Glacier Metal Co. Ltd, Wembley, Middx.

I. MECH. E. (1967) 'Recent developments in PTFE based dry bearing materials and treatments', 5th Lubrication and Wear Convention, Institution of Mechanical Engineers.

INFORMATION SYSTEMS FOR DESIGNERS (1971, 1974 and 1977) Proceedings, Publication Services, Worthing.

LEEDS TRIBOLOGY UNIT (1978) *How long should a ball bearing last?* Technical Note No. 10.

MARSHALL and MORGAN (1965/66) 'Review of porous metal bearing development', *Proc. I. Mech. E.*

NEALE, M. J. (ed.) (1973) *Tribology Handbook*, Butterworths.

SOUTHAMPTON UNIVERSITY (1974, 1977 and 1979) *Information Systems for Designers*, Publication Services, Worthing.

VANDERVELL PRODUCTS, *The Influence of Crankshaft Design, Machining and Finishing on Bearing Performance*, Vandervell Products Ltd, Maidenhead, Berks.

5

Fastenings

5.1 A logical approach to secure bolting

Archimedes developed and recorded the first spiral screw in 250 BC. He used it for lifting irrigation water. Up until about 1450 AD, the screw was used only as a power transmitting device. Gutenberg used a screw-driven printing press in 1450 to make the first machine-printed Bible; and a few years later clocks with the first slotted head screws appeared. In 1568, Benson designed a crude screw cutting lathe; however, it was not until the Industrial Revolution began in the later 1700s that William Wyatt and Jess Ramsden mass produced screws in England. At the turn of the century Henry Maudslay in England contributed to the first interchangeable screws and nuts by designing an accurate lathe. This, coincidentally, was at the same time that Eli Whitney in Connecticut was promoting and proving the principles of interchangeable production parts (Industrial Fastener Institute, 1974).

Today, according to a US government survey, assembling parts constitutes half of all the manufacturing labour in the USA. Five per cent of the assembly cost is the fastener itself; nuts, bolts, rivets, pins, etc. Next to the common nail, screw products are the most useful fasteners ever developed. They do however have limitations which are not always well understood or avoided. It is, therefore, well worth while to look at how a screw fastener works.

5.1.1 Getting the right clamping force

When someone buys a nut and bolt, he is with but few exceptions buying just one thing — clamping force. He wants to be able to predict what the force is going to be and how long it will stay at that value. In addition, at the end of a period of time, he may wish to remove the clamping force. Nuts and bolts supply this function well, but must be engineered properly to give satisfactory long-term results.

We tighten a screw or bolt by applying a torque to the head. A clockwise torque makes the bolt to nut distance shorter. If a resistance is met (such as when clamping a flange), the bolt will continue to rotate until a balance is obtained between the torque applied to the head and the sum of bolt tension and friction. The distribution of torque between these three factors is shown in Table 5.1.

The equilibrium relationship is often expressed mathematically as $T = KDF$, where T is the torque (N m) or (lb-in)*, D is the nominal diameter of bolt (m) or (in), F is the induced force or clamp load (N) or (lb), and K is the empirical constant which takes into account friction and the variable diameter under the head and in the threads where friction is acting. (It is not the coefficient of friction although it is related to it.)

Values of K can be determined experimentally (see Table 5.2). (For a mathematical analysis of force and friction see Section 5.1.5.)

The variation in friction and, therefore, K is wide since it is the result of extremely high pressure between surfaces which may be rough, smooth, oxidised, chemically treated, and/or lubricated. Oily steel has a K value which varies between 0.11 and

---

* *A note on the use of units of measurement.* Despite efforts in recent years to encourage the use of metric units in the specification of fasteners, approximately 40% of today's production is manufactured to standards based on Imperial units. In addition to the ISO metric standard, many standard bolts and machine screws conform to the UNC and UNF systems. Thus much of the quantitative information in this chapter is expressed in Imperial units.

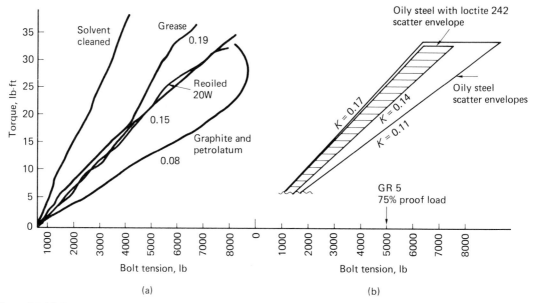

Figure 5.1 (a) Torque tension averages for Grade 5 steel; (b) torque tension envelopes for Grade 5 steel

Table 5.1 Torque absorption in a tightened bolt

| | Percentage of tightening torque | |
	(UNC)	(UNF)
Bolt tension	15%	10%
Thread friction	39%	42%
Head friction	46%	48%
Tightening torque	100%	100%
Loosening torque	70%	80%

Table 5.2 Typical K values* — lubricating threadlockers on various materials

Substrate	Oil	Lubricating threadlocker
Steel	0.15	0.14
Phosphate	0.13	0.11
Cadmium	0.14	0.13
Stainless 404	0.22	0.17
Zinc	0.18	0.16
Brass	0.16	0.09
Silicon bronze	0.18	0.24
Al 6262-Ta	0.17	0.29
Dry degreased fasteners		
Steel	0.20	0.20
Phosphate	0.24	0.14
Nylon	0.05	0.13
Zinc	0.17	0.15

All specimens were dipped in a 5% oil solution and dried before the threadlocker was applied. (Heat Bath Corporation, Lab Oil 72D.)

* The range of values for any lot of fasteners was ± 15%; however, different fastener lots can increase the variation to ± 20%.

0.17 or ± 20%. In addition, friction absorbs 80–90% of the tightening torque (see Table 5.1). It is prudent to test a particular combination in a torque testing device (such as a Skidmore-Wilhelm Hydraulic Bolt Tension Tester) to determine proper torque values for assuring good control of bolt tension. Technical data for lubricants and other thread materials will often have the K values plotted in a torque tension curve, as shown in Figure 5.1.

The slope of these straight line plots, that is torque divided by tension, is equal to factor KD and is constant. Since D is also a constant (0.375 in or 9.5 mm) then each plot has a computable constant K. $K = T/FD$. K is the same for all diameters. Knowing the friction constant K, the designer can compute the torque tension relationships for other sizes of bolts. To simplify the computation, a nomograph has been drawn as shown on the right-hand side of Figure 5.2.

In addition to plotting the graph of the expression $T = KDF$, another critical calculation $S = F/A$ has been interrelated on the same nomograph where S = bolt stress in lb in^{-2}. With this nomograph, a complete fastener design can be approximated for rigid clamping by starting with an allowable stress for the steel grade or material selected. Typical manufacturer's catalogue material concerning allowable stress is shown in Figure 5.3. Non-rigid joints

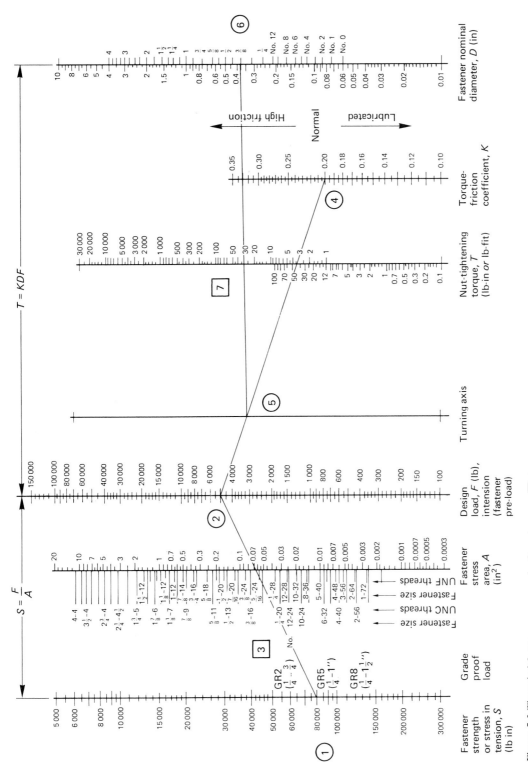

Figure 5.2 Threaded fastener nomograph: O, unknown; □, known

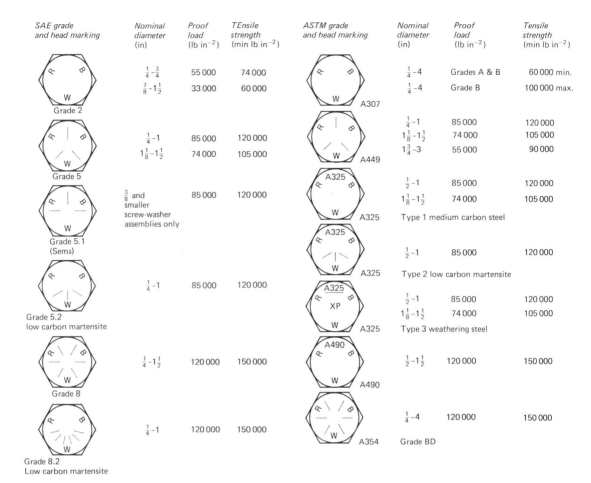

Figure 5.3 Allowable stress and head markings.
(Courtesy R, B & W Corporation)

require further analysis (see Section 5.1.6, 'Gasketing flange bolting').

5.1.2 Loosening tendencies of bolted joints

5.1.2.1 Clamping of soft materials

The information obtained from Figure 5.3 will be satisfactory only for fairly rigid joints. When clamping a soft joint, such as a gasketed cover, it is often necessary to determine the bolt tightness by the capability of the gasket to support the load (Anderson *et al.*, and Section 5.1.6). This means that if bolts are chosen that are too large, they will be stressed at a very low value. Since a steel bolt elongates 0.001 inches per inch of length for 30 000 lb in^{-2} stress, a lower stress means less elongation. If a gasket shrinks or creeps under load, the load

loss is very rapid when stresses are initially low. For instance, a 2 in bolt stressed at 60 000 lb in^{-2} will elongate 0.004 in. If the gasket shrinks 0.001 in, it will lose 25% of its load. If, however, a larger bolt has been chosen which gave the same load at 30 000 lb in^{-2}, then the elongation would be 0.002 and if the gasket shrank 0.001 in, 50% of the load would be lost. The lesson here is to use the longest, smallest bolt possible which will supply the maximum permissible gasket load.

Bolt locking materials, at first sight, do little good if the clamped parts themselves are shrinking away from the bolt. However, whenever shrinkage of gaskets occurs, there will also be increased movement of parts in a sliding and longitudinal motion (relative to the bolt). Therefore, a threadlocking material or device is beneficial in preventing catastrophic loosening (see below). It also provides thread sealing.

5.1.2.2 Brinelling of bearing surfaces

Even hard flanges and gaskets can collapse under the clamping load if there are burrs under the head or poor finishes on the threads. A relaxed condition can be produced if hard washers are not used under the bearing face of the nut and/or bolt, whichever is to be turned. The primary function of the so-called lock washer is to provide a hard bearing surface at very small cost. It has virtually no securing function in spite of its name (see the transverse shock and vibration tests described below).

5.1.2.3 Transverse sliding

All standard bolts and nuts are made with a clearance between them to assure easy assembly. Class 2A, the most common, will have from 0.0013 to 0.0114 inch. lateral clearance. Now consider that the helical thread is nothing more than an inclined plane with the nut sitting on it, held against sliding by friction (Figure 5.4).

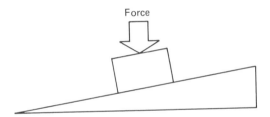

Figure 5.4 A nut on an inclined plane

This condition can be simulated by placing a small memo pad or block onto the side of a slippery book. Tip the book until the pad almost slides. Now try to slide the pad sideways (Figure 5.5) and watch what happens. The pad slides downhill every time you push sideways. You don't have to push it downhill. Its weight moves it by itself. This is exactly what happens to a loaded thread which is made to slide sideways. The higher the load, the faster it slides downhill provided side movement is present.

From this experiment and others, we can conclude that if sidewise sliding is produced on screw threads, then the threads will unwind all by themselves. The higher the clamping force, the less likely there is to be side movement; but if side movement occurs, the higher force will unwind the threads even faster.

Transverse sliding is a common phenomenon in bolted assemblies. It can be caused by bending of the assembly (see Figure 5.6). It can also be caused by differential thermal expansion, such as exists on the head of a car engine (see Figure 5.7). The differential expansion of a six-cylinder in-line engine has been measured to be as long as 0.060 inch total under extreme temperature cycling.

Sliding can be caused by internal pressures as shown in Figure 5.8.

Sliding of bolt threads in a nut can be produced directly by axial forces on the nut which cause it to dilate; see Figure 5.9.

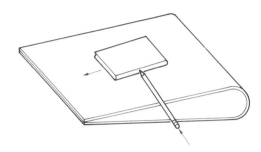

Figure 5.5 Sliding experiment with memo pad on book

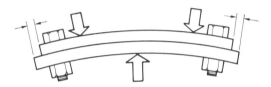

Figure 5.6 Transverse sliding

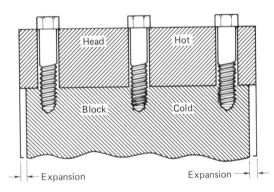

Figure 5.7 Differential thermal expansion on the head of a car engine

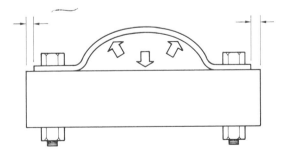

Figure 5.8 Sliding caused by internal pressure

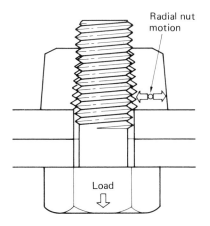

Figure 5.9 Sliding due to axial forces

5.1.2.4 Keeping the joint tight — prevention of thread rotation

Many technical devices have been used to prevent unwinding of nuts and bolts. A few such nuts and bolts are shown to indicate the ingenuity which has gone into this effort (Figures 5.10 and 5.11). Most devices are directed at preventing rotary motion and have been successful in a limited way. Worth noting are the nuts with compressible inserts and the nuts with teeth on the bearing surface. The insert is a prevailing torque type which prevents rotation with a heavy friction drive. By its nature, it resists going on as well as coming off. It does not prevent side motion, and therefore has a definite limit to its effectiveness. The serrated tooth nut is free spinning and works by digging into the clamped material. It is very effective in preventing rotation. Unfortunately, the digging doesn't stop at the cessation of tightening but continues during use, and on short bolts causes loosening without turning. It can also cause failure of the clamped part because the digging may initiate cracks. It is also possible for either the bolt or nut to turn so both may need some locking features. The cost of mechanical devices exceeds that of complete thread fillers as shown in Table 5.3.

5.1.2.5 Prevention of thread movement

The most effective way to prevent unwinding of threads is to prevent all thread movement in any direction. This is accomplished with liquid threadlockers which fill and cure in all the open space between the threads, thereby preventing:

(1) sideways thread movement,
(2) rotational thread movement,
(3) tipping thread movement, and
(4) dilation thread movement.

Figure 5.10 Locking nuts and bolts — prevailing torque type

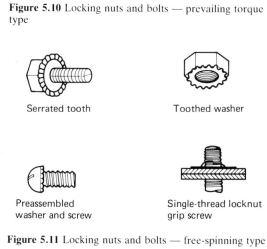

Figure 5.11 Locking nuts and bolts — free-spinning type

Table 5.3 Relative cost of locking methods

Method	Relative cost (%)
Threadfilling anaerobic and STD nut	100
Free spinning serrated head	137
Nylon ring	177
Distorted nut	116
Nylon patch	128

See Figure 5.12. As one might expect, this system is the most effective of all as has been proven by laboratory tests and field experience.

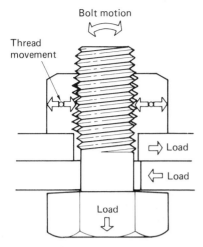

Figure 5.12 Filled thread prevents unwinding

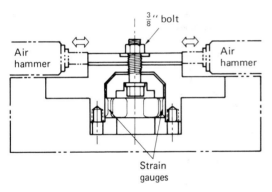

Figure 5.13 Test machine

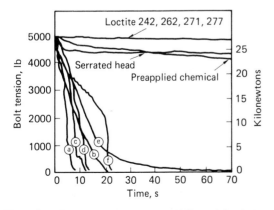

Figure 5.14 Transverse shock test on 3/8″ × 16 Grade 5 bolts: (a) lock washer — 5 to 12 s; (b) root interference lock nut — 6 to 8 s; (c) bolt patch — 8 to 12 s; (d) control, no locking — 8 to 12 s; (e) distorted lock nut — 7 to 22 s; (f) nylon ring — 16 to 20 s

5.1.2.6 Testing with transverse shock

The most common and easiest way to test a bolted assembly is by artificially induced transverse motion. In the 1960s, G. H. Junkers designed such a machine which included a sinusoidal sliding motion between two plates clamped with a bolt. He found that as few as 50 cycles would loosen (20%) a standard nut and bolt (Junkers, 1969). A similar but simpler machine was designed by a European car manufacturer and is the basic machine which Loctite uses to evaluate threadlocking materials. A cross-sectional picture of this machine is shown in Figure 5.13. It is called a transverse shock and vibration machine, or more accurately a transverse shock machine. It is as capable of rating various locking devices as the Junkers machine even though it is not as versatile and measures only time to loosen and not stroke, energy, or cycles. It ends up with the same relative ratings, and more importantly can be correlated with field results.

The test is severe enough (Figure 5.14) to cause failure of most mechanical locking methods. Which doesn't mean that these methods are not useful to a certain degree; however on a function and cost basis they will be hard to justify.

From a functional standpoint the most common prevailing types interfere with the proper tightening. Figure 5.15 shows three individual runs on a nut with a ring type insert, whereas Figure 5.14 shows the averages of several specimens. Note, in Figure 5.15, that a 40% variation in torque is needed to produce the same target clamp load. Also, the better the anti-loosening performance, the less likely it is that the clamp load will be obtained. The chief features of mechanical devices are reusability, temperature resistance (all metal distorted threads), and inspectability.

The relative cost of some of the common methods is given in Table 5.3.

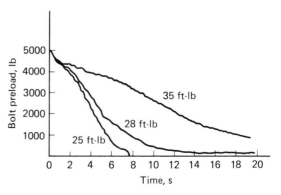

Figure 5.15 Transverse shock test: self-locking nut (plastic ring in cadmium nut), 3/8″ × 16 SAE Grade 5 phosphate and oil bolt, hard bearing surface

5.1.3 Selection of proper threadlocking compound

The selection of a chemical threadlocking material will depend on the following criteria:

(1) The ultimate shear strength of the fastener which must not be exceeded. This is usually important only for screws under 5/16 inch diameter.
(2) The severity of the loosening tendencies.
(3) The size of the threads, and therefore the viscosity of the material to assure thread filling.
(4) The method of application and requirements for testing or putting into service.
(5) The environmental requirements of temperature and chemical resistance.

5.1.3.1 Ultimate fastener strength

The disassembly of bolts or screws without fastener damage is usually important. The ultimate strength of soft screws with slotted or Phillips heads should be determined by experiment. The driving system may fail before the shank. Most high-strength fasteners use an internal or external hexagonal drive which is capable of shearing the fastener without harming the drive system. The ultimate strength of these nut tightening systems can be found as follows:

(1) Using the recommended tightening torque nomograph (Figure 5.2), follow the directions to pick the appropriate tightening torque for your bolt material to give a stress 75% of proof load. Thirty per cent of this tightening torque should be the maximum breakaway or augmentation torque for your bolt size and for any selected locking material.
(2) Enter the chart on Figures 5.16 or 5.17 at a torque augmentation equal to 30% of the tightening torque. This 30% torque value will add to the normal loosening torque so that the torque on break loose will be about equal to the original tightening torque. Go up to the curve for your bolt size and left to the columns showing material performance on various surfaces. Select a material which gives a stress within $\pm$ 25% of the line you have drawn. Use higher strengths for severe situations and lower for the more usual. Product numbers are for Loctite materials. Other materials may be evaluated by the shear stress given on the ordinate axis.

5.1.3.2 Selection of material for loosening severity

For bolted elements which may see severe occasional overloads which can cause very rapid loosening, use the strongest material commensurate with the strength of the bolt. Otherwise, pick a medium or low-strength material, as these will prevent loosening in most situations (Figure 5.14).

5.1.3.3 Selection of viscosity to assure thread filling

Select a viscosity which will apply easily, not run off, and will fill threads which have the maximum clearance (see Table 5.4).

Preapplied dry materials are available for application situations where liquids are not acceptable. They are easy to inspect and provide some reuse. The application is usually carried out by a bolt supplier. These are supplied in at least four formulations:

(1) low-strength locking and sealing,
(2) medium-strength — plated fasteners,
(3) medium-strength, and
(4) high-strength.

Table 5.4 Selection of viscosity to assure thread filling

Material	Viscosity	Suggested bolt range	(Class 1) maximum diametrical clearance
	(cP and Pa s)	(in)	(in and mm)
Low-strength thixotropic	1000 (1)	2 to $\frac{1}{2}$	0.016 (0.4)
Medium-strength thixotropic	1100 (1.1)	$\frac{1}{4}$ to $\frac{3}{4}$	0.022 (0.6)
High-strength thixotropic	1500 (1.5)	$\frac{3}{8}$ to 1	0.025 (0.6)
Very high-strength newtonian	750 (0.8)	$\frac{3}{8}$ to 1	0.025 (0.6)
Very high-strength newtonian	7000 (7)	$\frac{5}{8}$ to 1+	0.025 (0.6)
High-strength wicking newtonian	12 (0.012)	2 to $\frac{1}{2}$	0.016 (0.4)

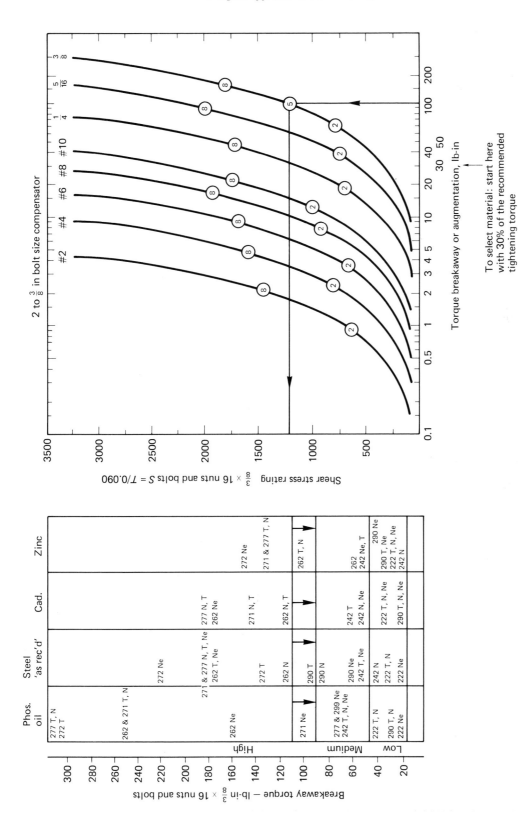

Figure 5.16 Thread-locking performance chart: UNC nuts and bolts. Example: 3/8″ × 16 Grade 5 recommended torque is 360 lb-in (30% is 108 lb-in); materials below the horizontal line are safe to use with standard nut. T, primer T; N, primer N; Ne, no primer

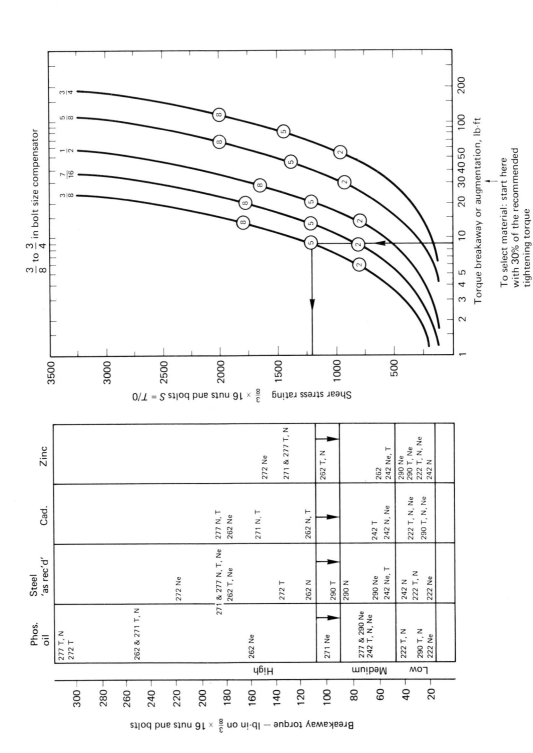

Figure 5.17 Thread-locking performance chart: UNC nuts and bolts. T, primer T; N, primer N; Ne, no primer

5.1.3.4 Selection of the method of application and cure speed

If quality control checks or functional stress are to be applied soon after assembly, then be sure that enough cure has taken place to avoid failure. Cure speed and breakaway torques can be selected from the manufacturer's product data sheets.

5.1.3.5 Environmental requirements of temperature and chemical resistance

Chemical resistance: With time, temperature, and aggressive environments, the strength of the adhesive may decrease. Pick a stronger material or more resistant material if environments are severe (see Table 5.5).

Hot strength: Threadlockers, like most organic materials, lose strength at elevated temperatures. Most show good strength up to 150°C. Hot strength formulations can increase this temperature to 230°C for those applications requiring it.

Application and equipment: For medium or high production it makes economic sense to automate the application process. Many types of equipment are available which are beyond the scope of this paper.

Check with an equipment manufacturer who specialises in anaerobic materials for help in automating the process. The equipment pays for itself in both labour and material savings. It also provides a degree of dependability to the process which is difficult to obtain by hand application.

5.1.4 Torque augmentation

Normal loosening torque of a UNC bolt will be about 70% of the torque to which it has been tightened (UNF = 80%).

The application of a threadlocking compound adds to or augments the normal loosening torque. The amount that it does this is called the torque augmentation. This is shown in the shaded area in Figure 5.18.

The value of torque augmentation is related to the breakaway torque[*] and may vary between 70 and 140% of the breakaway. For products 222, 242, and 262, augmentation is equal to breakaway.

Most structural fasteners are torqued to at least 75% of their minimum yield strength (proof load). To prevent shearing of a locked bolt while being loosened, a locking material should be used which has an augmentation or breakaway that would make

Table 5.5 Solvent resistance tested per MIL-S-22473-D: percentage retained strength after 30 days at 188°F

Thixotropic materials

Solvent	Low-strength (%)	Medium-strength (%)	High-strength (%)
Air reference at 188°F	100	100	100
Motor oil (% of reference)	67	100	100
Water (% of reference)	35	27	100
Glycol/water (% of reference)	27	30	98
Transmission fluid (% of reference)	88	100	100
Gasoline (% of reference)	67	95	86
Skydrol (% of reference)	82	95	78

Newtonian materials

Solvent	High-strength thin (%)	High-strength thick (%)	Ultra thin (%)
Air reference at 188°F	100	100	100
Motor oil (% of reference)	70	83	86
Water (% of reference)	110	64	74
Glycol/water (% of reference)	65	59	74
Transmission fluid (% of reference)	95	90	90
Gasoline (% of reference)	50	90	90
Skydrol (% of reference)	70	90	90

[*] Breakaway torque is the torsional strength of adhesive on an untorqued bolt (e.g. pretorque = zero).

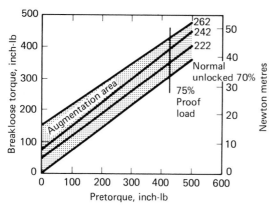

Figure 5.18 Torque augmentation. 'As received' 3/8″ × 16 phosphated and oiled Grade 5 bolts with 'as received' plain steel nuts

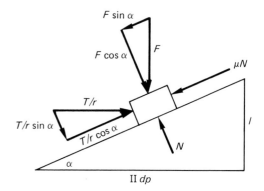

Figure 5.19 F, force applied by the bolt; T, torque applied to the bolt; N normal force on friction surface; μ, coefficient of friction (0.15); dp, diametrical pitch; helix angle whose tangent = $l/(\Pi dp)$; l, lead of thread

the break loose torque roughly equal to the tightening torque as stated above.

Therefore, as a design rule to prevent shearing on loosening, select a material so that:

Breakaway = 30% of tightening torque
or breakaway = 40% of normal loosening torque

For a thread engagement of 0.8 diameter (standard nut) on $\frac{3}{8}$ in × 16 P & O bolts: low-strength threadlockers give 13% augmentation; medium-strength threadlockers give 25% augmentation; and high-strength threadlockers give 40% augmentation.

Augmentation values are plotted in Figures 5.15 and 5.16 for many bolt sizes and surface finishes.

5.1.5 The mathematics of bolt tightening

A simplified mathematical solution to the torque tension relationship gives results very close to test results. To start the analysis, one 360° thread segment of a bolt is figuratively unwrapped. The fact that the face is tipped 30° from the plane normal to the bolt axis is ignored. A diagram can then be drawn (Figure 5.19). The block represents an element of the nut bearing against the ramp formed by the unwrapped and flattened thread. Since the system is in equilibrium, all forces, with due regard to direction and sign, will balance another. In other words, all the forces acting parallel to the ramp will sum to zero (1), and the sum of all forces acting normal to the ramp will equal zero (2):

$$T/r \cos \alpha - \mu N - F \sin \alpha = 0 \qquad (1)$$

$$N - F \cos \alpha - T/r \sin \alpha = 0 \qquad (2)$$
$$\text{or } N = F \cos \alpha + T/r \sin \alpha$$

where $T/r \sin \alpha$ represents a small value drop.

Putting Equation (2) into (1) gives

$$T/r \cos \alpha - \mu F \cos \alpha - F \sin \alpha = 0$$

$$\text{or } T = r \left(\mu F \frac{\cos \alpha}{\cos \alpha} + F \frac{\sin \alpha}{\cos \alpha} \right)$$
$$T = rF (\mu + \tan \alpha)$$

In lb-ft

$$T = \frac{dp}{24} F (\mu + \tan \alpha) \qquad (3)$$

Using Equation (3) for $\frac{3}{8}$ in × 16 UNC we have:

$$
\begin{aligned}
F &= 5000 \text{ lb} \\
\alpha &= 3.5° \\
\mu &= 0.15 \\
dp &= 0.330 \text{ in} \\
F \cos \alpha &= \mu = 4990 \text{ lb} \\
N &= 750 \text{ lb}
\end{aligned}
$$

so $T = 14.5$ lb-ft

For $\frac{3}{8}$ in × 16 UNF we have;

$$
\begin{aligned}
F &= 5000 \text{ lb} \\
\alpha &= 2.2° \\
\mu &= 0.15 \\
dp &= 0.344 \\
F \cos \alpha &= \mu = 4996 \text{ lb} \\
N &= 750 \text{ lb}
\end{aligned}
$$

so $T = 13.5$ lb-ft

The conclusion is that fine thread requires less torque for the same force.

5.1.5.1   Friction force under the head

Again, with a 5000 lb preload and assuming an effective bearing diameter of the nut of 0.4 in, the torque required (in lb-ft) to overcome the friction bearing is:

$$T = r\mu F = \frac{de}{24}\mu F = \frac{0.4}{24} \times 0.15 \times 5000 = 12.5$$

where T = moment arm × force; de is the effective diameter of the bearing surface ($\frac{3}{8} = 0.4$); and $T/r = \mu F$.

5.1.5.2   Total torque

UNC	UNF
14.5 (54%)	13.5 (52%)
12.5 (46%)	12.5 (48%)
———	———
27 lb-ft	26 lb-ft

5.1.5.3   Loosening torque

Loosening torque can be calculated in a similar manner. Again for F = 5000 lb and μ = 0.15:

Thread loosening, T (in lb-ft) =
6 for UNC $\frac{3}{8}$ in × 16, and 8 for UNF $\frac{3}{8}$ in × 24.

It is higher for fine thread and is less than 60% of on-torque.

Total loosening (add 12.5 for the head) is 18.5 and 20.5, respectively. Now the tightening torque was 27 and 26, respectively. So the UNC loosening torque is 70% of the tightening torque and the UNF loosening torque is 80% of the tightening torque.

If one assumed that the screw thread was 100% efficient and that there was no friction, then the torque to produce a 5000 lb load would be:

	UNC	UNF
	4.19 15%	2.7 10%
or to induce preload	15%	10%
to overcome thread friction	39%	42%
bearing surface friction	46%	48%

from which it can be seen that friction is the key factor using up 85–90% of the total input.

5.1.6   Gasketed flange bolting

The use of a gasket in a joint changes the considerations for bolt selection. The flexibility of the joint increases the possibility that the bolt will experience most of the applied load.

Most of the force for producing minimum sealing pressure in a gasket has to come from the bolts (a small amount may come from gasket adhesion and gasket swelling from chemical and pressure effects). It is, therefore, necessary that the bolts produce the designed stress in the gasket both on initial assembly and throughout its life. There are four reasons why bolts may fail to produce and hold the desired stress in the joint. They are:

(1) bolts which are too large or too small,
(2) improper tightening,
(3) extreme movement or vibration of the clamped surfaces, and
(4) improper material selection with excessive gasket relaxation.

5.1.6.1   Bolt sizing for compressible gaskets

The strength of the bolt must be high enough to support the preload which in turn must be high enough to produce the minimum stress which will seal the internal pressure or applied loads. In general, the tension which the bolt supports is not increased by the applied load in a solid metal-to-metal connection. Certainly the preceding statement is not quite true, but it is sufficiently true to enable designers of machine joints to obtain adequate designs based on this assumption (*Machine Design*, 1967).

If the general statement of the previous paragraphs were true, it would be possible to build an infinitely rigid structure. However, according to Hooke's law, deflection is proportional to applied force. In most joints the ratio of rigidity to fastener rigidity is high enough to discount almost any addition to tension already in the bolt produced by any externally applied load.

However, in a flexible joint with a soft gasket between bolted parts (Figure 5.20), the rigidities of the joint and the bolt are quite different; here, a

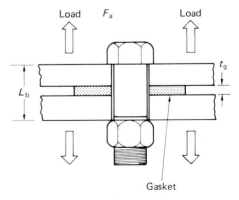

Figure 5.20 Joint assembly with flexible gasket

much greater proportion of the externally applied tension load is added to the bolt preload. The reason for this may become more obvious by studying the following equation:

$$P = P_i + CF_a \qquad (1)$$

where P is the final load on the bolt (lb); P_i is the initial preload or clamping load developed through tightening (lb); F_a is the externally applied load (lb); and the constant

$$C = \frac{(E_b A_b)/L_b}{(E_b A_b)/L_b + (E_g A_g)/t_g} \qquad (2)$$

where E_b is the modulus of elasticity of the bolt (lb in^{-2}); E_g is the modulus of elasticity of the gasket (lb in^{-2}); A_b is the effective cross-sectional area of bolt (in^2); A_g is the loaded area of gasket (in^2); L_b is the effective length of bolt (in); and t_g is the gasket thickness (in).

The value of the constant C falls between 0 and 1. The term $(E_g A_g)/t_g$ in Equation (2) will be large in comparison to $(E_b A_b)/L_b$ if the gasket is hard, thin, and large in area. Then the constant C approaches zero. When no gasket is used between members in a rigid joint, $C = 0$. For very soft gaskets, C approaches 1. It is important to remember that Equation (2) is only valid as long as the gasket remains in contact with joint members. If the bolt stretches to the point where the gasket is no longer in contact, Equation (1) is simply $P = F_a$.

Fatigue effects: The fatigue strength of a bolt joint must be evaluated two ways — fatigue of the bolt, and fatigue of the bolted material. The properly tightened bolt will not fail in fatigue in a rigid joint. Initial bolt tension will stay relatively constant until the external tension load on the joint exceeds the bolt load. Designers do not permit the calculated service load to be greater than the bolt preload. The bolt will experience no appreciable stress variation, and without stress variation, there can be no failure by fatigue, regardless of the number of load cycles on the joint.

This is not the case where considerable flexibility is present. Variable stress in screw or bolt fastenings increases with the flexibility of the connected parts. If flexibility is too great, the variable stress present may be high enough to cause eventual fatigue failure of the fastener regardless of the initial bolt preload.

The greatest single factor which can eliminate cyclic stress variation due to cyclic loading is proper pretensioning or preloading of the fastener. Test results indicate that rigid members bolted together by relatively elastic bolts offer the best method to prevent fatigue failure.

5.1.7 Summary

The logical approach to secure bolting consists of four simple steps:

(1) Select a bolt appropriate for the require clamping force. This can be done from the nomograph Figure 5.2. At the same time, find the proper tightening torque to produce this load.
(2) Using 30% of the tightening torque enter Figure 5.15, and note the proper strength threadlocking materials for the size and finish of the bolt selected.
(3) Check the viscosity, cure speed, and environmental requirements and select the best one of the proper strength materials.
(4) Call in your anaerobic equipment supplier to consult on automating the whole process.

5.2 Selecting a fastener

Fastening systems, whether they be adhesives, nuts and bolts, welding and brazing or any other method for that matter, are inherent in the design of a product or structure destined to be assembled as a 'one-off', by batch production or on a high volume flow line. However, despite the growing popularity and advantages of industrial adhesives as a fastening medium, mechanical fasteners continue to be regarded as essential to the joining of a product's components. By mechanical fasteners is meant the considerable range of bolts, nuts, screws, rivets, pins, clips and other categories of hardware currently available to the designer and production engineer. But, unless sufficient care is taken in their selection, the installation of such fasteners can lead to an increase in the labour costs involved and, possibly, a decrease in the required level of mechanical efficiency or in-service reliability of the finished product or individual joint.

This section, therefore, is written to give the fastener specifier some guidance in the selection of the right fastener for the job taking into account the true cost of fastening and the savings that can be accomplished.

5.2.1 In-place costs

Unquestionably, one of the major factors related to any fastening application is not so much the tremendously wide choice of systems or hardware available but rather in installation cost, assuming that the fastener meets with all criteria in terms of function, performance and aesthetics. In-place costs is a well worn, but still little appreciated term. Nevertheless, it is the key to economic assembly and, as such, is probably the most important factor in the selection process. This is particularly applicable to the more commercial areas of product manufacture where both costs and performance have just about equal priority unlike the fields of high technology, such as the aerospace industry where performance, reliability and safety are the major considerations. In the commercial areas, car production, domestic appliances, office furniture, toys and so on, the slightest increase in costs of screws or rivets is seen as an erosion of profitability because the assembly lines, laid down for mass production, are operated on a very carefully worked out cost basis and because the final selling price of the product determines the level of return on what is usually a heavy capital investment.

Obviously then, in terms of fasteners alone, the cost/performance ratio is finely balanced indeed. So, how are these costs determined? In analysing the cost of a single fastener that has to be installed under mass production conditions, the factors involved include product design time, materials, unit cost per fastener, installation costs, tooling, inspection and invoicing. Also to be taken into account are wastage, after-sales service and spares replacement. On this basis, therefore, the product manufacturer, that is the fastener user, should choose a fastener system that will perform satisfactorily under all conditions of in-field use and, at the same time, reduce the labour content of the installation to a minimum. It should be remembered that assembly is a highly labour intensive operation which can account for more than 60% of a product's total manufacturing costs.

The cheapest fasteners are not necessarily the least expensive to instal. As an example, consider the original fastening system used by a manufacturer to secure the brake/hub assembly to the axles of caravans and trailers. These consisted of bolts, nuts and washers; all standard products and relatively inexpensive. However, they were difficult and time consuming to instal and, moreover, the nuts had to be torqued to a predetermined value to assure security. A lockbolting system was considered as an alternative since it was later discovered that dismantling of the assembly was unlikely. At first sight the price, in terms of a percentage of the cost of the assembly – 14.09% for the lockbolt and collar as against 4.93% for the bolt, nut and washer – appeared to be excessive. But the ease and speed of the lockbolt system resulted in an installation cost of only 13.33% compared with the bolt, nut and washer's installation cost of 33.33% per unit. Translating this into financial terms, the company achieved a total cost saving of £7900 per annum.

5.2.2 The correct approach to fastening

Before choosing a fastener system to meet the design and performance requirements of the product to be assembled the designer, preferably in collaboration with the production engineer, should consider the factor of performance, function, properties, and in-place costs, and then pose a number of questions, the answers to which should provide the necessary guide to the ultimate – and correct – choice. For example:

(1) Is the fastening really necessary?
(2) Will the minimum number of fasteners specified be consistent with reliability and safety, as well as economy in production?
(3) Will the fastener specified perform its task efficiently?
(4) Will it be simple to instal and be capable of being placed by automated methods?
(5) Will the fastener have to be removed during service for maintenance and repair, and will it be readily accessible with standard tools?
(6) Will the fastener material and finish be compatible with that of the product?
(7) Bearing in mind the additional cost involved, will it be necessary to specify a 'special' fastener instead of a standard one?

Having asked the questions, now consider the possible answers:

(1)   Is the fastening really necessary?
It is probably true to say that with careful design and with the application of value engineering techniques which embrace advanced production methods, a considerable number of the fasteners that go into an assembly could be eliminated. Informed fastener selection can bring about a reduction in material costs, lower fastener inventories, reduced assembly costs without loss of quality and product performance.

(2)   Will the minimum number of fasteners specified be consistent with reliability and safety, as well as economy in production?
With the move toward product liability legislation there could be a tendency for the designer to 'over engineer' his product in terms of materials and fasteners in order to 'play for safety'. This, however, can be seen as groundless concern if the properties of the fastener are fully evaluated at the outset. Failure to assess minimum and maximum strength requirements and in-service performance can create serious problems, including accidents and breakdowns; equally, it can result in wasteful over-engineering. As an example of the latter it has been known for a non-critical inspection plate on a

domestic appliance to be retained with four screws. With thought, the plate could be retained with only one screw or, alternatively, a quick release fastener.

(3) Will the fastener specified perform its task efficiently?

The choice of fastener systems currently available is almost bewilderingly wide, but it is the designer's responsibility to select from the right category, to assess performance from suppliers' data and to consider its in-place cost. It must be remembered that a fastener that fails in service is not only unreliable, but is also uneconomic. The conditions under which the product will operate must therefore be known and the fastener selected must resist such conditions, which might include corrosion, extremes of temperature, vibration and impact loads. Another point to remember is that even the right fastener will not overcome faulty design or poor assembly. It should also be selected at the time the joint or the product is on the drawing board. If there are any doubts then this is the time to call for the advice of the fastener supplier.

(4) Will it be simple to instal and be capable of being placed by automated methods?

Much depends on the application, but many of the fasteners in use today — screws, bolts, nuts, inserts, rivets, etc. — can be installed automatically, but obviously not all can be removed. If possible, therefore, it is advisable to specify one-part fasteners suitable for automated assembly or power tooling. If the component to which the fastener is attached will be subjected to painting or plating prior to final assembly then it is advisable to specify a fastener which can be installed after the finishing process. This could obviate the need to retap to clear clogged threads. It has been established that, on average, 80% of the total cost of fastening derives from its application on the assembly line. Therefore, a mere 10% saving in assembly costs can be more significant than a 40% saving in piece part costs.

(5) Will the fastener have to be removed during its service life, and will it be readily accessible with standard tools?

This important consideration is all too frequently overlooked and insufficient thought is given to easy accessibility for maintenance and repair. The designer's responsibility does not end when the finished product leaves the factory because in the event that the product needs to be dismantled to rectify faults, or for routine servicing, the time involved should be kept to the minimum. Remember, the service engineer's time has to be paid for. It is equally important, bearing in mind Question 1, to assess whether the assembly really needs to be dismantled.

(6) Will the fastener material and finish be compatible with that of the products?

As every manufacturer knows only too well, material costs are a part of the inflationary spiral. Fastener materials must be chosen with the same care as the design to meet the requirements of the product being assembled. Modern plating and coating processes provide effective protection against corrosion, and mild steels can, unless specific conditions demand, provide more than adequate strengths. In addition, plastic fasteners are strong, reasonably inexpensive and capable of fulfilling many fastening needs in the assembly of domestic appliances, cars, TV and radio, electronic equipment and for many other industrial applications. Similarly, brass and aluminium alloy fasteners can be specified for a good many roles in place of steel. The tendency to over-engineer often stems from data or specification sheets prepared for long obsolete products and it is important for the designer to remember that just as improvements are continually being made in product design so too are advances being made in fastener technology.

(7) Bearing in mind the additional cost involved, will it be necessary to specify a 'special' fastener instead of a standard one?

The majority of fasteners specified for a joint or assembly are standard; that is, they can be bought literally 'off-the-shelf', which usually means from the supplier's catalogue. Such standard fasteners are used to good effect to achieve the right balance between performance, application and cost. However, there are occasions when a 'special' becomes necessary to achieve a particular function. But if such a fastener is required it generally means that its cost, despite the advances being made in fastener production, will be higher than the equivalent standard. This is due to the additional design time it required, plus higher tooling and production costs and possibly increased assembly time on the shop floor.

Sometimes 'specials' can be avoided if the product is suitably modified at the design stage to allow a standard to be used, providing it meets all other performance requirements. The general recommendation is, however, don't use a 'special' if a standard can be found to do the job equally well.

5.3 Bolts, screws, nuts and washers

In many industrial applications standard screws, and bolt, nut and washer combinations, are still the most efficient means of assembling two or more components with a high degree of security, providing that the correct techniques are employed.

The family of threaded fasteners is extremely wide, embracing screws of various types, bolts, studs and studding, special fasteners and a great variety of nuts and inserts. All of them are supplied in a variety of head styles, configurations, lengths, diameters, thread forms and materials including mild steel, alloy steel, stainless steel, high tensile steel, non-ferrous metals and a number of exotic materials. In broad terms their advantages include availability, high pre-tension and clamp-up characteristics, high ultimate tensile and shear strengths and reusability.

In high volume applications, however, bolt and nut combinations can be costly in terms of material and labour, as well as alternative investment in powered assembly tools. Access is required on both sides of the work-piece and time can be wasted in the assembly of washers and nuts, even before clamping takes place. Moreover, pre-tensioning can be inaccurate without proper equipment and weight can be increased to an unacceptable degree. Therefore, as in the case of other types of fasteners, due consideration must be given to the type of joint to be assembled before specifying any given type or size of bolt and nut.

5.3.1 Bolts and screws

A bolt can be defined as a headed fastener with a thread rolled or machined on to a predetermined length of the full shank. Screws, on the other hand, generally have their threads taken right up to the underside of the head, although this is not a hard-and-fast rule. If the screw does have a shank, then this is known as a 'scant shank'. Headed screws are normally called machine screws, while those without

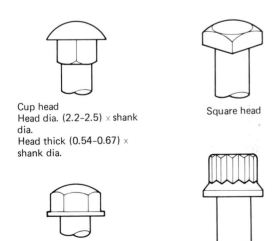

Cup head
Head dia. (2.2–2.5) × shank dia.
Head thick (0.54–0.67) × shank dia.

Square head

Raised hexagon washer head

12 point head

Figure 5.21 Typical bolt head forms

heads are referred to as 'set' or 'grub' screws. Some of the more common bolt head forms are shown in Figure 5.21 and those for screws in Figure 5.22.

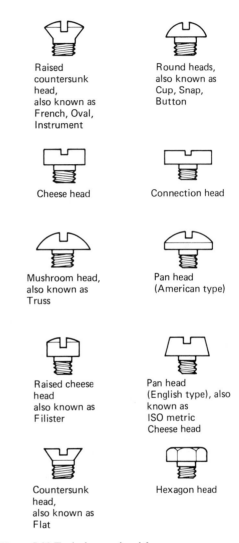

Raised countersunk head, also known as French, Oval, Instrument

Round heads, also known as Cup, Snap, Button

Cheese head

Connection head

Mushroom head, also known as Truss

Pan head (American type)

Raised cheese head also known as Filister

Pan head (English type), also known as ISO metric Cheese head

Countersunk head, also known as Flat

Hexagon head

Figure 5.22 Typical screw head forms

5.3.2 Self-tapping screws

These screws fall into two main categories: true self-tapping screws which, like a tap, cut their own threads in a prepared hole, and thread-forming screws which, under similar conditions, form their threads by a rolling or swaging action. Typical of the latter are the proprietary types Taptite and Swageform. Taptite incorporates machine screw threads formed on a trilobular shank and the Swageform has special lobes at 120° intervals along the tapered

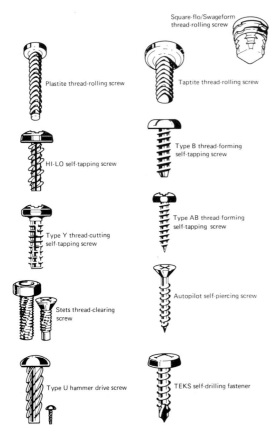

Figure 5.23 Self-tapping and thread-forming screws

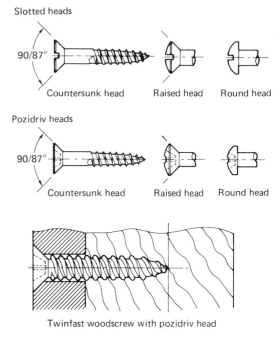

Figure 5.24 Wood screws

portion of the shank to impart a 3-dimensional swaging action to form the threads.

Self-tapping screws are widely used in the assembly of sheet metal components in which the thread cutting action results in a good fit, and resistance to vibration and shock loads. Thread-forming screws are particularly applicable to thicker materials and blind holes where their retentive power is especially valuable.

The self-drilling versions, e.g. Teks and Drill-kwick, are designed with a true drill point to produce the necessary pilot hole for the threads. Although they are more expensive than conventional self-tapping screws, their in-place cost benefits are greater because they eliminate the need for pre-drilling.

5.3.3 Woodscrews

The majority of woodscrews are produced from mild steel, brass and stainless steel although other materials, including plastic, can be specified. While most are of the single start type, two-start threads

(Doublegrip) and some with threads right up to the head are also available. Long woodscrews may have a relieved shank, i.e. a shank with a diameter less than the major diameter of the threads. The usual head forms are countersunk, raised and round head, with slotted, Philips, Pozidriv and Supadriv driving recesses.

A common mistake in the use of conventional woodscrews is to drive them directly into the wood. To be fully effective, and to reduce strain on the screw head, woodscrews require pilot holes which, for soft woods, should be about 70% of the screw core diameter and, for hard woods, about 90%.

5.3.4 Nuts

The family of nuts is so great that it is virtually impossible to do more than place them in their particular categories.

5.3.4.1 Free-spinning nuts

Free-spinning nuts are effectively plain nuts, although their profiles range through various shapes including square, hexagon, flanged hexagon, washer collar, wing, dome, etc. Typical forms are shown in Figure 5.25. These also include slotted and castle nuts which are designed to be mechanically locked to the bolt or stud by means of wire or cotter pin.

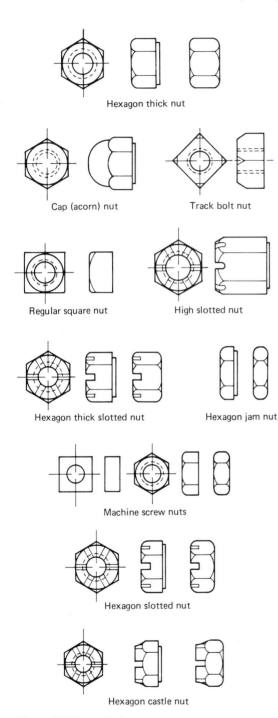

Figure 5.25 Free-spinning nuts

5.3.4.2 Lock nuts

Lock nuts also spin freely on the bolt threads but develop a locking action on contact with the workpiece. This is achieved either by increasing the

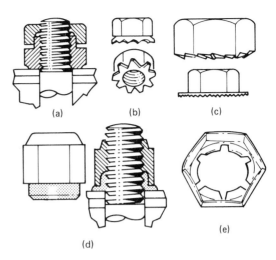

Figure 5.26 Free-spinning lock nuts: (a) upper half of two-piece nut presses collar of lower half against bolt; (b) captive tooth washer provides locking with spring action; (c) ratchet teeth bite into bearing surface; (d) nylon insert flows around bolt to lock and seal; (e) arched prongs of single thread lock unit grip screw

friction between the underside of the nut and the mating face or by increasing the friction between the mating threads as the nut is finally tightened. Once popular, the latter form has tended to decline in recent years.

5.3.4.3 Stiff nuts (prevailing torque nuts)

Stiff nuts generally incorporate a locking element of another material to generate an elastic contact between the nut and bolt threads or, alternatively, differential pitch or deformed threads to create the required friction between the mating threads. The usual form of differentiation is to call the former a nylon insert nut and the latter an all-metal locknut. The choice of such nuts is largely dependent on environmental conditions but, in all cases, it is recommended that the advice of the supplier is sought before specifying for a particular application.

5.3.5 Washers

Washers are used for a variety of applications in fastener assemblies but their prime function is to act as a seating for bolts, nuts, screws and even rivets in order to distribute loads over an area greater than that provided by the bearing surface of the fastener itself. They are also used to bridge oversize holes, to insulate, seal, improve appearance and to act as a spring take up between the fastener and the workpiece and prevent movement between the parts.

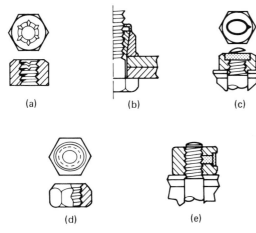

Figure 5.27 Stiff nuts: (a) deformed thread has depressions in the face of the nut to distort a few threads; (b) slotted section forms beams that deflect inward and grip bolt; (c) threaded elliptical spring-steel insert produces locking; (d) and non-metallic plug insert grips bolt threads; (e) out-of-round threads cause wedging action

Washers are divided into three main categories: standard, flat and tapered washers, which are covered by BS 3410, are available in a variety of metallic and non-metallic materials. This category also includes special washers for high strength friction grip bolts (BS 3199), tab washers and cup washers. Spring washers embrace single and multi-coil washers and their variants and a multitude of special purpose, non-standard types for different applications. Lock washers cover the full range of toothed 'Shakeproof' types and certain helical spring washers which incorporate positive locking characteristics.

5.4 Special fasteners, including blind fasteners

Special fasteners generally fall into two distinct categories:

(1) those that have a 'unique' character, i.e. they are designed and manufactured to customers' own requirements to suit a specific application only, and

(2) those that are produced to certain 'standard' forms in a range of dimensions but which incorporate one or more special features which yield cost saving and/or performance benefits. Also in this category are the modified standards which are changed in relation to dimensions or mechanical properties to meet a particular requirement.

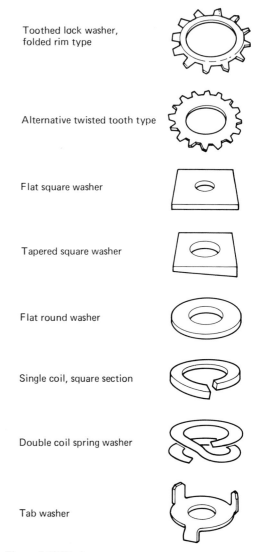

Figure 5.28 Washers

5.4.1 *Custom made fasteners*

These category (1) fasteners usually have capabilities over and above those of the standard fasteners mainly because they are designed to be multifunction parts. The cost of these parts is generally high, but the benefits in terms of lower in-place costs, or a reduction in the number of parts in an assembly, can be considerable. Nevertheless, a degree of caution is necessary when designing or specifying fasteners in this category because of the possible difficulties in manufacture. These parts can be produced either by turning from bar or by cold forming and, therefore, some understanding of both processes in relation to the quantities required is essential.

Most manufacturers of custom made specials strongly recommend close collaboration with the customer when the project is in the initial design stages to avoid the risk of costly mistakes. Furthermore, the experience of the fastener manufacturer may reveal that the use of a standard fastener is possible following minor, but cost saving, modifications to the product itself.

5.4.2 Standard form specials

The specials in category (2) are much more numerous and may include threaded fasteners in ferrous, non-ferrous, plastic and certain exotic materials; spring clips, self-sealing fasteners, latches, quick release fasteners, clamps, pins and many others. Because they are so numerous, space does not allow more than a brief mention of some of the different types.

5.4.2.1 Threaded fasteners

Examples of modified standards are difficult to illustrate largely because they are usually produced to a user's own — and often confidential — needs. However, modifications can include non-standard lengths, diameters, threads and the provision of shoulders, shank reductions, dog points, etc. A more common example of a modified threaded fastener is the addition of a self-locking element in the form of a fused nylon patch, micro encapsulated adhesive or the milling of a slot in the threads to accept a nylon strip.

5.4.2.2 Spring steel fasteners

Although these include certain standard parts, for example 'J' nuts, caged nuts, etc., most spring steel fasteners are designed for specific applications. Produced quickly and cheaply from hardened and tempered steel strip, they are used in non-critical applications in the car, electronic, domestic appliance and sheet metal component industries, either in

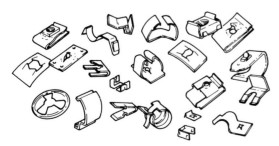

Figure 5.29 Spring steel fasteners. (Courtesy Canning Brett Ltd)

association with self-tapping screws or as clips to retain internal and external trim, small parts, cable runs, shafts and panels.

5.4.2.3 Plastic fasteners

These products are divided into two categories: standard bolts, nuts, screws and studding machined from nylon stock and those moulded from nylon or other high-strength plastics. While some of the latter, such as the 'Plasti-rivet' and 'Dart' clip, are produced as standards, the majority are made to customers' own requirements, even though they may appear in the manufacturers' catalogues as clips, turnbuckles, retainers, cable straps, etc. Advantages include good retention, toughness, resistance to corrosion and many chemicals and the availability of matching colours.

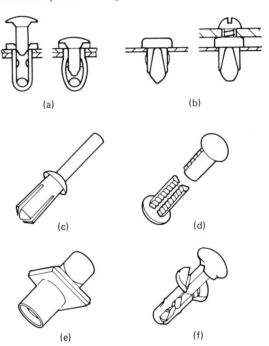

Figure 5.30 Plastic fasteners: (a) dart-type clip; (b) nylon expansion nut; (c) plasti-rivet; (d) rachet rivet; (e) plastic rivet; (f) Triploc rivet

5.4.2.4 Quick release fasteners

These are designed to provide a high degree of security combined with rapid closure and release. Accordingly, they are widely used for securing demountable panels, doors and covers demanding ease of access. The main types available are rotary stud, press button, slide and toggle latches, but magnetic catches and 'Pip' pins are also included in this category. Their uses include aircraft, domestic appliances, electronic control cabinets, office machinery, cars and commercial transports. These fasteners are normally only available from specialist manufacturers, and while they are not cheap in relation to piece part costs and assembly time compared with screws and nut and bolt combinations, their convenience and speed of operation on equipment requiring routine servicing, makes them particularly cost effective.

5.4.2.5 Self-sealing fasteners

Bolts, screws, nuts, washers, and rivets can be modified by the incorporation of a sealing element in applications where it is necessary to seal the fastener hole against leakage of liquids or gases. Pre-assembled seals can be made of neoprene, butyl rubber, natural rubber, polyethylene, nylon, soft metals and other suitable materials capable of maintaining a leak-proof seal under certain conditions of temperature, pressure and corrosion. The choice of the material, as well as the fastener, is dependent on these in-service conditions.

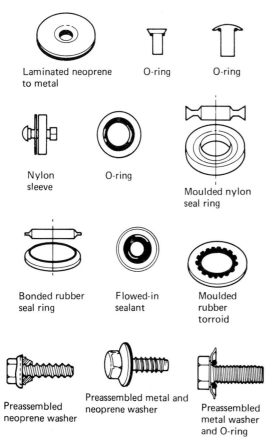

Figure 5.31 Self-sealing fasteners

5.5 Rivets, including blind rivets

In general terms rivets are low-cost permanent fasteners suitable for both manual (hand tool) and automatic (machine) setting. They can be classified as solid (large and small), semi-tubular, tubular, bifurcated and blind, all of which are available in a range of head styles, lengths and diameters. Materials include mild steel, stainless steel, titanium, monel, brass, copper and aluminium. However, certain special applications may require more exotic materials such as gold, silver and their alloys. Typical finishes are plating, passivating, stove enamelling, chromate dip and lacquering depending on customers' requirements.

The installed cost of rivets varies widely according to type. Solid rivets often require two operatives for manual setting, but if the work is done by machine setting then costs are greatly reduced, as are those for blind rivets which require only a single operative. Apart from their role as fasteners, rivets can also be used as pivots, spacers, electrical contacts and stops. Tensile and fatigue strengths are lower than those of equivalent sized bolts or screws, but shear strengths are generally adequate. Riveted assemblies cannot be dismantled without destroying the rivet; this usually means the specification of oversize replacement rivets.

5.5.1 *Joint design and preparation*

Correct joint design and preparation, together with the right fastener, will ensure a strong, trouble free and cost-effective structure. The following points, briefly outlined for guidance, are applicable to both solid and blind rivets but, in every case, it should be stressed that during the rivet setting process, the rivet shank exerts radial pressure on the material through which it passes; in the case of solid rivets, this force is quite considerable and can cause excessive buckling. Thus, the rules applying to distances between hole centres, rivet diameter and distance from the edge in relation to sheet thickness must be observed to avoid the risk of material distortion. For more detailed guidance refer to BS 449, Part 2: 'The Use of Structural Steel in Building'; BS 4620, 1970: 'Rivets for General Engineering Purposes'; BS 1473, 1972: 'Wrought Aluminium and Aluminium Alloys for General Engineering Purposes — Rivet, Bolt and Screw Stock'.

(1)   The hole may be formed by piercing or drilling but, in each case, the prescribed tolerances must be controlled. These depend on the type and size of rivet and its hole-filling properties.

(2)   It is important that the rivet effectively gathers or clenches the material together during setting.

(3) The rivet must be compatible with the material being fastened to reduce the possibility of corrosion, otherwise effective corrosion resistant treatments must be specified for the joint.

(4) To avoid tearing around the rivet hole the tension members must be designed with due regard to the reduction in cross section of the material at the hole. This means positioning the holes in accordance with recommended practice.

(5) Due allowance must be made for the accommodation of the setting tool, particularly in confined spaces.

(6) When specifying rivet size, the shank diameter should not be less than the thickness of the thickest sheet being riveted, nor more than $2^1/_2$ to 3 times the thickness of the outside sheet of the joint.

(7) When using long rivets, it is recommended that the grip length should not exceed four diameters.

(8) Burrs must always be removed from the edge of the hole before riveting, otherwise trapped swarf will cause fretting and possible joint failure.

(9) When riveting materials of differing thickness and compressibility, the rivet should be set against the stronger of the sheets so that the softer material is always under the rivet head.

5.5.2 Solid, tubular and bifurcated rivets

Solid rivets, both large and small are essentially structural fasteners with applications ranging from bridge building to small sheet metal assemblies. Such riveted joints are generally strong due to the characteristic grain flow of the rivet material during setting. Normal tolerances on major dimensions are +0.005 in, although closer shank diameter tolerances can be specified and held.

5.5.2.1 Semi-tubular rivets

Semi-tubular rivets have a straight or tapered hole drilled in the shank end to a depth not exceeding 1.12 times the shank diameter. The hole wall thus achieved provides the material for clinching, either by means of a punch or by spinning. To all intents and purposes, therefore, the semi-tubular rivet is a solid rivet with comparable shear and compression strengths.

5.5.2.2 Tubular rivets

Tubular rivets usually have a hole drilled almost to the head, although hole depth may be specified by the user. Shank length is determined by the amount

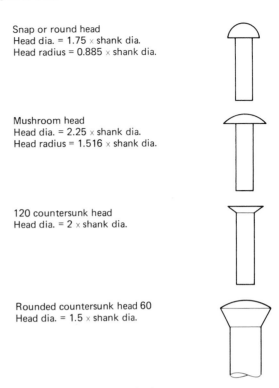

Snap or round head
Head dia. = 1.75 × shank dia.
Head radius = 0.885 × shank dia.

Mushroom head
Head dia. = 2.25 × shank dia.
Head radius = 1.516 × shank dia.

120 countersunk head
Head dia. = 2 × shank dia.

Rounded countersunk head 60
Head dia. = 1.5 × shank dia.

Figure 5.32 Examples of solid rivets

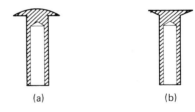

(a) (b)

Figure 5.33 Semi-tubular rivets: (a) ordinary oval head; (b) ordinary flat head

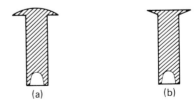

(a) (b)

Figure 5.34 Tubular rivets: (a) ordinary oval head; (b) ordinary flat countersunk head

of material required for clinching and the total thickness of the assembly. Widely used in both metallic and non-metallic applications, shear strengths are less than those of equivalent sized solid and semi-tubular rivets. Self-piercing versions with a thicker wall are available which can punch their own holes in thin metals and non-metallic materials. More recent developments have resulted in self-piercing rivets capable of punching holes in materials up to 4 mm thick.

5.5.2.3 Compression rivets

Compression rivets are two-part fasteners comprising a tubular rivet and a solid rivet which, when joined in the assembly, form an interference fit resistant to reasonably high pull-out loads. Advantages include uniform flush heads on both sides of the component and their use in wood, plastic and brittle materials without risk of splitting.

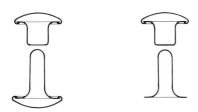

Figure 5.35 Compression rivets

5.5.2.4 Bifurcated rivets

Bifurcated rivets are made from solid rivets, the two prongs usually produced by sawing down through the shank; hence the alternative name of split rivet. Normally used in non-metallic applications such as wood, leather, plastic and fibrous materials, the rivet is clinched by the spreading of the prongs.

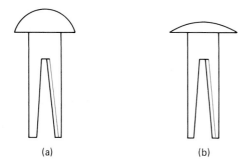

    (a)   (b)

Figure 5.36 Bifurcated rivets: (a) button head; (b) ordinary oval head

5.5.3 Blind rivets

Blind riveting systems are undoubtedly one of the most cost effective and technically efficient on the market today since they permit components to be joined at a high rate from one side of the workpiece only. Thus, they offer low in-place cost advantages coupled with high shear and adequate tensile

strengths, a wide grip range and good hole filling properties.

In principle, rivet closure is accomplished by a flared or headed mandrel which is drawn by a tool through the tubular body of the rivet. The action of drawing the mandrel through the rivet causes the rivet to expand in the hole and create a form of head on the blind side. The two main types of blind riveting systems are *the breakstem rivet* and *the repetition, or pull-through mandrel, rivet* both of which are set by an associated manual or air operated tool.

5.5.3.1 Breakstem rivets

The breakstem rivet comprises a hollow body with a pre-assembled mandrel in the bore. To set the rivet, the rivet mandrel is engaged with the jaws of the tool and the rivet shank inserted into the hole in the workpiece. Operation of the tool causes the mandrel to be drawn through the rivet body, at the same time pulling the parts together until the mandrel fractures at a predetermined pressure. This leaves the head of the mandrel to plug the body of the rivet, thus increasing shear strength and making it weather tight. Since the setting operation takes less than a second, it will be seen that even large assemblies can be joined by a single unskilled operator quickly and efficiently.

For more critical, high-strength structural joints, such as those required in the aerospace industry, special versions are available. Typical of these is the Avdel Monobolt blind riveting system which combines high ultimate shear and tensile strength with excellent pre-tension. When set, the mandrel stem is locked in position by a positive engagement between the stem and the rivet body to achieve a pressure tight seal.

5.5.3.2 Repetition rivets

The repetition rivet is also a tubular fastener but, unlike the breakstem rivet, the mandrel is drawn right through the body expanding the rivet in the hole and forming a head on the blind side. Up to 50 rivets, supplied in a paper tube, are loaded on to a high tensile steel mandrel the end of which is threaded into the setting tool. The shank of the first rivet, which protrudes from the nose of the tool, is then inserted into the hole in the workpiece and the tool actuated to set the rivet. As soon as setting is accomplished, the next rivet automatically presents itself for installation. The process is fast and there are no spent stems to be cleared. It also prevents wastage through loose rivets. However, since the mandrel is drawn right through the rivet, weather

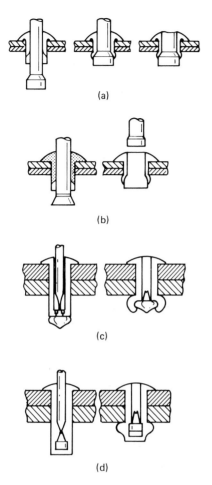

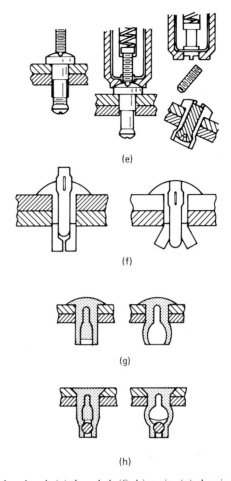

Figure 5.37 Blind rivets: (a) pull mandrel, non-break; (b) pull mandrel, pull-through; (c) pull mandrel, break mandrel, open end; (d) pull mandrel, break mandrel, closed end; (e) threaded; (f) drive pin; (g) chemically expanded, open end; (h) chemically expanded, closed end

sealing can only be achieved by the use of special plugs which are tapped into the hole with a hammer.

A simple form of blind riveting can be achieved with the drive pin rivet which is available in steel, aluminium and plastic. This is also a hollow rivet with an integral pin and a slotted shank. The rivet requires only a hammer to drive the pin into the rivet body and flush with the head to lock it in the workpiece hole. This low-cost fastener has many non-critical applications, particularly in joining parts to tubes and channel sections.

Bibliography

ANDERSON, HAVILAND and TOKARSKI, *Sealing Technology*, Loctite Corporation, pp. 16–24.

INDUSTRIAL FASTENERS INSTITUTE (1974) *The Heritage of Mechanical Fasteners*.

JUNKERS, G. H. (1969) 'New criteria for self-loosening of fasteners under vibration', SAE paper 690055.

MACHINE DESIGN (1967) 'Fastening and joining', *Machine Design* magazine, reference issue, Penton Publishing.

MACHINE DESIGN (1972) 'How much shake can bolted joints take?' *Machine Design* magazine, Penton Publishing.

6

Fluid power

6.1 Understanding basic oil hydraulics

An ever-increasing amount of hydraulically operated machinery is being employed in industry today,
a proportion of which is of a highly sophisticated
nature. However, the basic principles of hydraulic
function still apply. Hydraulics is often looked on as
some form of mystery, but it is often easier to apply
hydraulics, in terms of calculations and formulae,
than it is to find the solutions to mechanical engineering problems.

Oil-power hydraulics is basically the employment
of an enclosed and controlled column of oil to
transfer power from the original source to any linear
or rotational motion. The most common medium is
a mineral oil. Oil has a compressibility factor of
approximately 1% at 1400 N cm^{-2}, this compressibility factor may be ignored for most practical
purposes. In moving the column of oil, there will be
losses from the original input power as a result of
friction within the pipework. Other losses will result
from leakage across working surfaces of the pumping elements and across circuit control valves and
actuators. These losses must be taken into account
in the final specification for an application and will
be covered in a later section. For simplicity of
explanation in this particular section, these losses
have been ignored.

The fluid power industry has been developed on a
fundamental law of physics discovered by Pascal in
1650. This law states: 'A pressure applied to a
confined fluid at rest is transmitted with equal
intensity throughout the fluid'. This law is illustrated
in Figure 6.1, which shows a bottle of oil and a
stopper with an area of 1 cm^2. When a force of 10 N
is applied to the stopper, the oil, which is not
compressible, transmits a pressure of 10 N cm^{-2} to
every part of the inside wall of the bottle.

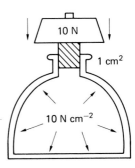

Figure 6.1 Pascal's law of pressure

If in the base of the bottle we now insert a stopper
with an area of 10 cm^2, a downward force on the top
stopper would give a multiplied force of 10 to 1 on
the bottom stopper. 10 N on the top stopper would
exert a force of 100 N on the bottom stopper; see
Figure 6.2.

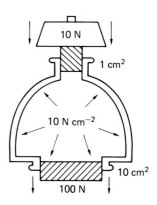

Figure 6.2

This basic principle is used in its simplest form in a hydraulic jack as illustrated in Figure 6.3. This is an alternative visual interpretation of Figure 6.2. When a force of 10 N is applied to the small 1 cm^2 piston (the pump), the oil is pressurised to 10 N cm^{-2} in all parts of the interior of the jack. When the pressure is exerted on the 10 cm^2 area of the large piston (the ram), the resulting force is:

$$10 \text{ N cm}^{-2} \times 10 \text{ cm}^2 = 100 \text{ N}$$

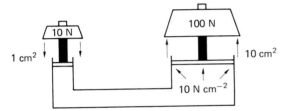

Figure 6.3 The principle of the hydraulic jack

If valves which allow free flow of oil in one direction and a closed condition in the other direction are now introduced and an oil reservoir added to feed the pumping chamber, a simple hydraulic system is produced; see Figure 6.4. By a continuous up and down movement of force A, B with a force of 100 N can be raised.

An excessive load at B may be beyond the input power available, or given sufficient input power, may require a force beyond the mechanical strength of the pump or the connecting galleries from the pump to the ram. The dotted line and valve V$_4$ represent a safety (pressure relief) valve which opens at a predetermined pressure allowing a bleed-off of oil to the reservoir. The force which can be exerted on the load is therefore limited to that for which the system is designed. Given an excess of input power, the load is also protected from an excess of force.

Ceasing operation of the pump lever with a manually operated hydraulic lifting jack, stops the load from continuing to rise. When man-power is changed to an electric motor, it is unusual and

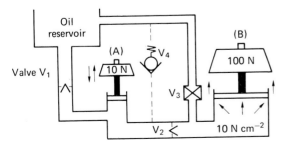

Figure 6.4 A simple hydraulic system

normally unacceptable to stop and start the electric motor in order to control the load. It is more usual to allow the pump to be driven continuously and to divert the oil back to the reservoir (off load), by a directional control valve. This valve will also perform the function of V$_3$ of the previous illustration.

Translated into the graphic symbols used by the hydraulic industry, Figure 6.5 shows a simple hydraulic circuit used to operate a single-acting cylinder (a cylinder which will return as a result of influence of the load or by means of a spring in the rod end of the cylinder exerting an influence on the piston). Valves V$_1$ and V$_2$ of Figure 6.4 are incorporated in the pump.

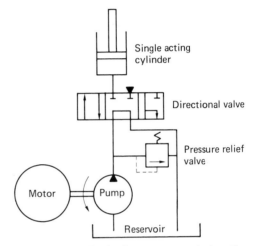

Figure 6.5 Hydraulic circuit to operate a single-acting cylinder

The power absorbed in an hydraulic system is dependent on the energy required at the work load. Given a prime mover (an electric motor or engine) of sufficient power, the system pressure is determined by the work load, not by the pump. The power absorbed is a factor of the volume of fluid being moved and the system pressure. A given input power can be absorbed in any combination of speed and power ratios within the limitations of the total power available, by changing the volume ratio of pump and actuator (hydraulic motor or cylinder). In the illustration with a pump piston area of 1 cm^2 and a cylinder piston area of 10 cm^2, the force is multiplied by 10, but for every centimetre of pump piston movement on the oil, there is only one tenth of a centimetre of movement of the cylinder piston.

There are many applications in which the cylinder is required to do work in both directions of travel, or where having performed a function of work on the forward stroke, it needs pressure on the return stroke to overcome mechanical load or friction, or it needs to retract under control. In these cases, a double-acting cylinder is used, and to retract the cylinder, oil is diverted to the rod side of the cylinder piston. Figure 6.6 shows a double-acting cylinder circuit.

When feeding the oil flow to the rod side of the cylinder, the power available is identical to that when fed to the piston side, but the area of reaction is reduced by the area of the piston rod. The force transmitted as work will therefore be lower, but as the piston rod takes up space in that side of the cylinder there is a lower volume of oil required to move the piston and so, with the same pump flow, the cylinder will retract more quickly than its forward stroke. The piston side of the cylinder is referred to as the full area and the rod side as the annulus area. In a particular application there would be a defined force requirement, and it would be necessary to determine the input power. A formula is available that can be used to find an input power, but this does not account for loss of efficiency at the pump, control valves, pipework and actuators. These losses will vary, depending on the type of equipment employed and the number of circuit valves, lengths and restriction caused by pipework.

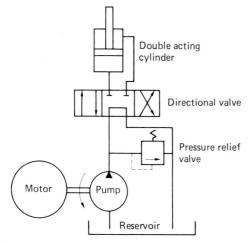

Figure 6.6 A double-acting cylinder circuit

The retraction speed is dependent on the cylinder rod diameter, which will vary according to the application; firstly a minimum size will be determined by a mechanical need, and a larger diameter by any determined requirement of retraction speed.

The power required may be in the form of a linear or a rotary motion. In both hydraulic cylinders and hydraulic motors, the power at the actuator is a combination of the system pressure and the area of reaction of the moving member. In the case of a cylinder the moving area is the piston; with a motor, the area on which the oil force is reacting will be a gear tooth, piston or sliding vane. The larger the area of reaction the greater the force exerted, but

volume of oil required for a given speed of movement is also greater. In sizing the hydraulic system, the first requirement must obviously be to know the force necessary to do the work, the speed of operation required and the linear movement or rotational speed.

A preference for a medium-pressure system (up to 2000 N cm^{-2}) or a high-pressure system (up to 3500 N cm^{-2}) must be considered. Systems are available above these pressures, but they are specialised and the choice of supply is very limited. The load itself may in fact dictate the pressure range to be used — having decided on a preference for medium pressure, the large size of cylinder thus indicated may be too large for reasons of physical size or cost. Again, the speed of operation required may result in a pump flow delivery that is unacceptable for similar reasons. The power required may be obtained by using more than one cylinder in parallel; the flow required may be achieved by taking the deliveries of more than one pump in parallel. The maximum power input available may require a sacrifice of speed to obtain the necessary power. The choice of action is wide, but there are not normally more than two solutions to a particular problem which are both technically and economically correct. The right choice is therefore very important.

Remaining at this stage with a simple circuit to operate a double-acting cylinder, it is necessary to touch briefly on the control valve which diverts oil to and from alternate ends of the cylinder. The valve used would be a four port type, the ports being connections for pipework or hoses; to carry oil from the pump, another back to the oil reservoir, and two service ports, one for each end of the cylinder. The diverting operation is performed by sliding a spool in a bore across the flow path, which in so doing changes the through passages within the valve body, and therefore the direction which the oil will take, see Figure 6.7.

Movement of the spool affects both through galleries simultaneously. This simultaneous diversion of both galleries is a necessity, determined by one of

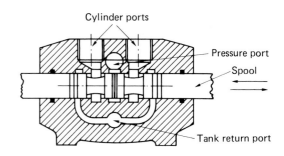

Figure 6.7 Spool valve

the principles of hydraulic pressure. It has been shown how force is multiplied by the ratio of pump reaction member to the area of the cylinder piston. The force is transformed into work by the cylinder rod. When diverting oil flow to the full area of the cylinder, it is essential that there is free passage of oil out from the rod area; this is achieved by the simultaneous opening of both valve ports, or the opening of the port controlling oil from the rod area slightly in advance of oil entering the full area. Where this configuration of valving is not possible, it is necessary that a safety (pressure relief) valve is fitted in the line from the annulus area, set to limit the pressure to a maximum of that allowed by the pressure relief governing the full area pressure. There are good reasons for stressing this point, in that failure to take simple precautions can damage or possibly destroy expensive system components. The danger is from what is referred to as pressure intensification, and is illustrated in Figure 6.8 where a cylinder has oil flow open from the pump, but closed from the annulus area.

Where a cylinder has been designed with a large rod diameter and resultant small annulus area in order to obtain fast cylinder retraction, the ratio between full area to annulus area can well be as high as 3:1, which would give three times the pressure at the rod or annulus end of the cylinder. According to Pascal's law this pressure would be transmitted with equal intensity throughout the fluid. This excessive pressure would therefore be applied to the inside surfaces of the rod end of the cylinder, to the pipework to the closed-off valve, and to the valve itself.

6.1.1 Pressure intensification (by design)

Providing that the design of cylinder and system equipment has been arranged to accept the higher pressures, the intensified pressure capability of the oil at the rod end of the cylinder may be utilised by design to obtain high pressure from a medium pressure capability pump. If oil is fed from the annulus area to the full area of the cylinder actually transmitting force to the work, the force can be multiplied, although the speed of work is reduced by the same ratio. To obtain a higher ratio of intensification, oil intensifiers are normally purpose designed units, and there is no exposed piston rod. The intensified force is applied from the area of the internal rod within its own bore, and ratios in excess of 4:1 are quite common. Figure 6.9 illustrates a force applied by utilising a pressure intensifier.

6.1.2 Oil flow intensification

If it is possible with an intensifier to increase force with a decrease in oil displacement, it follows that by feeding oil into the small piston area of the intensifier, the volume swept by the large piston is increased by the ratio of one area to the other. Figure 6.10 illustrates an intensifier used to increase the approach speed of a cylinder beyond that which would be achieved by the same pump connected directly to the cylinder.

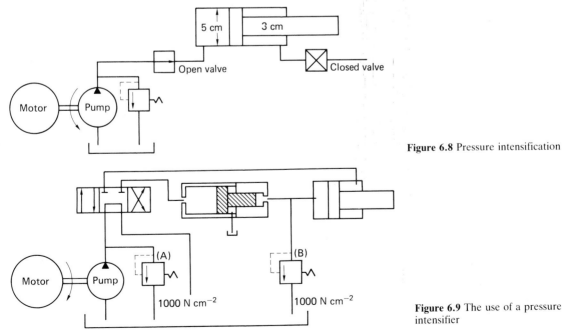

Figure 6.8 Pressure intensification

Figure 6.9 The use of a pressure intensifier

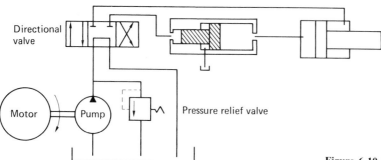

Directional valve

Motor   Pump   Pressure relief valve

Figure 6.10 Flow intensification

On its own, the circuit in Figure 6.10 serves no useful purpose except to illustrate the principle of flow intensification, as the same input power could achieve the same force and cylinder speed by utilising a smaller diameter cylinder, and a smaller pump capacity at a higher system pressure (without the use of the intensifier). However, it is possible by introducing a flow intensifier and adding various valves into the system, to achieve a fast cylinder approach at low force capability, and to switch automatically to a slow speed with a high force. There are several alternative ways of achieving this: one can use a double pump system, i.e. a dual pump with one section giving a high volume and low force capability, and a small delivery pump with a high force capability. The large delivery pump would be unloaded as the work load demanded a higher pressure. A pre-fill valve system will achieve the same effect using separate cylinders for approach and force. An accumulator can be used to give speeds above that derived from the pump, where there is time between operating cycles for the storage capacity of the accumulator to be charged. To a lesser degree, a regenerative system can also allow a dual speed/force capability. The need for a dual speed and force system is determined by the application. In many instances, and particularly in a press application, high force is not necessary until near the end of the cylinder stroke, but a fast approach speed is required to achieve a short cycle time. The input power can be drastically reduced by using a dual speed/force system. It also becomes possible, depending on choice of system, to reduce valve and pipework sizes, and to reduce oil cooling requirements and oil reservoir capacities.

6.1.3 Regenerative systems

This method of operation may be used to add to the cylinder approach speed, but again circuit valves must be added to retrieve the high force necessary to perform work at the end of the approach stroke. The change to high force may be achieved automatically on a rising pressure, or by a limit switch set at

a distance along the approach stroke. In a regenerative system, the pump feed is to the full area of the cylinder, and the oil being forced from the annulus area is fed back into the full area, together with the pumped oil. In calculating the speed of approach with a given pump capacity, the factor is not of full area and length of stroke, but the rod area and length of stroke. Both sides of the cylinder piston are in fact under pressure together, but the larger area will have the greater reaction, and the cylinder will move out. The force achieved however is only that which can be calculated from the force on the rod area, i.e. the full area less the annulus area. To obtain high force at the time required, the interconnection between full area and annulus area must be blocked, and the annulus oil taken back to the oil reservoir.

6.1.4 Double pump system

This system gives the advantage of fast approach and fast return by utilising both high- and low-volume pumps at low pressure together, and unloading the large volume when pressure rises, thus allowing the work to be taken by the low-volume high-pressure pump. The maximum power required is that needed by the small pump at high pressure plus the large pump unloaded.

An important factor to be remembered from the applications illustrated so far is that in each circuit there will be differing flows and pressures in various parts of the circuit. It is very important that these oil flows and pressures are noted in order to make the right choice of size of valves and pipe runs and of pressure ratings of equipment to be incorporated in the system.

6.2 Hydraulic motors

Hydraulic motors are the means used to convert back the fluid energy of an hydraulic system into rotational movement. There are two basic types of motor, the slow-speed high-torque motor suitable for speed ranges normally of between 1 and 600 rev min^{-1}, and medium- to low-torque motors with a medium to high speed capability of up to 7000 rev min^{-1} depending on type, but with a minimum speed of 100 to 200 rev min^{-1}.

The output torque of an hydraulic motor is dependent on the area of the motor reaction member and the system pressure. The pressure that can be utilised is limited to that specified as a maximum by the manufacturer, or the upper limit of the particular hydraulic system — only a larger displacement motor will then give increased torque. It follows that the larger the displacement of oil for each revolution the greater the mass of the working parts; the maximum speed of revolution is therefore limited to avoid excessively high peripheral speeds, or, in the case of radial piston motors, an unmanageable high velocity of large moving masses. The moving parts against which the fluid force is reacting are changing direction at least once in every revolution, and a break-up of components could result from a speed higher than that for which the motor was designed.

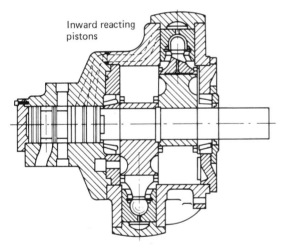

Inward reacting pistons

Figure 6.11 Radial piston motors

Slow-speed high-torque motors are invariably of the radial piston type, with several radially disposed pistons under pressure reacting inwards on a central cam which is an integral part of the output shaft, or in other cases pistons reacting outwards on a circumferential cam ring which is part of the motor body. Valving to pressurise each piston in turn, and to exhaust, is either face valving or rotational pintle, both being automatically sequenced by means of a relationship to the revolving shaft. A reasonably high torque can also be obtained from the ball piston type motor, but this is a more recent development. These are basically similar to radial piston motors, except that the reaction on the cam is produced by

steel balls backed up by pistons. These may be radially or axially disposed.

Higher speed motors are small in size, and are of the external gear type, axial piston, radial piston, vane, cam rotor, internal gear, or gerotor type. Greater torque outputs than those relating to the hydraulic actuator can be achieved by taking the output via reduction gears. Output torque is increased by the ratio of the gear reduction, and of course speed of rotation will be reduced in the same ratio. This can well be an economic alternative to high-torque motors where the requirement is for something at the bottom end of the range, and some types of medium-torque motors incorporate a built-in reduction between the oil pressure actuator and the output shaft.

Most types of hydraulic motor can be supplied for single rotation, or for dual rotation by diverting the feed oil to alternative ports. All motors have a certain amount of leakage from the pressure elements into the motor case and the area of the shaft seals, and it is therefore essential that these leakages are allowed to drain at low pressure. Slow-speed high-torque motors are invariably drained externally, even when operating in one direction of rotation only, but in most other cases, single rotation motors are drained internally by allowing the leakages to connect internally with the main flow of oil to the motor outlet. Dual rotation motors will normally have external drain ports, but some types offer an alternative internal drain, diverted automatically by check valves to join internally with whichever port is the outlet. It should be remembered that an internal drain gives a direct connection by galleries from the outlet port to the low-pressure case area of the motor. If the motor is being hydraulically controlled from the outlet side of the motor, where more than one motor is in series, or where the back pressure on the outlet port exceeds the manufacturer's drain pressure limit, external drains must be used and piped separately to the reservoir.

6.2.1 Motor selection

The sizing of hydraulic motors for an application is a little more complicated than for cylinders, and torque must be taken into account.

The starting torque of an hydraulic motor is always less than its running torque, by extents that vary depending on the type of motor. The load to be driven will also have a torque requirement characteristic that varies from starting to running speed. In some case the running torque can be less than the starting torque, for instance in vehicle drives or conveyor drives, but electrical generator drives or air moving fans or compressors require increasing torque. It is therefore essential that the torque curves of both driver and driven are carefully studied. The use of a variable delivery pump to feed the motor enables downward variation of flow on a higher pressure requirement, thus adjusting itself to the torque output required. Pressure will drop and flow will increase as the torque requirement decreases and allows an increase in motor speed. The use of this type of system will normally allow for a lower input, but will involve a higher initial cost. Where a fixed delivery pump is used and highest torque is required on starting, a motor should be selected which has the required running torque at a pressure calculated as a percentage below the maximum allowable pressure of the motor or the maximum system pressure whichever is the lower. The percentage referred to will be the percentage difference between the starting torque and running torque of the hydraulic motor. With a gear motor for instance, the starting torque may be 80% of the running torque; if the system pressure is to be 2500 $N\ cm^{-2}$, then a motor should be selected which gives the required running torque at 80% of 2500 $N\ cm^{-2}$, i.e. 2000 $N\ cm^{-2}$. On start-up, the system pressure will be 2500 $N\ cm^{-2}$ and will gradually fall to 2000 $N\ cm^{-2}$ as the load gains speed. Where the torque requirement increases beyond that required for breakaway the motor must be selected with a running torque to match the highest requirement at the system pressure decided upon.

Where the highest torque is merely required for periods of a few seconds before levelling off, and it is known that the system will accept higher pressures than calculated for running torque, and the prime mover (electric motor or engine) will accept momentary overload, it is in order to size the motor and input power for the normal running torque. The system relief valve will however require to be set to allow the system pressure to rise to its momentary peak requirements.

6.2.2 *Motor applications*

The construction of an hydraulic motor is almost identical to the equivalent type pump, and so if the load is allowed to take over from the motor and drive the motor from the shaft as opposed to being driven, the motor will operate as a pump, and will attempt to draw in oil at the motor inlet port. With the possibility of the motor over-running, it is essential to ensure that while the motor is rotating sufficient oil is available at the inlet to match the motor displacement until the motor comes to a standstill. Insufficient oil under these circumstances will cause what is known as cavitation, and will almost certainly result in severe damage to the motor.

In certain motor applications, for instance where a fan is being rotated at high speed, it is necessary to allow for over-run; blocking both motor ports and attempting to bring the load to a sudden stop would cause an unacceptable pressure peak on the outlet side of the motor. This danger exists with any rotational load which has a tendency to continue rotation when the oil flow is stopped.

There will be other applications where it is necessary to retain control of the load in both directions, for instance in a conveyor system where the load is conveyed up an incline and on a downward slope. Where a load is being lowered by a crane or hoist, it is necessary that the load does not gain momentum of its own accord, and it is also essential that on stopping there is a smooth but effective braking action. Different applications each present their own problem of control.

Earlier in this section, when dealing with the torque requirements of a system, we dealt only with a single motor drive. Torque output can be increased by driving several motors in parallel. The torque outputs may be harnessed to a single output via a gearbox, or they can be harnessed individually, for instance to the separate wheels of a vehicle. The speed of drive will be reduced, as the pump flow must be shared between all the motors which are coupled in parallel. Once the load is moving and the torque requirement is reduced, the required speed may be recovered by taking the motors out of parallel circuit and into series.

6.3 Hydraulic cylinders

We have already shown how hydraulic cylinders are used to convert the hydraulic energy of the pumped oil into a linear force for pushing, pulling, raising or lowering. In most cases, the reaction to the oil is provided by the piston attached to the piston rod. The piston must slide up and down inside the cylinder (or barrel), and must be supplied with seals which offer as low a friction as possible on piston movement, and at the same time form an oil-tight seal between one side of the piston and the other. In double-acting cylinders, seals must be provided to contain the oil pressure operating on either side of the piston. It is also necessary with double-acting cylinders to seal at the cylinder end where the rod extends from the cylinder, and to fit a wiper seal to avoid ingress of dirt to the main rod sealing area. Cylinders may be constructed with their ends welded to the barrel, or screwed, or with components assembled together with tie rods. The front end of the cylinder must of course be removable to allow for the extraction of the rod and piston assembly for servicing and seal replacement. Surface finishes of the cylinder bore and the piston rod must be extremely good to reduce friction and to ensure good sealing.

There are many alternative standard type cylinder mountings and rod ends available, some of which are illustrated. Apart from single and double-acting cylinders, which are available in a variety of dimensions in a standard form, there are other more specialised types.

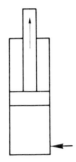

Figure 6.12 Single-acting hydraulic cylinder extended by oil pressure and returned by influence of the load

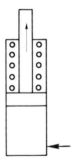

Figure 6.13 Single-acting hydraulic cylinder extended by load and returned by the force of a spring compressed on the forward stroke

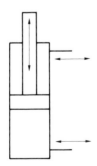

Figure 6.14 Double-acting hydraulic cylinder extended and returned by directing pumped oil to alternative ports

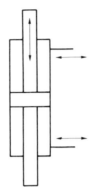

Figure 6.15 Double-acting hydraulic cylinder with through rod

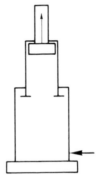

Figure 6.16 Single-acting hydraulic cylinder extended by pumped oil and returned by influence of the load

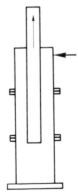

Figure 6.17 Displacement rams are constructed with no piston, and therefore the 'barrel' or body internal bore can be left in a relatively rough condition. The rod will probably have a retaining collar to avoid it leaving the body. The force exerted by a displacement ram is pressure × rod cross-sectional area. One application is in service lifts, where the body of the cylinder can be several flanged lengths of tube bolted together and dropped into a bore hole. Because there is no piston, the oil port can be the rod end of the cylinder, and the alignment of the several connected barrels is unimportant

The effective stroke of work of a cylinder can be increased for some applications by the addition of ropes and pulleys. The additional stroke results in a corresponding decrease in power, but a larger diameter cylinder is necessary to retrieve the required power, and is often more easy to accommodate than is increased length.

6.3.1 Cylinder cushioning

Where the total stroke of cylinder is being utilised, cushioning can be incorporated to slow down the movement at the end of the stroke. This can be for either direction of operation, and is achieved by an extension of the piston restricting the oil leaving the cylinder when it reaches near the end of stroke. An external adjusting screw is normally fitted to enable control of the oil flow.

6.4 Hydraulic pumps

Hydraulic pumps convert mechanical energy into hydraulic energy. In piston pumps, which are driven by a rotating force (an electric motor or engine), there are several pistons moved by a cam; these pistons are at any one time under a varying influence of a stroke from the cam, either taking in oil on a suction stroke or forcing oil out on a pressure stroke. The valves used to isolate suction from pressure are either of a spring-loaded poppet type that are opened by pressure or suction, or are rotating face valves sequenced by rotation of the pump drive shaft. Piston pumps are either of the radial type with pistons disposed radially on a central shaft driven cam, or the axial type having pistons in line with the shaft and operated by reaction from an angled cam plate. In some cases the piston barrel rotates on a stationary cam plate, and in others the cam plate is rotated by the shaft.

6.4.1 Radial piston pump

Radial piston pumps are capable of producing high pressures, in excess of 5000 N cm^{-2}. In the more general high pressure applications up to 3500 N cm^{-2} they are therefore working at nowhere near their maximum pressure, and their efficiency should be maintained for a long period under these conditions. It makes good sense when employing pumps in continuous operation that they are not used at their maximum rated pressures; although this may necessitate specifying a larger diameter cylinder, there will almost certainly be a worthwhile saving in extended pump life and less system failure and down time. Figure 6.18 represents a radial piston pump.

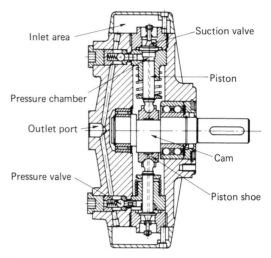

Figure 6.18 A cross-section of a radial piston pump

The illustration shows that the pumping elements in a radial piston pump are spring returned, and that the pressure and suction valves are of the seated poppet type, and are also spring loaded. Although there will be a vacuum created at the suction port, to ensure that the pressure chamber becomes completely full on suction stroke, it is necessary for the pump to be gravity fed or immersed in the reservoir. In immersed applications the protective end caps covering the suction valves will be mesh covers. When gravity fed, it is necessary to bleed air from the suction valve covers to ensure a free flow of oil to all chambers from the suction port. The arrangement of individual pressure valves for each piston lends itself to splitting pump outputs. Small drillings from the piston to the bearing side of the piston shoe allow oil under pressure to act as a bearing between shoe and cam.

6.4.2 Axial piston pump

Axial piston pumps are also available for high pressures, but excepting specialised pumps for specific high pressure applications they are not normally rated above 3500 N cm^{-2}. Because the piston movement is controlled by the rise and fall around the surface of an angled cam plate, this design of pump is often available as a variable output pump. The variation is achieved by a change in the cam plate angle, thereby varying the length of piston stroke. A typical axial piston design with a stationary cam plate is shown in Figure 6.19.

Valving is achieved by openings in the face of the piston barrel passing across a valve porting plate. It will be seen from the figure that the piston shoes are reacting under pressure against the cam plate; there is a free running 'slipper plate' between the shoes

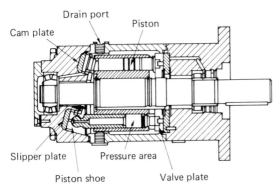

Figure 6.19 A cross-section of an axial piston pump

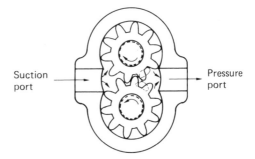

Figure 6.20 An external gear pump

and the cam, but careful pressure balancing is necessary to avoid piston shoe burn-up.

There are several variations of axial piston pump design. Where the cam plate rotates and the piston block remains stationary, poppet type valving can be incorporated, thus enabling higher pressures. The bent axis type pump has no cam plate, the piston block rotating at an angle to the input shaft; rotation of the shaft and the piston block causes the pistons to move in and out of their bores.

It is important to remember that in any hydraulic apparatus where there are reciprocating or rotating elements transmitting fluid, there is some leakage of fluid across the elements from the pressure area to the low-pressure side of the system; without leakage there would be no lubrication of contact surfaces. In a single rotation pump, this leakage is allowed to connect internally with the suction or inlet of the pump. With an axial piston pump it is essential that the low-pressure case area is allowed to fill with oil in order to lubricate bearings. This will only happen if there is no air trapped in the case, and a case drain must be connected to the reservoir with a slightly positive head of oil. When immersing pumps, the drain must be left open below the oil level, and it is essential to ensure that the pump is immersed so that the oil level is always above the level of all internal bearings.

6.4.3 *Medium pressure pumps*

By far the commonest hydraulic pressure pumps in use are in the medium-pressure range (up to 2000 $N \, cm^{-2}$), and of these external gear pumps are the most common. This is due to their simplicity compared with other types, and their relatively low cost. The basic design is shown in Figure 6.20, one gear is integral with the pump drive shaft, while the second (idler) gear is driven by meshing with the driver gear.

The gears are rotated so that the teeth which are meshing are moving towards the inlet area. As each

pair of gear teeth intermesh, entry of the meshed teeth into the inlet area and parting will increase the volume of the inlet area by the displacement of two teeth, and oil flows into the space. The equivalent amount of oil is carried between the teeth and the pump case to the outlet side of the pump. On the outlet side, the intermeshing gears operate in reverse, squeezing into the system the oil which has been carried round between the gears and the pump gear housing. The pressures which can be achieved are limited by loads on the gear shaft bearings, the amount of leakage which can be tolerated across the faces of the gears, or a limitation of the pressure which can be exerted on the plates between which the gears are running before making the pressure balancing of these plates ineffective. Any increase in hydraulic efficiency would almost certainly be offset by mechanical inefficiency. It must be pointed out however that gear pumps are now coming onto the market that are designed and rated for higher pressures. Gear pumps are readily available as double, triple, and even quadruple units, allowing a great deal of versatility in systems where several independent drives are required, or where there is a need to supply various stepped flow outputs. There are also units available as standard that comprise a medium-pressure gear pump and a high-pressure radial piston pump with a common drive shaft.

There are several other types of medium-pressure pump in common use, such as the vane type, the Gerotor and the cam rotor.

The choice of pumps is wide, and each type has certain advantages for particular applications, be it pressure requirement, initial cost or replacement cost, noise level, or the degree of contamination control necessary in a system to ensure an adequate running life of an expensive unit; there is little point in using sophisticated machinery if the environmental conditions are not sufficiently controlled to sustain the equipment in working order.

Apart from a very obvious need to maintain the hydraulic fluid in good condition (clearances between working surfaces are in many cases in the order of 5 μm), the second most common cause of pump failure is the drawing of air into the inlet, or a

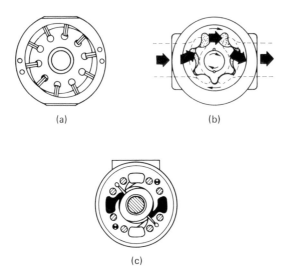

Figure 6.21 A variety of pumps: (a) vane type; (b) gerotor type; (c) cam rotor type

restriction that prevents sufficient oil from entering the inlet. Both these faults will result in cavitation and severe pump damage.

Having discussed the fundamentals of the major components in an hydraulic system the most important design aspect is the hydraulic circuit. This must enable the functions to be carried out efficiently at the lowest energy cost. Circuit design is vitally important and it is wise to consult hydraulic equipment manufacturers or circuit specialists before getting to grips with details of the total design as the circuit will influence the choice of valves and the necessary ancilaries.

6.5   Compressed air*

All matter consists of molecules which are in constant motion, but which are held together with molecular forces. In a solid the molecules are closely packed and arranged in such a pattern that the influence of the molecular forces is very strong. This gives the solid its consistency and form. Molecular motion consists largely of oscillations around points of equilibrium. In a liquid the molecules are about as close to each other as they are in a solid, but they are not arranged in a pattern and their cohesive forces are weaker. The molecules are more mobile in relation to each other, and as a result the characteristic liquid phase develops — the liquid accommodates itself to the walls of its containing vessel, and its free surface aligns itself horizontally in response to the force of gravity.

* With acknowledgements to Atlas Copco Ltd.

In a gas, however, the molecules are farther apart, and they move freely about each other because the molecular forces are not as strong as in liquids and solids. A gas therefore expands through space and mixes with any other gases present. The total volume of the molecules that comprise a gas is very small in relation to the volume the gas occupies in space. A gas can therefore be compressed into a very small fraction of its original volume.

All gases deviate in their behaviour from the ideal described by general gas law to some degree, and in some cases the deviation is rather extreme. The deviation increases with the density of the gas and with its nearness to the liquid state. It is sometimes necessary to take these deviations into account in compressor calculations.

Compressor processes are polytropic, which means that temperature increases with the pressure ratio. The work of compression increases as the temperature rises. To limit the temperature rise and thus improve the compression efficiency, compression is normally carried out in stages with the gas being cooled between each stage.

Multi-stage compression also increases the volumetric efficiency as the pressure ratio over the first stage is decreased. Perfect intercooling is attained when the temperature of the air leaving the intercooler is equal to the temperature of the air at the compressor intake. With perfect intercooling the minimum power consumption is obtained when the pressure ratios of all stages are alike. On one hand by increasing the number of stages, the compression efficiency increases; but on the other, the compressor becomes more complicated and expensive. For each pressure level there exists an optimum number of stages, depending on the use for which the compressor is intended.

6.5.1   Heat recovery

It is possible to recover all the work expended in compressing the air by cooling the air to the intake temperature. This statement may sound like a paradox, but the explanation lies in the fact that the temperature of the air after its expansion will be lower than if the heat had not been recovered. The energy necessary to raise the temperature of the expanded air is taken from the surrounding air. By recovering and utilising the heat content of the compressed air it is possible to have the air compressed seemingly without the expense of any work. All the energy cannot be recovered, but with different arrangements rather high efficiencies can be reached.

6.5.2 Intercooling

In order to dissipate the compression heat it is usual to cool the compressor cylinders, the cylinder covers, and any other surfaces that can affect the temperature, as far as is possible. However, cooling the air between the compression stages is the most important means of controlling the temperature. The device used for this purpose is the intercooler, which may be liquid-cooled or air-cooled.

Air-cooling is also used for relatively large compressors, particularly in open-air installations or where the heat can easily be dissipated from the premises. Air-cooling is the most convenient alternative because it eliminates the problem of water supply, the danger of freezing, etc. However, to make an intercooler that reduces the air temperature to that at the compressor air intake presents a difficult problem.

6.5.3 Survey of compressor types

The two basic groups are displacement and dynamic compressors. In the former the pressure rise is obtained by enclosing a volume of gas in a confined space, after which the volume is reduced by mechanical action. Well-known members of this family are the reciprocating piston compressor and the rotary screw compressor. Some displacement compressors (screw compressors, vane compressors, etc.) have a fixed (built-in) pressure ratio.

In a dynamic compressor the pressure rise is obtained by imparting kinetic energy to a continuously flowing gas and converting this energy to pressure in some form of diffuser. Ejectors, centrifugal compressors and axial compressors are all of the dynamic type. The capacity of a dynamic compressor varies with the working pressure. The more common compressor types are shown in Figure 6.22, their main characteristics being described below.

6.5.4 Displacement types

6.5.4.1 Reciprocating compressors

Piston compressors: This is the oldest and most common type of positive-displacement compressor. Single-acting compressors are usually of the trunk type, while double-acting compressors use a crosshead design. Reciprocating compressors are available both in lubricated and non-lubricated versions. Non-lubricated compressors have piston rings and use bands or skirts of polytetrafluorethylene (PTFE) with various fillers.

6.5.4.2 Rotary compressors

Screw compressors: The screw compressor is a positive-displacement machine with a built-in pressure ratio. The absence of inlet and outlet valves and of unbalanced mechanical forces enables the screw compressor to operate at high shaft speeds. Conse-

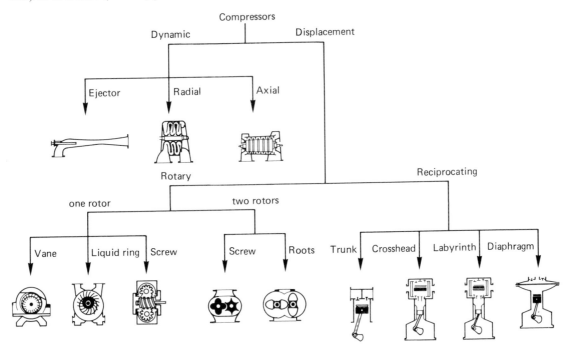

Figure 6.22 Basic compressor types

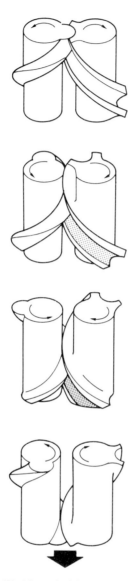

Figure 6.23 Working principle of a screw compressor (simplified)

quently it combines high capacity with small exterior dimensions.

Dry type screw compressors use external timing-gears to synchronise the counter-rotating male and female rotors. As the rotors touch neither each other nor the casing, lubrication is not required within the compression space. The delivered air is oil-free.

To maintain the compressor efficiency at low capacities requires very high shaft speeds. However, by injecting oil into the compression space it is possible to use a lower shaft speed. The injected oil has three functions:

(1)   to seal the internal clearances,
(2)   to cool the air during compression, and
(3)   to lubricate the rotors.

This internal lubrication makes it possible to dispense with the timing gears.

The injected oil is reclaimed and recirculated after compression. As the maximum oil temperature can be kept low it is possible to reclaim practically all the oil.

Oil-flooded screw compressors were first used as portable compressors. However, the development of new, more efficient rotor profiles has also made them viable as stationary compressors.

A new version uses water-injection to deliver oil-free air. The drawbacks are that the compressor's interior must be protected against rust, and that complicated seals are necessary to separate the compression space from the oil-lubricated bearings.

A special variant is the oil-flooded single-shaft compressor. A single screw-rotor meshes with two symmetrically located gate-rotors. To ensure a tight seal between the screw and the gate-rotors, the roots of the screw threads are located substantially along an arc of a circle. This means that the core of the screw has an hour-glass shape. Air is aspirated through inlet ports in the end plate. The outlet is formed by two triangular holes in the casing bore. The number of screw threads determines the built-in pressure ratio.

Capacity regulation or unloading of screw compressors is usually done by having a valve that shuts off or throttles the air supply to the compressor.

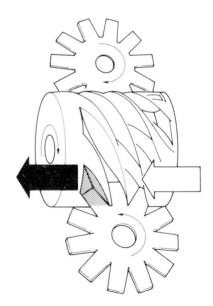

Figure 6.24 Working principle of a single-screw rotor compressor

Vane compressors: The rotary vane compressor is a single-shaft, positive displacement compressor with a built-in pressure ratio. A rotor with radially movable blades is mounted eccentrically in a stator housing. When it rotates the vanes are pressed against the stator walls by centrifugal force. Air taken into the compressor enters the space between the vanes in their most eccentric position, where the pocket between two vanes is largest. As the rotor turns, the pocket volume decreases and the air is compressed until the discharge port is uncovered by the leading vane of each pocket. This working principle has also been widely used in air motors.

The most common vane materials are phenolic resin-impregnated laminated fabrics, such as asbestos or cotton cloth. Today vane compressors are usually of the oil-flooded type. For oil-free service bronze and carbon/graphite vanes are used.

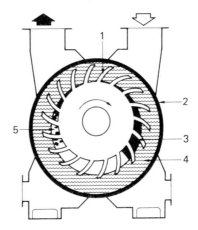

Figure 6.26 Liquid ring compressor: 1, impeller; 2, casing; 3, intake port; 4, working liquid; 5, discharge port

cylinder, the inner wall of which varies in its distance from the rotor, as does the cylinder wall. Thus the volume between the blades varies cyclically, as in the vane compressor. To avoid radial thrust, the liquid-ring pump is often designed with two symmetric compression spaces opposite one another.

The cooling of liquid-ring compressors is direct. Because of the direct contact between gas and liquid, the final discharge temperature can be held close to the liquid inlet temperature. However, the discharge gas is saturated at the discharge temperature with the compressing liquid. These compressors are used in processes where only a small temperature rise throughout the compression cycle is acceptable, in other words with approximately isothermal compression.

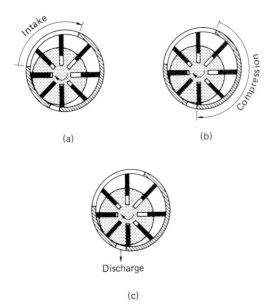

Figure 6.25 Working principle of a rotary vane compressor. (a) As rotor turns, gas is trapped in the pockets formed by the vanes; (b) gas is gradually compressed as pockets get smaller; (c) compressed gas is pushed out through discharge port

Liquid-ring compressors: The liquid-ring compressor is an oil-free, positive-displacement compressor with a built-in pressure ratio. It has a rotor with a series of fixed blades mounted in a cylinder. The blades are so arranged that the clearance between the blade tip and the cylinder varies cyclically during each revolution of the rotor.

The cylinder is partly filled with a liquid. During operation the liquid is carried around the cylinder by the action of the rotor blades. Due to centrifugal force, the liquid forms a solid ring around the

Rotary, two-impeller blowers: These blowers, often called Roots' blowers, form a type of valveless displacement machine. There is no internal compression. The compression takes place by backflow from the discharge side each time a rotor tip uncovers the discharge port. The *pV* diagram is thus rectangular which means a low efficiency. This restricts the use of this compressor to rather low-stage pressure ratios. Usually they operate as single-stage machines, but two- and three-stage versions exist.

Two identical, usually symmetrical, two-lobed rotors rotate in opposite directions inside a cylindrical casing. The rotors intermesh, but their internal clearance is maintained by a pair of timing gears. The compression space is not lubricated and these compressors are normally air-cooled.

Labyrinth piston compressors: This is a special type of oil-free, positive-displacement reciprocating compressor, working without piston rings. The seal

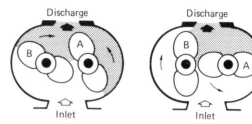
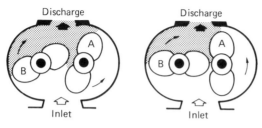

Figure 6.27 Working principle of a two-impeller blower

between piston and cylinder wall is produced by a series of labyrinths. The cylinders have a finely-grooved inner surface, and the piston skirts have a sharp-edged thread cut into the surface. The piston rod packing is also of a labyrinth type. The internal leakage is higher than for designs using piston rings, but on the other hand the piston-ring and packing-box friction work is saved. The delivered air is extremely free from contamination.

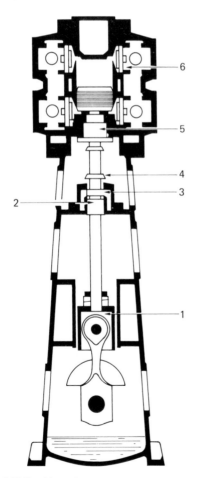

Figure 6.28 Double-acting labyrinth compressor: 1, crosshead; 2, guide bearing; 3, oil scraper; 4, oil thrower ring; 5, stuffing box; 6, disc valves

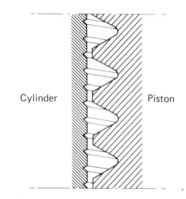

Figure 6.29 Labyrinth piston surface

Diaphragm compressors: The diaphragm compressor is an oil-free, positive-displacement reciprocating compressor, but instead of a piston reciprocating within a cylinder a flexible membrane or diaphragm is employed. The diaphragm may be mechanically or hydraullically actuated.

Mechanically-actuated diaphragm compressors are only manufactured for small capacities and moderate pressures and for vacuum duty. Hydraulically-actuated units are well suited to generating high pressures.

6.5.5 Dynamic types

6.5.5.1 Radial (centrifugal) compressors

This compressor type is characterised by radial flow. The gas is fed to the centre of a rotating wheel with radial blades known as the impeller, which throws the gas to the periphery by centrifugal force. Before being guided to the centre of the next impeller the gas passes a diffuser where the kinetic energy is converted to pressure. The stage pressure ratio is determined by the amount of velocity change, and the density of the gas.

Centrifugal compressors are well suited to inter-cooling between stages or stage groups, which makes the compression nearer to isothermal and improves the efficiency. The coolers are rather large, as dynamic compressors are sensitive to pressure drops.

Centrifugal compressors below an effective pressure of 4 bar are not usually cooled. Operating speeds are high compared to other compressors. 50 000 to 100 000 rev min⁻¹ are common in the aircraft and space industries where mass is a major factor. Most commercial centrifugal units now operate at around 20 000 rev min⁻¹, with a strong upward trend.

The minimum capacity of a centrifugal compressor is mainly limited by the flow through the last stage. 160 litres per second at the outlet of a horizontally-split type can be taken as a practical limit. The efficiency of dynamic compressors, at a normal working pressure of 7 bar, is not as high as that of displacement compressors except at very high capacities.

6.5.5.2 Axial compressors

This compressor type is characterised by having its flow in the axial direction. The gas passes axially along the compressor through alternate rows of rotating and stationary blades which impart velocity and then pressure to the gas. The minimum capacity of this type is around 15 m³ s⁻¹. Cooling between the stages is difficult to arrange with axial compressors. This is one of the factors that limit the pressure ratio over each casing.

Axial compressors, due to their smaller diameter, operate at higher speeds than centrifugals for the same duty. Usually the operating speed is about 25% higher. Axial compressors are mostly used for constant-flow applications and for moderate pressures. With the exception of the compressors used in jet aircraft engines the maximum pressure ratio is normally limited to six for each casing.

The axial compressor is best suited for plants requiring large, but constant quantities of air. A typical application is blast furnace blowing. Axial compressors are normally used for capacities about 65 m³ s⁻¹ and for effective pressures up to 14 bar.

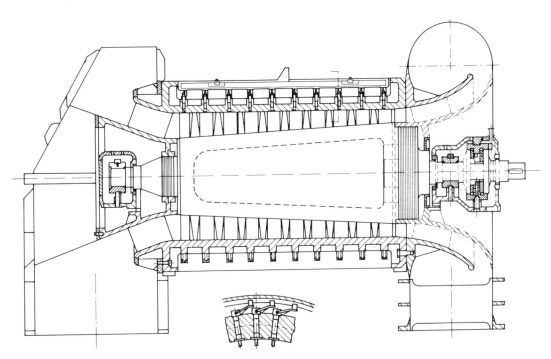

Figure 6.30 Section through a nine-stage axial compressor with adjustable stationary vanes

7

Design aspects of production processes

7.1 Basic forming processes

There seems no doubt about how to make a certain object; it may be well designed for its purpose, easy to produce and good to look at. But the facts tend to change. Since the original design was made, the quantities may have increased or decreased: the balance of material costs and production costs may shift. New methods become available. Old and new products both need looking at from the production viewpoint. Sometimes it pays to combine two into one, sometimes to subdivide one object into two parts. If we expect a list of simple do and don't rules, we find relatively few don'ts but many alternative do-decisions to choose from.

The policy adopted here is to look at each process in turn and discuss not only the points to avoid but the opportunities which the process presents to the product designer. To make good use of the available space, some processes are treated briefly, whilst some points common to the many processes that are based on a two-part mould have been summarised.

Machining has not been given a separate section; it is assumed that all engineering designers have received some machine shop training on the basic forms of machining such as turning, boring, drilling, tapping, milling and grinding. Readers are reminded here of some quantity production methods often excluded from basic training schemes: broaching, disc or belt sanding, circular milling (including thread-milling), thread and spline rolling. The economies made possible by such processes and the restrictions they place upon detail design are concerned as much with the particular equipment's tool access and work-holding capabilities as with the fundamentals. It should be part of the designer's duties to be familiar with the equipment available, even to the extent of suggesting the purchase of new equipment to facilitate the production of cheaper or

better-designed products. To some extent these remarks also apply to inspection methods.

7.1.1 Sand and strengthened sand casting (silicate + CO_2 or others)

The general design points that aid successful casting are common to all forms of the process and will be reviewed later. The points specific to green sand and to a lesser extent to strengthened sand methods arise from the relatively weak nature of the sand. Adequate draft to aid pattern withdrawal is one. Fillets are also important, as are core prints.

The reason these points are important is that sharp internal corners on the casting call for protruding edges of sand in the negative (the mould) which are liable to break off when hit by the flowing metal, as is well known. What is not considered so often is the location of the cores. A big core in a bath of molten iron or bronze has considerable buoyancy and tries to float up. The casting should whenever possible be designed to give good large core prints, arranged symmetrically about the centre. Two prints that are off-centre are liable to let the core rotate; under these circumstances a third print would help.

There is little point in saying that undercuts cost money, every designer is well aware that the pattern must be withdrawable, hence undercuts create complications. We must remember that the great virtue of casting is the freedom of shape that it provides. The avoidance of undercuts must not take precedence over other considerations. Basically sand casting is not a mass-production process in the sense of ten products per minute; if such rates are needed they are achieved by clustering many objects into one larger cast.

A sand foundry is used to placing cores into moulds, so it may not be hard to persuade a foundry to place inserts. Mild steel inserts in cast iron have been used from time to time; the low solidus of cast iron allows quite thin steel parts to be cast-in. It may be wise to use an indented outline to avoid a stress-raiser on a line of weakness. The best-known uses of steel inserts are in the car industry, for example as heat-flow barriers in small brake drums and as resilient centres in certain flywheels. Steel or cast iron inserts are also practicable in light alloys.

Protruding lugs or brackets must be designed not only for their function but to be strong enough to withstand the rough handling that castings get during sand removal and fettling. A large and difficult casting which carries a risk of too many wasters or gross distortion can sometimes be redesigned as two or three separate castings. This will rarely pay with iron since the subsequent joining will create extra machining requirements, but in steel castings it is worthwhile considering welding several sub-units into one; with a little extra fettling, it is possible to compensate for distortion.

In view of the great freedom of shape, the designer can include location points P for machining (Figure 7.1), holding-down holes and slinging points for heavy work. Work-holding features can be particularly helpful in Computer Numerical Control (CNC) work since the programming is much easier if it need not include special path restrictions to avoid clamps, or stops to allow for the shifting of clamps. In other words, production planning should start at the product design stage to some extent.

As a final thought, it is not always essential to knock out the cores; some years ago a machine tool bed was cast with no core outlets, the core being located only by chaplets, and it was claimed that the trapped sand helped to damp out vibration.

A guide to likely tolerances is given in Table 7.1 at the end of Section 7.1.

7.1.2 *Shell moulding*

This is the ultimate in strengthened sand casting. The sand is resin bonded and sets as a thin shell around a heated pattern. It generally takes precedence over sand casting for small objects as soon as quantities are large enough to justify a metal pattern, perhaps a few thousand if the shape is complicated, much fewer if it is simple. Undercuts would be created by external cores, but are likely to be very unpopular as we are now talking in terms of quantity production. The normal procedure is to make two half-shells and glue them together lightly. Rather than undercuts with external cores it may be worth considering a three-way or four-way parting, from separate sub-patterns, with good locating pips, to create the required mould from several sub-shells. This method is similar to the use of segmental moulds in casting bronze sculptures. To avoid problems here the main lesson is keep to two halves if you can, with no undercuts.

Thanks to the metal pattern and the strong bond the finish and tolerances of a shell moulded casting will be better than those achieved using green or strengthened sand.

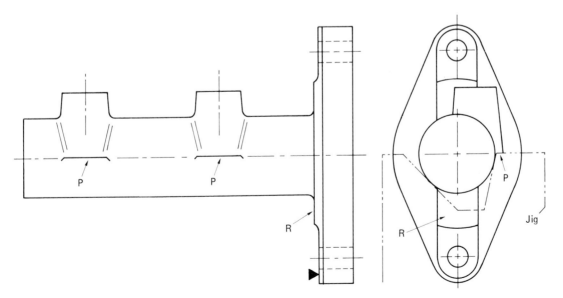

Figure 7.1 Inclusion of location points

7.1.3 Investment casting

This is a two-stage process in which an original with a shrinkage allowance has to be made in wax for every article required. This wax original is stuck onto a feeder, etc., usually as a cluster of many similar pieces, surrounded by a shell of refractory plaster and then melted out. The cavity left behind is then filled with molten metal. For the next cast a full set of fresh originals is needed. Originally an artist's method, it is now well established in dentistry, where it is used to cast plates and crowns from a thermoplastic mould created round a patient's palate or tooth base. It has caught on industrially because of its freedom from shape restriction since no pattern withdrawal is needed. Moreover as the mould is never opened, but is destroyed around the finished cast, size and shape tolerance are substantially better than sand or shell moulding can achieve. Investment casting is justified where these merits are important, i.e. when working with those shapes and materials that are usually costly to machine or polish. Cores are possible with this method; they must be placed in the wax original with the ends protruding so that the plaster can grip the core and hold it when the wax has gone.

There is no absolute reason for using refractory plaster; the original could be packed with ordinary foundry sand. This is a good method for casting test-bars, prototypes and small one-offs generally. The usual original in these cases is not wax (though it could be) but polystyrene foam. A (relatively) high density, fine-grained foam such as aeromodellers use can be cut and sanded to a reasonable finish. The required object, with its runner system for the metal, is built up from foam pieces stuck together; it is then used just like a pattern but the mould is not opened. Molten metal is poured in and destroys the foam, taking its place in the mould. Nothing is left of the foam except a puff of unpleasant fumes.

7.1.4 Slush casting

Designers should be aware of this casting method which can be used with any of the above mould forms. Metal is poured into the mould and very quickly much of it is poured out again, into a crucible or an ingot mould. This leaves a relatively thin hollow casting, thus saving material. We can use the object hollow as in statues, chocolate rabbits etc., or it can be back-filled with a cheaper core of lead, concrete, plaster, zinc, or anything of lower melting point.

7.1.5 Gravity and pressure diecasting

These processes have much in common. Both are quantity-production processes. Gravity diecasting uses cheaper, lighter dies and machines but is slower, has less design freedom and gives a rougher though quite attractive surface. Most of this section refers predominantly to pressure diecasting.

A diecasting mould is relatively expensive even if the product is relatively simple since it requires cooling passages and a good surface finish. Except for short run gravity work, the dies are made of hot-die steels, and every casting design needs some development on the die before the feeding and venting arrangements are satisfactory. Hence we look for minimum orders of 5000 on the simplest, flat, core-free objects, to 30 000 for more complex ones. Retracting cores at all sorts of angles are a normal feature, so we can have holes or external bosses ad lib if the quantities justify the die cost.

The materials commonly diecast are BS 1004 zinc alloys, Mazak brands, aluminium alloys notably the aluminium-silicon eutectic with small additions, and certain magnesium alloys. Bronze can be diecast in normal steel dies but reduces the life of dies, shot tubes and plungers. Some forms of cast iron are regularly diecast in steel dies, notably for exhaust manifolds. For carbon and stainless steels the Ferro-Di process, which is also suitable for bronze and copper, is applicable. This uses normal diecasting machines but with special die and shot tube materials. The material is fed in solid slug form and is induction melted immediately before injection. This reduces oxidation, etc. See GKN Projects Ltd (page 187).

In the general alloys we form holes by means of retractable metal cores. In Ferro-Di we place refractory cores into the mould. If complex holes are needed in aluminium or zinc, potassium chloride cores are used, which are then dissolved out. The cores themselves can be diecast, at higher temperatures of course.

Many of the design points are common to all casting and plastic moulding, and are listed at the end of Section 7.1. The use of ejector pins is specific to diecasting and plastic moulding. These leave a visible mark and have a slight flash. The product designer should show where such pins are acceptable, preferably at strong-points such as a junction between ribs, in the concave part. If the flash must be removed it helps to bring the pin positions into the general base plane which can be trimmed by belt sanding.

Where the finish is part of the sales appeal it is important to avoid sink marks. If the underside of a visible surface has ribs or bosses thicker than half the main wall and/or the ribs have needlessly large fillet radii, a shrinkage dimple will be visible, both in diecasting and plastic mouldings. It can be disguised by external ribs, fluted or textured patterns, etc.

The favoured way of designing lettering for names, instructions, etc. is to use raised letters in a sunken panel. This protects them from damage and makes for easy changes or repairs by means of an engraved block let into a pocket in the die.

The merits of diecasting include material saving. In zinc pressure diecasting thicknesses of $\frac{1}{2}$ mm are feasible and strength comes from having well-designed shapes, aided by ribs, etc. The same facility allows good detail reproduction. Full screw threads are possible using dies with rotating parts, though often a machining operation is more economical. Split threads with a gap at the parting line are preferred to full threads (Figure 7.2).

Provided it is not detrimental to function or styling, a flat parting line (and side cores in the parting plane) leads to cheaper dies.

Non-functional hollows to save material and avoid thickness variations are often justified even if they make the die more complex, but each case must be judged on its merits.

The use of inserts is well established. Small squirrel cage rotors can be diecast in pure aluminium around the lamination stack, with helical windings, complete with cooling fins.

Iron cores in flywheel magnetos are a similar example. Pistons can have steel or Invar expansion control inserts, strengthening plates, etc. A certain amount of flash must be expected around the insert location points. An insert which protrudes is humorously but commonly called an outsert. Diecasting is used to assemble two or more outserts together, using lead-antimony or other low-melting alloys, generally in small machines that are reminiscent of type-casters.

The design aspects are ease and security of placing since an out-of-place insert can damage a costly die, and the provision of enough strength around the insert since diecasting alloys contract more than the insert material. This ensures a secure grip but demands a well-considered surround.

7.1.6 *Sintering*

Sintering is the popular name for the application of the powder metallurgy process to the production of engineering components. It competes directly, as an alternative production technique, with casting, forging, fine blanking, deep drawing, etc., and, above all, machining. It has few characteristics which are inherently superior to those achieved by the other techniques, and hence it is used principally because it is, or can be, the cheapest production method, provided the quantities are large enough and the shape is suitable for the process. A selection of such components is shown in Figure 7.3.

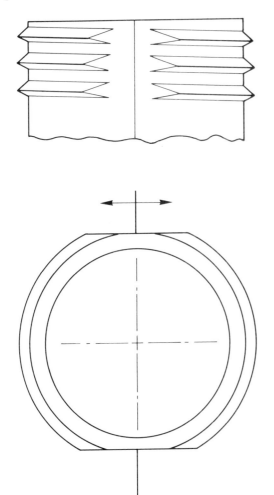

Figure 7.2 Split threads

Figure 7.3 Components produced by sintering

The powder metallurgy process comprises the steps of:

(1) producing the metal in the form of a fine powder in an annealed condition,
(2) blending together the powder to give the required alloy composition, and adding a small amount of pressing lubricant,
(3) compacting the powder mixture in precision tools at a pressure of less than 600 MN m^{-2},
(4) extracting the compact from the tools, and
(5) sintering the compact in a reducing atmosphere at a temperature below the melting point of the alloy.

After sintering, the alloy is in an annealed condition and thus the component can be repressed in coining tools to improve the dimensional precision by removing any distortions which may have occurred during the sintering. Coining is also used to improve the surface finish, to emboss certain small features not incorporated in the powder compacting tools, and to reduce the porosity where the pressure at the powder compacting stage has been less than that necessary to achieve the required density. In this latter case, the densified component may be re-sintered to enhance further the mechanical properties. A typical flow diagram is given in Figure 7.4.

The powder compacting step imposes a number of design limitations which need to be understood. Metal powder is not infinitely compressible. As the soft powder particles undergo plastic deformation, the metal work-hardens, and thus resists further plastic deformation. Before compaction, the loose powder bed has a relative density of about 38%. During compaction the volume of this powder bed can be reduced by a factor of between 2 and $2\frac{1}{2}$, depending upon the work-hardening characteristics of the alloy. Hence the relative density of the formed compact is generally just less than 90%. This means that there is just over 10% porosity at this stage, and this porosity will generally persist through the sintering stage. Hence the effect of this residual porosity in the finished component has to be separately considered and details of these effects and how they can be dealt with are given later on.

Another design limitation, imposed by the powder-compacting step, arises from the need to apply uni-axial compression. Three typical powder compacting sequences are illustrated in Figure 7.5. From these it will be noticed that those dimensions

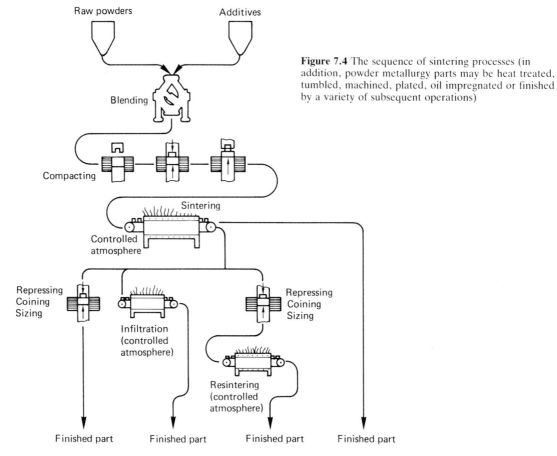

Figure 7.4 The sequence of sintering processes (in addition, powder metallurgy parts may be heat treated, tumbled, machined, plated, oil impregnated or finished by a variety of subsequent operations)

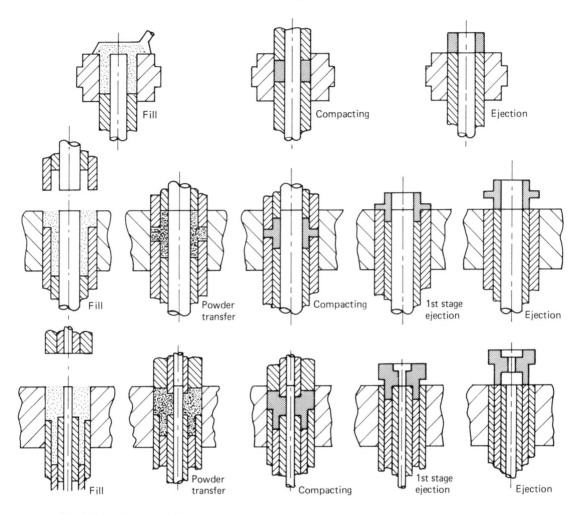

Figure 7.5 Typical powder compacting sequences

which are at right angles to the direction of pressing are defined by the dimensions of the tools, whereas those dimensions which are in the direction of pressing are defined by the movement of the punches used to compact the powder. Hence the dimensional tolerances which can be achieved in these two directions are different, with those dimensions defined by the tools being held to a closer tolerance than those defined by the motion of the punches.

Another characteristic of powder compaction is the way in which the pressure is transmitted in the direction of pressing. Due to the friction between the tool surfaces and the powder compact in contact with those surfaces, there exists a pressure gradient in the direction of pressing. Figure 7.6 illustrates the variation in density which is produced, first with single-end compression and secondly with double-end compression, for three length-to-diameter ra-

tios. To minimise the density gradient in the pressing direction, double-end compression is employed and the length to diameter ratio is kept as small as possible.

It must also be remembered that the compacting pressures are high and approach the yield point of the alloy steel punches which are applying the pressure. For these reasons slender fragile punches must be avoided. Similarly, where a chamfer is required to be formed, a sharp edge on the punches, which is likely to be damaged at high pressures, must also be avoided.

Let us now consider how these various limitations affect the design of components to be produced by powder metallurgy.

As illustrated in Figure 7.7, reverse tapers cannot be produced, as they would prevent the component being ejected from the tools. Similarly cross holes and screw threads cannot be formed.

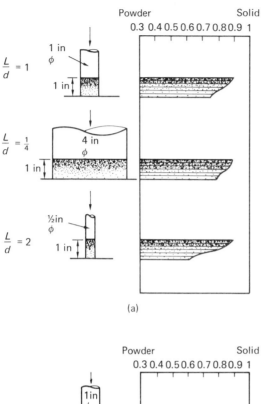

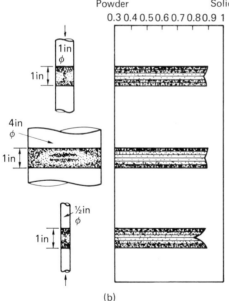

Figure 7.6 Variation in density with single-end and double-end compression for three length-to-diameter ratios

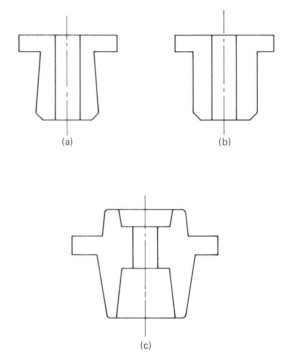

Figure 7.7 Reverse tapers to be avoided

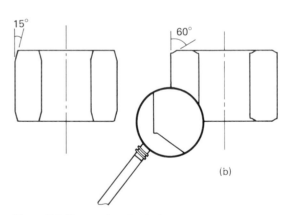

Figure 7.8 Correct chamfer design

In Figure 7.8 the correct design of chamfers is illustrated. The shallow angle, 60°, and the small flat, about 0.2 mm, ensure that the punches will have a satisfactory life in service. Similarly in Figure 7.9 the usual design requirement of avoiding sharp corners applies not only to the component but also to the tools.

Figure 7.10 illustrates a further two design criteria which apply to powder metallurgy components, avoiding thin overhanging sections and shapes which require punches with knife-edges. Figure 7.11 illustrates the problem of producing small steps which require thin fragile punches.

Figure 7.12 shows one way of avoiding a density gradient in the direction of pressing. As a casting this cam form would normally be on a *flat* circular base. However, as a powder metallurgy part it is

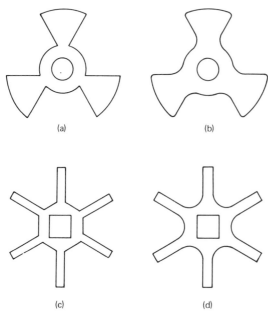

(a)   (b)

(c)   (d)

Figure 7.9 Avoid sharp corners (a) and (c)

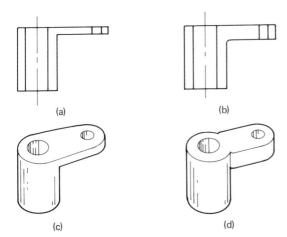

(a)   (b)

(c)   (d)

Figure 7.10 Avoid thin overhanging sections (a) and (c)

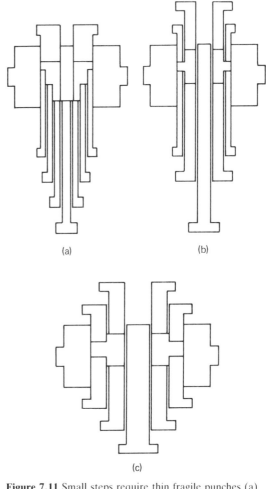

(a)   (b)

(c)

Figure 7.11 Small steps require thin fragile punches (a)

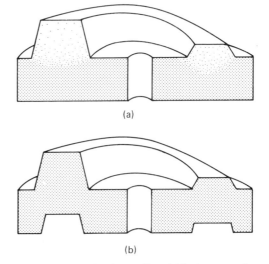

(a)

(b)

Figure 7.12 Avoid density gradient (a) by incorporating a recess (b)

necessary to compact fully the powder forming the cam form. This achieved by having a corresponding recess on the circular base. This not only ensures that the cam form is of correct density, but also reduces the weight of raw material used, thus producing a further cost saving, as the extra cost of producing the reverse cam form on the punch, spread over the life of the punch, is very small.

Figure 7.13 illustrates the sort of design changes to a machined component which are necessary to facilitate manufacture by powder metallurgy. The undercut where the flange joins the body, in order to achieve a sharp corner, has to be turned through

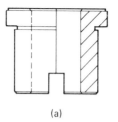
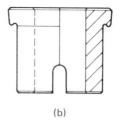

(a)   (b)

Figure 7.13 Design changes (b) to produce (a) by powder metallurgy

90°. The slot at the bottom, produced by milling, has a flat top. With a powder metallurgy pressing this flat top would create an undesirable density gradient, and it is avoided by either an angled or rounded bottom to the slot, which allows the powder to flow round the projection on the punch forming the slot.

Figure 7.14 illustrates another component designed to be produced by machining and the changes necessary to enable it to be produced by powder metallurgy.

Figure 7.15 shows how it is possible to replace an assembly of two gear parts produced by machining, with a single powder metallurgy part. Figure 7.16 reminds us that knurling, normally cross-knurling on a machined part, can be replaced by straight knurling built into the powder metallurgy tooling.

The tooling costs for production by the powder metallurgy process are very high and for complicated shapes would be several thousand pounds. Nevertheless their life could run to several hundred thousand pieces. For this reason, the powder metallurgy process will show considerable cost savings only when the quantities are large enough to offset the high cost of tooling.

The mechanical properties of powder metallurgy alloys are, due to their residual porosity, inferior to the same alloy with zero porosity. However, many engineering components are made in a mild steel because it is the cheapest material available, rather than because the properties of mild steel are required. In such cases a low alloy powder metallurgy material at modest density will often be sufficient to meet the service requirements. If a greater strength is demanded a higher alloy powder metallurgy material is available. Figure 7.17 gives, by way of example, the tensile strength and elongation of a typical powder metallurgy ferrous alloy at densities from 6.4 to 7.0 g cm^{-3}, in the 'as sintered' and the 'as heat-treated' conditions. It will be noticed that these properties vary almost linearly with density.

The technology of powder metallurgy has advanced considerably over the past 40 years, and Figure 7.18 shows the effect of these advances (in both raw material purity and alloy composition) on the mechanical properties which have been achieved. This will be of interest to design engineers

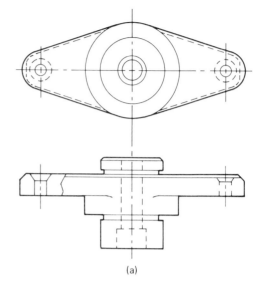

(a)

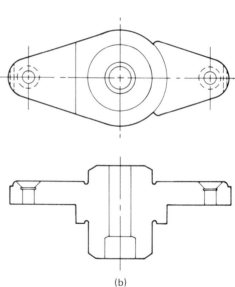

(b)

Figure 7.14 Design changes (b) to produce (a) by powder metallurgy

who have in the past tried powder metallurgy components and found that the properties which were then available were insufficient for their needs, because the strength and toughness of today's alloys are a considerable advance on what was available in the past.

However, it must not be forgotten that the price of powder metallurgy components is a function of their mechanical properties. An increase in density not only means more weight of material, but frequently a more compressible powder, which being softer and purer is more expensive, and to achieve a very high density may involve additional pressing

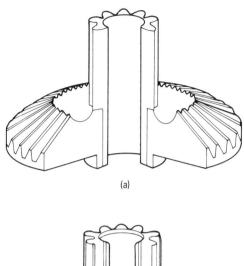

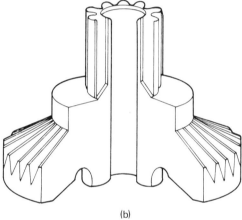

Figure 7.15 A single powder metallurgy part can replace an assembly of two gear parts

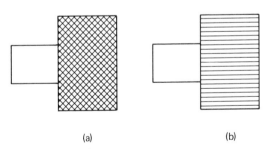

Figure 7.16 Straight knurling (b) can be built into the tool

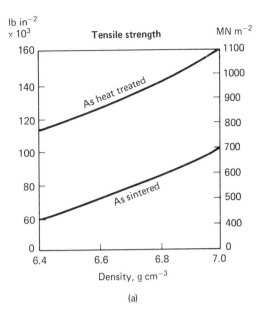

(a)

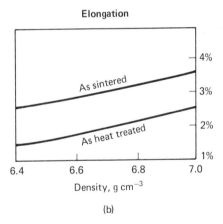

(b)

Figure 7.17 Tensile strength and elongation of a typical powder metallurgy ferrous alloy

and sintering operations. Similarly the achievement of greater strength through expensive alloy additions imposes a cost penalty; and it is sometimes more economic to increase the section thickness of the critical parts of the component.

In some cases the residual porosity can be an advantage. By impregnating it with oil the surface becomes self-lubricating, which is particularly useful in sliding applications. In cases where pressure tightness is required the residual porosity is impregnated with an inert plastic. Other techniques for eliminating the effects of the residual porosity include infiltration with a lower melting point metal, and compressing the sintered component at an elevated temperature. This hot repressing operation is called 'sinter forging' or 'powder forging' and results in a fully dense component.

From the above few pointers it will be appreciated that the choice of the best design and material to achieve the maximum cost saving with powder metallurgy is a complex study. It is therefore recommended that the manufacturers should be consulted at an early stage in the design process.

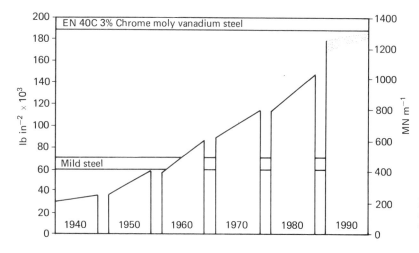

Figure 7.18 The effects of advances in powder metallurgy on mechanical properties

In the domestic appliance and motor industries, where large quantities of identical components are required, the design engineers are fully aware of the advantages of discussing their needs with the powder metallurgists at an early stage in the design process.

Finally we outline the features which may lead the designer towards sintering. Sintering offers:

(1) a wide choice of materials from bronze and iron to hardenable and stainless steels, carbon-metal composites, magnets, carbide tips, alloys free from segregation, controlled porosity (filters, etc.);

(2) a lubricant-retaining surface which often permits the use of iron instead of bronze;

(3) minimal or zero machining, hence elaborate shapes such as cams, ratchets, gears, integral keys or driving-flats become economical (eliminates key, assembly and weakness due to key-way stress-raiser, not to mention the danger of missing keys);

(4) low-cost joining by assembling several green pressings and fusing together during sintering;

(5) large quantities to pay off die cost, generally over 50 000 off, though shorter batch runs may be acceptable, giving a gap for die maintenance; and

(6) the sintered structure is believed to confer good high-temperature properties — this has certainly been shown with aluminium sintered-particle sheet.

It is not possible to give cost guidelines in view of the rapid rate of absolute and relative cost changes, but the examples cited should be enough to confirm that sintering is one of the leading low-cost product routes.

For some high-duty applications the powder is compressed in all directions. This is called isostatic pressing. It is a much slower process in which each article is compacted enough to hold it in one piece, then it is enclosed in a membrane and subjected to very high fluid pressure in a chamber, followed by further heat treatments. It applies more to ceramics and ceramic-plus-metal mixes than to simple metals.

7.1.7 Injection moulding, etc.

The following remarks apply chiefly to injection-moulded thermoplastics. The slower processes used for thermosets call for similar design features with regard to even thickness but are less prone to sink marks. Foamed plastic moulding is dealt with in Section 7.2.

Injection moulding is very similar to pressure diecasting; to a great extent the general casting remarks apply, as do the notes on pressure diecasting. The chief extra care needed in the design of injection-moulded products arises from the viscous nature of the melt and its low thermal conductivity, coupled with the point that many thermoplastic products are visible to the user in the as-moulded state, not polished or painted.

These make it important to aim at good flow, uniformity of thickness in the main parts, variation of not more than say 2:1 except near the feeders. Sink marks are particularly conspicuous over bosses and ribs. Disguises can take the form of shallow flutes, slight dummy ribs, etc. Textured finishes also serve but are liable to hold dirt, as are sharp-cornered recesses. Appreciable distortion can be expected in large thin parts, and only experience can provide guidance as to the probable extent of this.

When designing handles, etc. it is most helpful if the designer can make the trimming of flash easy, say by a slight ridge on the parting line and dummy ridges at 90° or 60° from it (for styling reasons); see Figure 7.19(a).

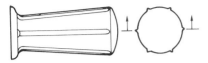

Figure 7.19 Dummy ridges to match flash lines

Inserts tend to be unpopular with the moulding operator, though this problem will diminish with the use of robots. The points to watch out for are cracking of the plastic due to thermal shrinkage over the insert (plenty of thickness needed), giving the insert a shape and production tolerance to ensure easy insertion and secure hold in the die or on the core pin, and heat conduction along the insert, especially in electrical fittings with brass inserts. This can be cumulative, and distortion can give poor contact, leading to arcing, which gives more heating. Location in the moulding needs a sense of structure: the insert should *not* produce a stress-raiser at its corners, therefore chamfers are desirable. Knurling is not always sufficient; grooves are safer. Anti-rotation flats or notches are a good precaution for tapped inserts.

Thanks to the resilience of many thermoplastics, undercuts are possible, normally on the inside. To help in pulling the object off the core, compressed air fed into the underside is useful. In rubber and soft PVC quite deep undercuts are possible; in Polythene and nylon rather less. Examples are a closable bottle cap for fizzy drinks (Figure 7.20(a)) and a protective cover for aerosols (Figure 7.20(b)), held on by two or three short ridges. A full circular ridge is not advisable in the more rigid plastics. The short ridges can be made helical, to suit screw-necked fastenings (not shown). Internal undercuts, produced by split core motions, are becoming more popular: Figure 7.20(c).

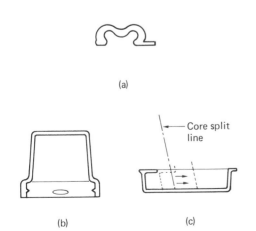

Figure 7.20 Examples of undercuts that can be made with injection moulded thermoplastics

7.1.8 Summary of general casting and moulding design points

(1) Avoid sharp internal corners. They cause high stress, unfavourable grain growth, loss of sand in sand moulds (which turns up elsewhere), and thermal crazing of dies. Conversely, avoid the thick lumps that result from needlessly large radii.

(2) Be prepared for cavities in thick lumps. Often they are harmless; if not, design them out.

(3) Make gradual transitions between thickness changes to cut down metal turbulence and stress concentrations.

(4) Aim to keep thickness changes within a 2 to 1 ratio, except in pressure diecastings.

(5) Use imagination to minimise external undercuts, e.g. four ribs, not three, six or eight; ridges R rather than raised bosses (see Figure 7.1).

(6) Don't be too ambitious with long cored holes; drilling may be cheaper.

(7) Beware of hot tearing, but beware also of remedies that make the structure more floppy such as staggered rib junctions, bent spokes, etc.; these may affect the function.

(8) Facilitate flash-trimming by keeping outlines convex and plain; e.g. cast or moulded gears can have a flange as in Figure 7.21 (which also adds strength).

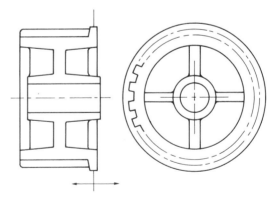

Figure 7.21 Flange to facilitate flash trimming

(9) Make covers slightly convex rather than flat or they may turn out concave when cold. Slight convexity tends to look better and reduces residual stress.

(10) Expect sink marks over ribs and bosses. If necessary, disguise these with external fluting or texturing. If the rib thickness is less than half the wall thickness the marks will be slight provided the radius is also small.

Table 7.1 General impression of process capabilities

Process	Maximum length (m)	Minimum thickness (mm)	General ± tolerance in die (%)	normal to die (%)
Sand casting	15	4	$1\frac{1}{2}$	3
Shell moulding	1	$2\frac{1}{2}$	$\frac{1}{2}$–1	1–3
Investment casting	$\frac{1}{2}$	1	$\frac{1}{2}$	$\frac{1}{2}$
Pressure diecasting	1	$\frac{1}{2}$	$\frac{1}{4}$–$\frac{1}{2}$	2
Plastic moulding	2	$\frac{1}{2}$	$\frac{1}{4}$–$\frac{1}{2}$	1–2
Sintering	0.15	1	0.2	3–5
Open forging	no limit	1 (cutlery etc.)		5–15
Die forging	$1\frac{1}{2}$	2	1	5–10
Fine blanking	$\frac{1}{4}$	0.1	0.1	–
Extrusion	see Sections 7.3.3 and 7.3.4			

	Diameter (mm)	Length or thickness (mm)
Turning & boring (milling)	±0.03	±0.05
Diamond turning, grinding	±0.015	±0.01
Honing, superfinishing	±0.005	

(11) Provide jigging aids (see Figure 7.1), holding-holes for machining, slinging holes for heavy work, flats or dimples to aid drilling, and anti-misassembly features.

(12) Consider providing integral rivets and stakes for assembly in diecasting and mouldings. Even zinc can be riveted over to some extent. Provide extra stakes if a repair facility is needed. To a lesser extent this applies to all casting methods.

(13) If long thin cores are needed consider using inexpensive refractory tubes, such as thermocouple insulators, and subsequently removed by carbide-tipped drills. Metal rods may be put through for support.

7.2 Specialised processes

7.2.1 *Foam-cored moulding*

7.2.1.1 Preamble

The commonest form of loading on components occurs in bending. Material near the neutral axis is only needed for shear; hence I-beams rather than solid bars are used for bending loads. A foam-cored moulding is an approximate equivalent to an I-section beam. It allows a thick section for stiffness,

with an economical use of material, because the foam core is of relatively low density.

In stiffness calculations the important requirement will be to find the second moment of area, I. The normal expression for homogeneous materials:

$$I = \frac{bh^3}{12}$$

where b is the width of the beam, and h is its thickness (see Figure 7.22), is modified for the beam section shown to include terms which can be derived from the respective densities of the solid and foamed parts of the foam-cored moulding. The modified expression is

$$I = \frac{bh^3}{12}\left\{1 - \left[1 - \left(\frac{D_f}{D_s}\right)^2 g^3\right]\right\}$$

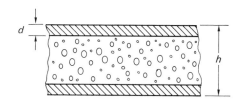

Figure 7.22 Typical cored material

where D_f is the density of foam core, D_s is the density of solid polymer, and

$$g = \frac{\text{foam thickness}}{\text{section thickness}} = \frac{h - 2d}{h}$$

No attempt is made to find the density of the foam core by direct measurements; in any case it is probably not uniform. Instead, the reduction in density occasioned by foaming is found. Tables for finding g are available of which Table 7.2 is an example.

Table 7.2

Reduction in density	g	
	$h = 5\text{–}10$ mm	$h = 10\text{–}15$ mm
30%	0.8	0.9
20%	0.7	0.8
10%	0.6	n/a

D_f is now found from:

$$D_f = \frac{D_c - D_s(1 - g)}{g}$$

An alternative approach, if it is required to calculate the deflection, δ, from for example

$$\delta = \frac{PL^3}{3EI}$$

in the cantilever shown in Figure 7.23, is to use a reduced modulus, E_{red}, which is found from

$$E_{red} = \frac{E_s}{e}$$

where E_s is the elastic modulus of solid polymer, and e is the blow ratio (often taken to be 1.8:1).

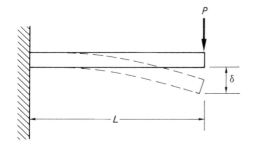

Figure 7.23 Cantilever deflection

Hence

$$\delta = \frac{PL^3}{3E_{red}I}$$

For a given deflection

$$I = \frac{PL^3}{3E_{red}\delta}$$

and $I = bh^3/12$ can be used directly to find beam thickness h.

In all such calculations, due account must be taken of the effect of creep and the modulus at the appropriate time must be used. These can be found from published creep modulus/time curves.

7.2.1.2 History of the processes

There are two complementary processes for the production of foam-cored mouldings. The earlier one gives structural foam (SF), and the later one gives sandwich moulding (SM). This process was pioneered in about 1970 by ICI, and was evolved to overcome some of the shortcomings of SF. The SM process has been available commercially since about 1976. In 1974, ICI withdrew from the development of SM. Machinery for it is available only from Battenfeld (in West Germany), who are licence holders and patentees, and Billion (in France).

The processes are developments of injection moulding. For structural foam it is possible to adapt existing equipment. However such changes would be far-reaching, and normally special equipment would be installed. Sandwich moulding is a much more sophisticated process and requires specialist equipment from the suppliers mentioned above. However, such equipment is normally designed to be capable of structural foam and normal compact (solid section) injection moulding as required.

The principal way in which both SF and SM differ from conventional (compact) injection moulding is the foaming of the core in the mould. The mould is fed with a 'short shot' and the expansion of the foam is used to fill the mould. This means that the clamping force required is much less than that for compact injection moulding. The secondary advantage offered by these techniques is therefore that large mouldings can be made, with large projected areas, without the need for high clamping forces.

7.2.1.3 Structural foam

In this technique, a compressed gas or a chemical blowing agent are contained in the moulding compound. If the gas method is used, compressed gas, usually nitrogen, is fed at $1400\text{–}2000$ N cm^{-2} via a vent in the extruder barrel. The screw carries a decompression zone at this point. As the compound injects into the empty, cold mould, the gas expands. Where the foamed molten polymer touches the mould surface, the foam collapses, and a solid skin forms. The cellular structure is retained in the centre.

7.2.1.4 Sandwich moulding

In this technique, separate injections of skin and foam core are made. They are injected simultaneously and concentrically (Figure 7.24) hence the alternative name for the process — coinjection. Two separate extruders are required, one feeding skin compound, the other foam-core compound. The process thus may be regarded as having evolved from co-extrusion as well as injection moulding.

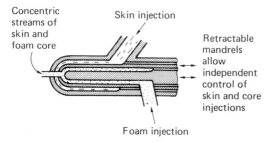

Figure 7.24 Cross-section through a coinjection nozzle

Since the skin and core are separately injected, they may be of different materials. Another possibility is the use of regrind in the core.

Because of its complexity, the capital cost of coinjection plant is very high.

7.2.1.5 Properties of foam-cored mouldings

The advantages of stiffness by virtue of thickness, and the relative ease with which large mouldings can be made, have already been mentioned. Foam-cored mouldings are also free from sink marks in thick sections, a fault which limits thickness in compact injection moulding. Sink marks are avoided because the foam expansion presses the skin against the mould surface, even during cooling. There is a minimum thickness, about 5 mm, below which the foam does not expand, and solid sections form.

The main disadvantage possessed by SF is its poor surface appearance. Such mouldings always have swirl patterns, caused by the bursting of the foam cells as they contact the mould surface.

If a moulded surface of good appearance is important this is a serious drawback. Although techniques

to modify the effect have been developed, they are expensive and difficult to use.

Sandwich moulding has been developed to overcome these problems and the separately injected skin of SM gives a perfect moulded surface, the equal of a compact moulded one. A brief comparison can be tabulated as in Table 7.3.

Table 7.3 Comparison of structural foam and sandwich moulding

Compact	SF	SM
Good surface	poor surface	good surface
Sink marks	no sink marks	no sink marks
4–5 mm thickness limit	thick sections: minimum 5 mm, 10–15 mm possible	thick sections as for SF
High clamping force	low clamping force	a little higher force than SF
Expensive steel moulds	lightweight moulds	steel moulds

7.2.1.6 Materials

Structural foam products are moulded in the normal range of polymers used for compact injection moulding. Polystyrene and its copolymers are widely used as well as polyethylene, polypropylene, polycarbonate, Noryl, nylon and others.

For sandwich moulding, there are no restrictions on material choice, except those imposed when skin and core are different from one another. In such cases good adhesion between the two polymer types is necessary, and their shrinkage rates upon cooling must match well. If these restrictions are neglected faulty mouldings will be produced.

7.2.1.7 Products

Both simple and complicated mouldings can be produced, especially in SM. The special design skill for complicated shapes lies in correct balancing of the sprue system. Where sensitive areas such as corners are involved, thickness of moulding may be reduced to less than 5 mm to allow a solid section to form, thus improving impact resistance.

Product design is usually characterised by thick, load bearing sections, which would be unsatisfactory in compact moulding (a) economically, because of the weight of polymer involved, and (b) technically, because of the problems of moulding thick sections.

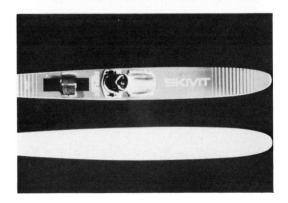

Figure 7.25 Examples of products produced using foam-cored moulding

Examples (some of which are shown in Figure 7.25) include

(1) Television screen frames, with sections thick enough to hold the weight of the tube. These are moulded in HIPS (high-impact polystyrene).
(2) Water cisterns, in HIPS, where surface finish and stiffness are paramount.
(3) Garden and indoor furniture, in which joints, etc. are eliminated (styrene acrylonitrile).
(4) Cabinets for hi-fi equipment, televisions, etc. in polystyrene.
(5) Cash register and computer cabinets in Noryl, with grained finish to withstand constant scuffing in use.
(6) Trolleys and box pallets.
(7) Skis.

7.2.2　Resin-bonded fibre composites

The main point of this method is to take advantage of the high strength and stiffness per unit weight of boron, carbon, glass and some stretched polymer fibres. A minor point is the mere wadding effect of holding a liquid resin in position while setting in the required shape. It is particularly appropriate for small quantities since the mould can be light and simple, only one half being needed. The other face is left free; if pressurising is needed it can be applied by an air-bag. For high-strength resin systems an autoclave with a bag membrane is used to provide heat and pressure.

As far as shape is concerned, the general moulding remarks apply. Undercuts are possible but cause complications such as split moulds or side cores.

The design points include the following:

(1) The fibres can be laid in the directions of stress, or they can be cross-layered, or random. Random layering gives the least strength and uses the most resin. Extra thickness is readily producible where loads are greatest or where damage is expected. Example of load-dependent layers are filament-wound pressure vessels, linear pull-truded rods (like wire-drawing) for electrical insulators, and an ever-growing range of sports equipment.
(2) Reinforcing ribs can be formed by laying in fillers of wood, foamed plastic provided it is not soluble in the resin system, and metal tubing if it is compatible from a corrosion point of view.
(3) The main danger point is high compressive stress, particularly if associated with local bending with curvature in a direction in which the fibres could buckle and de-laminate. Once a transverse buckle starts it can grow readily, sometimes explosively.

(4) Sandwich panels with a soft core have low shear stiffness unless the edges are specially braced against shear (which is difficult to arrange effectively in wide panels). The possibility of buckling should not be ignored.* The nominal compressive stress at which buckling is liable to start is $\sim \frac{1}{2}(E_f E_c G_c)^{1/3}$ in practical panels, where E_f and E_c are the Young's moduli of the face and core, respectively, and G_c is the core's modulus of rigidity.
(5) If reinforcing ribs are curved sharply there may be an appreciable force trying to tear the rib from the main wall. If this coincides with a cusped empty space as in Figure 7.26(a), the rib wall may try to break away. In such a situation, if the stresses are thought to be severe, the fibres may be laid both ways, partly around the filler and partly over it, as shown in (b).

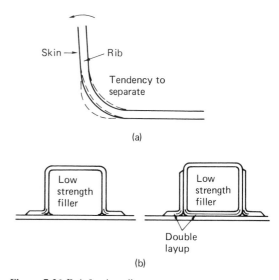

Figure 7.26 Reinforcing ribs

The nearest approach to mass-production is the use of pre-impregnated sheets and tapes of fibre and uncured resin (pre-pregs). These are placed in the mould, after stripping off the packing film. Multiple layers are used as required to give directional strength, extra thickness, etc., and are placed progressively to minimise air bubbles. The cure is quite quick once the right temperature is reached, down to a few minutes for some resins. Then the moulding is removed and may be clamped in a light jig to finish curing; the jig minimises distortion whilst freeing the mould for the next cycle. This affects the designer since he may be expected to provide handling and clamping points, possibly to be cut off later.

---

* For data on this point see Hoff and Mauner (1945) *J. Aero. Sci.*, vol. 12.

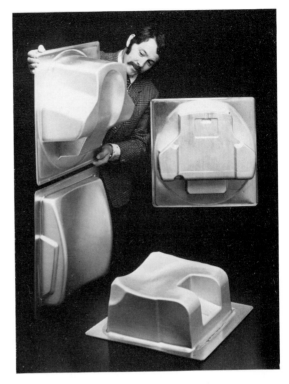

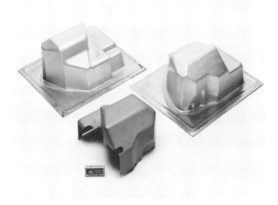

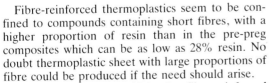

Figure 7.27 Examples of products made by superplastic forming

Fibre-reinforced thermoplastics seem to be confined to compounds containing short fibres, with a higher proportion of resin than in the pre-preg composites which can be as low as 28% resin. No doubt thermoplastic sheet with large proportions of fibre could be produced if the need should arise.

The designer will consider using fibre-reinforced composites instead of metal where the simplicity of the mould is an advantage, or where the outstanding strength or stiffness-to-weight ratio is attractive, or where the low thermal conductivity and electrical

properties are needed, or where the corrosion resistance is valued; this property is outstanding provided that some surface weathering is acceptable. The chief catch is some uncertainty about fatigue life.

7.2.3 *Superplastic forming*

This process is an extreme form of deep-drawing sheet material, taking advantage of the extremely

Male or Female Forming

The SUPRAL alloys can be formed on either male or female tools. Using the simpler female forming technique the sheet of metal is blown down into a single female mould. Male forming involves a more complex technique, but still only requires a single tool.

Male forming offers somewhat greater design freedom, and in particular ensures a more uniform distribution of metal around the component. Other factors entering into the choice between male or female forming are; (a) the size of the component, (b) tolerances, (c) corner radii, (d) the necessity to reproduce fine detail and (e) whether the component has to be anodised.

Each of these factors is discussed below.

	Male Forming	Female Forming
1. Sizes of forming machines and their capability for male and/or female forming.		
600 mm x 600 mm (2 ft x 2 ft)	YES	YES
900 mm x 600 mm (3 ft x 2 ft)	YES	YES
2100 mm x 1200 mm (7 ft x 4 ft)	NO	YES
2. Starting gauges available	0.8 mm 1.2 mm 2.0 mm 4.0 mm 1.0 mm 1.6 mm 3.0 mm	AS MALE

3. Limiting Aspect Ratios

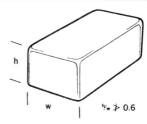

$h/w \not> 0.6$

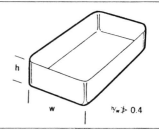

$h/w \not> 0.4$

4. Draft Angles

$\not< 2°$ $\not< 3°$

5. Tolerances

The Tolerances on the cast tools are ±0.005 in per inch (±0.5%). Cast tolerances can be improved by machining.

Note: With male forming, tolerances are on the inside of the component, i.e. the side in contact with the mould.

Note: With female forming, tolerances are on the outside of the component, i.e. the side in contact with the mould.

6. Corner Radii

(a) Plan Radii

R_1 $R_1 \not< 5x$ starting gauge

R_1 $R_1 \not< 15x$ starting gauge

(b) Section Radii

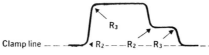

$R_2 \not< 5x$ local gauge
$R_3 \not< 3x$ local gauge

All radii shown are those on the inside, i.e. the side in contact with the mould.

Note: Local gauge for male forming can be approximated as follows:

Local gauge $\simeq$
starting gauge X. $\dfrac{\text{Plan area of component}}{\text{surface area of component}}$

Note: R_3 may need to be relaxed as the Limiting Aspect Ratio approaches 0.6.

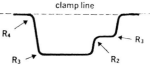

$R_4 \not< 5x$ local gauge
$R_3 \not< 5x$ local gauge
$R_2 \not< 5x$ local gauge

All Radii shown are those on the outside, i.e. the side in contact with the mould.

	Male Forming	Female Forming

7. Small Ridges / Grooves

Male / Female features on either male or female tools.

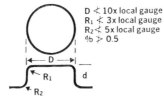

$R_1 \nleqslant$ 3x local gauge
$R_2 \nleqslant$ 5x local gauge
$^d/_w \ngtr$ 0.7

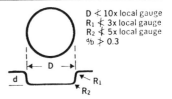

w $\nleqslant$ 5x local gauge
$^d/_w \ngtr$ 0.4
R $\nleqslant$ 3x local gauge

Note 1. The spacing (pitch) between such male features must conform to the Limiting Aspect Ratio for Female Forming:

i.e. $\frac{d}{pitch}$

Note 2. The end condition for such male features is critical. A length not less than 2d must be allowed to return the detail to the plane of the sheet.

Note. The end condition for such female features is critical. A length not less than 2d must be allowed to return the detail to the plane of the sheet.

8. Cylindrical Bosses / Depressions

Male / Female features on either male or female tools.

D $\nleqslant$ 10x local gauge
$R_1 \nleqslant$ 3x local gauge
$R_2 \nleqslant$ 5x local gauge
$^d/_b \ngtr$ 0.5

D $\nleqslant$ 10x local gauge
$R_1 \nleqslant$ 3x local gauge
$R_2 \nleqslant$ 5x local gauge
$^d/_b \ngtr$ 0.3

9. The Forming of Fine Detail

SUPRAL alloys are capable of reproducing fine detail from the moulds. The maximum definition will be obtained on the side of the sheet which has been in contact with the mould. For certain decorative components this may be a determining factor in the choice of male or female forming. Normally only 0.8 mm starting gauge would be used for such applications.

10. Anodising

SUPRAL 150 has a cladding of pure aluminium on both sides to a nominal thickness of 10% each side. This allows components to be etched or brightened and anodised giving excellent corrosion resistance. Note that SUPRAL 150 cannot be mechanically polished prior to anodising.

Wherever possible components for decorative anodising should be designed such that the critical surface was not in contact with the tool. The exception to this is where fine detail is required to be reproduced as in section 9 above.

TI SUPERFORM offer components anodised with either a light etch or chemical brightening pre-treatment. Additionally gold, copper, bronze or black coloured anodic finishes with the same pretreatments are available.

SUPRAL 100, which is unclad, can be anodised but the finish is matt grey, and the resistance of the film to atmospheric attack is not so great as on the clad alloy. The anodic finish is, however, perfectly satisfactory as a pretreatment for painting.

11. Painting

The SUPRAL alloys can be painted using the standard pretreatments for aluminium; and all commercially available paint formulations can be applied and stoved.

TI SUPERFORM offer components finish painted.

12. Jointing

The SUPRAL alloys can be spot welded and TI SUPERFORM offer a spot welding service. The alloy can also be fusion welded and advice is available to customers who wish to do it for themselves.

Adhesive bonding is an alternative method of jointing and again TI SUPERFORM offer this service.

13. Mechanical Properties

TI SUPERFORM offer components only in the as formed condition. The alloys can be heat treated and advice is available to customers wishing to carry out heat treatment for themselves.

The following Creep Data has been produced for the SUPRAL alloys in the as formed condition at ambient temperature, 23°C.

Test Stress (N/mm²)	Duration (Hrs)	Creep Strain (%/Hour)
50	1425	0.00001
75	668	0.000015

No plastic strain occurred on loading at either stress level.

The total amounts of strain recorded were extremely low: to illustrate this the change in specimen length occurring as a result of changes in room temperature controlled to ±1.5°C, was of the same order as the creep strain.

Typical Mech. Prop. for the SUPRAL alloys in the "as formed" condition.

0.2% Proof Stress		Tensile Strength		Elongation on 50mm	Young's Modulus (E)	
N/mm²	t/in²	N/mm²	t/in²	%	kN/mm²	lbf/in²
120	8	220	14	16	69.64	10.1 x 10⁶

high ductility shown by some alloys at certain temperatures. Some of the earliest alloys were found to have elongations of over 900% in rod form. For sheet materials, the control of temperature and speed in relation to shape is critical since the effect is strain-rate dependent; hence the work is normally subcontracted to experts.

Figure 7.27, reproduced by kind permission of Superform Metals Ltd. of Worcester, shows some products in aluminium alloy or alloy clad in pure aluminium. Note the remarkable depths achievable in a single draw, also the sharpness of detail. This is useful both functionally and in allowing crisp styling. At normal temperatures, the material loses its special softness and behaves like NS4 alloy.

Though slower than conventional pressing, superplastic forming normally requires only a single press tool and thus eliminates the cost of a matched punch and die set. The process is thus ideal when quantities are too low to justify high-cost matched tools.

An outline of the design limitations recommended by Superform Metals is reproduced on pp. 166–7.

Superplastic forming is not confined to aluminium alloys. Two types of high-strength stainless steel, namely 3Re60 and IN744, of 450–500 N mm^{-2} proof of stress and 700–780 N mm^{-2} UTS can be formed to relatively intricate shapes superplastically, likewise the very strong Ti-6Al-4V alloy and the commoner stainless steels, 304, 316 and 430.

The particular merits of using the superplastic properties, when compared with cold pressing, are

(1) obtaining the required shape with no springback and little residual stress,
(2) good detail and close tolerances on the outside of the component since the process uses a female mould,
(3) sharp radii can be produced if required although large radii are preferred, and
(4) low tool costs.

Figure 7.28, reproduced by permission of MPD Technology Ltd, shows a group of products, some of which are still in the commercial evaluation stage. Economical numbers tend to come between 75 off and 20 000 off.

7.2.4 Thermoplastic holloware

7.2.4 Vacuum moulding (vacuum forming)

This is very economical way of forming even-thickness thermoplastic objects using only a one-sided mould. This obviously is very much easier than two exactly-fitting halves. Also, as the mould need not be of hard metal, many substances can be used.

Figure 7.28 Examples of superplastic formed parts

The main part of the process is control over the temperature of the sheet which forms the starting point. It must be at a particular temperature to start with and must not chill in the wrong places until the shaping is complete. The basic plant layout is very simple. Figure 7.29(a) shows the simplest form of operation. A mould is made to represent the outside of the product, it is surrounded by a flat surface incorporating a seal. The warm sheet, which can be almost any of the usual thermoplastics, is placed on the top and held down by a clamp. Suction is applied to the box. For very thick work it may be necessary to enclose the top and apply compressed air. This variant is not shown. If we prefer to define the inner form, or if we want to produce very long objects, a male former (b) is used and is jacked upwards gently while suction draws the sheet onto the former. Some development work is needed on new designs to avoid forming folds (webs). This may be called plug-assisted vacuum forming.

Undercuts are quite feasible. If the numbers are enough to justify a machine with split die halves like a diecasting machine, the suction can be applied to the closed die just as if it were a single box. For smaller numbers, loose pieces within the mould can be used (c). The finished wall thickness varies according to the severity of stretch.

The main feature that could give problems is a male former with sharp corners. This would encourage folds.

Applications range from thin food containers to bubble packs for the retail trade and as protective packing for engineering spares, up to complete

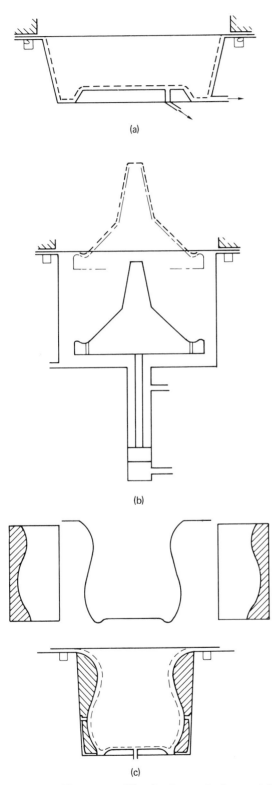

(a)

(b)

(c)

Figure 7.29 Vacuum moulding for thermoplastic material

dinghy bodies. The main shortcoming for large work is the inability to produce integral strengthening ribs.

7.2.4.2 Blow and rotation moulding

As far as the product designer is concerned, both these processes are ways of making holloware of uniform thickness, with well-defined exteriors and a self-generated inside shape.

Blow moulding is the plastics equivalent of glass blowing and like glass blowing it is largely self-regulating in that the thinnest parts cool fastest, thus preventing excessive thinning. Wall thicknesses of a fraction of a millimetre are possible as are achieved in the long-established celluloid toy trade, leaving only a very small blow-hole. With thicker walls it is used for bottles. A screw thread is readily produced in the mould but if a seal is needed it may be necessary to machine the flash away at the top, or make special moulding arrangements to obtain a flat face.

Rotational moulding is slower but more versatile, being appropriate for larger objects. It is a controlled version of slush casting which was mentioned and briefly described in Section 7.1. Instead of pouring in and then pouring out the excess, a measured quantity of plastic is fed into the mould in the liquid state. The mould is slightly cooler than the plastic and is rotated in all directions to make the plastic flow by gravity until all surfaces are covered by a solidified layer. By arranging the movement and timing, thicker layers can be produced where extra strength is needed. Its special features are freedom of shape, notably the ability to form containers with integral handles, usually hollow, and the possibility of forming slight ridges to protect the base.

The shape can be anything which can be withdrawn from the mould; two-piece moulds are usual for ease of temperature control. There is no fundamental reason why side cores or multi-piece moulds should not be used, except the additional cost of developing the right amount of heating/cooling in all parts. The method is used not only for containers but also for heavy-duty toys, sports goods, garden equipment etc.

7.3 General shaping processes

7.3.1 Light press work

7.3.1.1 Introduction

Light press work, as distinct from drop-forging or suchlike, falls into three classes:

(1) thin-wall work involving not only blanking, bending and drawing but also lock-seams, var-

ious other fastenings, beading, rubber bulging, ironing to reduce wall thickness and lengthen drawn cups — at the extreme end this becomes closed-end extrusion, see Section 7.3.5;

(2) specialised deep-drawing as in car-body work; and

(3) medium-gauge general engineering work.

Class (1) work is illustrated in Figure 7.30. To see what is feasible, the designer need only take a close look at common containers for biscuits, tobacco, drinks, shoe polish, etc. and general household durables.

Class (2) involves specialised experience, often backed by much development, and it is too varied to be discussed here.

This section accordingly concentrates on the general run of medium-gauge engineering press-work.

7.3.1.2 Designing for presswork production

To reduce the production cost of any component it is always wise to try to redesign it as a pressed part. We need only to look as far as the modern car for examples: track rods from simple channel pressings, rigid axle beams welded from two pressings, sheet metal axle beams with torsion bar action.

Presses produce more parts per minute than any other process. The wastage is less and tool maintenance is much lower relative to the number of parts produced, but there are certain aspects of pressed parts that give more trouble (and expense) than others. It is the purpose of this section to illustrate these features and how to overcome them.

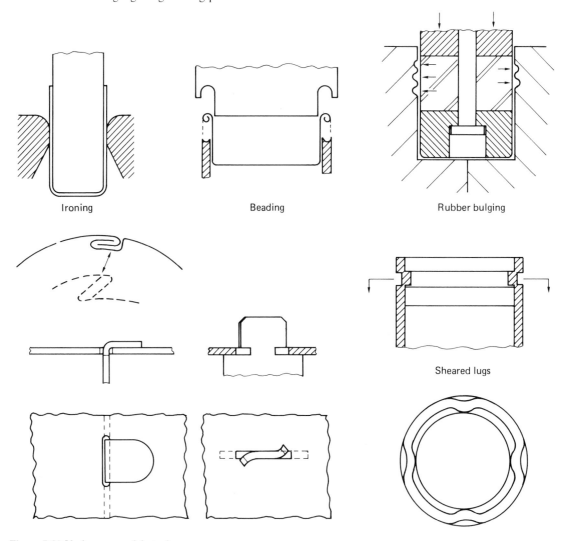

Ironing   Beading   Rubber bulging

Sheared lugs

Figure 7.30 Various pressed fastenings

7.3.1.3 Flat and bent work

About 75% of all work in most press shops is of the pierce and blank variety, so a large part of this section will be devoted to this part of the process and to looking at some of the things to avoid if cost is to be kept to a minimum. Some of the more troublesome features are tolerances that are too fine, edges that are to be square and smooth, and holes that have to be parallel all through the bore.

It is possible to do all these things providing special machines are bought for the purpose (this will be discussed later), but with ordinary presses a tolerance of less than 0.08–0.1 mm should be avoided: not that press tools are unable to produce a finer tolerance, but the tool maintenance increases in direct proportion to the fineness of tolerance.

The reason for avoiding square edges or parallel bores on pierced and blanked components is shown in Figure 7.31 which illustrates a piercing and blanking action, shown at the bottom of the cutting stroke. It will be noticed that the apertures in the

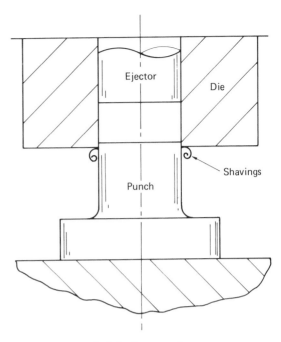

Figure 7.32 A typical shaving operation

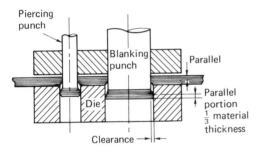

Figure 7.31 A piercing and blanking action

dies for piercing and blanking have to be larger than the punches; this varies from about 3% of stock thickness all round, to 15% all round, depending on the class of work. The larger the clearance the better the tool life, but the worse the squareness of the blank. The parallel portion is about one third of the material thickness and the 'fall away' behind it is equal to the clearance between punch and die. For example, a part made of 6 mm mild steel with a 10% all round clearance between punch and die would have a 0.6 mm fall away behind the hole, and only about 2 mm depth of the hole would be to punch size. The same conditions apply to the perimeter of the blank, where only a third of the thickness is to size.

If these conditions are not good enough for the design requirement a component needs to be made with excess material allowance for shaving off as a second operation.

Figure 7.32 shows a typical shaving operation. The blank is placed on a punch which is a fine fit into a top die; the die descends and shaves off the surplus material leaving a good square edge. If a really good

edge is required two operations are required: the first taking off 10%, and the second taking off 5%. Since these shaving tools are usually hand fed the cost of an apparently simple component begins to escalate.

A typical example of this sort of component is the pad abutment plate which is in every motor car disc brake, shown in Figure 7.33. This part has to be flat within ± 0.12 mm and the edges have to be square within ± 0.05 mm. The two elongated holes have to be parallel for at least half the depth of the bore.

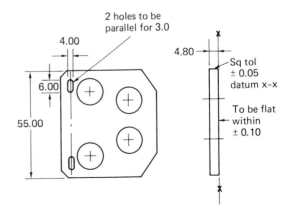

Figure 7.33 A pad abutment plate, part of a car's disc brake

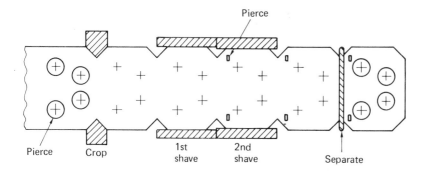

Figure 7.34 Layout of press feeding equipment

This part was normally produced in the following sequence:

(1) pierce and blank,
(2) planish to flatten,
(3) first shave, and
(4) second shave and pierce elongated holes.

With a progressive tool this can be done with no intermediate handling. Press feeding equipment, aided by location holes and pilot pins, can place the work correctly for each stage.

The layout of such an arrangement is shown in Figure 7.34. The strip material is first pierced and a portion of the profile cut away; the subsequent stations shave the edges and pierce the two oval holes; the final operation completes the profile and at the same time separates it from the strip. The component then falls down a chute into a work bin.

An additional bonus when using this type of tool is that the component remains flat partly because a heavy pressure pad holds the material when it is being cut and because the surplus material is removed a bit at a time. On ordinary blanking tools the component tends to bow into the die when it is cut.

Many flat components can be produced in this manner, but sometimes the profile is unsuitable for this method of production. By using a fine blanking-tool the whole component can be produced at one stroke of the press and holes and profile will be beautifully square and smooth. The component will also be perfectly flat, but the special press and the special tools for fine blanking are quite expensive and unless a very large output is needed it is best to sub-contract the work to the many firms that have the necessary equipment.

Figure 7.35 shows a cross-section of such a tool: the strip material is fed over a bottom punch and a very heavy pressure pad holds it firmly in position. A clamping ring, which has a raised ridge positioned around the profile, grips the strip against a top die which descends, cutting the material and piercing holes at the same time. The die then goes back up taking the component with it. At the top of its stroke

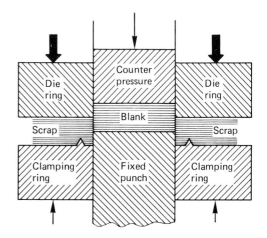

Figure 7.35 Cross-section through a fine blanking tool

the component is ejected and is blown off by an air jet into a work bin.

The punches and dies have to be a push fit into one another, and special knowledge is required to produce them. The manufacturers of these presses will supply all the expertise for this work and run courses for people who are interested.

When components are designed the function of the part is the prime consideration of the designer, but very often a component is asked for that unnecessarily runs up the cost. Some of the most difficult features to produce are holes that are too near the edge of the component, or too near to another hole.

If a hole is too near to the edge it distorts the edge, or breaks through if there is a variation in the stock width.

Holes too near to each other require a very thin die wall which tends to collapse; the material between the holes also tends to distort. A distance of at least $1\frac{1}{2}$ thicknesses of stock material is required.

Another trouble-maker is the hole that is positioned too near to a bend. If the hole is pierced first — as it would be on a progressive tool — it will be pulled out of shape when the bending takes place, unless at least two thicknesses of material is allowed between the edge of the hole and the centre of the bend — Figure 7.36.

One innocent-looking feature that component designers often ask for is the bend with one very short leg — Figure 7.37. If the short leg is less than two thicknesses beyond the centre of the radius it is virtually impossible to bend it. Often tool designers will leave a longer leg than is asked for to make sure that the bend will be more satisfactory and then a secondary milling operation is used to cut off the surplus. This is an expensive business, especially if the short bend was a component designer's artistic whim rather than a functional requirement.

Figure 7.36 Hole position relative to bend

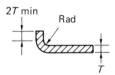

Figure 7.37 Minimum flange width

A not so frequent, but nevertheless troublesome, feature is the bend that is near a blending radius — Figure 7.38. If possible a rounded relief notch should be included in the design.

One final but most important consideration in the design of a part that includes a bend is that the inside radius should be at least as much as one thickness of material. A component that has a very sharp corner may look very nice, but in terms of tool cost it is an expensive luxury.

To recapitulate:

(1) keep tolerances as large as possible, especially on flatness;
(2) remember that square smooth edges cost money;

(3) the longer the parallel part of a pierced hole, the more difficult it is to produce;
(4) keep holes as far as possible from edges, bends and other holes;
(5) always allow enough material on bends to give the tool a 'purchase' on the material; and
(6) keep the radius of bends as large as possible, especially if they are parallel with the grain of the material.

7.3.1.4 Draw work

No account of press work would be complete without a comment on forming cup-shaped parts.

To produce a shell in one operation, the depth must not exceed 60% of the diameter (in mild steel) — Figure 7.39 — and the minimum inside radius should be four times the stock thickness. If this proportion of depth to diameter is exceeded a further operation would be necessary, and as further drawing operations only increase the depth by 25% — or less — a cup that is very deep may need three or four drawing operations.

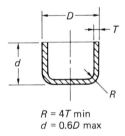

$R = 4T$ min
$d = 0.6D$ max

Figure 7.39 Cap forming

A component that sometimes raises its ugly head is the box shape — Figure 7.40. To form it in a drawing tool from a blank is very difficult, as the blank has to be developed after many trials and even then the top edge is usually very uneven.

To avoid these difficulties it is worth considering cutting notches in the corner of the blank to remove the troublesome excess material — Figure 7.41. If this is not possible then the corner radius should be

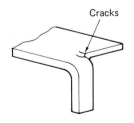

Figure 7.38 Blend radii

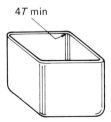

Figure 7.40 Box-shaped component

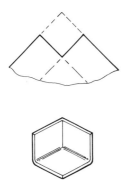

Figure 7.41 Removing excess material

at least four times the material thickness and, if it does not affect the function of the part, a small flange around the top will facilitate trimming off the uneven edge. In thin work of the tin-can class, the corner radius is also related to the depth; it helps if radius/depth is $\frac{1}{2}$ or larger.

7.3.1.5   Cold formed work

One of the most expensive and wasteful aspects of engineering production is the turning of studs, bolts and similar components; these can be much more cheaply produced by special presses for cold forming.

These presses usually have four stations and normally operate horizontally — the stock material is in the form of coils of wire ranging from about 5 mm to 14 mm in diameter. The wire is fed into the machine automatically where it is straightened and cut in the first station to the required length, then a transfer head picks up the piece and moves it through the various stages until it is completed and ejected into a work bin. These machines can produce studs and bolts at a hundred a minute or more.

An example of the sort of part that could be produced by cold forming is the mild steel pivot pin — Figure 7.42. If this component had been produced by turning from the solid bar, more than half the material would have been made into swarf, but by cold forming every scrap of material is used. An

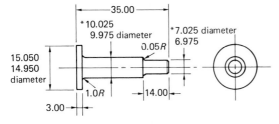

Figure 7.42 Mild steel pivot pin.* Roundness tolerance, 0.050 T.I.R

additional bonus is gained by the increase in the material's strength caused by the pressure and deformation.

Figure 7.43 shows some of the methods used in cold forming — most types of turned parts can be produced by using a combination of these processes.

The firms that make these machines are only too willing to supply any interested party with plenty of literature showing the full range of parts that can be cold formed.

As in normal presswork the designer should avoid radii that are too sharp as this reduces tool life and, unfortunately, there cannot be undercuts where there are shoulders so any mating parts need radii to clear the radii on the cold-formed component.

Designing parts with presswork or cold forming in mind greatly increases production and reduces cost, but the limitations of the press tools must be the first consideration.

7.3.2   Drop-forging

Drop-forging is basically a way of producing articles requiring large forces to create the required shape changes without buying very large presses. The impact of a falling mass hitting a large anvil is a crude but effective way of producing such forces. It has an additional advantage that the rapid blow is more nearly adiabatic than a squeeze in an hydraulic press; because of this, or perhaps in addition to it, rapid strain rates allow more severe changes without cracking than the equivalent slow squeeze.

As far as the product is concerned, any shape which will come out of the die can be drop-forged if the material is made hot enough, and is hit hard and often enough. Drop-forging is not used merely for the shape, which can be created by casting — even highly stressed objects such as Otto engine crankshafts and connecting rods can be satisfactorily cast. Yet diesel engine components are usually forged. The virtues of forging are that it results in the closing of pores and the realignment of grain flow. This is important since grain boundary weaknesses and slag inclusions are forced into favourable directions. On the other hand, drop forging is not exempt from the danger of cold-shuts (as occur in castings).

The severe forces could cause the work to wedge securely in the die, hence adequate draft should be provided, especially when forging steel. A favourable profile is shown in Figure 7.44(a), with a 7° draft and an inside radius of the same order as the height of rise, to help the flow. Obviously this is not always economical; one of the objects of forging is to get close to the final shape, saving material and energy by minimising machining. It is also helpful if the height of rise is fairly uniform over the whole object. In some cases mechanical ejectors are built into the die to reduce the draft requirement.

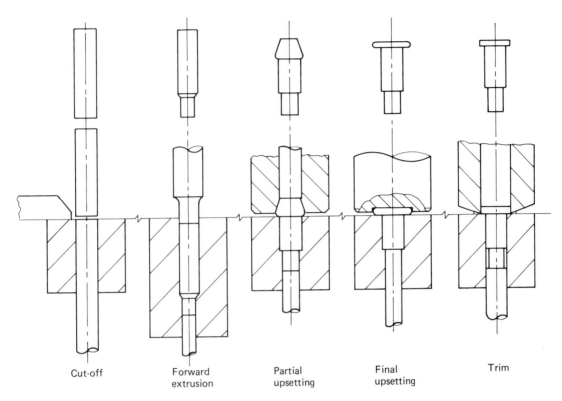

Cut-off   Forward extrusion   Partial upsetting   Final upsetting   Trim

Figure 7.43 A range of cold-forming techniques

It is usual to expect a certain amount of thickness variation. This is due to the varying mass of blank, and also varying temperature which results in the amount of deformation before the work cools not being constant. One way of reducing this variation is to extend the die beyond the expected flash region (Figure 7.44(b)), and to keep hitting until faces F meet. Expert knowledge is needed as to the amount of flash thickness to allow, otherwise the die may not be filled when the faces meet.

There are few non-hollow shapes that could not be drop-forged. The first forging is naturally made as nearly flat as possible, but the designer should not restrict his imagination to such bodies. Crankshafts are regularly twisted into multi-throw angular forms after being forged in the flat; levers and suspension members are cranked, bent or joggled as required in secondary operations.

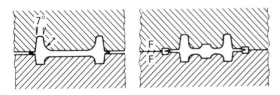

Figure 7.44 A favourable drop-forging profile

7.3.3 Closed-end extrusion

This method is generally well known; at one end of the scale it is the standard method for the manufacture of toothpaste tubes and the like in pure aluminium, and is also used to make certain medical products in pure tin. Within limits it is also the general press-shop operation used on vertical presses or horizontal forging machines. Combined with ironing through ring-dies, or better still through roller-dies, it is the regular method of making gas storage cylinders in which the ends are hot-spun if they are thick enough, or else pressed tops are welded on.

The main theme of this section is to show how accurate this process can be, producing hydraulic or pneumatic cylinders with very little machining of the bore, plus providing the saving of a separate end fitting, and the facility for a non-circular external shape. Figure 7.45(a) shows an aluminium alloy pneumatic cylinder. The square body is not just a styling feature, it provides for the fitting of flange studs which are preferred to a threaded end fitting, particularly in an aluminium body which carries the risk of thread stripping after repeated disassembly. The enlarged portion can serve as an air duct to the

Design aspects of production processes

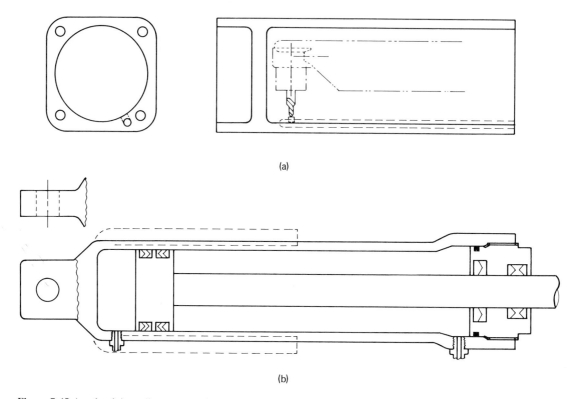

(a)

(b)

Figure 7.45 An aluminium alloy pneumatic cylinder

base, the connection being by cross-drilling and plugging, or by special angle drilling. This avoids the need for an external hose which is an advantage in clean work, such as in the food and medical industries.

Another successful combination of features is shown in Figure 7.45(b). The long hydraulic cylinder is formed by backward extrusion to approximately the dotted shape, and is then redrawn so as to leave an enlarged portion with a smooth transition. The upper hydraulic feed hole is drilled into this portion; then no special precautions are needed when inserting the piston and its seals into the bore. The main bore is produced to 89.65 mm minimum, 89.80 mm maximum diameter, straight to 1 in 2000 (this information is reproduced by kind permission of Mr T. Kelly, Technical Executive, TI Reynolds). The bore is merely honed afterwards, not so much for accuracy as to provide a suitable finish for the piston seals. The spade end for the lower pivot is extruded forward at the same time as the primary cup is extruded back around the first punch.

The upper end can be run out plain as shown, in whatever wall thickness is needed for screw fittings, and it can be beaded for extra strength or flanges can be formed if preferred.

The strength and soundness may be judged from

the nature of the process. Shapes which are extruded only, without subsequent drawing, will be at least as sound as normal long extrusions; probably sounder as a consequence of the pressure needed for reverse flow. Redrawn work is likely to be at least as sound as the corresponding drawn tubing.

The limitations of the process are dependent on the size of the presses available rather than on fundamentals, so the range worth considering is extremely wide, from individual cigar or tablet tubes in soft aluminium, through motor vehicle gudgeon pins, to heavy gas cylinders or torpedo tubes. In the absence of re-drawing, in steel, there will be a limit set by the strength of the punch in compression and buckling; 20 mm is suggested as a minimum bore. Wall thickness may vary by 5% in warm-extruded thick walls, down to 2% in cold-extruded thin walls. There is thought to be a self-centring action since it takes more pressure to force metal into a thin annulus, hence thinning at any point automatically provides a correcting effect. Length-diameter ratios are given as 7 maximum for aluminium alloys, presumably without considering redrawing, and 12 in steel. Maximum diameters of 200 mm in precision bores and 300 mm or more in container applications are available. In large sizes it would be worth while trying to fit the design to existing punches and dies.

7.3.4 Continuous extrusion

This method is of course well known. It would be used more widely if designers realised how economically a new die can be produced — under 1% of the cost of a complex diecasting die. Moreover there are many die forms already in existence from previous work.

The most usual materials for continuous extrusion are aluminium, ranging from 99.8% pure for corrosion-resistant trim profiles to the high-strength alloys such as 6062, and the brasses.

Some idea of the benefits the method can bring may be gathered from Figure 7.46. Masts and booms with integral tracks are too well-known to need a picture, so are curtain rail and window frame profiles.

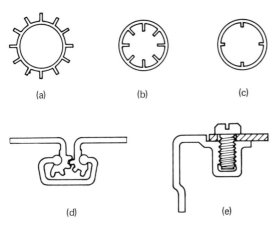

(a)   (b)   (c)

(d)   (e)

Figure 7.46 Round tubes with cooling fins on the outside (a) or inside (b). Smaller anti-buckling ridges (c). Patented interlocking hinge sections (d), courtesy of Indalex Ltd of Cheltenham. (e) Slots serrated on opposite sides with a half displacement provide a secure, non-machined screw retention profile, normal thread or coarse (e.g. self-tap screw thread), courtesy of Alcan Ltd of Banbury

Continuous extrusion allows a great deal of design freedom. The least thickness should not be less than 1/80th of the greatest width in large sections; in small ones there is a limit on minimum thickness as such but this depends on the profile itself. Round tubing can be made to smaller thickness than some complex shapes. Concave radii should be over $\frac{1}{2}$mm. Variations of thickness in any one profile should not be excessive, though it is difficult to be specific.

Extrusions tend to come out slightly bowed and twisted, of the order of 2 mm and/or 2° per metre. This can be eliminated by means of a stretching operation. Very unsymmetrical profiles come out rather worse than this.

Profile sizes are maintained to within 1 to 2%.

Very small holes may wander due to deflection of the plug which defines the hole.

Maximum size depends on the supplier's equipment. For example, Alcan, from whom a design brochure may be obtained, offers pieces up to 115 kg and over 300 mm across corners.

When considering a design which requires cutting up an extrusion into short pieces the cost of deburring after cutting up must be taken into account. Extrusion will be favoured if the numbers are too small to justify a diecasting die, bearing in mind the vast difference in die costs mentioned above.

7.3.5 Spinning and flow forming

Spinning is a long-established process for producing circular hollow work when the numbers are too small to justify deep-drawing or when elaborate shapes or very soft material, such as pewter, are involved. It uses a lathe, a roller tool and a series of formers to deform flat sheet gradually into a cone and eventually a cylinder. The diameter reduction is analogous to deep drawing without supporting the blank, hence much care is needed to avoid wrinkles. This tends to involve intermediate annealing as well as many successive formers.

It is possible to work without formers using a backing-roll or lubricated pad held against the rotating work.

In heavy work, spinning is a regular method of forming dished end-covers for pressure vessels.

One of the special advantages is that undercuts can be formed, freehand or against a split former (Figure 7.47), which otherwise would call for rubber bulging. Increasing the diameter is of course free from wrinkling danger; the author has belled-out copper tube successfully in a lathe with just a lubricated steel bar.

Flow forming is an extension of spinning. It uses a lathe with very strong spindle bearings. The roller is pushed and traversed hydraulically with enough force to reduce the material thickness substantially; thus it is the rotary equivalent of ironing. The type of product that best exploits the particular virtues of flow forming is a thin casing with a heavy flange,

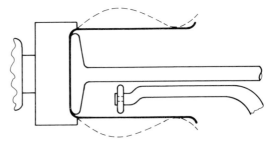

Figure 7.47 Forming undercuts by spinning

such as a pressure case for a filter. This would start with a sheet of flange thickness which would be coned and thinned down plastically. In cylindrical work flow forming can compete with closed-end extrusion where the number required is small. In addition it has the following unique facilities: conical forming, local thinning, thickening of the final flange and building up of intermediate stiffening ridges, and of course end closing, corrugation and bulging. In quantity work it may be worth while starting with simple cupping in a press tool so that the flat blank is supported against wrinkling during the most severe diameter reduction.

The cost will increase with the number of passes, i.e. with the thickness changes as well as the amount of diameter reduction.

Suppliers of flow-turning lathes may be found in buyer's guides, under the terms flow-forming, Flo-turning, Hydro-spinning, etc.

Spinning and flow forming are not sufficiently common skills to be taken for granted. Before designing with them in mind it is necessary to ensure that the service is obtainable, and then to confirm whether the particular design is suited to the facilities available.

Figure 7.48 shows a few sketches of the type of product for which flow-forming is either uniquely appropriate or may be found to be competitive.

7.3.6 *Electroforming*

This is a tool-making rather than a production process. Its history extends into printing plates and gramophone record moulds. The favoured primary metal is nickel, which can be backed by copper plating, or by cast low melting point alloys.

Any competent plating shop should be able to make a fair attempt at electroforming using a technique of intermittent de-plating at high current densities to suppress the humps that tend to form on thick deposits.

The key problems are starting and stripping. The starting surface can be a wash of colloidal graphite, followed by an electroless nickel coat. This is formed by certain nickel salts which, in the presence of a reducing agent, form a coherent film of metallic nickel in the same way that glass is silvered to make mirrors. On the base coat the main deposit can be built up until it is thick and strong enough to survive. The master can sometimes be stripped off whole, or it can be melted, dissolved or broken up in some way if it is not needed again. It is possible to make moulds which are excellent replicas of lace, snake-skin, etc.

One interesting application is to make a number of identical close-fitting masks for spray-painting when a two-colour scheme is required on toys or ornamental objects. Another is the chief production application, diamond-impregnated cutters. If the right amount of diamond grit is sprinkled on during the plating process, each grit is surrounded by several times its own size of metal, to hold it in place; the base can be a thin saw, a trepanning cutter for taking rock cores, etc. and can be new or being reconditioned.*

For the product designer the interest lies in prototype work rather than in quantity production, and in the possibility of making dies for decorative objects with nature-based surface effects.

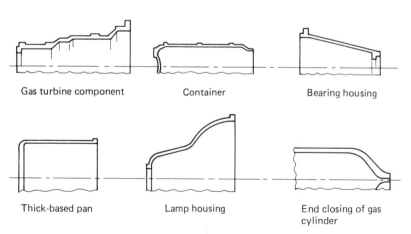

Gas turbine component   Container   Bearing housing

Thick-based pan   Lamp housing   End closing of gas cylinder

Figure 7.48 A range of product types that are suitable for flow-forming

* A recent book on this topic is *Electroforming* by P. Spiro, published by Draper, Teddington, Middlesex.

7.4 Joining and surfacing processes

7.4.1 *The commoner welding processes*

7.4.1.1 Arc welding

It is assumed that the reader is familiar with the processes of arc welding, and standard weld preparations where necessary, etc. This section reviews briefly some strength aspects of the process, before moving onto production points.

The fillet weld has the advantage of not needing much preparation, but it has two danger points: the root is weak in tension owing to the inevitable fissures, etc. — the integrity of the joint results from the tension from final shrinkage. Any bending loads which tend to open up the roots should be guarded against. The other danger is the tendency for the shrinkage to start a tensile crack in the base metal at the toe of the weld. Design features such as very gradual run-outs (Figure 7.49(a) and (b)), so

that the pull is distributed, can minimise this. Sloping, relatively blunt runouts produce little or no benefit.

A butt weld between unequal thicknesses should if possible be given some preparation to reduce the discrepancy locally. In some classes of work this is mandatory. The type of preparation involved may be as shown in Figure 7.49(c) or (d).

Some of the production points to note are:

(1) access for vision, electrodes, filler rods and possibly for gas nozzles may dictate some of the details or the assembly sequence, e.g. in Figure 7.49(e) the bulkheads may have to come last;

(2) the need to avoid excess penetration by using backing strips (which tend to be stress raisers); if critical, one may consider specifying refractory backing strips which come off easily;

(3) distortion control — this is a matter for the specialist welding engineer rather than the basic designer, and may require compensation to be designed-in;

(4) cleaning up — flux residues are corrosive. If cleaning up is difficult due to poor access, consider using carbon dioxide or inert-gas-shielded welding, which has become widely available in recent years.

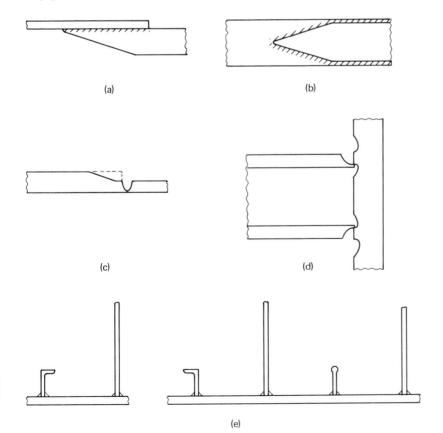

(a)

(b)

(c)

(d)

(e)

Figure 7.49 Preparation for butt welding

7.4.1.2   Resistance spot and seam welding

From a design point of view these techniques raise a few points. A spot weld is usually made to have a diameter of four to eight metal thicknesses. Its static strength is approximately the shear strength of the metal at the periphery. In fatigue the strength is three to five times weaker, i.e. the stress concentration factor may be taken to be 3 to 5.

When joining flat parts it is helpful to stagger the spot welds. A seam weld is statically stronger, but has its heat-affected zone and stress raiser all in one line.

It should be remembered that a spot- or seam-welded joint is a corrosion trap; if the environment is corrosive, the free edges should be sealed in some way to avoid preferential corrosion in the crevice and stress corrosion at the weld itself. The outsides are not unduly sensitive in this way.

Spot-welding equipment can be adapted for hot-riveting.

7.4.1.3   Flash-welding or stud welding

This is an extremely fast and economical process for relatively small parts. In very small sizes, e.g. instrument work, capacitor discharge provides a simple and controllable source of energy. With a little trial and error over capacity and voltage, wires can be joined by merely being made to touch each other while connected across a charged capacitor. In larger work the appropriate machines are used. These produce an arc between the parts for a short time, then press the hot parts together. An intermediate part can be welded into the joint at the same time. It does require a simple weld preparation, with a raised centre so that during the pressing together the oxide and scale in the joint are forced outwards into the flash. There is always some flash but it is usually acceptable visually.

Significant design aspects are access, the facility for gripping the parts and backing for the force pressing the hot parts together.

7.4.1.4   Friction welding

A slightly slower process than the above (it has cycle times of up to one minute rather than seconds), this uses a lathe-type machine to heat the joint faces by friction. It is used mainly for circular work in diameters from 2 mm (at very high rev min^{-1}) up to 150 mm. Some dissimilar metals can be joined in this way. A large flash is produced which may need removing, but ipso facto the joint is very clear of scale, etc. No flux is used. A shortening takes place due to the quantity of metal displaced into the flash; the amount varies from design to design but is consistent in any one product. Non-circular work is friction-welded by means of small-amplitude high-frequency oscillations. This is well established in thermoplastics rather than in metals. Ultrasonic welding of plastics is similar, since it depends on pressure plus a certain amount of friction.

7.4.2   Electron beam welding (EBW), incorporating laser welding and drilling

Electron beam welding is becoming well established in small and large quantity production, both in unique and in competitive applications.

7.4.2.1   Materials

The following materials can be readily welded using EBW techniques:

(1) low-carbon steel if fully killed (300 series stainless steels),
(2) precipitation-hardening steels,
(3) non-heat-treatable aluminium alloys, zinc-free copper alloys,
(4) Titanium, molybdenum, columbium, tantalum, platinum, gold, silver, lead, uranium,
(5) copper-to-nickel, and other fully miscible combinations except zinc.

Materials that require special techniques or which can be welded only with reduced strength are:

(1) low-carbon steel that is not fully killed (other than 300 series),
(2) medium to high-carbon steels (tool steels),
(3) sulphur or phosphorus-bearing free-cutting steels,
(4) various solution-hardening, and other low alloy steels,
(5) magnesium alloys,
(6) tungsten, tungsten carbide, and other sintered metals, and
(7) copper, and copper-to-steel combinations.

Aluminium to steel, titanium-to-steel combinations, and high zinc brass are unsuitable for EBW.

7.4.2.2   Pros and cons

The advantages of EBW are that it offers low distortion, low heat generation, long reach focusing, it welds thick or thin or thick-to-thin, has negligible oxidation, no flux, and produces residual stresses that are lower than with arc welding. It is not expensive, and is well established as a competitive method in mass production. A subcontracting service is available in several centres.

However, EBW takes place usually (though not always) in a vacuum chamber, it requires good jigging and joints preferably made up of straights and circles, although full CNC and automatic tracking along joints is available on some machines together with microprocessor beam deflection systems. It also requires a certain amount of expertise and development on new jobs to cope with beam wobble and location (the beam is naturally very fine and may need weaving to and fro, setting off-centre, etc.).

7.4.2.3 Some applications

Figure 7.50 is an aerospace instrument, note its size. By contrast, Figure 7.51 shows some Super-Phoenix reactor tubes, with a wall thickness of about 1 mm. Figure 7.52 is a gear for an earth-mover automatic gearbox. This is a competitive application; other ways of arriving at this object would involve a single forging of elaborate shape, probably with much machining, or two to three forgings and expensive joints. Figure 7.53 is a vacuum capsule of beryllium copper 0.13 mm thick, C, welded to a nickel base, D. Figure 7.54 is a nitrided mild steel arm welded to an alloy steel cam. For speed, this is welded by rotating the beam rather than the component, production rates being twenty-four per minute. This kind of rate requires a multiple fixture since vacuum chambers take some time to pump down after loading — not less than 6 seconds with a small

Figure 7.52 A gear for an earth-mover automatic gearbox

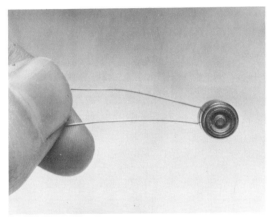

Figure 7.50 An aerospace instrument produced by electron beam welding

Figure 7.51 Super-Phoenix reactor tubes

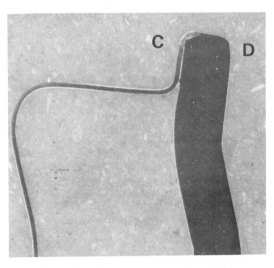

Figure 7.53 A beryllium vacuum capsule welded to a nickel base

chamber, minutes with larger ones. Figure 7.55 illustrates the design possibilities when thinking EBW into a product. The multi-plate clutch and shaft are built up from several cheap simple components using three or four welds. Figures 7.56 and 7.57 show the compactness made possible by EBW. The gear teeth are cut and may be hardened before the EBW or may be left soft for a final shaving. To correct for final distortion, the bores or journal diameters may be finished last, locating from the gear teeth.*

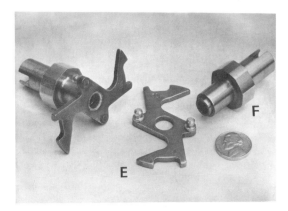

Figure 7.54 A nitrided mild steel arm welded to an alloy steel cam

Figure 7.55 The design possibilities of EBW

* Figures 7.50 to 7.52, 7.55 and 7.56 are reproduced by kind permission of Torvac Ltd. Figures 7.53, 7.54 and 7.57 are reproduced by permission of Sciaky Ltd.

Figure 7.56 Building up gears by EBW

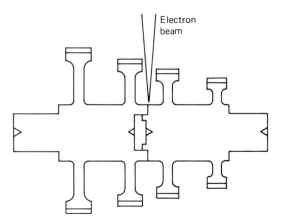

Figure 7.57 Building up gear train by EBW

7.4.2.4 Some unique features of EBW

Interrupted joints are no great problem. This makes possible the welding of wire mesh, and the joining up of cylindrical filters either mesh to mesh (if alignment is maintained successfully) or to a solid joining-strip of compatible material. In some cases, i.e. if the gauge is thin relative to the beam voltage, the interruption can be in the beam direction to join stiffened panels to end plates or to each other, one pass penetrating several thicknesses though with some dispersion. Hollow turbine blades with internal stiffeners, partitions for coolant flow, etc. can be produced in two or three pieces and welded together. Hollow tool handles are easily assembled from pressings. High-speed steel tips are weldable to plain steel bodies, e.g. hacksaw blades, milling cutters etc. Aircraft repair work is a valuable application, from engines to structures. For work which cannot be easily brought into a vacuum chamber special variants of machine use a small beam port letting the beam out into open space while maintaining vacuum within by powerful pumps.

For high-production work the pump-down time of the vacuum chambers can be speeded up with rotary displacement blowers (possibly with reservoirs) for the initial lowering to rough vacuum.

7.4.2.5 Some detail design aspects

It is an advantage if parts are self-locating and have one chucking diameter so that they can be loaded into standard remotely operated fixtures like Figure 7.58 (or larger equivalents) which index and rotate the assembly under the beam; this saves making specific jigs. A slight press-fit is a great advantage

Figure 7.58 Standard rotating fixture

since it offsets the shrinkage as the joint cools. A heavy press-fit should be avoided since the parts must be oil-free which would make a tight fit difficult to assemble. If a press-fit is not desired, then a shoulder location and a slight coning or joggle can be used (Figure 7.59). Axial joints are relatively free from the shrinkage problem but still need location.

The joint must be thick enough to give the required strength bearing in mind a slight sinkage at the top and some porosity at the root. The underbead or flash can be left on in most jobs since it is free from flux, etc. and cannot cause corrosion.

To minimise distortion requires some expertise and some experimentation. Important welds start with tacks at diametrically opposed points, then the main weld is made with gradual run-in and run-out; finally the work is straightened by reheating one side. It may be possible to stress-relieve in situ with a de-focused beam.

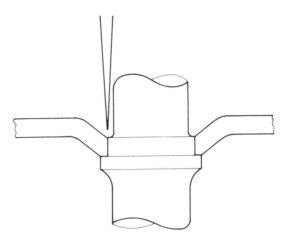

Figure 7.59 Shoulder location

Variants on the basic method are:

(1) pre-placed extra material on top to avoid sinkage,
(2) backing pads or rings to control flash or underbead runaway and consequent porosity, may need machining off,
(3) brazing with copper shims, which is faster than furnace brazing for small to moderate quantities with less heating of the assembly but it is more difficult to secure complete fusion.

7.4.2.6 Use of lasers

Laser beams are highly energy-intensive like electron beams, and hence are to some extent able to do similar work without requiring a vacuum chamber. This is a great advantage, but is offset by some drawbacks. The work still needs to be enclosed since laser light is reflected by molten metal and is dangerous to the eyes. A powerful laser, such as is needed for deep penetration is a large, expensive tool. In deep work the laser beam is accompanied by a helium or other gas jet to disperse the vapour which would absorb too much of the light. In thin work generally, laser methods should be considered at the same time as EBW. The design aspects are similar.

The laser is particularly advantageous in drilling (perforating rather than forming accurate holes) especially in refractories, diamond included, rubber and plastics which are too soft to drill easily (except with freezing), metal removal during dynamic balancing. Holes down to 0.01 mm diameter are possible though these will be tapered, with a fused surface. Shallow drilling can be used for engraving serial numbers, making it easy to identify individual components. This is of some importance in detecting the use of unauthorised spare parts in aircraft work.

Finally, although it does not affect design, lasers are well established in cutting up sheet, allowing more parts per sheet since the cutting loss is small. We may yet see the laser replacing the timber saw-mill.

7.4.3 Plasma-assisted surface treatment

There are many instances when the designer needs different properties within one component, e.g. the base material to be softer, tougher or cheaper than the surface material. Ancient examples are scythes with a thin cast steel blade encased in wrought iron, giving toughness and some degree of self-sharpening; also the self-sharpening plough-share achieved by local chill-casting to give a hardness gradient. The differential cost aspect is illustrated by gilding, Sheffield plate, etc.

The regular engineering methods of case-hardening, salt-bath or gas nitriding, Stellite-type welded overlays, sprayed layers, hard plating, Alclad and stainless-clad steel are well known and serve well in many applications. The purpose of this section is to bring to the designer's attention some less well known processes for those cases where the established methods do not quite meet the case, possibly due to residual stresses or to there being a relatively sharp boundary between coating and base.

7.4.3.1 Plasma nitriding of ferrous materials

This is metallurgically similar to simple gas nitriding but the intrusion of nitrogen into the base material is assisted by high-voltage glow-discharge. This gives a quicker, more even and more graduated effect and works at lower temperature, thus diminishing the softening of the base. The process penetrates into recesses and blind holes, though stopping-off is entirely feasible. In stainless steels the necessity for a vacuum chamber is turned to advantage, allowing the removal of the oxide layer to a more consistent extent than by chemical pickling.

Regular applications include internal-combustion engine valves, crankshafts, gears, press tools, die-casting and injection moulding dies and the wearing parts of the machines.

7.4.3.2 Ion plating

This is a generalisation and extension of the previous technique to a great range of materials. In essence it is a vacuum-chamber deposition process as in metallising, lens blooming, etc. but as in Section 7.4.3.1 it uses a high-voltage glow discharge to prepare and activate the surface and accelerate the coating material towards it. As a result, very high adhesion is obtained. Some applications belong

to aviation and space-flight, such as aluminium-coating of titanium, silver-coating steel, conductive or reflective coatings on non-metals. In other industries, applications are found where localised wear-points are needed on components that must otherwise be light, or soft and ductile. The coatings can be relatively thin if required to maintain surface contours, in contrast with the following process which is appropriate for thicker coatings and may need subsequent finishing operations. There is some similarity between these processes and hence some overlap in potential uses.

7.4.3.3 Detonation-gun plasma spraying

Sprayed coatings of metal and ceramics are well-established for protection against corrosion and oxidation, for reclamation of worn surfaces and for abrasion resistance. The Surface Coating Division of the Welding Institute at Abington Hall, Cambridge, is a good source of information, and many qualified spraying operators may be found. For exceptionally heavy duties, a process which combines high velocity impact with the high temperatures associated with plasma may be appropriate. This is the detonation gun process operated by Union Carbide UK Ltd. One of the favourite wear-resistant coatings is tungsten carbide in cobalt; others are alumina, chromium oxide, molybdenum, nickel, copper alloys and mixtures of these. The base materials are usually iron or steel but copper alloys and even Tufnol (phenolic resin with woven fibres) have been coated and found successful.

7.5 Electrical machining methods

This section discusses some design aspects of electrical discharge (spark) machining (EDM) and electrochemical milling (ECM). Their common features are that they reproduce a master shape or a master outline, either from a physical master or from a computer program. The method is force-free, burr-free and independent of the hardness of the material being worked. The swarf is in fine suspension or is actually in liquid form. These features together make operator supervision unnecessary, whereas in cutting processes there is always a chance of swarf blockage, tool breakage, etc. Some design points will become apparent as we discuss the details.

7.5.1 Spark machining

This comes in two forms, full removal (sinking) or wirecutting. The sinking procedure is generally confined to small numbers or to toolmaking: a master shape is machined from carbon, copper or some other substances, it is brought close to the blank and pulses of current are passed between them, vaporising mainly the workpiece. The vapour is condensed in the dielectric fluid which is pumped into the gap. This carries the swarf away in suspension. The fluid is filtered and re-used. The spark jumps at the point of closest approach so that the feed rate is readily controlled by sensing the breakdown voltage. The process is often done in two stages: a high current stage giving a rough finish, with some overcut beyond the shape of the electrode master, followed by a finishing stage with a fresh, slightly larger master. Electronic control over each individual spark pulse is used to suppress plasma production (arcing). Spark machining is coupled sometimes with reciprocating tool movements, and finishes down to a few microinches CLA can be achieved at reasonable speeds. The master shape can be reproduced to accuracies better than most machining processes. Tungsten carbide, hard steels and superalloys can be machined. As a production process it opens up endless design possibilities; shapes are feasible which the designer might have rejected as not being economically viable in the past.

Where the wire method is appropriate, production is much faster since only a thin band of metal is removed. Its natural application is in blanking-tool production. The electrode is replaced by a fine brass wire. A starting hole has to be drilled or spark-machined; the wire is fed through the hole and kept taut between two reels. It is gradually fed through the workpiece under computer control and is also slowly reeled from the supply spool onto the receiving one so that the workpiece finish is not affected by pitting and wear of the wire. For a typical blanking die one would cut the outline normal to the face, then a second cut would be made for the die relief. Modern machines would do both from the same program; the program also serves to cut a master for spark-machining the punch. Typical *production* applications would be short runs of motor laminations where a stack of 50 to 100 could be cut at one go, experimental blanks for press-tool development, short-run work generally. The limits of size and thickness depend on the particular machine, not on the process. Work sizes 1 m × 0.5 m × 0.5 m are by no means unusual; for large press tools, work tables over 2 m long may be found. As a guide to cutting rates, small thin jobs may take under half an hour, larger jobs are left to run overnight on self-monitoring machines.

7.5.2 *Electrochemical machining*

ECM or chemical milling is similar in effect to EDM but uses a (non-toxic) electrolyte, a very weak acid or mild alkali, to remove the swarf. It is the reverse of electroplating, but the removed material is not built up on the cathode, it is washed away and precipitated. Using up to 20 000 A at less than 24 V, up to 16 cm^3 per minute can be removed. Smaller machines, up to 2 000 A capacity, remove up to 3.3 cm^3 per minute. Naturally such a fast process is less accurate and gives a coarser finish than spark machining, 0.05–0.1 mm accuracy and 60 microinch CLA may be expected. It is conceivable that in a shop equipped with both types of machine, spark machining could be used to finish work roughed out chemically. Mass production uses of chemical milling are internal de-burring where the tendency of current to concentrate at high points gives a natural rounding-off tendency; this trend is also valuable when sinking oil-feed grooves into shaft surfaces, after hardening if necessary. This may be useful in highly loaded bearings. The main design merits of the method are in the production of difficult shapes much faster than by spark machining. A chemically milled surface is believed to be quite stress-free whereas a spark-machined surface may have a slight residual stress.

Chemical machining and spark machining are both suitable for deep hole drilling. The force-free nature of the process means that the electrode has little incentive to deviate from the straight and narrow path. Hypodermic tubing is used for fine holes, to provide a supply of the necessary liquid. If a non-circular hole is required, a suitable shape is put onto the end, not necessarily on the whole length. This enables the designer to call for holes with extended cooling surface, deep splines (helical if necessary) and other seemingly unmakeable shapes. With a special electrode it should be possible to join up two blind holes at the bottom, producing a U-shaped cooling duct.

Examples of designs made possible or much easier by electrical methods are illustrated in Figure 7.60 which is reproduced by kind permission of Matchless Machines Ltd., of Bletchley. Item (a) is a fan member with blade stubs formed by aerofoil outline by the plate electrode shown bottom left, having removed a substantial amount of interstitial stainless steel. The blade stub is hollowed out in two stages by the male electrodes shown forward of the plate electrode. At (b) we have a ring with slots, tabs and holes spark-machined. The time is not stated, but would be short. The plate at (c) in a Nimonic alloy could have been drilled, punched (with distortion problems) or laser drilled instead of being spark-machined. Laser drilling may have been competitive with EDM, the traditional methods would almost certainly be dearer and/or less satisfactory. A laser would fuse one hole at a time, EDM would use a multiple electrode. The rotor at (d) took 5 minutes per blade by chemical milling, in stainless steel. By end milling it may have been as quick, but with a less satisfactory finish at the thin tips on the trailing

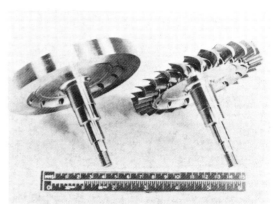

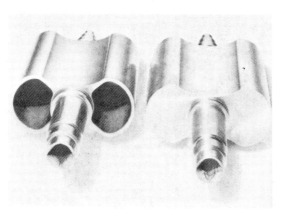

Figure 7.60 Examples of products made by EDM

edge. This seems a case for roughing by end-milling, finishing by ECM. The steel air rotor (e) has the square drive hole milled chemically, then the lightening pockets, followed by further lightening undercuts within the pockets. The lobes need sufficient thickness to keep the shape true at the open ends and minimise leakage; further in the walls can be thinner. Machining time is said to be 18 minutes.

Some useful addresses

Alcan UK Ltd, Southam Road, Banbury, Oxon OX16 17SN. Tel. 0295 4444. (Extrusion design brochure available, wide range of aluminium extrusions.)

Anodic Machining Technologies Ltd, 2nd Avenue, Axminster, Devon EX13 5HH. Tel. 0297 34567.

Battenfeld Maschinenfabriken GmbH, Postfach 1160/65, D-5882 Meinerzhagen 1, West Germany. (Foam moulding machines.)

Battenfeld (England) Ltd, Asheridge Road, Chesham, Bucks HP5 2DG. Tel. 0494 84855. (Foam moulding machines.)

BICTA, Royton House, George Road, Edgbaston, Birmingham B15 1NU. Tel. 021-455 8872. (Information on investment casting.)

British Powder Metal Federation, Ashton Court, 67a Compton Road, Wolverhampton, WV3 9QZ. Tel. 0902 28987. (Free booklet.)

Cold-Rolled Sections Association, Robson Rhodes, Centre City Tower, 7 Hill Street, Birmingham B18 6AS. Tel. 021-643 5494. (Information on and list of suppliers of roll-formed steel sections.)

Design Council, 28 Haymarket, London SW1Y 4SU. Tel. 01-839 8000. (The Design Council's field officers offer introductory visits; they can supply ideas, contacts, suppliers and sources of information.)

Fothergill & Harvey Ltd, Summit, Littleborough, Lancs OL15 9QP. Tel. Littleborough 78831. (Resin-bonded fibre, pre-preg and plain materials.)

Fry's Diecastings Ltd, Prince George's Road, London SW19 2PR. Tel. 01-648 0371.

GKN Projects Ltd, PO Box 19, Redditch, Worcs B98 UDR. Tel. 0527 2204. (Diecasting.)

GKN Bound Brook Ltd, PO Box 19, Lichfield, Staffs WS13 6HF. Tel. 05432 54101. (Design for sintering.)

Indalex Ltd, Kingsditch Lane, Cheltenham, Glos. GL51 9PD. Tel. 0242 21641. (Various extrusions, including hinges.)

Industrial Centre, University of Salford, Greater Manchester M5 4WT. Tel. 061-736 5843. (Ion plating with various metals.)

Matchless Machines Ltd, Spark Erosion and Chemical Machining Division, formerly Bilton Road, Bletchley, Milton Keynes, MK1 1HW. Tel. 0908 70912. (Electrical machining equipment and contract service; see also Anodic Machining Technologies Ltd.)

Morton-Jones, D. H., MSc, MRSC, CChem, University of Lancaster, Department of Chemistry, Bailrigg, Lancaster, LA1 4YA. Tel. 0524 65201. (Information on foam moulding etc.).

MPD Technology Ltd, Tempress Division, Wiggin Street, Birmingham B16 0AJ. Tel. 021-454 0373. (Superplastic forming of some stainless steels and titanium alloys.)

National Materials Handling Centre, Cranfield Institute of Technology, Cranfield, Beds. (Information on design to facilitate handling and storage.)

Rolinx Ltd, Ledson Road, Wythenshawe, Manchester M23 9WP. Tel. 061–998 5353. (Believed to make foam-coved mouldings.)

Sciaky Welding Machines Ltd, 212 Bedford Avenue, Slough, Berks. Tel. 0753 25551. (Electron beam and other welding equipment.)

SMPT Billion, BP 140, 22 Rue Brillat Savarin, 01104 Oyonnax, France. (Foam moulding.)

Superform Metals Ltd, PO Box 150, Worcester WR3 8TR. Tel. 0905 54392. (Superplastic forming of aluminium.)

Thomas Dudley Ltd, Dauntless Works, PO Box 28, New Birmingham Road, Dudley, West Midlands D71 4SN. (Foam moulding.)

TI Reynolds Ltd, Hay Hall Works, Redfern Road, Tyseley, Birmingham B11 2BG. Tel. 021-706 3333. (Closed end extrusion design and supply.)

Torvac Ltd, Windmill Lane, Histon, Cambridge CB4 4HE. Tel. 022-023 2646. (Electron beam welding machines and service at contracting centres.)

Unimation Ltd, Units A3 and A4, 4 Stafford Park, Telford, Salop TF3 3AX. (Robots.)

Union Carbide UK Ltd, Fountain Precinct, Balm Green, Sheffield S1 3AE. Tel. 0742 750011, also at Swindon 0793 488311. (Surface treatments.)

Welding Institute, Abington Hall, Abington, Cambridge. Tel. 0223 891 162. (Information on all types of welding and surface treatment.)

Wolfson Plasma Processing Unit, Department of Metallurgy, University of Liverpool, PO Box 147, Liverpool L69 3BX. Tel. 051-709 6022. (Plasma nitriding.)

Bibliography

The Canning Book of Electroplating, Publicity Dept., W. Canning (Materials) Ltd., PO Box 288, Gt. Hampton Street, Birmingham, B18 6AS.

SPIRO, P. *Electroforming*, Draper, Teddington, Middx.

8

Jigs, fixtures and tools

In the engineering factory the economic production of components depends upon several factors which include the type of machine tool available, and the size and shape of the components. Economic production is also influenced by the numbers required, and the possibility of repeat orders for small batches.

The choice of suitable machine tools for a new project is often a difficult one to make, since a wide range of manufacturing methods may be available in addition to the many different ways in which a part may be held during machining. The sequence of operations may be arranged in various ways, but in general the greater the number of parts required, the greater the amount of money that can be invested in tooling. Indeed, the cost of this feature may exceed the cost of the machine tool upon which it is employed. On the other hand, when a limited number of a given component is needed, consideration should be given to the use of standard equipment such as machine vices and chucks, modified with special jaws to hold the work.

The view is sometimes expressed that the machine designer should not be concerned with the manufacture of the components; if a machine functions efficiently, it is the duty of the jig and tool designer to sort out problems of manufacture. This, however, is a short-sighted policy, since consideration by the machine designer as to how a part is to be made may lead to simplification of the jig, a reduction in the manufacturing, and a saving in the cost of expensive tools. Thus the machine designer should aim at an economical design and avoid complicated structures or complex machining operations.

The material in this chapter first appeared in *Chartered Mechanical Engineer*, and is reproduced here by permission.

8.1 The function of jigs and fixtures

The function of a jig is to hold the work and guide the tools, usually by means of bushes. Thus jigs are used mainly for drilling and boring operations. A fixture, on the other hand, is a work-holding device, without actual provision for guiding the tools, but which may comprise setting devices so that a tool is held in the correct position for machining purposes. Either unit will enable high-grade work to be performed by unskilled labour, giving the assurance of interchangeability of the parts, whilst a primary function of both is to reduce costs by eliminating hand methods of marking out.

An example of a drilling jig is shown in Figure 8.1, the work location being on three points A in the horizontal plane, and in the vertical plane against two positive stops B by two screws, and against one stop C by a single screw. Any further locating points and screws will simply tend to distort the work and

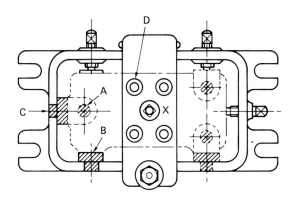

Figure 8.1 Drilling jig showing points of location

cause other points to be ineffective. The guide bushes D are held in a swinging latch which allows insertion of the work and which is then locked by a bolt with the work finally clamped down by screw X.

8.1.1 Standard units

Clamps, jacks, bushes and cams are available from specialist firms and may prove an economy. An example of a fixture which incorporates eight of these units is shown in Figure 8.2. The operation is that of milling the face A of the bracket which rests on pads and is held down by two clamps, one of them being cam operated by the lever. Two jacks are used to provide support against the cutting action, and positive location is obtained by two dowels.

8.2 Designing for production

Consideration for efficient production should begin at the drawing board stage, and while some of the examples given may seem elementary many machine designers have little experience of tooling difficulties and teething troubles occur which might have been foreseen by an experienced designer.

Figure 8.3 indicates points to avoid in detail design with improvements:

(1) Bosses and machined faces should be kept to the same height.
(2) Avoid drilling on inclined faces.
(3) If a larger hole terminates in a very small one, use a plug to avoid drill breakage.
(4) Tee slots on a machine table should have a clear run-out for milling them.
(5) To hold the headed pin for grinding is difficult, but if two circlip grooves are provided then the pin may be centreless ground, or made from ground stock.
(6) The cylinder drawing indicates a sharp corner at the end of the bore and a flat face. Tooling is simplified by a radius at A and a dimple at B.
(7) The bearing shown is difficult to hold for turning the shank, but the addition of a small boss, shown dotted, makes it a simple turning operation between lathe centres.
(8) The original design of a worm and wheel drive, A, can be simplified as shown in B. In A the worm wheel comprises a bronze ring on a cast iron hub, a common practice. Except on large wheels, this can be a doubtful saving when the cost of machining and fitting two parts is considered.

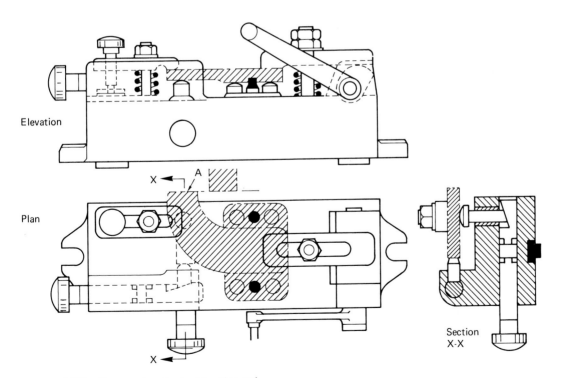

Figure 8.2 Milling fixture using standard locating and clamping units

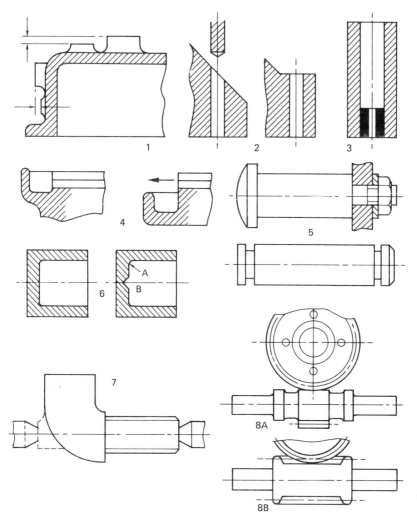

Figure 8.3 Designing for ease of production (see text)

Figure 8.3 gives some indication of how production can be simplified on various components, while other examples follow in the following sections.

8.2.1 Single-point cutting tools

The suitability of a material for metal cutting is decided by its ability to withstand the heat, pressure and abrasion caused by the cutting action of the tool and chip. Friction generates heat with temperatures up to 600°C on the cutting edge, while chip movement under heavy pressure tends to wear the tool.

The earliest cutting material was carbon steel, but its use is now restricted to intricate form tools, hand tools and small drills where toughness is important. The material is now improved by the addition of an alloying element such as chromium or tungsten.

8.2.2 High-speed steel

This is classified by its tungsten content, and while turning tools of this material have been largely replaced by carbides, drills and milling cutters continue to be manufactured.

8.2.3 Cemented carbide

This is the most common material used for machining metals, the term covers a range of tools of which the basic alloy is tungsten carbide held in a matrix of cobalt. The material is often used in tip form, electronic induction brazing uniting the tip to the shank. Because of the cost of grinding carbide tools an alternative to brazing is the 'throw-away' insert, either rectangular or triangular, which, after one edge is blunted, can be turned to present a new edge to the work. Cutting speeds range from 60–180 m min^{-1} for ferrous metals, and up to 1500 m min^{-1} for light alloys.

8.2.4 *Ceramic tools*

These have little resistance to impact, but have greater hardness and strength at high temperatures than carbides, thus higher cutting speeds can be used. The major constituent, up to 90%, is aluminium oxide. Inserts are of the 'throw-away' type set in a holder with an approach angle of 15° and a 7° negative rake. Suitable feed rates are 0.4—0.5 mm rev^{-1} with a depth of cut of 4–7 mm.

8.2.5 *Coated carbides*

Although carbide is the basic component, the new development comprises a thin layer of hard material bonded on top of the carbide to give either a longer life to the tool or the possibility of using higher cutting speeds. The Goldmaster process comprises a thin layer 0.5 μm of titanium carbide on the base material followed by a substantial layer of titanium carbo-nitride. The result is a strata combination which possesses low thermal conductivity while plastic deformation is reduced, thus giving long life to the cutting edge.

Using a Sandvik tool with a coating of titanium carbide 0.127 mm thick, the best economy for turning steel and cast iron is obtained at cutting speeds 20% higher than for ordinary carbide, and three times the average tool life can be expected. Figure 8.4 is a diagram illustrating the relative machining costs and tool life as a function of the cutting speed.

Borazon is produced by bonding a layer 0.5 mm thick of polycrystalline cubic boron nitride to a carbide substrate. Since borazon has a hardness only exceeded by diamond, it provides high resistance to wear and long tool life. As an indication of metal cutting, for turning hardened tool steels, a cut 6.3 mm deep can be taken at a speed of 22 m min^{-1} and feed rate of 0.25 mm rev^{-1}.

8.2.6 *Diamond tools*

Diamond is the hardest known material, but for turning and boring it can only be used where the cutting forces are small as in machining aluminium alloys, bronzes and plastics at high speed. Machining is not restricted to small components, since large drums and copper commutators are turned with a high surface finish, this being the result of the high Young's modulus and chemical inertness which prevents the formation of a built-up edge. Diamond

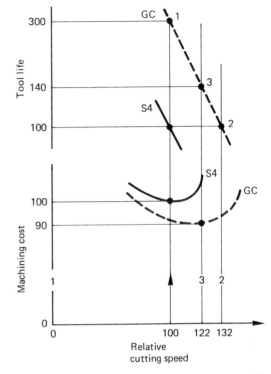

Figure 8.4 Chart illustrating machining costs and tool life

turning lathes and fine boring machines are used, a single-point (a) and facet edge (b) tool being shown in Figure 8.5, while milling operations are increasing.

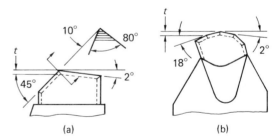

Figure 8.5 Types of cutting edges on diamond turning tools

8.2.7 *Isotropic diamond tools*

To increase the use of diamonds for machining, a material called Syndite has been introduced. This is a synthesised mass of orientated diamond particles in a metal matrix. When bonded on to a tungsten carbide substrate, the result is a material which can be used an an alternative to a conventional diamond tool. The advantages are that deeper cuts can be taken as the tool is more rigid. As an example of performance the number of pistons turned at 275 m min^{-1} was 1200 before tool failure for Syndite and 700 for a diamond tool. In milling silicon-aluminium 25 000 castings were machined, the operation being equivalent to 27 500 m of travel compared with 900 m for a carbide cutter.

8.2.8 Vibration problems

This increase in cutting speeds has its effect on jig and fixture design, in that vibration which was of a negligible order of magnitude at low cutting speeds assumes cardinal importance with modern tools. The greatest problem is when milling, but to show the development, the increase in the number of alternating stress repetitions based on a nominal shear pitch of 2.5 mm with a cutting speed of 10 m min^{-1} for a carbon steel tool, 30 m min^{-1} for high speed steel, and 100 m min^{-1} for carbide, the number of stress repetitions per minute is 3600, 10 800 and 36 000, respectively. Even though at higher speeds, and with different materials, the shear is less complete, the force fluctuations are severe. When machining cast iron, this is equal to 64–80 kg mm^{-2} of tool section and when machining medium and high carbon steel the values are 146–250 kg mm^{-2}.

8.2.9 Designing with hollow bar to reduce cost of manufacture

One of the ways in which the machine designer can assist in the reduction of tooling is by using hollow bar. The wide range of steels and close dimensional accuracy available open up new vistas of development with an increasing number of applications. In addition to the superiority of the tubular section in strength and torsional capacity, the elimination of drilling and boring the hole saves both time and cost.

An example of this feature is in the re-design of a lathe spindle. Originally, this was produced from a heavy flanged forging. Several hours of deep hole boring were required to produce a 75 mm diameter hole through the spindle. By purchasing the main length of the spindle as tube and welding the flange on one end, considerable savings in cost were obtained. Plugs in each end of the tube were used as locations for turning and grinding operations. Figure 8.6 shows another example where an 8 in (200 mm) flange is welded to the tube to form the spindle of a milling machine. Hollow bar is not limited to long components, for gear blanks, piston pins, and ball races may be cited as typical examples.

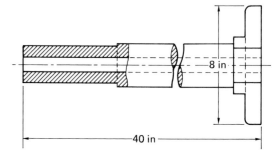

Figure 8.6 Milling machine spindle built-up of tubing

8.2.10 Manufacture of chuck screws

An example of re-design is in the manufacture of a range of screws for operating lathe chucks. These were made in six sizes in batches of fifty, and in the first instance were made from bar with one end gripped in a chuck as in Figure 8.7(a). The square threads were 8–6 tpi, left hand, so that a starting recess was required near the drive, and on completion of the thread the screw was cut-off and a $\frac{5}{8}$ in hole drilled in one end. This was then recessed at the

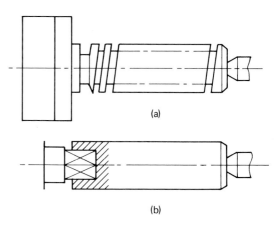

Figure 8.7 Alternative methods of manufacturing chuck screws

bottom, so that a slotting tool could be used to produce a square hole for use with the chuck key. This was a slow and expensive process and was superseded by drilling a square hole in one end of the screw blank and driving as shown in Figure 8.7(b) from a lathe centre with a square end. The square was produced by holding the work in a floating jig shown in Figure 8.8 and using a three-sided drill rotating in a square guide bush. The work is located in a vee and held by a clamp.

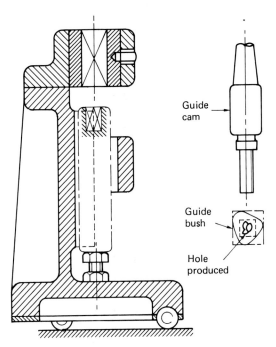

Figure 8.8 Floating jig for drilling square holes in chuck screws

8.2.11 *Tracer controlled copying*

Copy turning must rank as one of the great advances in production. By using a template mounted at the rear of the bed, a stylus in contact with the template will cause a cutting tool to produce the same shape on the workpiece. Even on small batches increased production can be achieved because cutting is conti-

nuous from end to end, and boring can be carried out with equal ease. To eliminate the usual driving dog when turning and allow the tool to cut along the full length of the work, hydraulic driving dogs are available. Figure 8.9 shows the arrangement with a face driver, clamping being by the centring of a spring-loaded centre A and the drive by pins B on the end face of the work. The pins are connected by an hydraulic system C. A feature to note is that the driving pins (whose distance X from the driving head is always constant), and not the centre, determine the stop length. It is important that the force should not be excessive, hence the revolving centre showing the holding pressure.

8.2.12 *Machining of spherical surfaces*

Copy turning is one method in which the cylindrical template has four centre holes, as shown in Figure 8.10. Two of the holes are used for grinding the template and the other two are offset from the axis so that the template can be mounted between centres. Copying starts at point B and terminates at C on the workpiece D. The front toolpost of the lathe is used for turning the shank and cutting the groove at C.

Figure 8.11 represents the machining of a spherical bore of a differential housing on a boring and turning mill. The tool holder is a sliding fit in its bearing and carries a roughing cutter C and finishing cutter D, both being in operation together as the table revolves. The cutter arms swivel on stud E and a connection between the arms and the holder A is made by two links F. To commence machining, the handle G is slackened so that the bar drops down

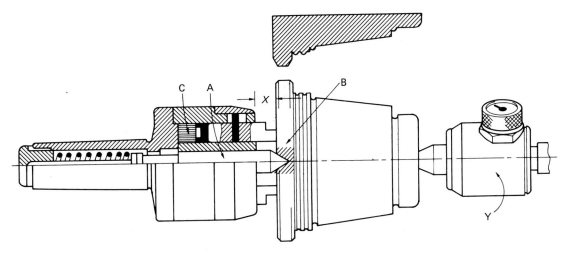

Figure 8.9 Face driver and hydraulic centre for copy turning

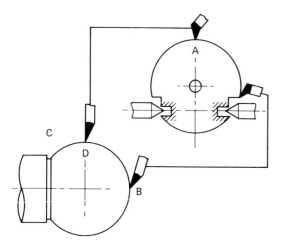

Figure 8.10 Machining of spherical surface by copy turning

and pulls the cutters to the horizontal position. The downward feed of the turret is then engaged, the relative axial movement between the holder A and the boring bar causing the cutters to move in an arcuate path, which by the revolving of the machine table generates a spherical bore in the casting, the machining terminating in the position shown.

8.2.13 Problem of cutting oil grooves

Cutting the grooves around the periphery of a universal joint was first envisaged as an operation involving a complex mechanism to traverse the tool, as in screwcutting, and simultaneously to feed it forward. The simple solution is shown in Figure 8.12 which shows a lathe face-plate having a spigot set at 45°. With the joint clamped on the spigot by means of screws in the split lugs, the operation is then one

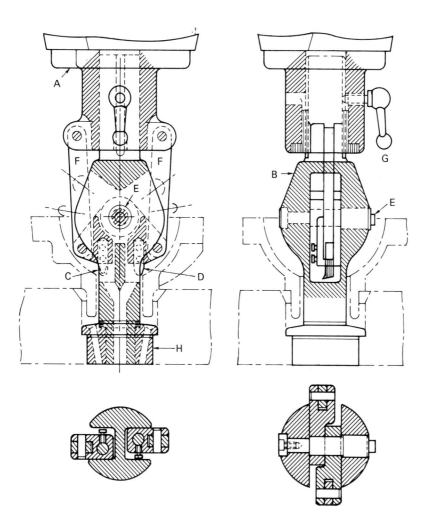

Figure 8.11 Production of a spherical surface on a boring and turning mill

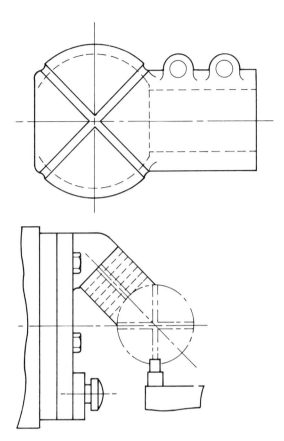

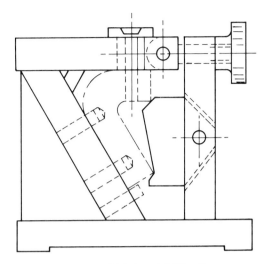

Figure 8.13 Example of fabricated drilling jig

Figure 8.12 Method of cutting oil grooves on a spherical surface

of cutting a simple groove without moving the tool longitudinally. After the first groove has been cut, the work is indexed to the opposite side to machine the second groove.

8.2.14 Drilling and boring operations

In view of the great number of holes in components, drilling is a major operation. Figure 8.13 is an example of a simple drilling jig. This is a fabricated unit which saves the cost of a pattern and reduces the machining of a casting. A more simple idea is to build up a jig from bright steel stock sections screwed together, which involves hardly any machining. In contrast, the ultimate in drilling is found on transfer machines built by Frederick Pollard & Co. Ltd. On such machines several hundred drills may be in operation, so provision must be made to detect drill breakage otherwise further damage may result to tapping units at the next station. Again, failure to drill a hole to the correct

depth or left-in cuttings may also cause tap breakage, thus probes and air blast are arranged to take care of these emergencies. Multiple drilling heads are available to suit any hole pattern, for example for close centre distances Dex Gears Ltd. have heads to drill 60 holes in areas of only 23 cm^2, or spindles can operate at 7 mm centres. One unit carries 500 spindles.

8.2.15 Modern drilling

Carbide tools have reduced time required for turning operations, but drilling has tended to lag behind. Now, impressive claims are being made for a range of drills claiming to operate at cutting speeds that are 10 times faster than normal drills, yet the feed rates of 0.1 to 0.3 mm rev^{-1} are similar to those of twist drills. The drills from 25 to 75 mm use indexable carbide inserts A and B (Figure 8.14) placed so

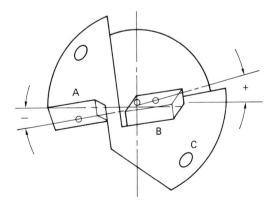

Figure 8.14 End view of drill showing indexable carbide inserts

that the cutting forces on each side of the drill centre
are the same but act in opposite directions. For chip
removal coolant from holes C forces the chips away
via two external V-shaped grooves.

8.2.16 *Unit head tooling*

The advantage of unit head tooling is that heads can
be assembled around a component, or arranged in
line as in transfer machines. Fine boring machines
are generally used to fit the heads, the front of the
machines being standardised in four sizes. An
example of unit head tooling is shown in Figure 8.15
which shows an end view of a boring jig for the holes
in the headstock of a Harrison lathe. Location is on
base A with downward pressure applied by swinging
link B on lever C through bolt D. As soon as the
handwheel is released, the weight E brings the lever
clear of the casting for removal or insertion of
another unit. End location is by means of screw F.

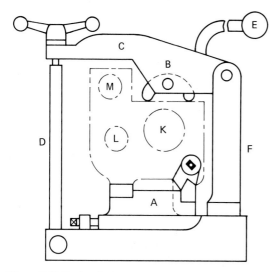

Figure 8.15 Boring jig for lathe headstock

The cutters on the three spindle units are shown in
Figure 8.16, the drive coming from the headstock
which connects by gearing to KLM. A cutting speed
of 6.3 m min^{-1} is employed, and cutting takes place
simultaneously on both ends of the headstock, the
floor to floor time being 23 min.To keep the cutter
bars short and rigid, each one is directly coupled as
at E. For the spindle bearing three cutters are used,
a front double rougher, a round sizing cutter, and a
recessing cutter.

Figure 8.17 shows sections of the bar at X and Y,
the centres of the cutters being offset 3.5 mm from
the centre of the bar, while the feature of the
roughing cutter is that one edge precedes the other
by 2.5 mm, and each cuts a different diameter. Thus

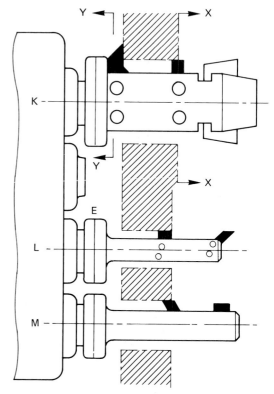

Figure 8.16 Types of boring cutters for machining
headstock

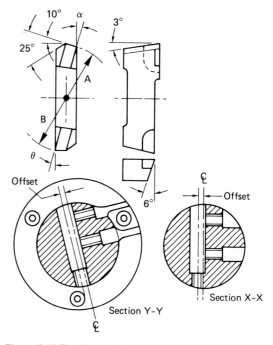

Figure 8.17 Details of boring cutters

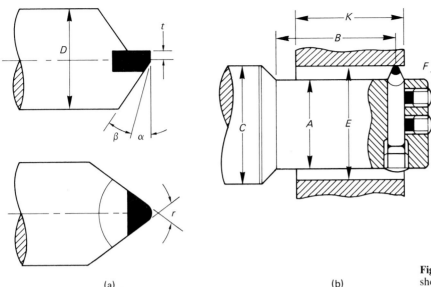

(a)   (b)

Figure 8.18 Diamond tool showing design requirements

while diameter A is 96 mm, B cuts 89 mm, the angle α being 9° and θ equal to 10°. The advantage is that B acts as a semifinishing cutter and leaves little metal to be removed by the sizing edge of A.

8.2.17 Diamond boring tools

As shown in Figure 8.18(a) a diamond can be brazed on to a round section shank which can be clamped in a boring bar. Standard tool sizes are available for bores ranging from $\frac{1}{2}$ to 3 in (13 to 76 mm) diameter, the diameter D varying from $\frac{1}{4}$ to $\frac{3}{8}$ in (6.5 to 9.5 mm). There are three angles to consider, namely the primary clearance angle α, the secondary clearance β, and the nose angle γ.

Figure 8.18(b) indicates the requirements for a true bore. A should be 80% of the work diameter, with B the minimum to clear the workpiece length K and should not exceed 5 times the bar diameter. C should not be less than E, and for clamping (as at F) copper pads should contact the tool.

For vibration damping the rigidity of a bar can be increased by using a material with a higher modulus of elasticity than that of normal steel. The rigidity is directly proportional to the modulus and the fourth power of the diameter and inversely proportional to the third power of its overhung length. Length to diameter ratios of 4:1 are suitable for steel, but may increase to 7:1 for bars of tungsten carbide.

8.2.18 Supported boring bars

For large components with long bores, the boring bar must be supported in the jig by guide bushes. As

an example of a lathe tailstock see Figure 8.19. The casting rests on the machined base on a face of similar contour to the lathe bed and is held down by a screw in the top plate. The pressure of the cut is taken against a stop, while end location is by means of the opposing screw. Note that a steel tongue is used to locate the jig in the tee slot of the machine table, and that for bolting down, lugs are preferable to bolt holes, since the jig can be lowered on to the table and the bolts slid into position. As the ends of the tailstock require facing, sufficient room must be left between the casting and the jig for the insertion of cutters.

Figure 8.20 shows the machining: (1) is a core drill for the first operation of roughing the bore, (2) is a second bar fitted with a single-point tool for

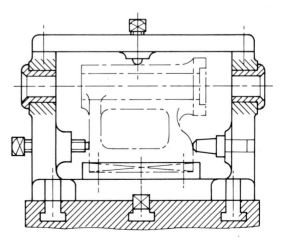

Figure 8.19 Boring jig for machining lathe tailstock

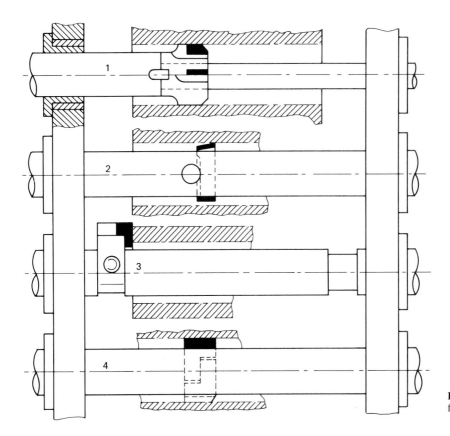

Figure 8.20 Tooling layout for boring lathe tailstock

straightening the bore, and with cutters (3) for machining both bosses, and (4) is a third bar carrying a floating cutter for sizing the bore. There are several alternatives for bringing the bore to size, such as using special floating reamers or by the honing process, described later.

8.2.19 Reducing costs in gear units

The production of accurate bores is not difficult, but facing operations can be long and costly. Consider a gearbox in which there are six shafts, each one having two bearings giving a total of 24 faces to be machined. The cost of facing to length far exceeded any other operation, and Figure 8.21 shows the means employed to eliminate all facing. The left hand boss shows the original design fitted with needle roller sleeves level with the ends of the machined bosses, while the right hand end shows the shortened bosses with the sleeves extending. With this second arrangement no accurate distance between the faces of the bosses is required, for the sleeves are inserted and clamped by the jig screws A in the proper position. Using the screws as drill

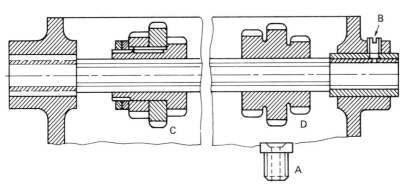

Figure 8.21 Details of re-design of gear box and units

bushes, a hole is drilled into the sleeve after the gears are in position, the screw is then removed and screw B inserted in its place.

To reduce tooling on gearing, there are two alternatives. C shows a cluster gear built up in units, this being necessary if the teeth are produced by hobbing and finished by grinding. For headstock drives this is desirable, but for many drives a one piece cluster gear produced by rack or pinion process is acceptable as at D. Grinding is not feasible, but recent developments in heat treatment are producing tough and accurate teeth so that further processes are not necessary, but such gears can be lapped if required. The saving in time and cost is obvious.

8.3 Tooling for producing plane surfaces

8.3.1 Milling

The advantageous feature of milling is that by mounting a gang of cutters several faces of varying heights and contours can be machined simultaneously. An example, Figure 8.22 shows the milling of lathe saddles with eleven cutters in action together, a set-up requiring a machine of high power and rigid work holding means. All cutters are carbide tipped with 6 teeth of 5° radial rake. Apart from the narrow cutters 4, 6, 7, 8 and 10, the teeth of the others are at an angle of 10° straight across the face. This is because for the operation of pendulum milling the cutters are operating at one fixture in

conventional milling and for down-cut at the other, spiral teeth being unsuitable for this latter.

With pendulum milling, the work is mounted in a fixture at one end of the table, so that after one casting has been machined, the cutters return to mill the other one. The important feature is that while two fixtures are required, only one set of cutters is used, as against two sets for equivalent work on two machines. Also the loading and unloading time is not charged for the operation, since the machine is working productively at the same time.

Cutting is at 60 m min^{-1} with a feed of 140 mm min^{-1} and an average depth of cut of 5 mm. Another example of gang milling lathe beds is shown under Hydraulic Fixtures. The tool designer should see that cutters with helical teeth are mounted right and left hand so balancing the end thrust.

8.3.2 Planing operations

In general milling will prove more economical than planing on small components, but modern planing practice is proving more efficient for machining heavy components. A carbide tipped tool is shown in Figure 8.23. Under the carbide insert is a nickel shim 1 mm thick having a high degree of elasticity. Semi-steel castings, hardness 280 Brinell, are being planed at 95 m min^{-1} with feed rates 1.2–3 mm stroke^{-1} and depth 25 mm.

Tool sharpening for a planing machine is simple in contrast to re-grinding a gang of milling cutters, and quick change multiple tool holders are proving

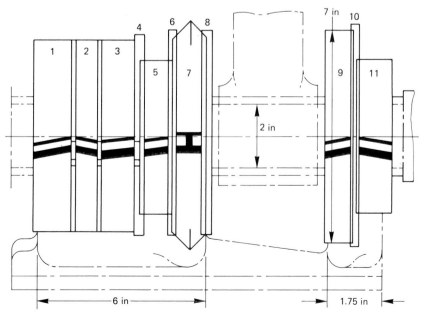

Figure 8.22 Set-up of cutters for pendulum milling operation

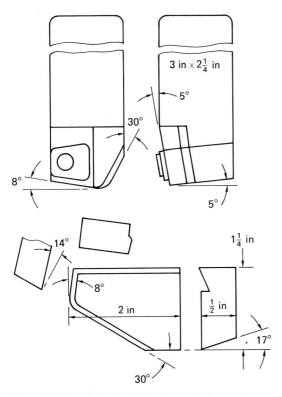

Figure 8.23 Example of carbide-tipped planing tool

time-saving. The tools are on steel plates pre-set remote from the machine, but the main feature in time reduction has been the re-development of double cutting. Table 8.1 shows a comparison of performance when planing a length of 5 m with a depth of cut of 13 mm and at a feed rate of 1 mm stroke^{-1}.

Another example of a planing machine is one operating on steel fabricated 18-cylinder vee-engine blocks. These weigh 18 tonnes each and measure $4200 \times 1270 \times 914$ mm in length, breadth and height. There is a vertical milling head for machining the top face, but the main machining is by four double-cutting tool boxes operating at 107 m min^{-1} with four tools cutting simultaneously in both directions. This sets up cutting forces in alternate directions and contributes to the low distortion of the fabricated block, as well as giving a 30% improvement in machining time over previous methods.

8.3.3 Surface broaching

Figure 8.24 shows the elements in the design of broach teeth, and unlike most machine tool operations the feed is not applied by the machine mechanism, but by the increase in height of each cutting tooth. The front rake angle is governed by the material but varies from 6° for cast iron to 20° for soft steel, 10° for aluminium, and 5° for hard brass. Pitch is based upon the length of the component, the nature of the material and size of chip, but an approximation is: pitch $= 0.35 \times$ (length of cut)$^{1/2}$

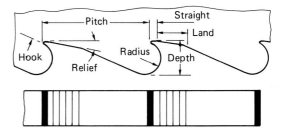

Figure 8.24 Elements of design of broach teeth

Carbide tips are being used for broaching Ford cylinder blocks, 2228 tips being used in the roughing stage; the average cutting life (eight edges) is 45 000 parts per cutting edge. For finishing cuts ground inserts are used, the average life before re-grinding being 60 000 parts. Cutting speed is 40 m min^{-1}.

As one of the problems may lie in determining whether broaching or milling will be the most suitable for a given operation, the following points should be noted.

Table 8.1

	Forward and return planing	Planing in one direction	
	$V_c = V_r$ $= 25$ m min^{-1}	$V_c = 25$ m min^{-1} $V_r = 50$ m min^{-1}	$V_c = 25$ m min^{-1} $V_r = 75$ m min^{-1}
Double-stroke time, s	26	20	18
Stock removal (double stroke)	7.3	3.7	3.7
Stock removal per second	0.28	0.18	0.2
Surface planed per second, %	100	65	72

(1) Faces to be broached must have all the elements parallel to the axis of the broach holder, and there must be no obstruction in the path of these edges.
(2) Broaching achieves good results because each tooth removes a fixed thickness of metal with light cuts for finishing. Roughing and finishing cuts are required to obtain the same result by milling.
(3) Broaching speeds are low and, because impact loads vary as the square of the velocity, wear is not as heavy on a broach as on a milling cutter where speeds are considerably higher.
(4) There is no slippage area when a broach engages the work, whereas there is in milling.
(5) Undercuts can be machined with a broach at the same time as other surfaces, whereas milling requires other set-ups and fixtures.
(6) The cost of a broach is higher than that of milling cutters and re-sharpening is a longer process.

8.4 Abrading processes

8.4.1 Grinding

In the car industry the main development in cylindrical grinding has been the use of multiple wheels and higher cutting speeds up to 2550 m min^{-1} and much experimental work has been carried out with wheels of Borazon. Another development includes the use of a machine with two spindles, one for external and the other for internal grinding. Figure 8.25 shows examples of high production grinding where in each case two operations proceed simultaneously with the external wheel approaching at an angle thus permitting the grinding of a face whilst also grinding the diameter. For internal work it is feasible to mount three wheels on one spindle, these being dressed simultaneously by three diamonds in one holder. Such an arrangement permits the grinding time of the bores of a drill chuck to be only 3 minutes.

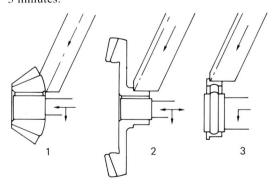

Figure 8.25 Set-ups for multi-wheel grinding operations

If re-design of a component allows it, consideration should be given to see if centreless grinding is possible, for even multi-diameter parts can be ground at such a speed that one centreless grinding machine can often cope with the output of six multi-tool lathes.

8.4.2 Wheel dressing

Diamond impregnated rollers are replacing the single diamond dresser, for a diamond roller, which in effect grinds the grinding wheel, can reduce dressing time from say 4 minutes to 8 seconds. Also, the life of a diamond roller is far greater than that of a single diamond so that a machine can run for years making the same part, without any stoppage as far as dressing equipment is concerned; only the wheels must be changed. The diamonds are set in the roller in a helical path and allow for dressing several wheels simultaneously, the roller diameter being from 150 to 400 mm.

Diamond rollers are expensive, costing as much as £6000 for a 150 mm diameter roller, while the means of applying the roller to the grinding wheel requires elaborate mechanism. The motor for rotating the roller is placed at the left hand end of the slideway, while a feed rate is applied by a ram driven by a ball screw and nut through a stepping motor. The roller is only required to make about seven revolutions for one dressing, while the feed rate is applied in steps of a few micrometres.

8.4.3 Honing

In this process a large number of cutting points are in abrading contact. This permits low stress application over a large work area, and ensures uniform metal removal at low temperature. The extremely low pressure is exerted at the lowest speed used in any mechanical abrading method, and Figure 8.26 shows the harmonic travel path of the grit. The crossing of the paths on the forward and return strokes gives a symmetrical cross hatch pattern which is characteristic of the process. Accuracy for roundness is maintained by the rotary motion of the hone, and accuracy for straightness by the reciprocating motion. The speed ratio of the two motions affects the work finish, but in general speeds for rotation for cast iron range from 60 to 150 m min^{-1} and from 15 to 21 m min^{-1} for reciprocation.

8.4.4 Diamond honing

Diamond honing is finding increasing use for units such as nitrided sleeves of pumps where geometrical tolerance can be as low as 0.0005 mm, while dia-

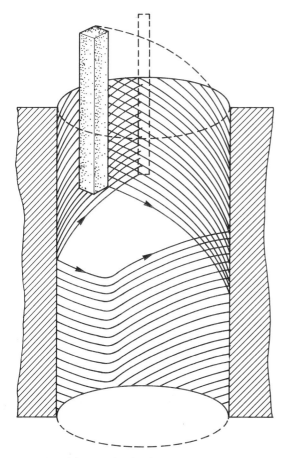

Figure 8.26 Diagram showing harmonic travel path of honing operation

mond hones will also operate on materials as diverse as carbides and ceramics.

8.4.5 Lapping

The process of surface finishing using a plate with applied abrasive is known as lapping, while the process of using a special grinding wheel for the process is known as lap honing. The work is placed between two wheels or plates and the upper member lowered to apply the cutting pressure. A rotary eccentric pin in the centre of the wheels is used to oscillate the work across the face of the wheel or lap. Figure 8.27 shows a fixture holding the workpieces which are triangular inserts for cutting tools. These are loosely held in gear shaped pockets, while rotation of the inner plate carrying pins which act as gear teeth causes epicyclic rotation of each work holding gear. Thus while the wheels rotate, the work holder gears carry the parts around the machine guided by the outer fixed pins and carry each part

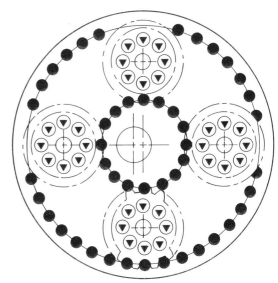

Figure 8.27 Lapping fixture for carbide inserts

across the full width of the wheels. Various abrasives are used including grits as fine as 1200 as well as diamond dust, paraffin being used as a lubricant. As an example production, gudgeon pins 25 mm diameter × 75 mm long are lapped at the rate of 500 per hour.

8.5 Pneumatic and hydraulic jigs and fixtures

It is apparent that any advantage of high speed machining is reduced if the loading and unloading of the machine results in delay. To reduce this drawback, particularly on light operations, pneumatic control is used. With air clamping the operator has a controlled and quiet medium which not only clamps the work, but can locate it or even eject it from the jig. The source of power can be transmitted to any part of a jig by flexible pipes, while the control valve lever and cylinder are standardised equipment. Refinements include pressure reducing valves and gauges, the first being useful in reducing the normal pressure of 55 N cm^{-2} for fragile components or to vary the speed of piston travel so that movements can take place in some definite relation, i.e. locating and then clamping. Standard cylinders are available in sizes from 40 to 150 mm diameter, giving pressures of 140 kg to over 1 tonne respectively, but any pressure can be increased by means of a lever mechanism.

Figure 8.28 shows the simplicity of construction using plate sections for a jig for drilling holes through an assembly of three pieces of a carbon brush holder. These are held in the same relative

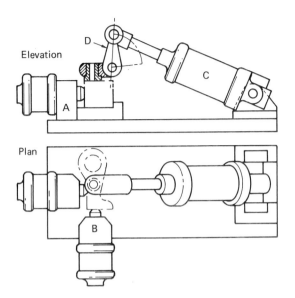

Elevation

D

A

C

Plan

B

Figure 8.28 Pneumatic drilling jig built-up from plate sections

position that they assume in the final assembly. There are two fixed cylinders A and B and the swinging cylinder C. The member D not only exerts clamping pressure but carries a drill bush. Actuation of a single lever causes all cylinders to operate simultaneously, while a two-way valve returns the pistons to allow the work to be removed.

8.5.1 *Hydraulic operation*

With hydraulic power being incorporated on many machine tools, means can be available for the control of jigs and fixtures. The advantages are similar to pneumatic control, but operating pressures are much higher, usually at 690 N cm^{-2}. A development in the problem of clamping, work transfer, and unclamping on spar milling machines and transfer machines has been solved by the incorporation of gas filled accumulators in the circuit. At one time the use of several pumps along the line was usual, but by fitting accumulators a small capacity pump has time during the machining cycle to build-up pressure in the accumulator which becomes available for clamping and other functions. Such a system has speeded up the operation to one-fifth of the time previously taken using a pump of the same capacity. On the machining of aircraft spares, 90% of the floor to floor time was taken by hand clamping, but 80% has been reduced by hydraulic operation, for by a single lever action the equivalent of 100 bolts can be tightened or released simultaneously.

8.5.2 *Hydraulic indexing*

On hydraulic machine tools having a circular table, it is advantageous to provide an accurate hole in the centre of the table for two purposes, one to locate jigs and fixtures, and the other for the supply of pressure oil for their operation. An example is an automatic machine for the manufacture of connecting rods. Four jigs are mounted on the table, three for machining and one for loading and unloading. The machining is by three fine boring machines at the machining stations, each one having two spindles for boring the large end of one rod and the small end of the other. The left-hand rod rests against a vee support with clamping by a similar vee at the top, while the right-hand rod is clamped in a similar manner but reversed. Both rods are held sideways by the long clamps operated by links and a hydraulic ram. Three boring operations are required for each hole, the rods being inverted after one revolution of the indexing table and completed at the end of the second indexing movement. The action is continuous once the machine is started, the operator merely loading, inverting, and removing the rods.

8.5.3 *Hand-operated hydraulic units*

A valuable means of clamping is by small hand-operated pump units operating at high pressure, the units being mounted on the job and being independent of any external oil supply. For milling operations the work must be well clamped to avoid any tendency to vibrate. Hydraulic clamping is by the hand units operating at a pressure of 1000 N cm^{-2}, the oil passing to a number of cylinders in the fixture. Pressure is applied by the capstan wheel, all clamps operating simultaneously, and being released by spinning back the wheel. A pressure gauge indicates the holding pressure, while a second unit is available for clamping another pair of beds while machining is proceeding on the first pair; this unit is shown at the bottom left-hand corner.

A similar unit (Power Jacks Ltd.) is used to hold a lathe tailstock for the boring operation (Figure 8.29). A previous example using mechanical clamping has been shown, but this did not possess the advantage of rapid and easy clamping obtained by fluid power. In this case pressure is applied at 823 N cm^{-2}, the first movement locating the casting sideways against the locating face and then endwise from the centre jack. Holding down pressures are applied by the clamps at different levels through the piping in the base of the fixture.

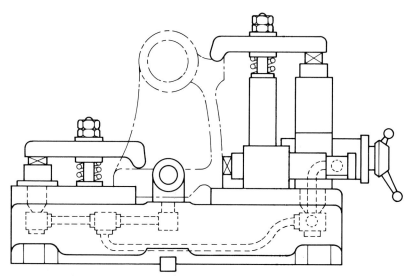

Figure 8.29 Hydraulic locating and clamping of lathe tailstock

Bibliography and addresses

JONES, E. J. *Production Engineering: Jig and Tool Design*, Butterworths, London.

TOWN and MOORE. *Manufacturing Technology* (Basic and Advanced), B. T. Batsford Ltd, London.

Section 8.1.1
Purefoy Unit Tooling Ltd, Frant, Tunbridge Wells.
WDS Tooling Aids Ltd, Newlay, Leeds, W. Yorkshire.
Destacs Units (1982), *Eureka*, Oct. 1982.
Standard Jigs and Fixtures, Sieweck Tool Co., New York.
Jig Bushes: Standards for Workshop Practice, Handbook of British Standards, Romheld Units, Ringspan Ltd, Bedford.

Section 8.2.1
'Optimising the machining of ceramics', *Production Engineer*, Feb. (1981).
De Beers (1981), 'Tool life – how synthetics rate', *Production Engineer*, Feb. (1981).
'Diamond and carbide', *Machinery and Prod. Eng.*, May (1979).
Modern Trends in Cutting Tools, SME Publications, Dearborn, Mich.
Machining – a process check list, Machinability Data Center, Metcut Research, Cincinnati, Ohio.

Section 8.2.6
SCRIVEN, A. (1979) 'Synthetic diamonds', *CME*, Oct.
'Diamond turns up trumps', *Production Engineer*, Feb. (1981).
SASON, H., *The Extending Field for Diamond Tools*, De Vries & Son Ltd., London.
ASPINALL and MYATT, *Diamond Milling Cutters*, BL Technology.
PER, A. C. 'Diamond Milling', *Machines and Tooling*, vol. XXXIX, no. 7.

Section 8.2.8
TOWN, 'Vibration', *Metalworking Production*, June (1982).
DAS, M. K. (1981), 'Machine tool chatter', *CME*, Sept.

Section 8.2.9
PROCTOR, S. (1978) 'Hollow Bar Economy', *CME*, Dec.
TI Desford Tubes Ltd., Wednesfield.

Section 8.2.11
Tracer Controlled Copying Lathes and *The Increasing Development in the Use of Copy Turning Lathes*, T.S. Harrison and Son Ltd., Heckmondwike.
TOWN, *Design and Construction of Machine Tools*, Butterworths, London.

Section 8.2.14
Photo-electric Devices, Ludwig Burger, Maschinenbaur, Germany.
Electronic Detection, Automotive Products Group, Leamington Spa.

Section 8.2.15
Osborn-Mushet super drill', 19th MTOR Conference.
'Drilling comes of age', *Machinery and Prod. Eng.*, Feb. (1979).
Carbide Tipped Drills, Yarker Holdings Ltd, Sheffield.
Komet Unisix Tool, Hahn and Kolb, Rugby.

Section 8.2.16
TOWN and MOORE, *Manufacturing Technology* (Advanced), B.T. Batsford Ltd, London.

Section 8.2.17
REVA, V. F. 'Fine boring with rigid bars', *Machines & Tooling*, vol. XXXIV, no. 4.
TOWN and MOORE, *Manufacturing Technology (Basic)*, B.T. Batsford Ltd, London.
Noise and Vibration Data, Trade & Technical Press Ltd, Morden, Surrey.

Diagrit Anti-vibration Bar, Diagrit Grinding Co. Ltd, Staplehurst, Kent.

Vibration-damping Tool Shank Material, Johnson, Matthey & Co. Ltd, London.

NEW, R. W. 'Chatter proof boring bars', Brunel University (Research).

De-vibrator Bar, Kennametal Ltd, Brierly Hills, Staffs.

Section 8.2.19

Ferritic Nitrocarburising, Wild Barfield Heat Treatment Ltd.

Section 8.3.1

DIES, R., 'Reciprocal or pendulum milling', *Workstatt und Betrieb*, vol. 87, Germany.

T.S. Harrison and Sons Ltd, Heckmondwike, W. Yorks.

Milling Machine Practice, Cincinnati Milling Machines, Birmingham.

Section 8.3.2

TOWN (1981), 'Planing Machine Developments', *CME*, May.

The Butler Machine Tool Co. Ltd, Halifax.

Kearney & Trecher Ltd, USA.

Double Cutting Machine, J. Stirk and Son Ltd, Halifax, for Canadian State Railways.

Numerically-controlled Planing, Gebr. Boehringer, Goppingen.

Section 8.3.3

MILES, K. E., *Broaching Research Results*, Denver Research Institute, USA.

Section 8.4.1

'Facts on forming for grinding wheels', *Production Engineer*, Feb. (1981).

Creep feed grinding, Bristol University Research programme.

'Abrasive belt grinding', *Machinery & Prod. Eng.*, Feb. (1980).

Section 8.4.2

NOTTER and SHAFTO, *Roller Dressing*, De Beers Diamond Tool Centre, Ascot.

C-C Grinding Machines, Henley-on-Thames.

SCHEIDEMANN, H. 'Thesis on Diamond Dressing Rolls', Institut fur Werkzeugmaschinen, Braunschweig.

WINTER, E. *Design of Diamond Dressing Rolls*, Norderstedt, Germany.

Section 8.4.4

JUCHEM, H. O., *Advances in Honing*, Technical paper, De Beers Industrie-Diamanten, Dusseldorf, W. Germany.

SHIPIRO, E. M. 'Pneumatic sizing on honing machines', *Machines and Tooling*, vol. XXXIX, no. 7.

Section 8.4.5

'Diamond powder for lapping', *Production Engineer*, Feb (1981).

Lapping Machines, Armstrong (Engineers) Ltd, Leeds.

Section 8.5

Air Jigs, Benton and Stone Ltd, Bracebridge St., Birmingham.

Maxam Equipment, Climax Engineering Ltd, Redruth, Cornwall.

Section 8.5.1

Pratt Precision Hydraulics, Bankfield Works, Halifax, W. Yorks.

Vickers-Sperry-Rand, New Lane, Havant, Hants.

Keelavite Hydraulics Ltd, Allesley, Coventry.

KUZHETSEV, 'Hydraulic appliances for machine tools', *Machines and Tooling*, vol. XXXII, no. 1.

Section 8.5.2

Electronic Indexing, A. A. Jones and Shipman Ltd, Leicester.

TOWN, *Automatic Machine Tools*, Iliffe, London.

Connecting Rods, Industrial Sales Ltd, Wilmslow, Cheshire.

Section 8.5.3

Newton Hydraulic Clamping (Power Jacks) Ltd, Hemel Hempstead, Herts.

Hydroclamp, Spencer Franklin Ltd, 11 London Bridge St., London SE1.

9

Spring design

In approaching spring-design problems, the designer must first decide on the spring configuration he will use. This is usually determined by the space available. Next, he will select material with respect to operating environment and endurance requirements as affected by application. Final solution is usually a compromise achieved by balancing many variables. The following compilation of spring design data will aid the designer in his choice of a spring to suit a specific use.

Nomenclature

b	width
C	spring index, D/d
D	mean diameter of coil
ID	inside diameter
OD	outside diameter
d	wire diameter
E	modulus of elasticity
f	deflection
G	shear modulus, or modulus of rigidity
K	design constant
K_w	Wahl constant
κ	spring rate
L	length
M	moment or torque
N	number of active coils or number of waves
P	load
r	radius
S	stress
θ	angular deflection
TS	tensile strength
t	thickness
μ	Poisson's ratio (0.3 for steel and nickel-base alloys, 0.33 for copper-base alloys)

With acknowledgements to Associated Spring, Barnes Group Inc.

9.1 Simplified material selection

Notations in the *For* and *Against* columns of Table 9.1 refer to the following specific material properties.

(1) Set point
(2) Tensile strength
(3) Ductility and formability
(4) Surface quality
(5) Fatigue properties
(6) Corrosion resistance
(7) Conductivity
(8) Temperature coefficient of modulus
(9) Relaxation
(10) High temperature properties
(11) Cost
(12) Delivery

9.2 Compression springs

9.2.1 Round-wire compression springs

The basic formulas for round-wire compression springs are:

$$\text{stress in torsion } S = \frac{8PD}{\pi d^3} K_w \text{ and } P = \frac{fGd^4}{8D^3N}$$

The materials used include music wire, carbon and alloy steels, stainless steel, copper alloys and nickel alloys.

The limitations include buckling — where the length is greater than five times the mean diameter of the coil there is danger of buckling. It is desirable to avoid a low ratio of coil diameter to wire size; D/d should preferably be between 5 and 10.

Table 9.1 Material selection (see p. 206 for key)

Material	For	Against
Flat materials		
0.90–1.05 carbon steels	1, 2, 5, 9, 12	3, 6, 7, 8, 10
0.70–0.80 carbon steels	1, 2, 5, 9, 12	6, 7, 8, 10
0.50–0.65 carbon steels	2, 3, 5, 9, 11, 12	6, 7, 8, 10
Annealed steels	3	
Pretempered steels		3
Wires		
Music wire	1, 2, 3, 5, 9, 12	6, 7, 8, 10, 11
Medium carbon steels	3, 11, 12	5, 6, 7, 8, 10
Carbon valve spring	1, 2, 3, 4, 5, 9	6, 7, 8, 12, 11
Alloy steels		
Chrome vanadium	1, 2, 3, 5, 9, 10, 12	6, 7, 8, 11
Chrome silicon-silico manganese	1, 2, 3, 5, 9, 10	6, 7, 8, 11, 12
Stainless steel	2, 3, 6, 9, 10	1, 7, 8, 11
Special wires		
Beryllium copper	1, 2, 3, 5, 6, 7, 9	8, 10, 11
Phosphor bronze	3, 6, 7, 12	1, 2, 8, 9, 10, 11
Silicon bronze	3, 6, 7, 11, 12	1, 2, 8, 9, 10
Inconel X 750	1, 3, 6, 9, 10	5, 7, 8, 11, 12
Ni-Span 'C'	3, 6, 9	7, 11, 12

9.2.2 Square-wire compression springs

The basic formulas are:

$$S = \frac{2.4PD}{t^3} K_w$$

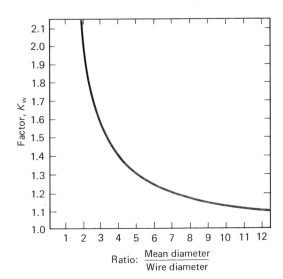

Figure 9.1 Total stress ($K_w \times S$) according to the Wahl formula

where t is the side of the square before coiling; and

$$P = \frac{fGt^4}{5.58D^3N}$$

The materials consist of carbon and alloy steels and (special) bronzes.

Square-wire compression springs are used where space is very limited and loads are heavy. Their limitations include stress raisers at the corners of the wire; the wire is not so readily available as round wire, nor is the quality as good; their service life is limited; and the wire keystones when winding to small indices.

9.2.3 Rolled- or rectangular-wire compression springs

For these

$$S = \frac{PD}{K_1 bt^2} \qquad P = \frac{K_2 Gbt^3 f}{ND^3}$$

where b is the width or larger dimension of section; t is the thickness or smaller dimension of section; and K_1 and K_2 are constants that vary with b/t.

The materials are the same as for round-wire compression springs.

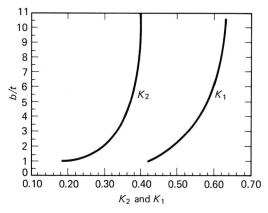

Figure 9.2 Constants for rectangular wire in torsion

These springs achieve a more advantageous use of space than do round wire springs. They can obtain smaller solid heights without altering the available space, and are often used as die springs.

Their limitations include the fact that ratios of width to thickness exceeding 3:1 become difficult to coil. They are also more expensive in material and more difficult to manufacture.

9.2.4 High-duty compression springs (valve springs, etc.)

The basic formulas for high-duty compression springs are the same as those for regular compression springs. The wire size should be the minimum within the area marked 'Area of safe stress range' on

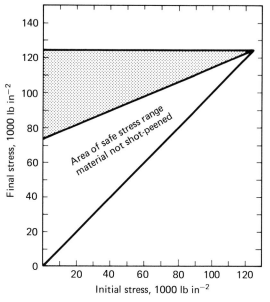

Figure 9.3 Stress range of pretempered wire (stress corrected by the Wahl factor)

Figure 9.3. To save material, a minimum number of coils should be used.

The materials consist of carbon-steel spring wire (ASTM A 230), pretempered when $\frac{1}{4}$ in (6 mm) in diameter or less, except when OD/wire size < 3, hardened and tempered after coiling when the wire above $\frac{1}{4}$ in is used. The following alloy steels are also used: silico manganese, chrome vanadium, chrome silicon.

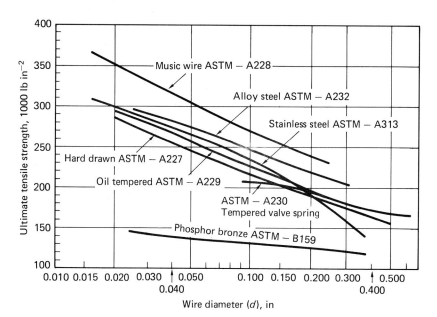

Figure 9.4 Minimum tensile strength of spring wires

High duty compression springs are used as valve springs for internal-combustion engines (car, aircraft and diesel); injector springs for diesel engines; and springs for certain electrical apparatus.

Temperatures in excess of 150°C will cause stress relaxation and loss of load. High temperatures necessitate the use of alloy steels.

9.2.5 Conical compression springs (single and double taper)

Where the taper is uniform from end to end, the same formulas apply to conical compression springs as to springs of uniform diameter, using the average mean diameter of the coils. But the formulas do not hold for any deflection greater than that required to close the weakest coil.

The materials used for these springs are the same as for round-wire compression springs.

They are used to provide a means of decreasing the solid height by the telescoping action to increase gradient and to connect large diameter and small diameter.

They are generally limited to springs of large ratios of diameter to wire size.

9.2.6 Volute springs

The basic formulas are, in general, the same as for rectangular wire springs. The materials used are flat strip steels: AISI 1065, 1075, 1095.

Volute springs are employed to provide self-damping — when coils are wound so that they rub as the spring is compressed; they offer a rapidly increasing change of rate (when coils on compression come down to the surface and bottom); and are very compact.

Their limitations are that rubbing action causes galling and wear, and thus reduces life.

9.3 Extension springs

Except for initial tension wound into extension springs, the same formulas apply as for compression springs. The stresses in ends are affected by bends.

Bending stress at point A: $S = \dfrac{16PD}{\pi d^3}\left(\dfrac{r_1}{r_3}\right)$

Torsional stress at point B: $S = \dfrac{8PD}{\pi d^3}\left(\dfrac{r_2}{r_4}\right)$

$P = P_i + kf$

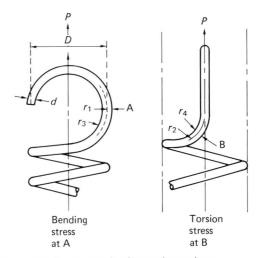

Bending stress at A   Torsion stress at B

Figure 9.5 Stress at ends of extension springs

where P_i is the initial tension, and S_i is the initial stress, 0.4 to 0.8 × (*TS/C*).

Their materials are the same as for compression springs. They have a wide range of applications, and do not suffer from buckling problems. No guiding is required.

9.4 High-temperature springs

The basic formulas for high-temperature springs are the same as those for compression and extension springs.

For temperatures in excess of 150°C and below 260°C stainless steel should be used. Between 260°C and 315°C, 17-7 PH should be used. Inconel 600 is generally appropriate for temperatures in the range 260°C and 343°C, and for temperatures between 343°C and 510°C Inconel X 750 should generally be used.

These springs are employed under the high-temperature conditions found, for example, in jet engines, reactors and high-pressure steam turbines. Their usefulness is however limited by the fact that their operating stresses are usually only moderate.

9.5 Torsion springs

The basic formulas for torsion springs are:

Round wire

$$\text{Rate} = \frac{M}{\theta} = \frac{Ed^4}{10.8DN}$$

$$N = \frac{L}{\pi D}$$

$$S = \frac{32M}{\pi d^3}$$

where L is the total wire length.

Rectangular wire

$$\text{Rate} = \frac{M}{\theta} = \frac{Ebt^3}{6.6DN}$$

$$S = \frac{6M}{bt^2}$$

where b is the axial dimension, t is the radial dimension and D is the OD radial dimension of the cross-section.

The materials are the same as for compression and extension springs.

Their applications are innumerable, where there is ample axial room.

The limitations are that they are usually not able to hold accurate loads because of friction from the mounting. Almost all these springs require some form of supporting member.

9.5.1   Torsion bars

The basic formulas for torsion bars are:

Round

$$\frac{M}{\theta} = \frac{\pi^2 d^4 G}{16L}$$

$$S = \frac{16M}{\pi d^3}$$

$$S = \frac{\pi d G \theta}{L}$$

Rectangular

$$\frac{M}{\theta} = \frac{\pi^2 G bt^3}{2L} K_2$$

$$S = \frac{2M}{bt^2 K_1}$$

The materials used are the same as for round-wire compression springs. Torsion bars offer efficient configuration (circular section best). Their end fastenings are, however, usually expensive (splined or milled).

9.5.2   Spiral (brush) springs

The formulas are:

$$S = \frac{6M}{bt^2} \qquad M = \frac{\pi Ebt^3 \theta}{6L}$$

where L is the length of the active material in the spring.

Spiral springs are made from carbon spring steel, stainless steel–beryllium copper, and phosphor bronze.

They are used where ample radial room exists; for locks, electric motors, and as brush springs.

They must be arbor mounted.

9.6   Power, motor or clock springs

The basic formulas for these springs are:

$$S = \frac{6M}{bt^2}$$

If the spring occupies half the space, then the length required is

$$L = \frac{D_D^2 - D_S^2}{2.55t}$$

where D_D is the ID of the drum and D_S is the diameter of the arbor.

The number of turns is

$$\theta = \frac{\sqrt{[2(D_S^2 + D_D^2)]} - (D_S + D_D)}{2.55t}$$

The arbor size should be approximately 15 to 25 times the stock thickness. The ratio of length of strip to thickness should be approximately 7000. Values in excess of 10 000 will cause a jumpy condition.

0.90 to 1.05 tempered carbon steel, 0.70 to 0.80 tempered carbon steel and stainless steel can all be used.

These springs find applications in spring motors, counterbalance mechanisms, reel returns and typewriter carriage returns.

Their limitations include hysteresis resulting from friction between coils and the fact that they must usually be retained in a drum.

Table 9.2 Design stresses for static service

Spring configuration	Yield point as % tensile strength			
	Ferrous materials		Non-ferrous and austenitic stainless	
	Residual stress zero	Residual stress max.	Residual stress zero	Residual stress max.
Helical compression*	45%	65%	35%	55%
Helical extension*	45%	65%	35%	—
Torsion bars	45%	65%	35%	55%
Helical torsion	—	100%	—	80%
Sprial springs	80%	100%	—	80%
Hairsprings	50%	—	50%	—
Flat springs	80%	100%	75%	110%
Belleville spring washers	120%	275%	95%	160%
Other spring washers	80%	100%	—	75%

If the spring is to be highly precise and must have minimum hysteresis, creep, and drift (zero point shift) in service, the above stresses should be halved.
*Stress is Wahl corrected.

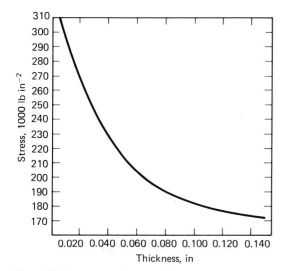

Figure 9.6 Average maximum solid stress

9.6.1 *Hairsprings*

The basic formulas for hairsprings are:

$$S = \frac{6M}{bt^2} \qquad M = \frac{\Theta \pi bt^3 E}{6L}$$

The materials used are high carbon steel; 18-8 stainless steel; NiSpan C; phosphor bronze; low-resistance bronze or MS; copper silicon; nickel silver; beryllium copper; silver.

Hairsprings find applications in clocks, watches, speedometers, meters, gauges and instruments.

Their limitations are light loads and low stresses.

9.7 Flat springs

9.7.1 *Cantilever-type flat springs*

The formulas for these springs are:

$$S = \frac{6PL}{bt^2} \qquad P = \frac{fEbt^3}{4L^3}$$

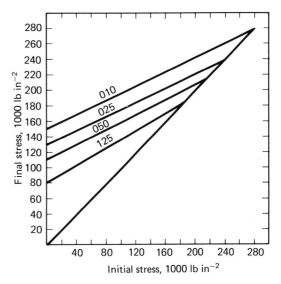

Figure 9.7 Safe endurance limits for 0.65–0.80 carbon-steel flat springs (45-48C Rockwell) tested as cantilevers

They are made from carbon steels either annealed or pretempered; alloy steels — chrome vanadium, chrome molybdenum, silico manganese; stainless steels — 300 or 400 series; phosphor bronze; beryllium copper; and Inconel X 750.

Cantilever springs may perform one or a combination of functions, and they offer unlimited scope for design, material selection and forming methods. On the other hand, they do not lend themselves to exact mathematical calculation, as do wire springs.

9.7.2 Beam-type flat springs

The formulas are:

$$S = \frac{1.5PL}{bt^2} \qquad P = \frac{4fEbt^3}{L^3}$$

The materials are the same as for the cantilever type. These springs also share the same application as the cantilever type, except when the load is to be supported at the centre, and the same limitations.

9.8 Spring washers

9.8.1 Curved spring washers

The formulas for curved spring washers are:

$$S = \frac{1.5}{t^2} PK \qquad P = \frac{4fEt^3}{(OD)^2 K}$$

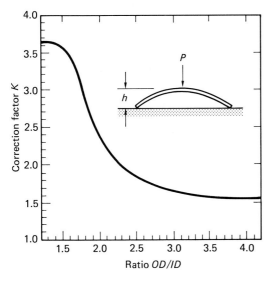

Figure 9.8 Correction factor for curved-spring washer design

They are made from the same materials as flat springs. They are used with light loads for relatively large deflections, and their limitations are usually associated with wide wall widths.

9.8.2 Wave spring washers

The basic formulas are:

$$S = \frac{3\pi PD}{4bt^2N^2}$$

$$P = \frac{Efbt^3N^4}{2.4D_W^3} \times \frac{OD}{ID}$$

$$b = \frac{OD - ID}{2} \qquad D_W = \frac{OD + ID}{2}$$

The materials are the same as for flat springs.

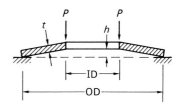

Figure 9.9 Wave spring washer

Wave spring washers are used where radial dimension is limited between a shaft and housing, and for medium loads and deflections. They are usually limited to narrow wall widths.

9.8.3 Belleville spring washers

The basic formulas for these springs are:

$$P = \frac{Ef}{(1 - \mu^2)\, Ma^2} [(h - f/2)\,(h - f)\,t + t^3]$$

$$S = \frac{Ef}{(1 - \mu^2)\, Ma^2} [C_1\,(h - f/2) + C_2 t]$$

where h is the free height minus the thickness, a is $\frac{1}{2}\, OD$; and S is the stress at the convex side of the circumference. For values of constants M, C_1 and C_2 see Figure 9.11.

The materials are the same as flat springs.

Belleville spring washers are used for heavy loads and small deflections; die springs, particularly used

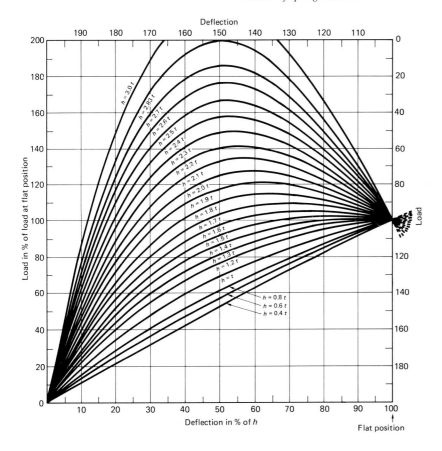

Figure 9.10 Load curves for Belleville spring washers

in combinations; and special-shaped load curves as shown in Figure 9.10. They are generally used for small deflections only.

If the washer is supported and loaded at its edges so that it is deflected beyond the flat position, then the greatest possible deflection can be utilised. Since the load/deflection curve beyond the horizontal position is symmetrical with the first part of the curve, Figure 9.10 has been labelled at the right and at the top to be read upside down for deflections beyond the horizontal. The dotted lines extending beyond the chart indicate the continuation of the curves beyond the flat.

9.10 Selection of spring materials

There is a wide variety of spring materials to meet the often conflicting needs of strength, cost, availability, surface integrity, and specialised properties. Selection of the specific materials that best meet the need usually represents a compromise among all the material characteristics. When the volume of material is large, the choice of material is highly important, for it will usually be the major cost

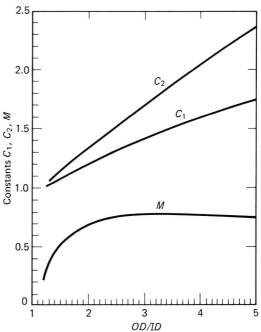

Figure 9.11 Compressive-stress constants for Belleville spring washer calculations

element. If the quantity is small, and particularly if quick delivery is important, immediate availability — rather than cost — often dictates the material choice. This is an area where consultation with the springmaker is essential.

Table 9.3 Properties of common spring materials

Common name, specification	E (10^6lb in^{-2})	G (10^6lb in^{-2})	ρ density (lb in^{-3})	Sizes available (in) Min	Max	Fatigue applications	Maximum service temperature (°C)
High-carbon steel wires							
Music ASTM A228	30	11.5	0.284	0.004	0.250	Excellent	120
Hard-drawn ASTM A227	30	11.5	0.284	0.028	0.625	Poor	120
Oil-tempered ASTM A229	30	11.5	0.284	0.020	0.625	Poor	150
Valve-spring ASTM A230	30	11.5	0.284	0.050	0.250	Excellent	150
Alloy-steel wires							
Chrome-vanadium AISI 6150	30	11.5	0.284	0.032	0.438	Excellent	218
Chrome-silicon AISI 9254	30	11.5	0.284	0.035	0.375	Fair	250
Silicon-manganese AISI 9260	30	11.5	0.284	0.025	0.375	Fair	230
Stainless-steel wires							
Martensitic AISI 410, 420	28	11	0.280	0.003	0.500	Poor	260
Austenitic AISI 301, 302	28	10.5	0.286	0.005	0.375	Good	315
Precipitation-hardening 17-7 PH	29.5	11	0.286	0.030	0.500	Good	370
Nickel-chrome A286	29	10.4	0.290	0.016	0.200	——	510
Copper-base alloy wires							
Phosphor-bronze ASTM B159	15	6.3	0.320	0.004	0.500	Good	93
Silicon-bronze ASTM B99	15	6.4	0.308	0.004	0.500	Fair	93
Beryllium-copper ASTM B197	18.5	7.0	0.297	0.003	0.500	Excellent	204
Nickel-base alloys—wire and strip							
Inconel 600	31	11	0.307	0.004	0.500	Fair	370
Inconel X750	31.5	11.5	0.298	0.004	0.563	Fair	593
Ni Span C902	27.8	9.7	0.294	0.004	0.500	Fair	93
High-carbon steel strip							
AISI 1050	30	11.5	0.284	0.010	0.125	Poor	93
AISI 1065	30	11.5	0.284	0.003	0.125	Fair	93
AISI 1075	30	11.5	0.284	0.003	0.125	Good	120
AISI 1095	30	11.5	0.284	0.003	0.125	Excellent	120
Stainess-steel strip							
Austenitic AISI 301, 302	28	10.5	0.286	0.003	0.063	Good	315
Precipitation-hardening 17-7 PH	29.5	11	0.286	0.003	0.125	Good	370
Copper-base alloy strip							
Phosphor-bronze ASTM B103	15	6.3	0.320	0.003	0.188	Good	93
Beryllium-copper ASTM B194	18.5	7.0	0.297	0.003	0.375	Excellent	204

10

Heat exchangers

The purpose of heat exchangers is to transmit thermal energy from one fluid to another which is at a lower temperature. Heat exchangers are used in a wide variety of industrial plant, buildings, transport and in the home. Major applications are to be found in chemical, petroleum and other process industries, power generation, vehicle building, space air conditioning and refrigeration.

In a few applications heat may be transferred by mixing the two fluids, the most notable instance of this being in water cooling towers. Figure 10.1 shows an example of such a tower. By direct contact between the water flowing down and the atmospheric air flowing up through the unit, the water is cooled and the air heated. Some evaporation of the water also occurs.

Most heat exchange processes, however, require that the two fluids are separated by an impervious heat-conductive intervening wall. It is this latter type of heat exchanger that is dealt with in this chapter.

Nomenclature

a cross-sectional area of conductive path

A total heat transfer surface in contact with a fluid

A_r apparent surface area of body in equation (1)

D characteristic dimension

D_e equivalent diameter of flow passage

E rate of heat transmission

f friction factor

g_c gravitational constant = 9.81 m s

G fluid mass velocity

h heat transfer coefficient fluid to surface

H height of plate

K thermal conductivity

l length of conductive path

Figure 10.1 Forced draught cooling tower

l_f height of fin

L length of tube

m ratio of area to heat flow through dividing wall to surface area in contact with fluid A

R ratio of surface areas in contact with fluids A and B

ΔP pressure drop

S specific heat (at constant pressure for gases)

t	thickness
T	temperature
ΔT	temperature rise/fall along conductive path
U	overall heat transfer coefficient
V	fluid velocity
W	fluid mass flow rate
α	absorptivity
ϵ	emissivity
θ	temperature difference fluid to surface
θ_{LM}	logarithmic mean temperature difference
μ	dynamic viscosity
ρ	fluid density
σ	Stefan–Boltzmann constant $= 56.7 \times 10^{-9}$ W m^{-2} K^{-4}

Subscripts

a,b	refer to fluids a and b
1,2	denote inlet and outlet
s,∞	relate to surface of body and surroundings respectively in equation (1)
w	refers to the dividing wall

10.1   Modes of heat transfer

10.1.1   Radiation

The experience of gaining heat by absorbing radiation from the sun is common to all. Heat can be transmitted by this mechanism in vacuo. It is a major mode of transmission in heat exchangers, however, only when the temperature difference between the two fluids is high, and is of principal significance in fired heat exchangers, particularly large boilers.

The basic equation for rate of heat transmission from a grey body radiating to its surroundings is:

$$E = A_r \epsilon \sigma \, (T_S^4 - T_\infty^4) \tag{1}$$

Equation (1) applies strictly only when the surroundings are completely black with no reflected radiation. When the body is absorbing heat from its surroundings ϵ may be substituted by α, the absorptivity of the surface, which may be different in value from ϵ. Values of ϵ vary from about 0.02 for polished copper to 0.95 for asbestos (ϵ is dimensionless).

In heat exchangers, heat is radiated between one body and another and is materially affected by what area of surface the one 'sees' of the other at a different temperature.

10.1.2   Conduction

The transmission of heat through a conductive material is analogous to electrical conduction, and for most metals thermal and electrical conductivity are directly related.

The relationship for thermal conduction (analogous to Ohm's law) is:

$$E = \frac{Ka}{l\Delta T} \tag{2}$$

In most heat exchangers, the thermal conductivity of the material that separates the two fluids is so high that it can often be regarded as infinite. Conductivity becomes important in the fins that extend from the separating wall and have a small cross-section in relation to their length (see Section 10.2.4).

10.1.3   Forced convection

When a fluid is forced by pumping to flow over a solid surface at a different temperature, heat is transmitted between the two. This is the most common mechanism in heat exchangers. The rate of heat transmission depends on a large number of factors, but is normally regarded as being related to the difference in temperature and to the surface area by the equation:

$$E = hA\theta \tag{3}$$

The heat transfer coefficient (h) itself varies with the properties of the fluid, its velocity of flow over the surface and the local configuration of the surface. It is usual to relate these by the use of the dimensionless parameters:

$$\text{Nusselt number, } Nu = \frac{hD}{K} \tag{4}$$

$$\text{Reynolds number, } Re = \frac{DG}{\mu} \tag{5}$$

$$\text{Prandtl number, } Pr = \frac{S\mu}{K} \tag{6}$$

For fully developed turbulent flow through straight tubes ($Re > 10\,000$) these parameters are related by the equation:

$$Nu = 0.023 \, Re^{0.8} \, Pr^{0.33} \tag{7}$$

and in the laminar regime ($Re < 2100$) by:

$$Nu = 1.86 \, Re^{0.33} \, Pr^{0.33} \, (D/L)^{0.33} \, (\mu/\mu_w)^{0.14} \tag{8}$$

Figure 10.2 is a graph of h against tube bore at various velocities for fresh water at 15°C.

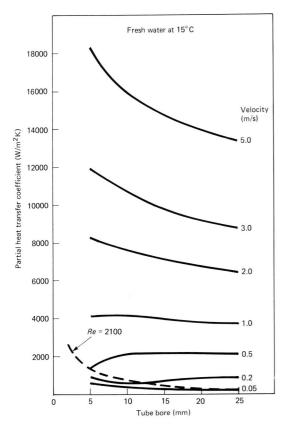

Figure 10.2 Heat transfer coefficient for water flowing through tubes

For flow over nests of tubes in a 'staggered' arrangement the relationship is represented by Figure 10.3 in which fluid properties are measured at a temperature mid-way between that of the wall and of the bulk fluid. G is measured at the minimum flow area between the tubes and D is the outside diameter of the tube. For a treatment of more complex forms of heat transfer surface, it is necessary to refer to specialist publications.

Typical values of h encountered in heat exchanger design under usual conditions are given in Table 10.1.

10.1.4 Natural convection

A fluid in contact with a heated surface will rise, due to the buoyancy effect created by the warming of the fluid in contact with the surface. This will cause a flow over the surface and will be transmitted. The usual domestic central heating 'radiator' depends mainly on this mechanism to transfer heat to the surrounding air.

The rate of heat transfer depends not only on the fluid involved and the difference in temperature between it and the surface, but also on the attitude, form and height of the surface. Natural convection usually has a negligible effect when the fluid is pumped or when flow is induced by a chimney.

Simplified equations giving heat transfer coefficients for natural convection to free, still air are:

For horizontal pipes

$$h = 2.9\,(\theta/D)^{0.25} \tag{8}$$

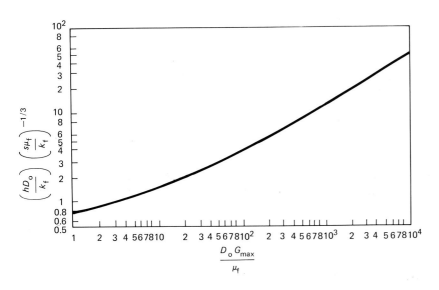

Figure 10.3 Heat transfer to banks of staggered tubes

Table 10.1 Typical *h* values in heat exchange design

	Through tubes (W m^{-2} K^{-1})	Over tubes (W m^{-2} K^{-1})
Water (including sea water)	4000–6000	5000–10 000
Lubricating oil		400–800
Air at atmospheric pressure		50–200
Air at 8 bar		200–500

For horizontal, upward-facing, flat surfaces

$$h = 2.0 \, \theta^{0.25} \qquad\qquad (9)$$

For vertical flat surfaces up to 600 mm in height

$$h = 1.35 \, \theta / H \qquad\qquad (10)$$

10.1.5 Boiling

The boiling of a liquid in contact with a surface at a temperature above its boiling point involves the migration of the generated vapour away from the surface and so a mass transfer as well as a heat transfer takes place.

There are various modes of boiling and the process is complex. Boiling rate increases with temperature difference but a point can be reached at which the vapour substantially blankets the surface, thus limiting access to the liquid phase. At this point the heat transfer rate falls.

Water is by far the most common fluid involved in boiling heat transfer and the various refrigerants probably rank next. For these, typical values of *h* are:

Water   5000–8000 W m^{-2} K^{-1}
Refrigerants   500–1000 W m^{-2} K^{-1}

The rate of vapour generation is, of course, related to the latent heat of the fluid.

10.1.6 Condensation

This is also a combined heat and mass transfer process in which molecules of vapour migrate to a surface which is at a temperature below the boiling point of the liquid and there they change to the liquid phase when in contact with the surface.

Condensation usually occurs in the film-wise mode, the surface becoming covered with a thin film of liquid. The heat transfer coefficient obtainable is increased by an order of magnitude in the drop-wise mode, in which the condensate forms into discrete droplets on the surface. As the latter mode cannot be assured, condenser designs do not rely on it.

For water and refrigerants typical values of *h* are:

Water   5000 W m^{-2} K^{-1}
Refrigerants   1000 W m^{-2} K^{-1}

Values are considerably reduced by the presence of a significant amount of any non-condensable gas.

10.2 Sizing heat exchangers

10.2.1 Required heat transfer surface area

The transmission of heat from one fluid to another through a heat conductive wall involves a drop in temperature between the hotter fluid and the wall, through the wall itself and then between the wall and the second fluid. This is represented in Figure 10.4. These temperature drops can be regarded as being due to thermal resistances, those associated with the fluids being the reciprocals of the respective heat transfer coefficients.

These are combined to give an overall heat transfer coefficient by the relationship:

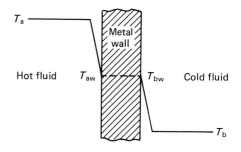

Figure 10.4 Temperature drops through element of heat exchanger

$$\frac{1}{U} = \frac{1}{h_a} + \frac{n}{h_b} + \frac{mt}{K_w} \qquad (11)$$

This is a statement that the overall thermal resistance equates to the sum of the individual resistances in series. The surface area required to achieve a given rate of heat transmission is then derived from:

$$E = UA_a \, \theta_{LM} \qquad (12)$$

When the flow of the two fluids through the heat exchanger is in substantially opposite directions (counterflow)

$$\theta_{LM} = \frac{(T_{a2} - T_{b1}) - (T_{b2} - T_{a1})}{\log_e \left(\dfrac{T_{a2} - T_{b1}}{T_{b2} - T_{a1}} \right)} \qquad (13)$$

and when in the same direction (co-flow)

$$\theta_{LM} = \frac{(T_{a1} - T_{b1}) - (T_{a2} - T_{b2})}{\log_e \left(\dfrac{T_{a1} - T_{b1}}{T_{a2} - T_{b2}} \right)} \qquad (14)$$

The value of θ_{LM} in these two cases can be obtained by using the nomogram shown in Figure 10.5. The former gives the highest and the latter the lowest possible value for given terminal temperatures. For other flow arrangements such as cross flow (which is met in the design, for instance, of vehicle radiators) the value lies between the two.

When there is no condensation or boiling of either fluid, the heat balance equation

$$E = W_a \, S_a \, (T_{a1} - T_{a2}) = W_b \, S_b \, (T_{b2} - T_{b1}) \qquad (15)$$

must be satisfied.

When there is uniform boiling or condensation on one side of the heat exchanger, the appropriate boiling point temperature may be used as the value for both terminal temperatures in the equations for logarithmic mean temperature difference.

If condensation of a vapour takes place when an inert gas cools (such as when chilling air in an air conditioning system) a strict analytical approach is complex and approximate methods of sizing are often employed.

10.2.2 Fouling of heat transfer surfaces

Not all fluids handled in heat exchangers are free of solid matter in suspension. Cooling water derived

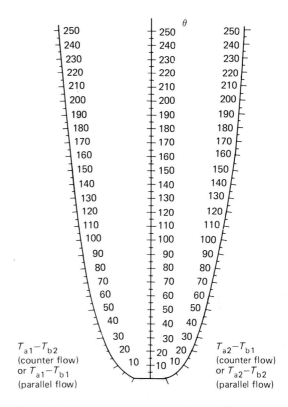

Figure 10.5 Logarithmic mean temperature difference

from the sea, a river or a cooling pond contains matter that will to some extent deposit on the heat transfer surfaces.

Allowance is made in Equation (11) for the thermal resistance of the deposited film by the addition of a term often designated the fouling factor. For cooling waters commonly encountered, values vary from $0.0001 \ m^2 \ K \ W^{-1}$ for fresh water to $0.001 \ m^2 \ K \ W^{-1}$ for untreated cooling tower water. Where a secondary surface is used on the other side of the dividing wall, this fouling resistance must be multiplied by n.

If the surface temperature is high enough (usually assumed to be above about 45°C) scale may form on the heat transfer surfaces caused by solids in solution in cooling water. This will progressively increase in thickness, sometimes to the extent of eventually blocking the water flow passages. This condition should obviously be avoided.

Some cooling applications in chemical plant give rise to relatively rapid and severe fouling as a result of the deposition of crystalline material from the process fluid. This can be so extensive as to require that the heat transfer surface area provided be several times that needed to meet the specified performance when the surfaces are clean, so as to avoid the heat exchanger having to be cleaned too frequently.

Fouling by atmospheric air, when it occurs significantly, usually takes the form of partial blockage of the inlet face of the heat exchanger, so increasing the resistance to air flow rather than imposing an additional thermal resistance on the heat transfer surface.

Where deposits are not readily removable by chemical means, those surfaces subject to significant fouling should be accessible for mechanical cleaning.

10.2.3 Secondary surface

Secondary (or extended) surface, usually in the form of fins projecting from the dividing walls of a heat exchanger, can greatly reduce its size, weight and cost.

Fins are exposed on both sides to the fluid with which they are in contact. They may be made of relatively thin material and can be placed as closely together as considerations of fouling by solid matter allow. In the right circumstances, therefore, relatively little metal may be used to increase substantially the density of heat transfer surface. Sometimes the secondary surface may be made of a cheaper material than that of the dividing walls.

Examination of Equation (11) reveals that if any of the terms on its right hand side is much lower in value than the others, then variation in the values of the others will have relatively little effect on the sum. In the great majority of cases, the thermal conductivity of the dividing wall material is so high that the term incorporating it gives a value that is much lower than either of the other two. It then becomes evident that, if either of the other two terms is substantially the lower, it will control the overall thermal resistance. There is, therefore, benefit to be gained in adding secondary surface on the side of the dividing walls where the heat transfer coefficient is much lower than on the other side, with the aim of making the first two terms in the equation roughly equal. It should be noted that if secondary surface is added to side 'a' only, m is equal or nearly equal to n in Equation (11).

Secondary surface is added to both sides in some instances where heat transfer coefficients are not widely dissimilar.

10.2.4 Fin efficiency

Heat flow through a fin is by conduction towards or away from the dividing wall. To minimise the cost of material, fins are usually very thin, particularly in air-cooled heat exchangers where 0.1 mm or less is

normal and as little as 0.025 mm is used. Although high thermal conductivity material is employed, this small thickness can give a significant temperature gradient along a fin, so reducing the overall effectiveness of the secondary surface.

Allowance for this is made by applying a fin efficiency factor to the secondary surface area. This is dependent on a parameter $l_f \sqrt{(2h/Kt)}$.

In Figure 10.6 fin efficiency is plotted against this parameter for the two cases of straight fins and circular fins on cylindrical tubes, the fins being of constant thickness. In most instances a fin efficiency over 90% is aimed at in heat exchanger design.

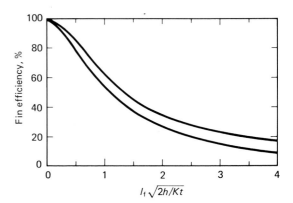

Figure 10.6 Fin efficiency

10.2.5 Pressure drop

Skin friction and form drag occasion a loss in the pressure of a fluid being pumped through a heat exchanger. With smooth-walled straight tubes of constant cross-section, the friction factor, f, has the discrete relationship with Re shown in Figure 10.7.

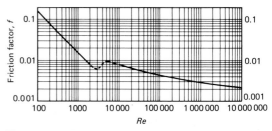

Figure 10.7 Friction factor through tubes

Friction factor is defined by the equation:

$$\Delta P = \frac{4f\rho V^2}{2g_c} \times \frac{L}{D_e} \tag{16}$$

Entry and exit losses should also be taken into account. As a rough guide these may be taken as $1.5 \, \rho V^2/2g_c$.

The pressure drop for a fluid flowing over a bank of plain cylindrical tubes on equilateral triangular pitch may be derived from Figure 10.8. The number of rows deep to flow is substituted for L in Equation (16) and velocity is based on the projected area of the bank.

Other forms of heat exchanger exhibit similar characteristics, many of which are available in published literature.

Where flow of a fluid over a heat transfer surface is induced by natural convection in an enclosed system rather than in free air (for example by use of a chimney) the buoyancy effect of the heated fluid determines the driving pressure available to promote the flow.

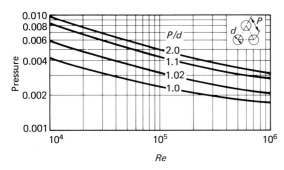

Figure 10.8 Pressure drop over banks of round tubes

10.2.6 Sizing procedure

The known variables necessary to determine a heat exchanger design are:

(1) required rate of heat transmission,
(2) inlet temperature of each fluid,
(3) flow rate of at least one of the fluids,
(4) physical properties of each fluid,
(5) limitation of pressure drop for each fluid, and
(6) operating pressure of each fluid.

The flow rate of the other fluid, if not fixed, can be used as a variable in the optimisation of the design: a value must be assumed so that the outlet temperature of both fluids can be determined.

An assumption then has to be made about the arrangement of flow (counterflow, co-flow or one of the many intermediate cases) to derive the value of θ_{LM}. This leads to a value of the product UA which must be achieved to satisfy the design requirements.

With knowledge of the heat transfer and pressure loss characteristics of the form of heat exchange surfaces to be used and assuming values of fouling factor for both fluids (where applicable), it is then possible to arrive at a design which will meet the stipulated thermal requirements within the limits of pressure drop. This is usually done by an iterative process of calculation.

In air-cooled heat exchangers, the cooling air flow is frequently a variable whose value can be selected by the heat exchanger designer, as is the cooling air pressure drop. This then requires the matching of the heat exchanger and fan characteristics.

Since there is often a choice of form of heat transfer surface, flow rate of one fluid and sometimes of flow arrangement, several designs may meet the requirements equally well.

10.3 Types of heat exchanger

There is a surprisingly large variety of constructions of heat exchanger, each designed for differing services. The following are amongst those most widely used.

10.3.1 Shell and tube designs

For heat exchangers between two liquids, and for many condensing applications having a liquid cooling medium (usually water), this is the most usual type.

It comprises a bundle of cylindrical tubes in either a triangular or a square pitch array, the tubes being secured and sealed to a tube plate at each end, usually by expanding the tube ends within corresponding holes in the plates. The bundle is enclosed within a cylindrical shell which contains the fluid in contact with the outer surfaces of the tubes, and is provided with branches for ingress and egress of that fluid. One or both tube plates may be sealed to the shell depending on the particular design. Headers, sometimes called channels, are sealed to the tube plates and distribute the fluid through the tubes.

Baffles are normally used to direct the flow of fluid over the tubes in applications that do not involve change of phase. There are two common systems of baffles which are shown in diagrammatic form in Figure 10.9.

In the segmental system, circular plates of a diameter to fit the shell each have a segmental

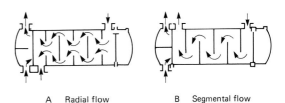

A   Radial flow   B   Segmental flow

Figure 10.9 Common baffle systems

portion removed to provide a 'D' shape. These plates, perforated with the appropriate pattern of holes to receive the tubes, are spaced along the length of the tube bundle, alternate plates having the cut portion diametrically opposite that of its neighbours. This system directs the flow from one side to the other across the whole diameter of the bundle. Tubes are usually sited within the cut, through which the fluid is transferred from one pass to the next.

Disc-and-doughnut and disc-and-ring are terms used to describe variants of the second common system whereby the fluid is caused to flow radially inwards and outwards in alternate passes over the tubes; this is achieved by the use alternately of discs materially smaller in diameter than the shell and discs with a large central hole but an external diameter to fit the shell.

This latter system is generally accepted to give a more predictable performance of heat exchanger as by-pass between passes as well as round the outside of the tube bundle can be better controlled. The segmental system is however more widely used in process plant heat exchangers.

This type of heat exchanger may be constructed with both tube plates permanently secured to the shell (fixed tubeplate design) or with the bundle made removable. The former construction is unsuitable where differential expansion of the tubes and shell may cause unduly high loads on the tube to tubeplate joints, unless the shell incorporates an expansion bellows.

In removable bundle designs, the header at the expansion end may be secured to the tubeplate or to the shell. In the latter case both the shell and the header are sealed to the tubeplate by means of joints which will allow relative movement. Interposing a separate ring between the two joints, as illustrated in Figure 10.10, mixing of the two fluids cannot occur due to joint failure. A typical heat exchanger of this type, having disc and doughnut baffles, is shown in Figure 10.11.

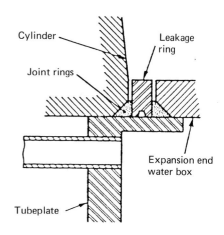

Figure 10.10 Safe expansion end sealing system

Other constructions are depicted in Figure 10.12. The internal floating head varieties are particularly suitable where the shell side fluid is usually hot, aggressive or at moderately high pressure. Under such circumstances, and particularly when one fluid is at very high pressure, a heat exchanger is often designed so that the high pressure fluid is inside the tubes, even though this may result in a unit that is substantially larger than if the fluid were on the shell side. The additional cost of a thick-walled shell, or one made from a more expensive material, is usually much higher than for the corresponding headers.

Whilst plain tubes are the most widely used in this type of heat exchanger, there are occasions, for instance in cooling oil by means of water, when secondary surface on the outside of the tubes can be beneficial. One form is obtained by rolling a thread form into the tube surface. Another uses fins, perforated with a pattern of holes, through which the tubes pass and to which they are bonded to provide a low thermal resistance path between them. An example of this is shown in Figure 10.13.

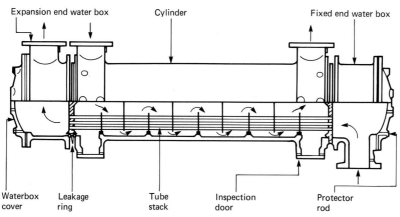

Figure 10.11 Shell and tube heat exchanger with disc and doughnut baffles

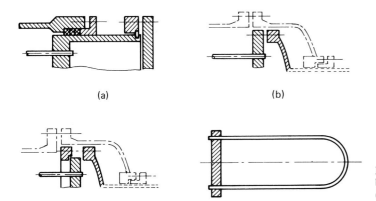

(a)   (b)

(c)   (d)

Figure 10.12 Varieties of removable tube bundles: (a) outside packed floating head; (b) pull-through floating head; (c) floating head with backing device; (d) U-tube bundle

Figure 10.13 Shell and tube heat exchanger with secondary surface

Secondary surface is occasionally used inside tubes, particularly in the refrigeration industry.

10.3.2 Plate type

Developed originally for milk processing, the demountable plate type is suitable for liquid-to-liquid heat exchange, liquor concentration and other applications involving steam heating. An exploded view of the heat exchanger is shown in Figure 10.14 and a heat transfer plate in Figure 10.15. It is widely used in food processing, partly because of its accessibility for mechanical cleaning, but has some application in the engineering and chemical fields. It is particularly advantageous when the required ratio of temperature change of one fluid to the available difference between the two fluids is large, such as in some heat recovery applications.

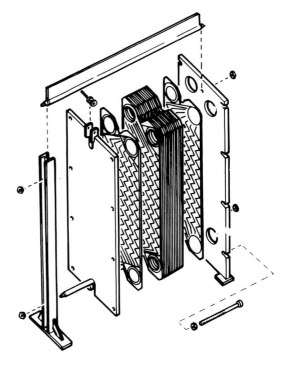

Figure 10.14 Plate heat exchanger assembly

The plates, pressed with a pattern of corrugations to provide greater strength and turbulence in the flow passages, are suspended from a rail and clamped together. Each plate has four ports which serve as conduits for the two fluids. A seal, housed within a peripheral groove pressed into the plate surface, allows access to one of the fluids from two of these parts at opposite ends of the plate, whilst denying access to the other fluid passing through the remaining two parts. This seal is reversed on alter-

Figure 10.15 Heat transfer plate

nate plates so that streams of the two fluids are interleaved, heat transfer taking place through the plates. Inlet and outlet branches fitted to the end plate communicate with the four ports.

10.3.3 *Air-cooled secondary surface types*

The use of fins in heat exchangers using air to cool a liquid is almost universal. The basic forms commonly used are illustrated in Figure 10.16.

Type A (top left) is limited to low-pressure applications and is used mainly for vehicle jacket water radiators. The flat-sided tubes minimise form drag for the air passing between them. The corrugated fins are often louvred to enhance heat transfer.

Type B (top centre) having fins perforated with holes into which the tubes fit, is suitable for use with

pressure inside the tubes up to about 10 bar. Tubes may be flat-sided or elliptical. Applications are for water, oil and compressed air cooling and some condensing duties. As with type A, tubes are usually bonded by soldering to the fins.

Type C (top right), having round tubes, can be used for still higher pressures but the air-side pressure loss characteristics are poorer than for the constructions with flat sided tubes. In one variant, tubes are expanded to give the necessary intimate contact with the fins. Because of the relatively low cost of construction of this type it is finding increasing favour for automotive radiators. This same form is used in the refrigeration industry for refrigerant condensing and in air conditioning for cooling air. A further application is in compressed air cooling.

Type D (bottom left) has a secondary surface bonded to both sides of the intervening walls. When joints are brazed, it has considerable strength and is used in the construction of small air-cooled oil coolers and of air-to-air heat exchangers for aerospace applications, the material being aluminium.

Type E (bottom centre) has a ribbon wound helically onto a round tube. These individual tubes form bundles in large heat exchangers extensively used in the petroleum and chemical processing industries.

Type F (bottom right) employs wire in place of the ribbon in Type E. This has the characteristic of higher heat transfer but also a higher pressure drop.

Heat exchangers are constructed with a single piece matrix of type A and B in which the tubes are sealed into tubeplates and headers attached by soldering as in the car radiator in Figure 10.17, or bolted on. Alternatively the matrix is built up from a multiplicity of narrow elements, each with its own headers connected to distribution manifolds, which can be readily removed for cleaning or replacement. This type is shown in Figure 10.18. It is employed for relatively large units.

Figure 10.19 illustrates a car radiator and Figure 10.20 an engine charge air cooler, both with matrices of type C. The small air-cooled oil cooler in Figure 10.21 is based on the construction of Type D.

Figure 10.22 shows a typical bundle of tubes of type E, with headers at each end. Larger air-cooled units are normally fitted with one or more fans to provide the required cooling air flow.

10.4 Materials of construction

The material of the tubes in heat exchangers varies with the application.

For sea-water cooled units, aluminium brass, 70/30 copper-nickel and 90/10 copper-nickel (see BS 2871, Part 3) are the most widely used.

Figure 10.16 Basic forms of secondary surface matrix

Figure 10.17 Automotive radiator

Figure 10.18 Sectional radiator

Figure 10.19 Motor vehicle radiator with thermoplastic headers

In air-cooled heat exchangers with matrices of types A and B, the tubes are mostly of 70/30 brass formed from foil and either a lock-seam or welded seam. Copper and aluminium are used in the construction of type C where the contact with fins is obtained by expanding the tubes. The tubes onto which ribbon or wire is wound in types E and F may be carbon steel or any other material suitable for the fluid being cooled.

Fins in all types of matrix must have high conductivity. Copper and aluminium satisfy this requirement and are relatively low cost and easily fabricated: they are almost invariably used. Heat exchangers based on type D matrix are normally constructed entirely from aluminium, the components being brazed or welded together.

Carbon steel is used for the fabrication of shell-and-tube heat exchanger shells and many structural components in almost all types of heat exchangers. Cast iron is also used for manufacture of shells and headers. For sea-water-cooled applications headers may also be made from gun metal.

For tube-plates in shell-and-tube heat exchangers, naval brass, aluminium bronze or Muntz metal are common for raw-water-cooled units but for process plants these may be of carbon steel.

The plates in plate heat exchangers are pressed from stainless steel for most food processing applications, but when saline water is involved titanium is the most usual material.

Non-metals are not extensively employed in heat exchangers except for seals. There is, however, a growing use of headers moulded from thermoplastic in volume-production car radiators.

Figure 10.20 Engine charge air cooler

Figure 10.21 Air-cooled oil cooler

Figure 10.22 Ribbon tube heat exchanger bundle

Bibliography

ASHRAE (1977) *ASHRAE Handbook – Fundamentals*, American Society of Heating, Refrigeration and Air Conditioning Engineers.

BUTTERWORTH, D. *Introduction to heat transfer*, Oxford University Press.

GRAY, W. A. and MULLER, R. *Engineering calculations in radiative heat transfer*, Pergamon Press.

KAYS, W. and LONDON, A. L. *Compact heat exchangers*, McGraw-Hill.

KERN, D. C. *Process heat transfer*, McGraw-Hill.

McADAMS, W. H. *Heat transmission*, McGraw-Hill.

ROHSENOW, W. M. and HARTNETT, J. P. *Handbook of heat transfer*, McGraw-Hill.

SIMONSON, J. R. *Engineering heat transfer*, Macmillan.

11

Computer-aided design

The advent of the computer has taken the drudgery out of many of the tasks that face the designer. Not only do computers help with numerical work, they also offer graphics facilities and automated draughting equipment.

Nevertheless the designer's skills are still required, and in fact new skills are required if a designer is to choose the right equipment for the task in hand. Even more difficult is choosing the right software, i.e. the right computer program, since programs are not all universally compatible; some can only be used with specific hardware.

In due course no doubt rationalisation will make the task of choosing software and relevant hardware easier. In the meantime the designer must carefully consider his options, possibly in conjunction with the various computer advice bureaux — both commercial concerns and those set up by the government and various institutions.

Several programs exist which can be used directly by a designer working at a computer terminal, and one of these is described below. It is described in the context of its use in the design of a building, and in particular of the ductwork associated with the structure.

11.1 COMPASS

COMPASS (Computer Orientated Manufacturing, Production and Scheduling System) is an integrated software system used by draughtsmen at all stages of the design process. It is a design aid which reduces

The material on COMPASS first appeared in *Chartered Mechanical Engineer*, and is reproduced here by permission. The COMPASS system was developed jointly by CADCentre, Cambridge, and Henry Hargreaves and Sons Ltd, Bury.

the tedious aspects of drawing, but retains the creative aspects of a draughtsman's work. Instead of working at a drawing board, he builds up his layout at a computer terminal. By use of simple commands, he creates a 3D model of the structure, e.g. of a building and the ductwork within it.

Using the interactive graphics facilities, he can view any portion of his layout from any angle. He may, therefore, produce isometric views extremely quickly. There are also facilities for perspectives and for the removal of hidden lines.

There are extensive error-checking facilities, but no attempt is made to rectify errors automatically. The draughtsman has the responsibility for modifying his layout to remove errors detected by COMPASS.

The output from COMPASS comprises fully dimensioned drawings and manufacturing, timing, and purchasing documents. When a layout is complete, the user is able to add dimensions and annotation to his final drawing. The 3D model of the ductwork and structure is held in database files, and this design data is transferred to a serial file to allow manufacturing take-off. The documents produced from COMPASS are suitable for use on the shop floor, since they contain all the necessary manufacturing information.

11.2 Design sequence

Ductwork components are manufactured from sheet metal and come in three cross-sectional shapes — rectangular, circular, and flat oval. The link from design to manufacture involves the production of shop floor instructions to cut and form sheet metal into the appropriate shapes. This scheduling function begins with the classification according to component type, shape, joint types, and other design

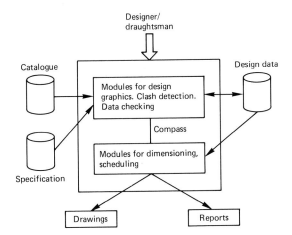

Figure 11.1 COMPASS structure

parameters, of every manufactured component on the drawing. Similar components are grouped together and allocated identical 'schedule numbers'. Programs are then run on a desk-top calculator in order to generate detailed manufacturing data. At this stage, documentation is also generated for use in requisition of materials, transportation, and finally erection of ductwork on site.

11.2.1 Component catalogue and design rules

Draughtsmen creating a design need to have access to a catalogue of standard components. In COMPASS, this catalogue is held as a database (i.e. a structured file) on disc. Therefore, one of the initial tasks is to create this catalogue data. For each ductwork component, a 3D geometrical model is built up out of standard primitives such as boxes, cylinders, tori, etc. This model is used to give a geometrical representation of the component on the drawing, and to provide parameterised dimensional information. In general, catalogue components do not have a fixed size, and dimensions are dependent upon parameters defined at the design stage — for example length or radius.

The task of creating a catalogue will only need to be performed once by an organisation using COMPASS, although modifications and additions will be required as manufacturing technology and standards improve. The draughtsman producing a drawing requires no knowledge of how to set up the catalogue, and in fact will not be allowed to modify it. This is the task of a system administrator.

As a complement to the catalogue, COMPASS also provides a specification facility. This allows design and manufacturing codes of practice to be held in the system. These codes are defined in terms

of a table, which is input to the system at the beginning of a contract. According to the values of certain component parameters — for example cross-section or radius — the table defines the particular catalogue component to be used. Manufacturing restrictions, such as maximum permitted cross-section dimensions, can be held in the specification and will be common to all contracts. However, there is the flexibility to incorporate any special customer requirements for a particular contract. Like the catalogue, the specification structure is hidden from the draughtsman and he will not need to modify it.

11.2.2 Detailed design

When a draughtsman begins a new drawing of, for example, a building, the specification and catalogue data will have been set up and are, therefore, available for his use. Working from marked up consultants' drawings, he first defines the structure of the building, including columns, walls, slabs, and restricted zones. These are created and positioned using simple commands. At this stage, the draughtsman also defines grid lines, required for reference when positioning items. The 3D capability allows him to verify his input by viewing the structure from any angle on a graphics screen. When he is satisfied that this structural input is complete and correct, he moves on to the next stage in the design process — defining the ductwork.

In the manual design process, the functions of ductwork layout and ductwork design are separated. COMPASS combines these into a single function, with the draughtsman designing individual components from the start. The only exception is that straight duct runs, and lengths of flexible ducting, do not need to be defined explicitly since there are automatic features to generate these.

Any ductwork layout contains a number of branches. Each branch contains a number of connected components and has a start and an end point, known as the 'head' and 'tail' of the branch. The draughtsman using COMPASS builds up his design one branch at a time, although there are facilities for making copies of branches.

For each branch, the draughtsman first defines the positions of the head and tail. He also defines some other branch parameters, such as its shape and the cross-section dimensions at the head and tail. He then designs each component in the branch in turn. Having defined the component type and other relevant parameters, such as length and off-sets, he uses a single SELECT command, which automatically selects the correct catalogue component for the situation. The rules for selecting components are held in the specification, which is input at the beginning of a contract. Therefore, the draughtsman is prevented from using components which cannot

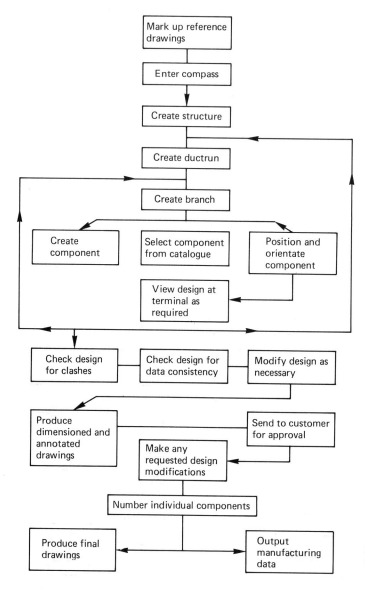

Figure 11.2 The process of ductwork design using COMPASS

be manufactured or are otherwise unsuitable. The SELECT command also automatically creates joints at the two ends of the component, again with reference to the specification and catalogue. Joint types are typically dependent upon the shape of the branch, its cross-section dimensions, and the velocity of the air which the ductwork is designed to pass. Having positioned the first component at the head of the branch, subsequent components are selected and then linked using CONNECT commands.

The draughtsman has many other design facilities available to him, enabling him to build up the design quickly and accurately. However, COMPASS does not automatically arrange the ductwork within the

available space. It is a tool which complements the draughtsman's skill and experience.

At any stage in the ductwork design process, the draughtsman can verify his design by displaying a portion of it on a graphics screen. By using a number of selected views of the ductwork and structure, he can very quickly detect any obvious errors.

However, more sophisticated error-checking facilities are provided by two modules within COMPASS. The first of these is a clash-detection module, which will check the 3D model of the ductwork and structure for clashes. If a clash is detected, an error message is produced and the draughtsman can then amend his design. Also built into COMPASS is a

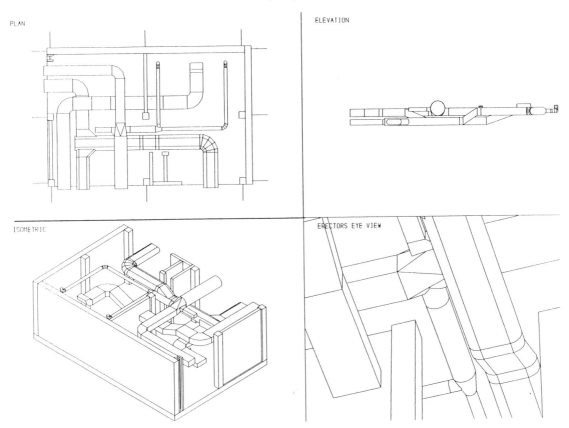

Figure 11.3 Plan, elevation and isometrics of a single area of COMPASS design

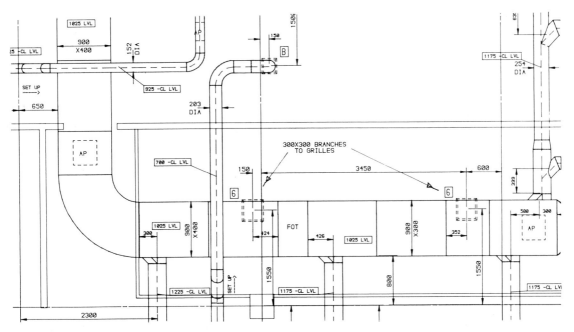

Figure 11.4 Part of a plan of a dimensional and annotated drawing produced by COMPASS

data-consistency checker. This enables the user to check that his design is consistent. For example, there are tests to confirm that all ductwork components have been positioned and orientated, and that there are matching joints between adjacent components. Again, an error message is produced for each error detected, and the draughtsman then makes the appropriate modifications.

11.2.3 Production of drawings

When a consistent, clash-free design has been obtained, the draughtsman produces drawings of it. At this stage, they will typically consist of a plan view of the ductwork and structure, with a number of elevations of selected areas. The draughtsman will not normally wish to show any lines on surfaces which are hidden from view, and COMPASS provides a facility for removing these 'hidden lines'.

The next stage is the dimensioning and annotation of the drawing. Working at a graphics terminal, the draughtsman specifies where he requires dimensions. Since positional information is held explicitly in the 3D model built up during the design process, COMPASS can calculate these dimensions automatically from the design data. Therefore, the user does not need to perform any calculations by hand. Notes and other annotation are also added to the drawing at this stage. At the end of this process, a fully detailed, dimensioned, and annotated drawing is produced. It contains all the information which would appear on an equivalent manually produced drawing. When complete, this drawing is output on a high quality plotter.

The initial design task is now complete, and the drawing is sent off to the customer for approval. Any modifications requested may be easily incorporated into the design by changing the design model. Drawings of the modified design are then generated. At this stage an automatic labelling facility within COMPASS will be used to put item numbers, required for manufacture, on individual components. A number of isometric drawings may also be produced to aid visualisation when the ductwork is erected on site.

11.2.4 Production of manufacturing information

As described earlier, a model of the complete design is held in a structured file on disc. Having produced the final drawing, the next stage is the generation of manufacturing and timing data, and any data required for requisition sheets or other documents. Given the type of component and its dimensions, algorithms can produce data such as the number of

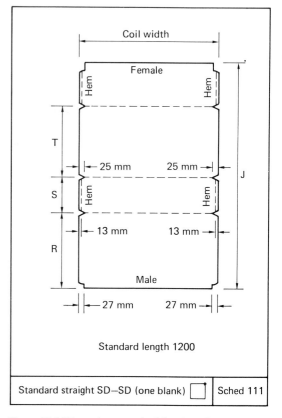

Figure 11.5 Dimensions required for shop floor manufacture of standard straights

blanks required, machine settings, time to manufacture, and other manufacturing data. To take full advantage of COMPASS, new algorithms can be written to determine component schedule numbers, and others to generate reports. Therefore, the whole scheduling function, which previously had to be carried out by hand, can be fully integrated into COMPASS. By the use of a limited number of commands, the complete set of design data generated by the draughtsman is processed to produce, as line-printer output, all the documents required for manufacture.

11.3 Benefits

The COMPASS system offers a number of obvious benefits:

(1) Two stages in the design process, layout and detailing, have been combined into a single design function. The scheduling function now simply involves the output of data already held in the system. Therefore, there is a significant reduction in the delay between drawing

approval and ductwork manufacture, and less possibility of errors.

(2) The use of a standard component catalogue and a contract specification, containing design and manufacturing restrictions, provides increased standardisation. Special components, which need to be manufactured from drawings, are expensive to produce. COMPASS enables the number of specials to be kept to a minimum.

(3) The full 3D modelling and associated visualisation features which COMPASS provides offer many advantages. In regions of limited space, where co-ordination is a major problem, the possibility of errors is greatly reduced. A design can be developed quickly and accurately.

(4) Design changes can be costly, and the consistent modification of drawings may be time-consuming. COMPASS enables these design changes to be made quickly and simply. The modified drawings and manufacturing data may then be generated automatically.

(5) COMPASS is popular with the draughtsmen who use it. It eliminates the task of drawing at a board, which can be tedious and time-consuming. However, it retains the creative aspects of their work, enabling their skills to be used more effectively.

The result has been the production of a software system of direct relevance to industry. It is an integrated system, from design through to manufacture, but it has been developed to allow for future interfaces to other packages, such as stock control. Links to NC sheet metal cutting machines are another future possibility. Sheet metalwork manufacture is a relatively low technology industry. However, the COMPASS development has shown how sophisticated CAD techniques, such as 3D modelling, can provide real benefits in such an application.

Bibliography

CONSTANTINOU, S., LEONARD, R. and RATHMILL, K. (1980) 'The operational procedures of a Computer Graphics Aided Design and Manufacturing System', Computer Graphics 80 Conference, Brighton.

CONSTANTINOU, S., LEONARD, R. and RATHMILL, K. (1980) 'The production of layout drawings by use of a 3D CAD system', Engineering Design Conference, Birmingham.

PART 2

12

Design—to expand or contract out?

12.1 To expand or contract out?

Over the past few years, either by good management, or by sheer necessity, greater attention has been given to staff complementing and the efficient control of man-hours per job and overtime costs. Nowhere has this exercise been more keenly applied than in the Design Department — Planning, Development Engineering and Drawing Offices. These functions are often considered as lump sum expenditures in a company's annual balance sheets, since it is difficult to assess their actual contributions to the profit and loss accounts. In times of financial crisis, when no new projects are being planned, the opportunity is invariably taken to cut back on the employment of the oft-called non-productive staff, with the inherent problems associated with re-expansion when more favourable conditions occur.

When confronted with the prospects of expansion, the Design Manager will hesitate before committing the company to recruitment of new personnel, even if the budget allowed for some modest increases. What then are the alternatives available to him to achieve the extra output required?

In general, so long as previous staff and work forecasts have been reasonably accurate and business policies and commitments have not been subject to panic measures, the design staff should be sufficiently flexible to cope with short-term urgent needs and long-term planned programme work. By shrewd management, staff can be utilised to ensure the successful handling of pressure loads, either by re-distribution of existing projects or by limited extra duty (overtime) schedules.

Occasions arise however when, due to the necessary restraints on recruitment and overtime, consi-

deration must be given to the alternative of engaging outside labour on a contract basis for clearing draughting and design bottlenecks. In certain cases it is worthwhile investigating the advantages of contracting out the whole of the project to an agency or consultancy with specialist knowledge of the product.

Whilst contract working is not the minefield which it used to be, there are still some limitations which the Design Manager must accept. Company staff will always have reservations, if not actual objections, to the necessity of employing outside staff, and consultation should be entered into as soon as the need for additional labour becomes apparent. As a general policy it is usual to restrict contract work to the clearing of back-log and day-to-day work of an urgent nature, or projects of a specialist nature not within the normal expertise of company staff.

The decision to recruit or contract will, in either case, commit the firm to extensive financial outlay; a wrong decision could well lead to delay or the possible failure of the new project. There could also be a disturbing effect on existing work output and staff relations, and the pros and cons must therefore be carefully considered. If a reasoned decision is to be reached, the situation should be treated as a design study, the factors being categorised and logically assessed – the reasons may need to be recalled for justification later.

Drawing Office Project and Work Record books contain, or should contain, all relevant details of present and programmed work. New proposals should be added and a total commitment chart prepared. This can be sub-divided into two categories: work within the company's normal expertise, and work outside the normal run. The pros and cons of in-house working or contracting out may be listed under each heading to form the basis for comparison.

The material in this chapter first appeared in *Chartered Mechanical Engineer*, and is reproduced by permission.

12.2 Considerations of in-house expansion

12.2.1 Advantages

12.2.1.1 Products within company's normal expertise

(1) Existing staff already have knowledge and experience which can be passed on to new entrants.
(2) Work can be examined at any stage by supervising staff.
(3) Previous jobs and designs held in file are available for comparison.
(4) Parts and sub-assemblies used on firm's other products are available for incorporation into new designs.
(5) Proposed methods of production, machines available, etc. can be discussed in-house; agreed alterations can be incorporated without delay.
(6) Management can directly obtain up-to-date information on state of project and progress report.
(7) Where products are of a confidential nature or where the firm's expertise, patent rights or methods of production need protection, the risk of leakage is minimised by keeping development in-house.

12.2.1.2 Products outside company's normal expertise

(1) Company will benefit by recruitment of new staff introducing knowledge of new techniques and experience hitherto not available.
(2) Expertise of existing staff extended by virtue of (1) above.
(3) New developments can be kept confidential to firm's staff.
(4) Research, development and design costs can be closely monitored; new manufacturing methods can be costed against standard practices to assess possible changes in production methods of existing ranges.

12.2.2 Disadvantages

12.2.2.1 Products within company's normal expertise

(1) Staff cannot be engaged for short-term periods. Hence unless a long-term programme is envisaged, there is a danger of under-employment of new staff.

(2) Unless extra staff are engaged overtime working can rise to unacceptably high levels.
(3) Continuous overtime tends to lead to a falling work rate and reduced work motivation.

12.2.2.2 Products outside company's normal expertise

(1) Prohibitive cost of assessing viability of new products, market research, development, etc.
(2) Danger of infringement of patent rights, standards and codes of practice, etc. not known to company's existing staff.
(3) Implications of liability for defective products due to lack of knowledge of difficulties involved in the production or use of the new product.
(4) Cost of training and educating staff selected to undertake design of new product.
(5) Difficulties and costs of setting up new production lines and testing procedures for new product.

12.3 Considerations of contracting out

12.3.1 Advantages

12.3.1.1 Products within company's normal expertise

(1) Contracting out eliminates the need to take on new staff for what may prove to be a short-term pressure period.
(2) The contract firm would bring new thinking on traditional design and manufacturing methods.

12.3.1.2 Products outside company's normal expertise

(1) A specialist firm having past experience and up-to-date state of the art development can be employed. The specialist would have knowledge of relevant standards and regulations regarding the proposed product.
(2) A contract price for design and development can be negotiated: this can be assessed against anticipated sales and profits to judge viability.
(3) Liability for defective design may be accepted by the contractor.
(4) Penalty clauses can be incorporated to eliminate losses due to non-fulfilment of contract, or faults arising from contractor's errors.

12.3.2 Disadvantages

12.3.2.1 Products within the company's normal expertise

(1) Direct and continuous supervision of design is lost unless a Project Leader is designated to work with the contractor.
(2) Company's own staff invariably show resentment at contracting out, especially where staff and their unions are already at variance with management on work load and staffing levels.
(3) Company's own expertise may become common to other firms to the detriment of future orders.
(4) Unless contract work rates are specifically agreed, costs may escalate out of proportion to the product value.

12.3.2.2 Products outside company's normal expertise

(1) As for (1) listed under Section 12.3.2.1 above.
(2) As for (2) listed under Section 12.3.2.1 above.
(3) Contractor's staff may change during design stages, causing a disjointed approach to the development of the project.
(4) Company's own lack of knowledge of a new product could lead to acceptance of an inferior or faulty design.

12.4 Discussion

Any one of these factors may be sufficient in a specific instance to outweigh all others in the decision to recruit new staff or go to contract. For example, a new project outside the company's design expertise, but within its manufacturing capability, may be expedited by placing a design contract with a specialist consultancy. Certain safeguards are necessary to achieve a satisfactory result.

The contractor must be aware of all standards (Company, National and International) that affect the project, and wherever possible should be given a definite specification of requirements, both in terms of the product design and of the drawings and diagrams to be supplied. The contractor must accept the company's supervision of work as a matter of course, and carry out any revisions and amendments as required.

Work charges need to be established and agreed in writing prior to commencment of any work, and if more than one firm is available for the contract, tenders should be obtained. As valuation of work often leads to differences of opinion and possible hold-ups of urgent work, important contracts should only be let to firms known to be reliable and having previous knowledge of the company's standards.

Despite general impressions to the contrary, the cost of employing contract agencies for draughting and design work is not inevitably higher than in-house costs. The higher hourly rates charged for contractor's designers is partly offset by overheads incurred when using company labour. Furthermore, if the project requires only short-term commitment, contracting costs would be considerably less than that of taking on new staff over a longer period.

The decision is therefore more likely to hinge on the outcome of comparisons of the factors listed above, rather than labour charges. If the need for complete confidentiality of a project is paramount, the preference is likely to be to engage staff with the necessary experience into company employment. Conversely, if the problem is one of urgent clearance of a backlog of day-to-day work then a contract drafting agency may well provide the answer. In other cases the factors may be weighed against the total commitment list to provide a balance. The traditional method of equating overtime being worked to staff required does not always give correct results.

Critical assessment of the man-hours or man-years of work estimated for each outstanding job is required to arrive at a figure of anticipated costs for draughting and design. These will provide a useful basis for comparison between in-house and contract working, as well as establishing costs to be set against expected profits.

Each job in the record book may be given weighting factors in terms of urgency, confidentiality (security rating) etc., and its anticipated work units in thousands of man-hours (kMH) assessed. For example ratings from 1 to 10 could be given for each factor. A simple program, giving preference for in-house working to high security jobs, whilst accounting for work units, degree of urgency, etc. can be fed to a small personal computer to give a readout of category groups for all listed jobs, as in the example shown in Table 12.1. Other factors appertaining to the company's specific needs may also be determined and included in the analysis. Totals in each category can then be compared with existing availability of staff to give the kMH figure and category of labour required. The program can readily be extended to give details of estimated labour costs, probable job duration, etc.

As may be seen from the very simple example in Table 12.1, an assessment can now be made:

(1) 6.5 kMH required for work needing to be kept in-house, i.e. nearly four man-years. The urgency will decide on numbers to be recruited.
(2) 3.9 kMH could be covered by overtime working, but this is impracticable and must be assessed in context with (1) for extra staff.
(3) 9.8 kMH of work would be suitable for contract working. The urgency of the jobs and the facilities offered by contractors will need to be

Table 12.1

Job	kMH	Urgency	Security	Category
1	2.3	6	8	REC
2	0.75	3	2	O/T
3	2.8	7	3	CON
4	4.2	3	7	REC
5	1.5	5	9	O/T
6	0.82	8	3	O/T
7	2.5	7	3	CON
8	0.85	4	4	O/T
9	1.8	9	3	CON
10	2.7	5	5	CON

REC   recruit new staff
O/T   cover by extra duty
CON   jobs suitable for contract

considered before making the decision to use contractors or to recruit. Accurate estimating of comparative costs is vital in making a final commitment to expand or contract out.

One further point should be noted, whether engaging new staff or placing contracts for design work: the provisions of the Health and Safety at Work and Consumer Protection Acts in respect of the design and supply of defective products apply to all articles made for sale or for use at work. Design Managers may need to see how far the clauses relating to design affect their interests.

13

Preparing a technical specification

How does a newcomer to writing technical specifications make a start, and where does the engineer look for guidance on preparation? This chapter is an attempt to provide a starting point. It is concerned with technical specifications for enquiry or tender offer, from the application of the simple data sheet and its development into more complex specification requiring a descriptive text. Also discussed are some of the pitfalls to avoid.

What are technical specifications? Quite simply they are documents which define in the written word, together with drawings and numerical data, plant and equipment which a purchaser wants a vendor to supply or conversely that which a tenderer is prepared to offer to a buyer. It sets down only the technical conditions of a contract. It does not discuss the commercial contract conditions which are usually the subject of a separate covering letter or other documents between the two parties. Primarily therefore the art of writing specifications is a skill of technical communication in print, the objective being to do this in a simple easily understood manner. Between the purchaser and vendor it thus forms the primary link on the plant requirements. The onus is on the purchaser to write a clear precise statement of what he wants, and on the vendor to read, understand (in the manner the purchaser intended), and make an offer in line with these requirements with an equally lucid technical tender presentation.

Theoretically one can commence writing a specification with a blank sheet of paper. However in practice one is not often faced with this dilemma, for industry has adapted itself to cater for this in easier ways. The simplest form of technical specification is

The material in this chapter first appeared in *Chartered Mechanical Engineer*, and is reproduced here by permission.

the equipment data sheet. Let us now consider its application.

13.1 Data sheets

Specifications for single plant items such as a pump, motor or control valve, etc., are commonly prepared using a data sheet for each piece of equipment. This contains all the design information necessary to specify the plant item. It is usually split up into sections presenting operating conditions, technical details, material requirements and general information such as design standards, inspection and shipping details. A typical centrifugal pump data sheet for example is shown in Figure 13.1. This would most probably be issued for tender enquiry together with a motor data sheet to cover the motor design requirements. It might also be supplemented perhaps by a short two or three page general pump specification describing the constructional requirements, characteristic, seal preferences, etc. Careful thought should be given to the layout/technical information to be included on each sheet for the particular plant item. For example a recent pump data sheet the author came across extended to three sheets, when all the information could have been neatly included on one sheet.

Data sheets need to have reference information, and typically every sheet should carry the company name and address, and space for the title, specification, sheet, contract and plant item numbers. In addition provision should be included for vetting signature and data (e.g. prepared, checked, approved), and a line space for revisions and updating. A line numbering system down the side of the sheet is also useful particularly to pinpoint revisions.

CENTRIFUGAL PUMPS								SPEC. No CP 1001			
								SHEET 1 OF 1			
OPERATING CONDITIONS											1
NO. OF MACHINES				WORKING				STANDBY			2
OPERATION		PARALLEL		CONTINUOUS				INTERMITTENT			3
LOCATION											4
AMBIENT CONDITIONS				VAPOUR PRESSURE							5
FLUID PUMPED				VISCOSITY							6
ANALYSIS				DENSITY							7
WORKING TEMP °C				pH							8
FLOWRATE		MIN. CONT.		NORMAL				MAXIMUM			9
PRESSURE		SUCTION		DISCHARGE				DIFFERENTIAL			10
ABSORBED POWER				NORMAL				MAXIMUM			11
NPSH		AVAILABLE		REQUIRED							12
PUMP CONSTRUCTION											13
MANUFACTURER				SEAL/GLAND TYPE							14
CASING				BALANCE ARRGT				DISC/DRUM			15
SPLIT				THRUST BRG TYPE							16
TYPE				JOURNAL BRG. TYPE							17
NO. OF STAGES				DRIVE TORQUE				F.L.			18
SPEED								STARTING			19
1ST CRITICAL SPEED				VALUE OF WR2							20
CONNECTIONS	SIZE	RATING	FACING	POSN.	FITTINGS SUPPLIED			VENT VALVE			21
INLET								DRAIN VALVE			22
DISCHARGE								SUCTION P.G.			23
EFFICIENCY								DISCHARGE P.G.			24
PERFORMANCE CURVE				DIRECTION OF ROTATION (FACING COUP)							25
GENERAL ARRGT.											26
MATERIALS											27
CASING				DIFFUSER							28
IMPELLOR				GLAND SLEEVE							29
SHAFT				GLAND PACKING/SEAL							30
SHAFT SLEEVES				NECK BUSH (SHAFT)							31
BALANCE DRUM/PISTON				LANTERN RING							32
CASING NECK RING				THRUST BRG.							33
IMPELLOR WEAR RINGS				BEDPLATE							34
DRIVER & TRANSMISSION											35
TYPE OF DRIVE				RECOMMENDED DRIVER POWER							36
SPEED RATIO				FITTED MOTOR POWER							37
DRIVER SPEED				MOTOR EFFICIENCY				POWER FACTOR			38
DRIVER		MANUF.		TYPE				SUPPLIED BY			39
SPEED REDUCER		MANUF.		TYPE				SUPPLIED BY			40
COUPLING		MANUF.		TYPE				SUPPLIED BY			41
GUARD		MANUF.		TYPE				SUPPLIED BY			42
BEDPLATE		MANUF.		TYPE				SUPPLIED BY			43
HOLDING DOWN BOLTS											44
DESIGN STANDARDS & INSPECTION											45
DESIGN CODE				SHIPPING WEIGHT							46
DESIGN PRESSURE				MAXIMUM ERECTION LIFT							47
HYDROSTATIC TEST PRESSURE				MAXIMUM MAINTENANCE LIFT							48
SHOP TESTS											49
SERVICES											50
ELECTRICAL		VOLTS		PHASE				CYCLES			51
COOLING WATER		PRESSURE		TEMP				FLOW			52
SEALING WATER		PRESSURE		TEMP				FLOW			53
STEAM		PRESSURE		TEMP				FLOW			54
					PREPARED						
					CHECKED						
					APPROVED						
REV	DESCRIPTION			APPR	DATE		ENGINEERING				
ANO	A N Other Co. Ltd Sometown, Placeshire			SERVICE							
				PLANT ITEM							
				CONTRACT							

Figure 13.1 Data sheet

The data sheet is the simplest most direct form of specification for single plant items, and is the way much of industry works today both for purchase enquiry and tender quotation. Prepared in a standardised format, a whole range of data sheets can be generated that are particular to your industry (mechanical, electrical, civil, etc.). These will save time and money, the engineer having only to complete the appropriate numerical data before it may be sent out for enquiry or tender.

13.2 Specification text

Considering now the development of more complex specifications such as a boiler or water treatment package, or still further to a complete process plant, involving a range of vessels, machinery, pipework, electrical and control plant, we cannot simply put together a collection of data sheets, because by themselves they do not tell the contractor the whole story. They need to be supplemented by a general specification text describing the design, what the plant is to do, how it is to operate, the construction, scope, extent of supply, etc. A collection of plant item data sheets will form the basis of the numerical design information for the specification and now appear as an appendix to the text. The specification is usually prepared under a number of formal headings. Table 13.1 shows a typical list of contents as a basis for more formal specifications.

13.2.1 Scope

This states the '*extent of work*' which a purchaser requires or a tenderer will provide for the plant he is offering. It is a statement of what he does, not what he supplies. It usually embodies a simple statement such as:

'*This specification covers the design, development, manufacture, supply, works testing, delivery, off-loading, erection and site testing, etc, of the XYZ chemical process plant the duty of which is defined in this specification.*'

Often this is all the scope says. The engineer might however consider the following clauses for inclusion also under this heading.

(1) A statement qualifying the extent of the specification, e.g. '*The complete specification shall comprise of sections (i) to (ix) together with appendixes (A) to (E) inclusive.*'

This clause may not be required if the specification is properly bound but if it is made up of

Table 13.1 Specification contents

(1)	Scope
(2)	Extent of supply
(3)	Terminating points
(4)	Design
(5)	Manufacture, inspection, works testing
(6)	Packing, delivery and storage
(7)	Site erection, commissioning
(8)	General
(9)	Documentation
Appendix A	Design data
Appendix B	Plant item data sheets
Appendix C	Drawings
Appendix D	Associated specifications
Appendix E	Documentation

a number of separate, loose documents/data sheets as the chemical industry so often does, then this statement has some importance.

(2) A statement should be made on the order of precedence of the main and supplementary specifications and standards (e.g. Appendix D BS Codes) so that in the event of a conflict of interpretation of the requirements between purchaser/vendor this is quite clear.

(3) Another useful paragraph a purchaser could incorporate is a statement regarding departures from specification such as:

'*This specification shall generally apply and any departure from this shall be clearly stated by the tenderer in writing. Absence of comment in the tenderer's quotation shall be interpreted as acceptance of the specification requirements. Departure from the specification must be approved by the purchaser in writing.*'

In a complex specification it may be advisable to request the vendor to specifically list the deviations in a 'Departures from specification' schedule, stating that only where so listed will they be considered, i.e. if there are miscellaneous deviations elsewhere in the document, the purchaser will nevertheless ignore them and assume the vendor is in compliance with the enquiry specification. In carrying out a project bid analysis the purchaser's engineer will of course make a detailed study of the tender offers. However, by incorporating the departures clause/schedule, this will be simplified.

(4) In the case of a purchaser it is useful to make a statement that '*The tenderer is to be responsible for all aspects necessary for the safe, reliable and efficient operation of the plant within his extent of supply.*'

13.2.2 Extent of supply

The extent of supply lists all the plant items which are to be provided under the enquiry/tender offer. It usually commences with a clause such as:

'*The Contractor's supply shall include all the equipment between terminal points on the XYZ flow system diagram necessary for the safe, reliable and efficient operation of the XYZ chemical process plant. The extent of supply shall include, but not be restricted to the following.*'

This is then followed by the extent of supply list which may comprise of any of the following.

Machinery
Vessels
Pipework and valves
Structural
Electrical
Control and Instrumentation
Civil works

The list should be as comprehensive as possible to avoid disagreements after the contract placement. For example a statement that the extent of supply shall include '*two boiler feed pumps*' is not nearly precise enough and should be rephrased along the lines:

'*TWO — Sets of 50% duty horizontal centrifugal ring section boiler feed pumps each c/w driving motor, bedplate, couplings, guards, automatic leak off NRV, cooling water and gland piping, and holding down bolts*'

The extent of supply should also list the exclusions which a contractor is not expected to supply. For example free issue valves into the contractor's system, civil works, motor starters, contactors, etc.

13.2.3 Terminating points

The terminating points can be either physical or process. Only the former are included under this heading, i.e. the mechanical, electrical and civil connections. It usually commences with a statement such as:

'*The following terminal point list is applicable to the XYZ chemical process plant.*'

This is then followed by the list of terminating points which should also be indicated where appropriate on any drawings under Appendix C, e.g. flow diagrams and layout drawings. The specification should state whose responsibility it is to make the terminal point, and how it is to be made. It is important to include look all conditions on the terminations, e.g. forces and moments, not just the physical point, for agreement by both parties. As just mentioned there may be process condition terminations. These are design conditions and are normally listed as such under Appendix A.

13.2.4 Design

Design can be subdivided into two sections, the system description which tells the contractor the design basis and operating requirements, and the equipment description which specifies the more general design construction requirements of individual plant items. The former describes in principle what the plant is, does or produces, and how it works. The latter describes the particular mechanical/technical requirements of the plant, e.g. the type of construction, codes, materials, welding standards, etc, which may be supplied or are offered. Complementary to these descriptions are the system and plant item data sheets in Appendix A and B, respectively. The latter are generally made up from the standardised sheets, and these two appendices thus provide all the numerical design parameters for the contracts. It is of note that in the process industry it is common also to make up many of the plant item descriptions on to standardised sheets. Table 13.2 summarises the design text requirements, the engineer using only those appropriate to the project.

Table 13.2 Design requirements

System description	Design basis operating requirements
Plant Description (which may comprise of any of the following) Machinery	Type of construction, codes, materials, welding details, stressing, etc. e.g. pumps, turbines, fans, mixers, etc.
Vessels	e.g. heat exchangers, boilers, condensers, etc.
Piping and valves	e.g. HP, LP, steel, GRP, lined, etc.
Structural	e.g. steelwork
Electrical	e.g. motors, electric heaters, cabling
Control & Instrumentation	e.g. control basis, instrument details
Miscellaneous	e.g. access, insulation, cleaning

Whether the design description is written separately under 'System' and 'Plant' depends on the contract. For a large process plant it may be ideal to do so, but in a majority of cases where simpler plant is concerned, the dividing line is often indistinct, and they are written as one.

The importance of plant being of a proven well established design should be stressed under this heading. A typical clause might read:

'*Plant shall be of proven well established design and manufacture, having achieved a high standard of reliability in service*'.

13.2.5 Manufacture, inspection, works testing

This section is concerned principally with proof that the product meets the design requirements in terms of construction and performance. This is the test/certification showing it is built to established codes, and will meet the manufacturer's performance claims. A typical specification clause to cover fabrication/construction codes might be:

'The contractor shall submit manufacturing certification to the purchaser for approval in accordance with the documentation data sheets (manufacturing), e.g. Appendix E.'

The latter would list the steelmaker's chemical analysis certificates, material test certificates, heat treatment records, mill certificates, welding certificates, X-ray and NDT examination, facsimiles of nameplates, etc. and identify those applicable. In addition hydraulic tests will be required on all pressure parts and a statement added to this effect, including the code.

With regard to performance the purchaser will usually ask here for a guarantee performance test e.g. *'A guarantee performance test shall be carried out on the plant to show that it meets the design requirements specified in Appendix A/B'*. It may be desirable, however, that the guarantee should take the form of a site rather than a works test (e.g. a site constructed boiler).

13.2.6 Packing, delivery and storage

This specifies the measures to be taken to ensure the product arrives at site in pristine condition. A typical clause might read:

'After manufacture and testing all plant shall be thoroughly cleaned from scale, rust, dirt and other deleterious matter, dried out and a suitable vapour phase inhibitor introduced, and all end closures plugged.'

We need say little more for it is in the supplier's interest to see that the plant arrives in its 'new' condition, because usually this is when he gets paid a large slice of the contract cost. If, however, the vendor is responsible for site erection then a clause regarding storage may also be advisable. Sites are notoriously muddy and dirty places and the plant may quickly deteriorate unless adequate protective measures are taken. A typical clause might read:

'Plant delivered to site shall be stored in conditions compatible with their nature, suitably protected against the environment, and placed on timber out of contact with the ground. All end closures shall be checked and inspected on a weekly basis'.

The importance of adequate packing preparation and storage conditions cannot be too highly stressed. The author recalls an instance of a tubular heat exchanger which on opening up at site was found to be severely rusted in the bores of the tubes. Somebody somewhere had not taken adequate precautions in the packing, delivery or storage preparations.

13.2.7 Site erection, commissioning

This section states a contractor's site responsibilities, e.g.

'The contractor's responsibilities shall include site construction, commissioning, setting to work for the first time and a performance test, etc'.

In a large plant such as a power station or chemical complex it is essential that the activities of the numerous contractors working on a site should dovetail into an overall plan. The purchaser therefore, besides stating the vendor's site responsibilities as above, will usually also ask him to submit a programme of his site activities for agreement. Site activities can get quite complex and cost a lot of money if the planning is not right, and consequently this aspect is usually covered by numerous contractual conditions (e.g. labour relations, site conditions, etc.), which do not form part of the technical specification.

13.2.8 General

There will always be a few clauses that an engineer wishes to incorporate into a specification, but which will not ideally fit in elsewhere. This is the heading to include them under. Typical examples might be:

Hazards — flooding, fire, windloading, chemical release, etc.
Development
Quality Assurance
Painting
Identification

13.2.9 Documentation

This specifies the design and manufacturing documentation to be produced during the contract. Design documentation consists of drawings, calculations, operating and maintenance instructions, etc., submitted for approval to satisfy the purchaser's engineer that the plant construction is in accordance with the specification, and so that he can co-ordinate this in with the design of other associated plant. It may also involve statutory insurance company clearance, e.g. for pressure parts. Manufacturing documentation is the constructional certification. A typical documentation clause might read:

'*The contractor shall provide documentation in accordance with Appendix E*'.

The latter would be split into two schedules for design and manufacturing respectively.

13.2.10 Appendices

From the above discussion the content of the appendices should be self-evident. However, Table 13.3 summarises the requirements.

Table 13.3

Appendix	Title	Content
A	Design data	System numerical design information
B	Data sheets	Plant item numerical design information
C	Drawings	Flow diagrams, layouts, etc.
D	Associated specifications	Supplementary specifications, BS Codes, etc.
E	Documentation	Design and manufacturing documentation requirements

13.3 Specification pitfalls

In preparing specifications there are a number of pitfalls to be avoided, and this check list might form a handy reminder.

13.3.1 Omissions

Omission or understatement in the extreme is like specifying a ship, but forgetting to ask for it to be complete with a rudder to steer it. Here of course the likelihood is that a tenderer would quickly draw attention to this obvious omission. Typical engineering examples in an enquiry specification might be forgetting to specify the supply of air pressure regulators for pneumatic controllers, or failing to explain fully some important process requirements.

Eliminating omissions calls for a clear methodical mind, checking back over a specification heading by heading to see that everything has been included. They are the most important of all pitfalls in specification writing to be aware of, and to do one's best to eliminate, but it is not an easy task.

13.3.2 Overstatement

Overstating technical requirements is like asking for a gold plated sink when an ordinary stainless steel one is quite adequate. An engineering example might be a process fed by $2 \times 50\%$ duty centrifugal pumps with two further 50% duty pumps as standby. Would not one 50% duty standby pump be adequate, or does the process even justify a standby at all? Overstatement in specifications results in an increase in either capital or maintenance and running costs, and often a combination of these. Purchasers who overspecify run the risk of paying more for their plant than they need have done. They may or may not get a better engineered job depending on just what was overspecified. Similarly tenderers who overspecify are offering plant which is more sophisticated than it need have been, it is likely to be dearer, and therefore the vendor risks being uncompetitive with other manufacturers.

13.3.3 Duplication

The technical requirements only need to be stated once and in the correct place. Restatement (i.e. duplication) merely adds words to the specification, and leads to the document becoming woolly, confused and ill-defined. Probably the most common case of duplication is stating numerical data in the text as well as in the design appendix. Where possible they should be restricted to the latter to avoid errors in correcting specification amendments.

13.3.4 Vagueness

If an enquiry is vague in some respect, then the likelihood is that the tenderer will either give an equally vague answer, or may ignore the issue altogether. In either case, he is entitled to do so because the specification is obviously deficient in some way. To be vague is to be imprecise and it implies therefore that the writer is unsure about some aspect. The solution is to take a firm approach, specify exactly what you want or are offering. In other words be precise.

13.3.5 Ambiguity

Ambiguity is not specifying or explaining matters in a clear logical manner. Such statements may have double meanings or perhaps be so confused as to make the interpretation rather doubtful. An example might be a conflict of requirements between the main enquiry and its supplementary specifications (e.g. BS codes).

13.3.6 Assumptions

Too often in writing a specification an engineer assumes certain information or data will obviously be known to a contractor. 'Of course the contractor will know this information', you argue, but will he? Should not the data be specified? The question to ask yourself is, 'If a contractor makes an incorrect assumption of certain information, will it significantly affect the plant design or the offer he makes?' If it does then clearly the data should be specified.

13.3.7 Poor grammar

Good specifications describe the technical details in clear, easily understood English. The prime requirement therefore is to have a sound command of the English language, and the ability to communicate this in the written word.

Specifications, like books, are split into chapters, paragraphs and sentences, etc. Poorly written documents do not obey these rules. Badly subdivided, what might otherwise have been a good specification can sometimes end up looking like a piece of dull endless prose. The reader becomes confused where one section ends and the next begins. Major headings, scope, extent of supply, terminations, etc. (i.e. the chapters), should at least be highlighted in underlined capitals, with subheadings in lower case, underlined. Most specifications also have a sectional numbering system for reference purposes.

Word repetition is another hazard, particularly in the same sentence. A dictionary is an invaluable guide to alternative phraseology, and every engineer should keep one handy for reference. Finally remember that you cannot expect your contractor to understand you, if you cannot explain yourself in good English.

13.4 Specification presentation

Specifications can be presented in many ways. One could simply type out the requirements onto plain paper, though it is desirable to encourage employees to prepare company specifications in a consistent format. Figure 13.2 shows some examples.

Style 1: A plain format suitable for the text of longer specifications, appendixes, etc.

Style 2: Suitable for the text of short specifications where space is required for reference data, etc.

Style 3: A lined format sheet, the basis of the equipment data sheet.

Many specifications are adaptations or developments of earlier documents, and only in extreme cases will the plant be completely novel. When a purchaser requests a contractor to tender for some new process plant, he will issue an enquiry specification. Presumably he will approach companies with experience in the particular field, so it is likely that the company already has information or specifications for the type of plant involved.

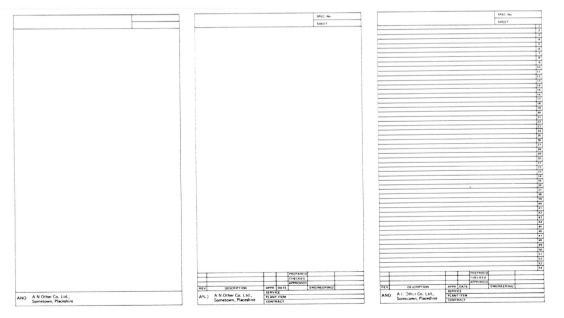

Figure 13.2 Style of specification presentation

The first step is to summarise the requirements, decide on major headings and collect together all the relevant company standards and data sheets. It will assist the purchaser in making his bid analysis if a vendor follows the enquiry specification. Copy the technical clauses of the enquiry and slot these in under the various headings chosen. They may duplicate already collated information but this way prevents omission of any special clauses. If company standards are better than the purchaser's data, the former should be used as the specification basis.

Review the document and check whether it states what is required, it is clear and easy to understand. Then check that all detail requirements and special clauses, etc., have been met. If any are impossible to meet, state so or refer these back to the contractor for clarification and agreement.

14

The design audit

A design audit is an independent review of a contractor's design and engineering of a process plant or equipment item following contract award. Its objective is to provide the management of the purchasing organisation with the assurance that the plant to be supplied will be capable of producing the specified output reliably, safely and economically. This chapter describes the technique and cost of design audits, and gives examples of potential problems identified by them and solutions recommended for overcoming them.

14.1 Why do a design audit?

The objective of a design audit is to provide assurance, to the management of an organisation which has contracted the supply of new or refurbished industrial plant and equipment, that it will perform in accordance with their expectations, not only during its acceptance test but throughout its useful life. These expectations are usually specified in terms of some or all of the following parameters:

- production volume,
- product quality,
- yield,
- energy consumption,
- environmental pollution,
- operational health and safety,
- trouble-free operation,
- operating and maintenance costs.

The experience of numerous plants all over the world, which encountered protracted teething problems after start-up or, indeed, never achieved their rated production capacity on a sustained basis, emphasises the critical need for design audits. Had the purchasers required design audits to be carried out on these plants, the majority of the serious process and engineering deficiencies which became apparent during service would undoubtedly have been identified and corrected at the design stage.

A design audit is particularly appropriate in situations where the design of a new plant or the enhancement of an existing plant incorporates one or more of the following features

- New or more advanced process technology designed to reduce capital and/or operating costs, improve product quality, reduce environmental pollution, etc.
- Scale-up of production capacity compared with earlier plants in terms of higher throughputs, batch weights, operating pressures, temperatures, speeds, etc.
- New construction materials to enable the plant better to withstand the high temperatures, abrasion and corrosion associated with the production process.
- Major engineering modifications aimed at overcoming problems encountered in the operation of earlier plants, reducing energy consumption and/or environment pollution, reducing downtime and facilitating maintenance.
- The plant, although based on proven process technology, is to be designed and engineered for the first time by a new licensee.
- A proven plant is to be constructed for a different raw materials input, duty or environment from that pertaining to earlier plants.
- Proven plant items are to be linked in a new production system.

In the present climate of financial stringency, projects involving major capital expenditure are very carefully prepared and evaluated by both the operating company's management and its potential lenders. The viability of the project, and hence management's decision to proceed, depends crucially on the expectation that the plant will follow the learning curve and attain stable operation in line with the forecast developed in the feasibility study; this in turns serves as the basis for the financial projections and estimates of profitability and debt service capacity. It is apparent that any failure on the part of the plant to achieve this expected performance will have an adverse effect on the commercial viability of the project.

Although suppliers generally offer guarantees of the performance of the plant, including capacity, quality, yields, energy consumption and possibly other parameters, such guarantees are difficult to enforce and the operator is seldom fully compensated for production and revenue losses arising from inadequate plant performance. It is against this background and the knowledge that prevention is better than cure that a design aduit is carried out to review the integrity of the proposed design, while it is still on the contractor's drawing board, and to identify and eliminate potential problems.

14.1.2   *Faults in conventional design assessment*

Following the decision to proceed with the project tender specifications for the plant as a whole or major plant items are drawn up. These generally take the form of a description of site conditions and performance specifications for the plant, complemented by standard specifications for its components, such as the civil, structural and building works, and the mechanical, electrical and control equipment. The tender documents typically stipulate hand-over and acceptance criteria, performance guarantee requirements and financial penalties in the event that the plant fails to meet these guarantees.

The specifications are normally drafted in such a way as to provide scope for the various tenderers to put forward a design of plant based on the production process for which they are licensed or with which they are most familiar. Following the submission and evaluation of tenders, a contract is awarded to the successful tenderer, who will then proceed to undertake the detailed design and engineering of the plant on the basis of the tender specification.

It should be appreciated that the purchaser's and the contractor's interests are divergent. The purchaser, on the one hand, is concerned to acquire a plant which can be depended on to give reliable and efficient service during its design life, produce a range of products of acceptable quality, meet occupational health and safety and environmental standards, and be readily maintained. The contractor,

on the other hand, having won the contract award often in the face of strong competition, will endeavour to deliver whatever the contract stipulates but no more. And this is where potential problems arise, because it is extremely difficult to draft the tender specification of a large industrial plant so as to comprehend every aspect of its design, operation and maintenance.

Consequently, such a situation calls for a design audit of the contractor's interpretation and development of the tender specification. That becomes necessary in order to assure management that its requirements will be properly addressed in the plant design and to draw attention to any potential deficiencies at a stage where corrective action can be taken easily and cheaply.

Most purchasers of industrial plant do not employ sufficient technical staff to undertake a comprehensive review of the contractor's detailed design — calculations, flowsheets, general arrangement and shop drawings, and material specifications — to ensure that it fully meets the intent of the tender specifications and that the resulting plant can be expected to perform satisfactorily in service. The banks and other lending institutions that may have appraised the project at the outset are not in a position to carry out such a review either.

Instead, the normal procedure is for flowsheets, general arrangement and shop drawings, and component and material specifications to be checked by the purchaser's technical staff by discipline. That is to say, the process engineers check the flowsheets, the civil engineers check the design of the foundations and buildings, the electrical engineers check the design of the substation, power distribution system, motor list and process control system, and so on. But it is rare for the production process as a whole to be evaluated at this stage. As a result, the impact of plant arrangement and specification on the operability, reliability and maintainability of the overall system is not evaluation. Also large sections of the plant design are often not checked at all, on the premise that the contract has a good reputation and can therefore be relied on to provide a suitable design. This view is often reinforced by management's somewhat naive reliance on the performance guarantees, which, although they may look watertight on paper, rarely turn out to be so if the worst comes to the worst.

14.2   Design audit procedure

The design audit is carried out in two distinct stages:

- system audit;
- component audit.

14.2.1 System audit

The system audit evaluates the contractor's overall plant design and engineering. Basic design features of the plant are studied with a view to identifying potential weaknesses in the system as a whole, such as equipment mismatches, production bottlenecks, inadequate provision for intermediate buffer stocks, low plant availability, insufficient standby equipment, unused waste heat, potential pollutants, safety hazards, inappropriate control facilities, or inadequate provision for maintenance.

A manual or computer based mathematical model is developed to represent the proposed system design. This identifies, in the first place, items of equipment that are critical to the performance of the plant so that they can then be subjected to a more rigorous examination in the component audit stage. In the next step, data on the performance of these critical components are collected from a variety of sources to enable a complete system reliability model to be formulated. This model is then used to predict the availability of the proposed plant and the contribution of various factors to plant downtime. Potential problem areas can then be identified and corrective action proposed.

14.2.2 Component audit

This is essentially an audit of selected critical equipment items aimed at evaluating their fitness for purpose under service conditions within the total system and identifying potential design weaknesses such as undersizing, unsuitable materials, inadequate protection against process temperature, wear and corrosion, incompatibility with other components, and restricted access for maintenance.

For example, computer methods can be used to analyse stress distributions in items of equipment, and thus to identify areas of potential overdesign or structural weakness. This procedure enables designs to be optimised, and results in a more effective use of materials and in reduced risk of catastrophic failure in service.

14.2.3 Skills required

As in the case of the more traditional audits, the design auditor needs to possess both professional and interpersonal skills in order to carry out this function successfully. This is particularly true to avoid giving the contractor the impression that the purchaser's requirement of a design audit is a reflection on his competence in, or interference with, the design of the plant.

On the professional side, the role of the design auditor calls for familiarity with the process technology of the plant, the design and selection of its components, and operational requirements, so as to command acceptance of his judgement as to the adequacy of the proprosed design.

On the interpersonal side, the design auditor needs to demonstrate independence and objectivity and a commitment to enhancing the design of the plant, within the parameters of the ocntract, so as to assure reliability, safety and economy of operation. This requires the design auditor to take conscious steps to conduct himself as a member of the design team and to put forward suggestions for overcoming potential problems in a constructive fashion. Above all, the contractor must feel confident that any design weaknesses revealed during the audit process will not become public knowledge and damage the contractor's reputation.

14.2.4 Implementing design changes

Generally, the design modifications resulting from a design audit are minor in scale and relatively simple to implement. The cost of incorporating these modifications in the original design are certainly far less than the cost to the purchaser of any loss of production on the one hand, and the cost to the contractor of redesigning and replacing equipment that has failed in service on the other. A design audit also lessens significantly the likelihood of the contracting parties engaging in potentially long drawn-out and expensive arbitration and litigation proceedings, and of the contractor being called on to pay liquidated damages or forfeiting his performance bond.

When the design aduit identifies an actual design deficiency, most contractors will not hesitate to correct it at their own expense. It is not uncommon, however, for the design audit also to identify areas of overdesign and to recommend redistribution of expenditure rather than an overall cost increase.

When the design audit identifies shortcomings which are not the fault of the contractor, the purchaser has the opportunity to consider the potential cost and benefit of implementing the proposed modifications. Most managements are willing to sanction a small increase in the contract price in the interest of enhancing the performance of the plant.

Managements should therefore look on design audits as a precautionary risk-reduction exercise which, for a comparatively low cost, provides assurance that the plant to be supplied will be capable of producing the specified output reliably, safely and economically. Figure 14.1 and 14.2 show typical design audit costs as a function of plant cost. Naturally the design audit cost will depend in each specific case on the type and complexity of the plant and the extent of the information contained in the

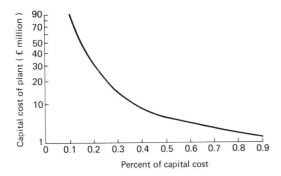

Figure 14.1 Design audit costs for plant above £1 million

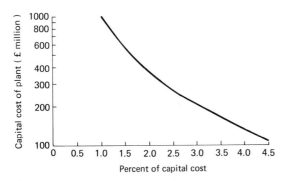

Figure 14.2 Design audit costs for plant below £1 million

tender specification. But the figures are representative of typical design audit costs and show that for a plant costing £20 million, the cost of undertakding a design audit would be approximately £60 000.

14.3 Examples of design audit in action

The following are four examples to illustrate the types of problem identified by design audits and the solutions recommended for overcoming them. It is worth noting that the original designs cited were all prepared by reputable international contractors, and that neither they nor the purchasers were aware of these problems before the design audit.

In a *major ironworks project*, a raw materials feed bunker was found to be undersized, because the contractor had not fully understood the intended mode of operation. This would have severely restricted throughput of raw materials and would have needed costly modifications in service. The problem was identified by a mathematical model of plant operation. A simple and inexpensive design change allowed the bunker to perform as required.

In a *major minerals processing project*, a front-end loader used in handling raw materials had been

incorrectly specified. This again would have restricted raw materials throughput. The problem arose because the machine was required to handle several materials of varying densities. Although the volume-carrying capacity of the machine appeared inadequate, the densest material introduced a weight constraint which had been overlooked by the plant designers. The remedy was to use a slightly larger and more expensive machine, but if this had not been revealed prior to purchase, a second machine would have been required soon after commissioning. This would have entailed for the operator an initial loss of production and subsequently greater operating and maintenance costs, and for the contractor greater expense in the provision of adequate mobile handling equipment.

In a *coalmining project*, a very large rotary coal-breaking machine was audited. The method of fixing and assembling the main structural beams of the barrel to the end rings was considered inadequate, and a change from welded to bolted design was recommended. The justification for this change was borne out when a similar but smaller machine which had been installed two years earlier failed catastrophically due to fatigue cracking in the weld zone at the end of the structural beams.

In a *steelworks project*, a continuous bloom casting machine was audited. The top cooling zone area was identified as being critical to plant performance for a number of reasons, particularly because of its vulnerability in the event of breakouts. In the light of these considerations a set of recommendations was developed aimed at simplifying top zone alignment, affording more protection to top zone components, and providing better access for inspection, adjustment and reinstatement after breakouts. The effect of this package of recommendations was to increase substantially the availability of the bloom caster.

14.4 Conclusion

These examples may be fairly obvious in hindsight, but they are typical of potential problems sometimes overlooked by plant designers as they strive to meet contractual deadlines and budgets. The systematic review which lies at the heart of the design audit can, however, be relied on to identify these problems and thus to provide an opportunity for them to be corrected before they occur in service. Consequently, a design aduit materially enhances the confidence level that management can place on the performance of new or refurbished industrial plant.

It follows that a design audit should routinely be required for all plant and equipment for which the contractor has to undertake a substantial amount of design, in much the same way as, and complementary to, quality assurance. By calling for a design audit the management of an industrial organisation can discharge their responsibility as to the adequacy of the plant to be supplied. A design audit reduces the incidence of design deficiencies which adversely affect plant performance, and benefits the contractor by largely obviating the need to redesign and replace equipment that proves unsuitable after commissioning.

Above all, it ensures that technical efforts are concentrated on the design of the plant and not on contractual disputes long after the plant has been started up. Provided the requirement for a design audit is expressed in the tender documents and allowed for in the implementation schedule, there is no reason why the purchaser, contractor and design auditor should not form a team in which each member will make a distinctive and valuable contribution to the overall success of the project.

15

Structure and organisation in design offices

Organisation is concerned with the relationship between work and the people who do it. The quality and efficiency of engineering design is affected by the structure and organisation of design activities within a company.

Traditional organisation theory prescribed the manner in which work should be allocated and jobs grouped. It described in specific terms formal organisation structures and the manner in which specialisation would be applied; design being one of these specialisations.

Basically, the proposition was that the planning of positions and departments should precede selection of individuals. This approach made it possible to state a group of principles about organisation structure, but said little about how people behaved or are likely to behave within the structure.

More recently the behavioural sciences have focused attention on the nature of individual and group interaction in an organisation — how people actually work together. Modern organisation theory uses traditional organisation theory as a framework which it complements with new concepts of organisational behaviour. It emphasises people rather than jobs. It concentrates on a description of behaviour rather than structure.

To put it more simply, every organisation must solve the problem of relationships among its people; every manager should be concerned with developing fruitful relationships with, and between, his subordinates.

The individual cannot usually work without the organisation and the organisation depends almost entirely on the individual. But their interests differ. The manager's job is to develop the proper balanced interaction of individual needs and organisation demands.

As Chris Argyris (1957) has written:

> The individual and the organisation are living organisms, each with its own strategy for survival and growth. The individual's strategy for existence is at crucial points antagonistic to the strategy that guides the formal organisation. This may lead to a continual conflict between the individual and the organisation. The conflict, however, can be a source for growth as well as a stimulant for disintegration.

Management has to solve problems within the context of the organisation. Solving design problems, for example, may call for considerable experience, technical knowledge and innovative thinking; but it also requires the exercise of psychological skills, for all problems in design have one common ingredient: people. Engineering design is a corporate activity involving teams of people whose job it is to provide a prescription of what is to be produced. How people interact can be determined by the shape of an organisation.

15.1 Management and organisation

In its basic objectives, the management of design is no different from other types of management. Basically it attempts to use the total resources of an enterprise in such a manner that maximum profit is obtained from minimum investment.

Management may be looked upon as both an art and a science. The art of management is based upon experience and skill, while the science calls upon an organised body of knowledge admitting of quantitative treatment. Management in its broadest sense is the organisation, direction and control of the total business process for specific ends.

Successful management in any field involves three essential abilities:

(1) the determination of objectives and of their order of priority;
(2) the devising and implementation of means whereby these objectives may be obtained; and
(3) the setting up of control systems to assess and improve progress towards the objectives set.

Management pervades all spheres of activity and is not therefore a separate profession. Even a one-man band has to 'manage' himself to achieve good results. Good engineering design is the result of a team led by an imaginative manager, who is able to organise work, so as to use resources economically, motivate and control people, and measure performance.

The resources of design are unlike production facilities. In a machine shop it is possible to pro-gramme work for optimum utilisation in accordance with machine capacities. But designers cannot be so programmed, and often their performance is unpredictable. But a design organisation is expensive and it is as essential to pay as much attention to the design unit — whether a team or individual — as it is to study a machine or machine shop.

A proper understanding of how a machine works is the only safe ground on which to build improvement in its performance or utilisation. The organisation of groups of designers, with attendant staff, into design teams, and the arrangement of paperwork and design data is a reasonably straightforward exercise, provided three things are known:

(1) the objective(s) to be achieved;
(2) how designers work; and
(3) the performance required.

The first requirement is that the right problem be tackled by the designer or design team. The second is the basis of optimum division of work between individuals; while the third sets targets, in terms of cost and time, etc. together with some appropriate measuring system to ensure that they are achieved.

Figure 15.1 shows, in generalised terms, the division of work in any engineering design. Here the work has been divided into three main areas — engineering, design and communication. It does not follow that three watertight compartments exist; indeed, it is possible that one person may perform all three types of work. The complete process is shown in Figure 15.2. Between the various stages certain information must flow and it is important to realise that the design process does not end with production. The process must continue with feed-back of user experience resulting in improvements. For many products in the military and capital equip-ment areas there will be erection and commissioning

problems that affect design work. Erection may, for this reason, be looked upon as a continuation of production at a different site and commissioning too is becoming more and more an extension of design work.

On looking at the nature of the work to be performed, it should be possible to decide the tasks and responsibilities to be assigned to designers. But if the engineering industry is to have a high grade of people in the design function, then the tasks given to them must be worthy of them; otherwise they will move to another firm or even to another function. If high grade people are employed in design, then its status will automatically improve. This is not unprecedented.

What has happened since World War II is that science and engineering, in that order, have at-tracted people with higher education into research and analytical thinking. These people have achieved a greater status than those employed in creative design. This trend can and must be reversed if British industry is to ensure our country's economic survival.

It is, in fact, a managerial problem within the technical area. Every manager of design must think clearly about the tasks to be performed, what sort of organisation is necessary for this and what sort of information is needed. Where will the necessary information come from, and can formal channels of communication be set up to ensure that it arrives in time? And above all, what kind of support in staff and equipment do first-class designers need to be able to spend their time creatively, rather than on soul-destroying routine work? Is it possible to use out of house facilities, such as contract designers, to enable rush work to be completed?

In Figure 15.1 the information required to under-take design work is set out. Basically this consists of three stages. The first stage consists of gathering information to enable an adequate design brief to be established, while the second stage sets out the core design activity where information is generated. Finally, the last stage prepares the design prescrip-tion for onward transmission to manufacturing and construction. Along the side of each stage is ar-ranged the programme of work which has to be undertaken by the design organisation.

15.2 Human factors in organisation

From the above it becomes apparent that organisa-tion is almost as much a process as a structure. It is a process of delegation and communication, and a process of adaptation — people adapting to the organisation while at the same time adapting the organisation to their own needs. It is a process

Engineering (Stage 1)	Programme of work
1 Collect all relevant information	1 Receive enquiry
2 Determine engineering job to be done, embracing such features as: (a) environmental conditions (b) performance, life and reliability (c) ergonomic factors (d) safety and margins for overload (e) cost (f) delivery	2 Evaluate enquiry
3 Definitions of feasible possibilities	3 Estimate office workload, particularly programme of technical work
4 Evolution of optimum solution within the constraints imposed	4 Define objectives: Primary, secondary and rank
5 Commissioning of plant	5 Appreciate state of the art
6 Review of performance of systems and products	6 Identify critical problem areas
	7 Feedback of results at end of programme

↓ Output

Basic engineering information to enable design to be performed
1 Specification of systems, products and components
2 Specification of such features as: performance, reliability, quality, life, serviceability, guarantees, cost, appearance, size, etc.
3 Definition of design parameters, such as: stresses, temperature, voltages etc., which have to be contained
4 Identification of critical features and areas of ignorance, and how these are to be dealt with – e.g. development of research work
5 Tests and inspection which must be made. (These include both analytical and physical tests.)

↓ Division of work in engineering design

Design (Stage 2)	Programme of work
1 Definition of outline and layout to contain critical factors within the constraints of: (a) materials (b) manufacturing facilities (c) transport and erection on site facilities (d) time available (e) cost	1 Receive authority to design
2 Choice of optimum solution and validation of performance	2 Identify problems and sub-problems
3 Realisation of selected design solution	3 Synthesise to establish realm of feasibility for possible design solutions
4 Checking and inspection of design work prior to delineation	4 Collect and generate data, analyse performance
5 Rectification of errors in design work	5 Validate performance in critical areas
6 Supervision of detail drawings, noted costs etc.	6 Division, delegation and detail programme of design work

↓ Output

Information from design office
1 Material specifications
2 Process specifications
3 Inspection, test and commissioning schedules
4 Information necessary for preparation of detailed production instructions
5 Logistics information about handling, transport, erection, commissioning, etc.
6 Packaging specification

↓

Technical communication office	Programme of work
(Drawing office) (Stage 3)	
1 Preparation of detail drawings of components, sub-assemblies and assemblies with standards	1 Define communication needs
2 Parts, material and process lists. Packaging schedules	2 Select communications media
3 Issue, withdrawal and amendment of drawings, instructions etc.	3 Prepare and transmit communications
4 Consideration of best media for transmitting instructions	4 Prepare final design review papers
5 Amendment and termination (a) rectify and modify instructions (b) revise performance specifications (c) amend records (d) classify and store records	

Figure 15.1 Division of work in engineering design

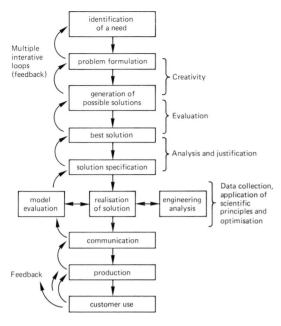

Figure 15.2 The design process

through which power, authority and influence are exercised, accepted or rejected.

No matter how good an organisation may be, it is its individuals who will make it work. Of all the resources a company has the most important are its people. It costs a great deal to hire people and care is necessary to ensure that they are placed, developed and used effectively. The education and training of designers is of great importance and will be discussed later. Here we are concerned with some of the personal aspects of using people in design.

Many engineers and managers overemphasise the rational approach to organisation. It is assumed that, because the structure is rational, behaviour within it also will, at all times, be rational. There is a surprisingly widespread belief that people will permanently suppress their emotions for the good of the organisation.

There is also the conviction that people, being rational, will welcome increasing doses of specialisation, since they must clearly see the logic of it; that they will also, in the interests of specialisation, suppress all their other talents and capabilities.

But it is not sufficient to provide a logical framework for people to work in. They must be allowed to develop in their jobs, in the emotional as well as the intellectual sense. Therefore the managers need an understanding, acquired or intuitive, of emotional as well as intellectual factors. They must learn to tolerate, indeed encourage, emotional conflict, without causing cataclysm.

15.2.1 *The individual*

A good deal of attention has been given to the needs of the individual as part of the organisation; research at one stage tended to concentrate on how best to satisfy these needs. One concept of motivation which has proven particularly useful in understanding individual behaviour within the organisation is Maslow's 'hierarchy of needs' (Maslow, 1971).

There are dangers in oversimplifying and there are some serious flaws in the hierarchical approach to motivation, but the concept does deepen understanding of individual behaviour.

15.2.2 *The hierarchy of needs*

Managers should try to provide opportunities for need satisfaction through doing the job itself so that people will enjoy doing good work. To do this, they must understand the basic types of human needs.

Physiological needs

People need food, drink, absence of fatigue, etc. It is important for managers to note whether the general working conditions satisfy these needs; e.g. lighting, temperature, ventilation, design of equipment, colour schemes, etc. Have the designers and draughtsmen and women got the right work stations, etc?

Safety needs

People need protection against danger. When workers feel threatened they look for security, often in irrational actions. In times of change a manager must realise that this need will be very strong. Total security may not be possible, but every effort must be made to remove even the appearance of a threat to jobs, status or earnings.

Emotional needs

People need the love, affection and warmth of family and friends. They have the need to belong and the need both to give and receive love. In the organisation this is provided by the immediate working group and also by recognition from the management. The converse aspect is loyalty and job satisfaction.

Social needs

Designers like to be thought well of by their fellow engineers and they also have a need for a certain amount of social contact during the day.

Status and self-esteem needs

People desire to be thought well of by colleagues and managers.

Some of these needs are often in mutual conflict.

In addition to positive need fulfilment, a manager will also have to use negative motivation to prevent some problems arising or to remedy others that have occurred. To be effective, disciplinary measures must be accepted as fair and reasonable. This can only happen if the manager normally uses the positive methods of motivation. Sanctions should be standardised for each offence and the rules on which they are based clearly laid down and publicised.

To motivate a working group managers must understand their staff, and the staff's needs and problems. They can then use the most appropriate incentives in any given situation. There are some incentives that may not be in their power, e.g. money, but every manager can contribute leadership and understanding of employees.

15.2.3   *The group*

People achieve through group action what individuals cannot achieve alone. They also achieve satisfaction from membership of groups. People belong to groups outside the working organisation, but they also belong to sub-groups within it. The needs of individuals are compounded by the needs of the groups to which they belong.

Groups differ in cohesion. Some are loosely bound and can only exercise a minimum of influence on their members; others are close groups that can put considerable pressure on their members.

The organisation is a larger group, and the way in which it works is modified by the behaviour of its sub-groups. Conflicts of objectives arise. For an organisation to work satisfactorily it is necessary to recognise both the formal and informal patterns within it and to use them to achieve objectives.

It is important for a manager to recognise that effective design groups pass through a series of stages of development which can briefly be described by reference to Figure 15.3.

In designing an organisation it must be appreciated that the various project work groups may be in any one of the modes indicated in Figure 15.3 and consequently some flexibility within the structure must be allowed.

15.3   Environment and design office work

An environment conducive to the effective utilisation of personnel is as important in a design department as in any other function. This is the responsi-

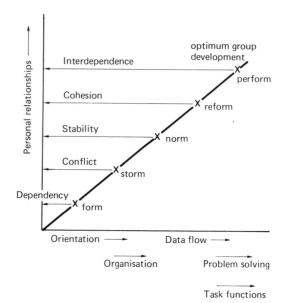

Figure 15.3 Design work group development

bility of the design manager. The Feilden report (1963) and the Koenigsberger NEDO report (Corfield, 1979) both stressed the need for a senior executive to be appointed to the board of companies who was responsible for design policy and its execution with due regard to its production and sales implications. Alas, this recommendation is a long way from being implemented in British industry. Consequently designers very often have to work in inferior surroundings with poor equipment, inadequate clerical services and inefficient — if any — data retrieval systems.

As regards the actual design office, there are two schools of thought: concentrated open-plan; or dispersed effort in small offices. People have strong feelings on this.

(1)   Those in charge believe that an 'open-plan' office is easier to control, facilitates communication, is more easily re-arranged, offers a higher packing density, is better for team spirit; but they know very well that it is universally disliked.

(2)   Those who have to live in the corral say it is noisy, distracting, humiliating, and positively hinders certain essential tasks. It does not offer any of the above advantages because people take every opportunity to be elsewhere.

(3)   Management distrust small offices because: they can't see what's going on; instead of communicating people appear to be reading what look like newspapers; space is wasted; too many telephones are needed; the radiators are all in the wrong places; you can't move people around; office occupation is an inflexible status symbol.

(4) Employees like small offices because they are quieter which helps one to think, confidential matters are more easily discussed, you can always be found because you are generally 'at home', and your own office gives you a feeling of importance and security.

(5) There is a general agreement that if the objective of an enterprise is quite clear to, and supported by, all concerned, people will work under the most appalling conditions without complaint.

(6) According to Parkinson, work and staff expand to fill the space available; and when an enterprise occupies the vast, specially built premises for which it has been waiting all these years it is already in decline.

The design office is sometimes split into two: one part, open plan, is for detailing, issuing modifications, etc. The other part is divided into small offices for development or project teams who do the creative work, if necessary to a degree of detail that will enable prototype manufacture to take place.

Alternatively, all design, at whatever level, can take place in one area; or designers may join with other engineers in feasibility studies or tender preparation.

The half-and-half system works well in a company making a few products where other influences ensure cohesion among the designers. Otherwise, morale in the detail office can be very low.

Centralisation may be ideal in theory, but is difficult to arrange when ready access is required by liaison engineers and advisory groups, and by development laboratories, printing departments, etc. A compromise can be valuable, especially when the objective is abundantly clear.

The best arrangements are difficult to find. Systems engineers need to be near computers, electronic circuit designers need a laboratory, and so on. Probably there is no ideal arrangement, flexibility is important. Therefore it is highly desirable to have easily removable partitions between offices.

It is also important to ensure that there is adequate lighting and heating, and that the appropriate equipment is provided for each designer. In this respect every design manager should be aware of the appropriate lighting glare index and minimum value of illumination (IES Code Recommendations).

15.4 Organisation structures

All organisations are in a continuous state of change. Very often these changes are imperceptible, at other times they are reminiscent of revolutions. The capacity of any organisation depends upon its ability to aid the necessary decision-making process. This always depends upon the quality of its information systems — are they adequate, accurate and timely? In this respect in an organisation the flow of information may be likened to the way organisms operate, and it is useful to recognise that doctors diagnose any malady in the human body by having two basic kinds of information:

(1) A thorough knowledge of the nature of human beings — this enables the doctor to know how the system should function.

(2) Knowledge given by measurements and tests on the human body at a given time.

In looking at design and development office organisation, managers need to have similar kinds of knowledge. They must understand the nature of their organisation — how will it respond to changes in environment? What are its component parts, etc? They must then know what specific measurements should be made for diagnostic purposes and how these should be interpreted.

There are many alternative structures which can be used to execute design work.

An organisation structure is appropriate if it furthers the objectives of the firm, whether or not it conforms to a prescribed pattern.

Organisation charts rely on certain conventions, such as that the vertical position on the chart indicates relative authority levels and horizontal lines depict collaborative links, etc. Staff functions are usually represented by horizontal lines off the main line functions as at 'A' in Figure 15.4.

This line and staff principle originated in military practice. The line officers are those who stand in the lines of combat, but the staff provide the administration and planning support: actually these are two distinct functions. But today in many manufacturing companies projects and products are created by so-called staff functions, such as R & D. This seems to be a wrong concept. Even the military have found the line/staff concept to fail at the accelerated pace set by the communication systems of today.

Improved communication has tended to concentrate line authority at the top while the power of decision-making by subordinate line managers has been weakened; they now merely co-ordinate activities in response to orders issued from the top. The staff, on the other hand, has a shorter chain of command to the top and its influence has been extended accordingly.

15.4.1 *Conventional structures*

The conventional line and staff structure might be depicted as in Figure 15.5. Here the Manager of Design and the Manager of R & D report directly to a Technical Director. Design is split between the message-creation phase where concepts are developed and feasibility proven and the message-

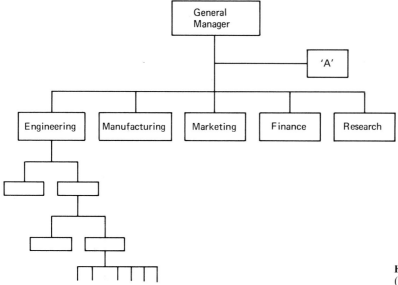

Figure 15.4 General management (functional) organisation

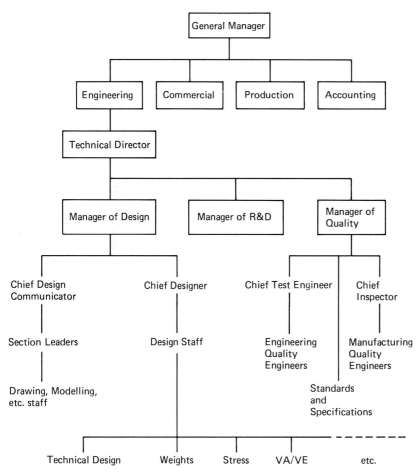

Figure 15.5 Conventional line drawing office structure

communication phase where the exact prescription of what is required is formulated for transmission to other interested parties.

In smaller companies inspection and test might be combined with R & D and standards, and specifications with design (communication), i.e. the Drawing Office. Normally the Chief Designer will be supported by a number of specialist sections such as Stress and Weights Offices, etc. as indicated in Figure 15.5.

Depending upon the technology being handled, there is a variety of ways in which detail design can be carried out and validated. In large companies Drawing Offices and Design Departments are often tied to particular product types. There may well be specialist design offices for gear boxes or hydraulic systems. Here an Organisational Structure providing each product group with its own Design/DO team is often more appropriate as depicted in Figure 15.6.

In such organisation structures new products or modifications to existing ones require close collaboration between production engineers, prototype shops and the design and drawing offices and they may often use common laboratory and experimental facilities.

For many capital goods the sale comes first and is followed by detail design and production: here design must be closely associated with marketing and a different structure is required. Similarly, for custom-built products, sales and design are closely linked since customer requirements have to be carefully interpreted and turned into contracts and specifications. In such cases the organisation will generally be more integrated as shown in Figure 15.7.

An organisational structure which has proved suitable for mass production work is depicted in Figure 15.8. Here the technical department has all the facilities to take development up to the stage of producing a working unit. They produce their own drawings down to the last detail, but do not design the tooling, etc. which is undertaken by a separate production design/drawing office. Sometimes these two roles are carried out by a single unit, but its internal structure generally reflects the two-fold role required to produce drawings suitable for mass production. It is naturally very important in any circumstances for the design team to take into account production capability so that close liaison with production departments is essential.

Clearly the conventional line-and-staff type of organisation shown in Figure 15.4, which might be called a general management organisation, is not really suited to all types of design work. Its advantage is its ability to preserve and enhance the company's technical expertise. It is well suited to mass production of items following a standard specification. Where slow evolution produces small product changes and derivatives it does allow all projects to

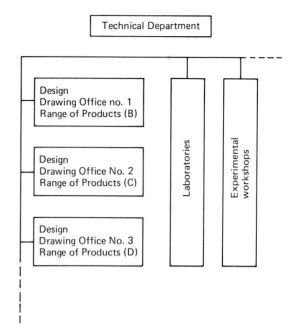

Figure 15.6 Drawing office structure for catalogue listed products

benefit from advanced and new technologies. However today, with complex technology to get people harmoniously working together, other forms of organisation have come into being and these have demanded a special type of management, namely product and project management. These will now be briefly discussed.

15.4.2 *Project structures*

Where complex large projects or high technology demand sophisticated systems and components, the conventional line/staff structures just discussed are unsuitable. Such projects involve multi-disciplinary activity, occur infrequently and are thus unfamiliar to the organisation. Generally some degree of novelty creates intricate interrelations of performance, time and cost relationships. The situation is confused by the fact that the Project Manager is not usually given complete responsibility for resources: generally he has to share these with the rest of the organisation.

For this class of work it is now generally accepted that a Project Manager is required. Like a Product Manager a Project Manager is responsible for seeing his project through from start to finish. In short he is responsible for running a business within a business.

The main characteristic of project organisation is the exceptionally strong lateral working relationships demanded, necessitating close co-ordination

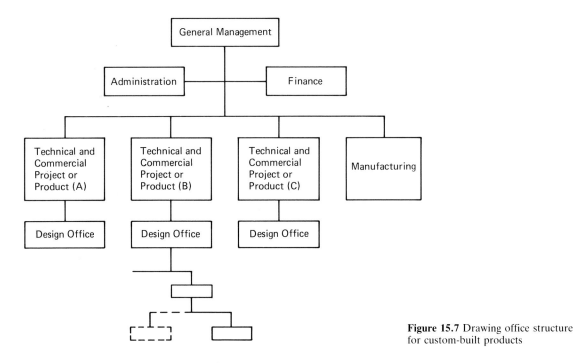

Figure 15.7 Drawing office structure for custom-built products

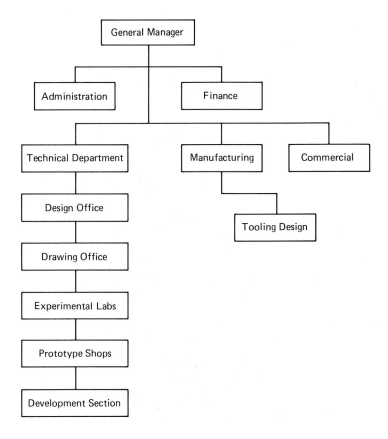

Figure 15.8 Drawing office structure for long and medium product runs

among many individuals in different functions. In achieving this a Project Manager will need to exercise sound common sense and tolerance if he is to succeed in the scramble for existing resources, no matter what the organisation structure is. There will also be vertical liaison in project management as additional expenditure will need to be approved by senior managers who will also wish to know current progress.

Certain organisational uncertainties are inevitable and many a project manager may find that his working relationships with functional department heads has not been clearly defined. Tricky questions can arise in connection with the urgency of design release for construction; new project features or modifications after field testing; spare parts scheduling; etc. At the same time a project manager may have to juggle with conflicting internal schedules laid down by departmental heads, to say nothing of changes necessitated by customers or subcontractors.

Before describing some of the standard types of project organisations that have been tried by industry to meet the above difficulties, some general observations might prove beneficial.

15.4.3.1 Bureaucracy

This type of organisation has a rigid structure of a steep pyramid with a long vertical chain of command. It was perfected during the industrial revolution, and is based on the division of labour into specialisms and operates within a system of rules and procedures that can deal with any work situation. The great strength of bureaucracy lies in its capacity to deal with predictable routine.

The threats to such a system are many, but perhaps the greatest is rapid and unexpected change. It is this, together with the complexity of modern technology, involving co-operation across departmental boundaries with professionals of very diverse specialisms, that has led to different types of organisation. The purely mechanistic value of bureaucracy often conflicts with the need to humanise the organisation and allow for professional growth. An organic and adaptive structure is required for harmony between individuals and to make their task meaningful, worth-while, creative and satisfying.

Anyone concerned with developing organisations to handle problems knows the difficulties of reconciling a rational structure with the need for maximum satisfaction of all those who have to work in it and make it work. Drucker has pointed out 'good organisation structure does not of itself produce good performance . . . but a poor organisational structure makes good performance impossible . . .' (Drucker, 1968). Here are some of the problems:

Integration: How to integrate individual needs with organisational goals. Such issues as incentives, rewards and personal motivation are involved. It seems likely that, as technology advances, society will demand a more human approach and may well be willing to sacrifice some efficiency to obtain this.

Collaboration: Management has to understand, and be able to resolve, conflicts. As organisations grow, they become more complex, fragmented and departmentalised. Interface conflicts quickly arise as tightly-knit group attitudes develop.

Adaptation: The present rate of change in society has upset the placid, stable and predictable environment of yesteryear. Old structures, with most power vested at the top and procedures laid down to cater for every routine, can no longer adapt to change and start to decay. The increasing interdependence of everything calls for new structures that have resilience and flexibility. To ensure their survival, organisations must, however, do more than respond to changes passively. They may have to try to shape the environment to meet their needs. This involves creating demands and needs where none existed before.

15.4.3.2 Standard types of project organisation

There are a number of variants on each of the four project organisations described below. It is also well to remember that many firms now reserve the term 'Project Leader' for those doing project work in the Design and Development Departments: in such cases they will often form part of a complete project team, headed by a Project Director or Chief Project Engineer.

Line or aggregate project management (see Figure 15.9). Here direct control over all matters concerning a project is vested in each project manager who has his own team of specialists. In effect, each Project Manager is running his own business. While this method does provide strong control by a single authority and has therefore a quick response time, it may fail to develop technical skills and there may well be a lack of interchange between project teams.

Shared staff project management (see Figure 15.10). Since it can be wasteful to multiply staff functions, some or all Project Managers may share control of staff departments, becoming in effect something like progress chasers.

Although, at first sight, this might seem a hopeless type of organisation, it can be successful at the small end of the project spectrum where there is a need for strong technical leadership. But it is useless

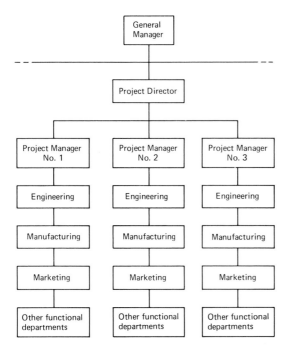

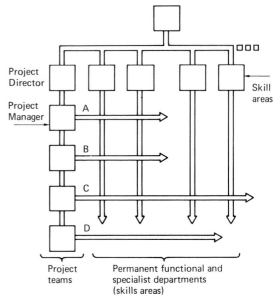

Figure 15.11 Matrix project management (dual control) structure

Figure 15.9 Line project management structure

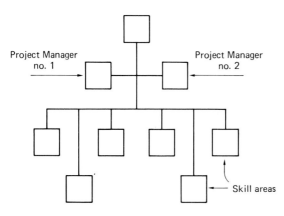

Figure 15.10 Staff project management (influence control) structure

functional areas. In effect, the Project Manager directs an element of each functional department on matters concerning his particular project.

All personnel are permanently assigned to a functional area and are responsible to their departmental heads on technical matters — the *how*. At the same time they are completely responsible to the Project Manager for *what* they do, and *when*.

The penalty paid for such a system is in the duplication of control and the length of response time, but it has the great advantage of preserving the continuity of the enterprise and of individual careers: with the line type of organisation (Figure 15.9) experience tends to be lost when a project has been completed. It can be difficult for specialists to operate under a dual accountability. Annual reviews and project priorities can also be constant sources of confrontations.

for larger projects and can prove frustrating and unrewarding to all but the specialists whose services have to be competed for by the various projects.

Matrix project management (see Figure 15.11).

This seeks to combine some of the advantages of the line organisation with those of the shared staff type. In Figure 15.11 all the functions are under a general manager. Each functional group is headed by a departmental manager responsible for its technical performance. Each project manager has programme responsibility which extends into the

Hybrid project management (see Figure 15.12).

This structure seeks the best compromise between 'line' and 'matrix' type organisations. In this case functional specialists are seconded to specific projects for the duration of the specialist work. On completing this they return to their functional departments. This results in better control but may lack flexibility to deal with sudden changes and fail to develop new techniques.

These four types can be compared as shown in Table 15.1 which sets out the respective advantages and disadvantages.

Table 15.1 Project management structures — advantages and disadvantages

Line or Aggregate Project Management	Staff Project Management
Advantages: Strong control by a single authority Rapid reaction time Good for performance, cost, delivery, trade-offs Leadership easy, personnel loyalty high Good customer contacts	Advantages: Very strong technical control Moderate reaction time Develops in-house technology and know-how Very good for developing project engineers
Disadvantages: Fails to develop continuity of technology Small opportunity for technical interchange between projects Inefficient use of manufacturing/construction facilities Difficulty in balancing work loads as projects come and go Lack of career continuity	Disadvantages: Poor schedule and cost performance due to multi-project situation Often poor customer relations Technical overload often reached Excessive time consumed on persuasion Little project-orientated planning
Matrix Project Management	Hybrid Project Management
Advantages: Helps to advance and keep new technology (project feedback) Facilitates technical interchange Good utilisation of resources Good external relations Moderate reaction time	Advantages: Very good deployment of personnel on project Better utilisation of collective experience Technical performance high Career development good
Disadvantages: Dual accountability Conflict of interest between project and functional line Profit and loss accountability more difficult	Disadvantages: Appraisal of individual's work more difficult Problems of personnel returning to line work Loyalties can conflict

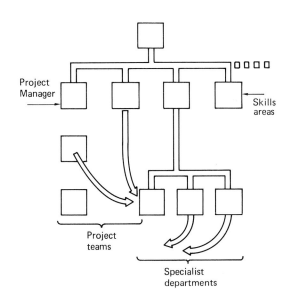

Figure 15.12 Hybrid project management (variable control) structure

In devising design and development organisations a careful balance between order and flexibility has to be obtained. Should a Design Office be centralised for several production groups, or decentralised? These and many other questions on organisation depend upon the nature of the technology. Where there is little or slow change, there may be formal policies, procedures and rules to obviate communication difficulties and aid delegation. But where change is continually occurring, an organic type of organisation is required where groups, or task forces, are continually being formed and disbanded as jobs progress. Where design work demands frequent changes, project teams are necessary to drive projects through the often amorphous conventional staff/line organisations.

15.5 The role of checkers and checking facilities

The problem with checkers is that if they remain too long on the job they eventually pass mistakes. Like 100% inspection they see what they want to see.

This does not mean that checking facilities should not be provided for they are especially desirable when a critical part of a design is being completed or a new procedure is being installed. But management must endeavour not to keep checkers on all the time since if they do section leaders and designer/draughtsmen/women can become slack and fail to check their own work.

From time to time management should apply a sampling check on individual work, but even this needs careful handling and may take up considerable time.

15.6 The use of contract designers and outside design bureaux

Very often design teams find themselves unable to cope with excessive overload which can occur for various reasons in spite of good planning. Figure 5.13 shows a typical design manpower build-up associated with the complete design process, while Figure 15.14 indicates what can happen to the manpower and costs build-up when a main contractor uses a sub-contractor for separate design

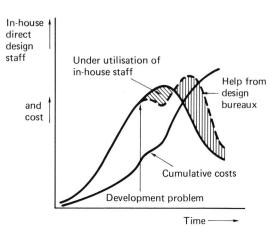

Figure 15.14 Build up of in-house design staff with help from design bureaux

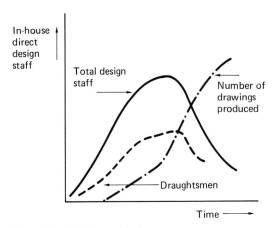

Figure 15.13 Build up of design staff

work. This may be due to a programme being 'crashed' or to some planning error, or to unexpected development troubles. A further instance occurs when variations on the main design may have to be made for different customers. An example of this can be found in the case of aircraft, where, say, an extended fuselage is required for operation on certain routes. Another case would be the uprating of a diesel engine involving additional or enlarged cylinders.

Separate design bureaux can also be useful for dealing with the following types of work:

(1) providing specialist design work,
(2) industrial design,
(3) technical illustrations and other handbook production, and
(4) peak load conditions.

To ensure a good working relationship with a separate design bureau is not easy and certain factors must be taken into account. Among these are the following:

(1) If a firm has a complicated project on hand, and needs additional help with the design, it must sub-contract complete portions of the work which can be well defined.
(2) Unless the complete design is to be given to a bureau the main scheming work should be kept 'in-house'.
(3) Whatever is let out to sub-contract should be written down in detail specifying all interfaces and clearly defining what is expected in the way of drawings, specifications, models, material lists, etc.
(4) Keep the bureau personnel away from the main firm once a contract has been let. Use a project leader to liaise with the bureau.
(5) Always have a resident designer on the bureau's premises to advise, supervise and liaise with your own design team.
(6) Ensure that the bureau is conversant with your own design and drawing office practices. (Data sheets may have to be supplied to the bureau.)
(7) Establish a modification procedure but only allow a sub-contractor to execute modifications under strict supervision. Always watch their paperwork on changes.

(8) Any contract should clearly state how modification work will be costed.

(9) Where necessary contracts should contain penalty clauses for late design work. Time and target dates must be agreed before the commencement of the work. Sub-contractor's PERT charts should marry up with main contractors.

(10) An agreed budget must be drawn up setting out cost targets.

Occasionally separate consultant designers may be employed as for example with industrial design. In these cases it is most important to have the consultant designer in as early as possible in the design process, preferably at the problem formulation stage (see Figure 15.2). He must be given a clear brief and will need to liaise closely with the in-house design team. His involvement with them tends to vary according to the phase of design activity but will generally be as indicated in Figure 15.15.

15.7   Education and training of designers

The training of engineering designers has, for too long, been left to chance. Many say managers and designers are born, not made. For some this may be true, but it does not mean to say that they would not be better managers and better designers if they were given some training.

Unfortunately the conventional higher educational system does not, on the whole, really cater for helping creative engineering designers. There are some exceptional cases where undergraduates are given design work and projects in their last year. But the greatest progress has been made in the postgraduate courses, and some of these are producing encouraging results, but they are few and far between (*Engineering*, 1975; Leech, 1975).

Much has been written and spoken about Design Education as both the Moulton and Corfield Reports show (Moulton, 1976; Corfield, 1979). But it will take some time before any changes in the established educational system bear fruit. So firms will need to carry out much training themselves. At the time of writing the Finniston report has not brought about the desired changes to the education of engineers. For design work of the future it is clear that more interdisciplinary courses are required which cut across the arbitrary divisions of Mechanical, Electrical, Chemical Engineering, etc. and which are orientated towards design and production.

For so long the engineering education system has concentrated on analysis. Present courses lay much emphasis on teaching fundamental laws and derived theory, but designers have to synthesise. In the

Figure 15.15 Effort and involvement of industrial design in the design process

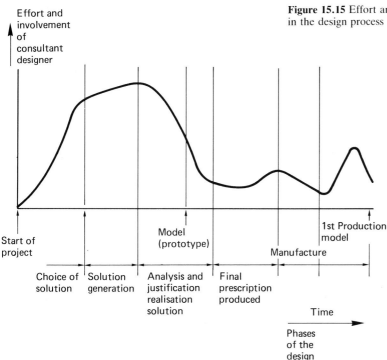

ever-increasing concentration on theory many teachers have unconsciously stifled design creative ability. Examination of architects' courses shows that much more time is devoted to practising design skills. They carry out abstract exercises, limited objective design exercises and total design projects, as well as live projects. Perhaps some engineers should be trained a bit more in this manner. If design is the heart of the engineering business, it follows that the very best people should be employed in this area of work. The quality and reliability of a product stem from the design office. Indeed it is true to say that the reputation of an engineering enterprise is largely determined by the competitiveness of the design and of its products. It follows, therefore, that designers need to be carefully selected, developed and deployed. This can be viewed from two aspects, on-the-job and off-the-job training (see Figure 15.16).

15.7.1 *On-the-job training*

Some firms have started to employ design tutors with the responsibility of aiding designers while actually employed in design offices. This can be of benefit since the tutor can act as an informed critic, thus causing the designer to defend his efforts and possibly re-evaluate them. However, designer managers must be responsible for developing those who work for them. Some of the ways of doing this are set out under the following sub-headings.

15.7.1.1 **Special assignments**

It may be possible to give a designer from time to time a special assignment in addition to his normal job. This may be to investigate ways of improving the productivity of the drawing office, or improving the information flow into the design office, etc. This

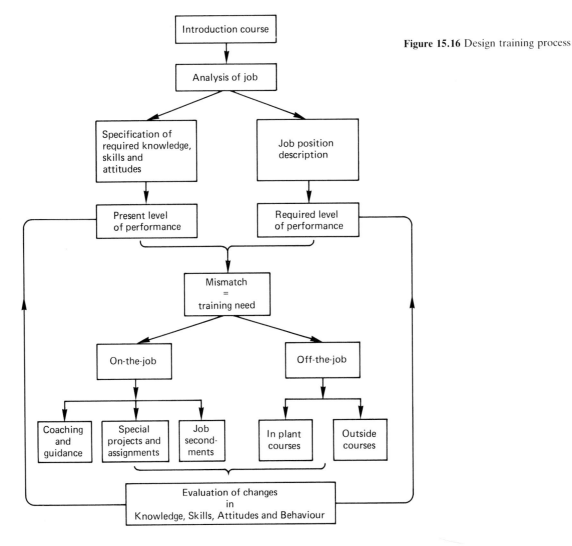

Figure 15.16 Design training process

causes a designer to move around and talk to other people outside his immediate section. It also requires that the designer gather information and arranges what is obtained, so as to present a readable report. If a designer is made to report back the findings to a panel of engineers, so much the better.

15.7.1.2 Planned visits

Too many designers are restricted in their vision and much can be done to help them by arranging for a series of visits. These may include visits to the sites where the products they help to design are in use, so that they can speak to the operators and clients and obtain first hand information on any difficulties experienced in operation and learn of good design points. Other visits may be made to exhibitions and research establishments to keep in touch with other competitors' products and gain an insight into future developments.

15.7.1.3 Secondments

Here a designer may be sent to another department for a period of time to see how they work. It is important to ensure, however, that when a designer is seconded for, say, six months, he is given a positive job to do. One example where this proved of great benefit was in connection with purchasing. A new product required certain special processes and had to be made by sub-contractors. By seconding a designer to the purchasing office help was afforded in getting satisfactory production achieved and the designer learnt of problems peculiar to the purchasing role, such as negotiating price procedures, vendor rating and the importance of adequate packaging, etc.

15.7.2 Off-the-job training

It is likely that designers who move up to become section leaders and then heads of departments will require supervisory and management training. Such training may be conducted by a company's own training staff, or by some outside agency. For large enterprises probably both are necessary, for knowledge of a particular company — its products, policies, organisation, trades union matters, etc. — is best given by its own people, whereas broad knowledge and new ideas may be better given elsewhere. Smaller companies may well have to rely entirely upon outside teaching establishments, where opportunity will be afforded for potential managers to rub shoulders with men from other concerns. Before sending a candidate on an outside course he must be told when he is going and what it is hoped to achieve by sending him on the course. After the course is over it is highly desirable for the

candidate to be monitored so that his performance may be assessed. This will require hard work by both the candidate's boss and the course tutor if true evaluations are to be achieved.

It is vitally important to ensure that off-the-job training is wedded to on-the-job training if effective results are to be achieved. On-the-job training should be able to identify a designer's weaknesses and strengths, and the golden rule of building up strengths should be followed by choosing an appropriate outside course for him to attend for these to be developed.

However, it is important to realise that in the last analysis management is learnt by managing and being managed. Designers can learn from the present way they are managed: some of the pitfalls to avoid and the good points to cultivate. They must learn for themselves how to encourage and bring on people as well as how to correct them.

For training in special techniques and design aids two methods may be used. The first might be called the project method. Here a design/make and build exercise can be used to teach, say, the use of value engineering in achieving an economically viable design. The second is by means of design workshops. Here groups of designers can be brought together to tackle design problems on a group basis. They are asked to bring a specific design problem of their own, and any possible situations they may have. Alternative ways of tackling the problem are then put forward by the group. Such work may be interspersed with lectures introducing new materials and processes, etc.

Education and training must be looked upon as a continuous process for all design offices. Basically it should be conducted at three levels.

15.7.2.1 New intakes and young designers

Young designers with any real drive will wish to extend their study to expand their technical ability. It may well be possible to do this by means of part-time release or even full-time courses. It is important to have agreed training programmes in this course with proper assignments scheduled for each team in technical college or industry. Where necessary assignments in other industries may be desirable. In this connection the EITB's Industrial Liaison Officer may be able to help with arranging suitable positions.

15.7.2.2 Junior designers

It is often very difficult for a junior designer to keep abreast of latest developments or even other work being carried out in his own section or department. To overcome this problem it is useful to conduct in-plant seminars. Junior designers should be asked to present short lectures on their own work at these gatherings. Time should be given to those with this opportunity to prepare visual aids, models, etc. Such seminars can be conducted after working hours, so that disruption to normal working hours does not occur.

15.7.2.3　Senior designers

This is possibly the weakest area in training, and our senior institutions have done little to help senior designers. Time must be given to allow senior staff to attend lectures, seminars, and conferences to talk with their colleagues. The Institution of Engineering Designers (IED) has done much to make this possible.

All senior designers should be encouraged to prepare papers for publication on their design work. The main benefits are not from the kudos obtained, although this may be quite considerable, but from the discipline required in crystallising their thoughts and presenting them in a logical way. In addition many new ideas may arise both from the preparation of the paper itself and from the discussion after it has been given. They should not be afraid to set down their failures as well as their successes. For it is only by overcoming obstacles that real design development takes place.

It is vitally important that every design manager should consider carefully how he can develop his staff and he must devote time to do this.

The goal of any engineer should be to utilise the knowledge and material of the physical world for the benefit of society. To achieve this end he designs and constructs physical objects, devices, structures, processes and systems. The problems which engineers seek to solve generally have many possible answers from which an appropriate solution must be chosen. An engineering designer's aim is really to optimise the usefulness of resources for mankind's benefit. It is a tragedy that so much of our engineering education and training is not directed specifically towards the designer's main aim. Much correction to new intakes has to take place by industry for this reason. The day cannot be far off when a proper science of Design will emerge as a teachable discipline, and it is hoped that this will percolate into our established teaching units (Turner, 1966; Turner *et al.*, 1974; Harris, 1980).

15.7.3　*Computer training and designers*

With the advent of the microcomputer it has become possible for many designers to have computers at their elbow. No longer will they have to pass infor-

mation to another group of people to use the machine. It will therefore be necessary to train existing and future designers in a programming language such as 'BASIC' so that the full value of computer aided design becomes a reality. Such training is best conducted in-house using a consultant.

For more esoteric work CAD (Computer Aided Design) may be used and such systems can produce neater and more uniform drawings with fewer errors. Where such systems are used for producing pipework, isometric drawings and printed circuit boards, etc. it is essential to give proper introductory appreciation courses and allow draughtsmen time to work the system on their own. Preferably they should be allowed about a month to familiarise themselves with such equipment and have available a tutor to aid them when necessary.

Bibliography

ARGYRIS, C. (1957) 'Today's problems with tomorrow's organisations', *The Journal of Management Studies*, **4**, no. 1.

BENNIS, W. G. (1966) *Changing Organisations*, McGraw-Hill.

BIM (1960) *Drawing Office Organisation*, British Institute of Management.

CORFIELD, K. R. (1979) *Product Design*, National Economic Development Council.

DRUCKER, P. (1968) *The Practice of Management*, Pan.

Engineering (1975) 'Design Can and is Being Taught, But . . . ', September.

Feilden Report (1963) *Engineering Design*, HMSO.

HARRIS, A. (1980) 'Can design be taught?', *Proc. I. Civil Eng.*, Part 1, August.

IES Code Recommendations for Lighting Building Interiors, S/D A.67, UDC.628.9.

IMechE (1963–64) *Engineering Design*, Proceedings of the Conference on The Practice and Education for Engineering Design, **178**, Part 3B.

IMechE (1966) *Organisation for Design*, Conference Proceedings.

IMechE, IED and Design Council (1977) *Engineers for the Drawing Board*, Report of a Seminar held on the 24th March.

LAWRENCE, P. R. and LORSCH, J. W. (1967) *Organisation and Environment*, Harvard University Press.

LEECH, D. J. (1975) 'Undergraduate training in design project management', *IJMEE*, **3**, no. 1.

LIKERT, R. (1967) *The Human Organisation*, McGraw-Hill.

MASLOW, A. H. (1971) *The Farther Reaches of Human Nature*, Penguin.

MIDDLETON, C. J. (1967) 'How to set up a project organisation', *Harvard Business Review*, March/April.

MILLER, E. J. and RICE, A. K. (1967) *Systems of Organisation*, Tavistock Publications.

MOULTON, A. E. (1976) *Engineering Design Education*, The Design Council.

PERROW, C. (1971) *Organisational Analysis*, Tavistock Publications.

PORTER, L. W. and ROBERTS, K. H. (eds.) (1977) *Communications in Organisations*, Penguin.

PUGH, D. S., HICKSON, D. J. and HININGS, C. R. (1971) *Writers on Organisations*, Penguin.

RAS (1976) 'Future developments in the organisation and management of design', Proceedings of the Royal Aeronautical Society, March.

STEWART, R. (1970) *The Reality of Organisations*, Pan Management Series.

TAGUIN, R. and LITWIN, G. H. (eds.) (1968) *Organisational Climate*, Harvard University Press.

TURNER, B. T., EVANS, W. G. and CHAMNEY, A. R. (1974) 'Tomorrow started yesterday', 17th Leonardo da Vinci Lecture of the Institution of Mechanical Engineers.

TURNER, B. T. (1966) 'A new approach to education for engineering design', Proceedings of the Conference on the Teaching of Engineering Design.

TURNER, B. T. (1968) 'Management of Design', *InComTec Manual*, December.

TURNER, B. T. (1978) 'Growth and industrial organisations, *Chartered Mechanical Engineer*, July.

TURNER, B. T. (1979) 'The engineering design and drawing office today and tomorrow', *J. Mech. & Gen. Tech. Eng.*, **90**, no. 2.

WEARNE, S. H. (1970–71) 'Systems of engineering organisation', *Proc. IMechE*, **185**, no. 3/71.

WEARNE, S. H. (1973) *Principles of Engineering Organisations*, Edward Arnold.

16

Design services

16.1 Engineering manuals

16.1.1 General

Engineering organisations vary greatly in complexity, depending upon their product(s). One that designs and manufactures lawn mowers, for example, would clearly be much simpler than one dedicated to major aerospace projects, such as airframes and engines.

However, each must have facilities for conceiving a design, then developing and producing it. In seeking to define the requirements of a particular section of the market, both must evolve and maintain a specification for the product towards ensuring that operational requirements are optimised with regard to quality and cost.

Aerospace engineering organisations rate among the most complex and sophisticated, encompassing specialists in such diverse fields as aerodynamics, stress, performance, electronics, reliability and metallurgy. In appropriate combinations these specialists must realise the specified objective — to produce effective, soundly engineered products, on time.

The prime task of engineering management is to create and sustain such an organisation and to direct it to the achievement of the declared objective. To this end, all personnel employed in the engineering function must be familiar with the organisation and comply with its policies, procedures and standards. These features must, therefore, be widely-communicated through a suite of engineering manuals.

Chapter 15 discusses structure and organisation in design offices, in general terms, while this chapter describes the organisation of a major aerospace company and the part played by manuals towards managing its endeavours.

16.1.2 Organisation documented

16.1.2.1 Functional organisation

A Chief Engineer is responsible for the evolution of each project into a cost-effective, well-engineered product, through project teams comprising design, development, performance, stress and product cost control representatives each under the control of a senior engineer. Project teams are assisted and advised by specialist departments or groups who provide the required expertise for all projects. Similar specialist groups are engaged on research into new and improved technologies to help maintain the pre-eminence of the organisation in its field.

16.1.2.2 Procedural control

To maintain required standards and ensure compliance with the requirements of external controlling authorities, engineering activities are governed by Control Procedures, while the contribution of each engineering department is controlled through its Manual of Operating Procedures.

16.2 Design and design services

16.2.1 Design area

The Design Area is organised into functional groups designated Project, Specialist or Services, each directed by a Chief Designer.

Project Groups undertake the overall design of a particular project or group of projects, whereas the Specialist Groups provide the complementary specialist designs for one or more specific feature or component, as required by each Project Group. The Services Group provides the expertise necessary to ensure that each project design is compatible with, typically, installation, maintenance and overhaul requirements and that the basic design standards comply with the requirements of the company and other interested or controlling authorities.

16.2.2 Design services

Complementary to the Design Area, the Design Services organisation comprises:

(1) The Engineering Drawing Office,
(2) Configuration Department,
(3) Management Systems,
(4) Photo-reprographic and Technical Services,
(5) Administration.

The main responsibilities of these departments are:

(1) *Engineering Drawing Office*: Translation of the requirements of Design Schemes into detail or assembly drawings suitable for use within the Manufacturing area, etc.
(2) *Configuration Department*: Processing and issue of design schemes, part numbers, specifications and other documentation, and order and stock control of development components.
(3) *Management Systems*: Compilation of technical procedures and the derivation, test and implementation of supporting manual or computerised systems, covering ordering of components, build schedules, unit history and data retrieval systems.
(4) *Photo-reprographic and Technical Services*: Provision of a comprehensive photographic facility, including a consultative service to all departments and a reprographic facility producing brochures and manuals.
(5) *Administration*: Provision of support facilities:
    (a) *The Technical Library*, a comprehensive library and information service of all aspects of aerospace activity;
    (b) *Translation and Interpreting Office*, a centralised translating and/or interpreting service for all subjects or activities;
    (c) *Central Typing Office*, a word processing and typing service to Design, Design Services and other departments as required.

16.2.3 Procedures, methods, standards and controls

16.2.3.1 Engineering standards

The Engineering Standards Department prepares documentation to cover standard parts, design standards and engineering specifications, as agreed by a Standards Committee. National and International Standardisation is taken into account, through Society of British Aerospace Constructors (SBAC) and BSI committees, which prepare aerospace standards, and through equivalent international bodies, e.g. ISO/TC20 Aircraft and Space Vehicles, ISO/TC1 Screw Threads, AICMA Commission Mécanique and the SAE E21 Design Standards and E25 Part Standards Committees in the USA.

Materials Properties Handbook: Deals with material properties and contains a rationalised range of approved materials.

National Standard Parts: National standard parts, e.g. BSI and SBAC, are specified wherever possible. New standard parts are promulgated through these national bodies so that they become available for use throughout the industry.

Company Standards: Provide information and recommendations to designers on standard parts and features (screw threads, splines, etc., processes and specifications).

Company Engineering Specifications: Cover procedures for manufacture, inspection, assembly, etc., necessary to meet engineering requirements.

16.2.3.2 Design Standards Specifications

Define the standards that are to be used for each project, towards ensuring consistent use of standard parts and design practices. Agreed between the Chief Designer for the project and the Engineering Standards Department, before agreement with the customer.

16.2.3.3 Drawing Control Procedures

Presentation, dimensioning and tolerancing methods, together with the issue and alteration procedures for engineering detail drawing, are laid down in various drafting documents.

16.2.3.4 Repair and Salvage Procedures

The Engineering Department administers these procedures, which cover:

Repair Drawings: Initiated by the Design Office (Repair), to cover anticipated basic wear problems; specific requests from repair shops and the Service Department; effects of modifications.

Fits, clearances and repair tolerance schedule: Comprises a list of standard dimensions and the resulting fits for new parts, together with their permissible worn figures, beyond which a component must not be used without repair action.

16.2.3.5 Concession and production permit

Concessions: Components which are found to deviate from requirements are made the subject of an application for a concession. Concessions are raised by the Chief Inspector and submitted for the approval of Engineering where they are endorsed accept or reject; salvage or repair action necessary for acceptance is specified. It may be necessary, also, to obtain the agreement of the customer.

Production permits: Authorise materials or the manufacture of components which differ from the approved drawing or specification. The authorisation is only valid for a pre-defined limited quantity or period. Approval is given by authorised signatories within Engineering, Manufacturing, and Quality Departments, and agreed by the customer.

16.2.3.6 Drawing introduction control procedures

Function: To establish and control the design standard of equipment to permit manufacture, overhaul and inspection. Ensures maintenance of the design acceptance standard and uniformity of product, both functionally and dimensionally. Enables design changes to be controlled and provides adequate data for contractual purposes.

Method of control: In order to meet production programmes, it may be necessary for manufacture to commence prior to the completion of approval tests. Therefore, where permissible, changes are embodied by domestic clearance until programmes or contractual terms are affected. At this point an official modification procedure commences, wherein design changes are classified as modifications or amendments, depending on the effect of the change on the contract and customer. A modification is a design change, authorised after release for full production manufacture, which affects one or more of the following: interchangeability; safety; performance; installation; cost of the unit or accessory and/or its spares; date of delivery; embodiment in units or accessories delivered; schedule of fits and clearances and repair tolerances; support equipment.

An amendment is a design change of a minor nature which does not affect any of the items listed above.

16.2.3.7 Design change control procedure

Engineering procedures for instructing an alteration to the approved standard of a product are designed to ensure that only validated changes are made. The procedures also ensure that the full commercial service, manufacturing and engineering consequences are investigated and appreciated.

Standardisation procedures ensure that only design changes which have been adequately validated by testing, or on the basis of a sound technical argument, are allowed to go forward for formal modification action.

16.2.3.8 Modification action

Following satisfactory testing and approval of a design change, the Design Office authorises preparation of a modification from data contributed by all departments concerned. This information is embodied on a standard pro-forma and submitted to a change control committee, consisting of senior representatives from Design, Development, Production, Service and Commercial Departments, with other members co-opted as required.

Following agreement, modifications are endorsed by an approved signatory before being submitted to the appropriate certification authority for final approval. The manufacture and introduction of modifications into new equipment and the supply of modification sets to the repair organisation or customers is initiated by the Commercial organisation, following instructions from the Engineering Department.

16.2.4 Advanced engineering

Clearly, advanced engineering is an important activity in an aerospace organisation and its overall function is as follows:

(1) To specify the functional design of main components and associated systems and to collaborate with other departments in the translation of the functional design into practical hardware.

(2) To provide specialist assistance and data in support of work programmes aimed at verifying the compatibility of the product with specified requirements, and to assist in overcoming problems arising during all phases of design, development and service.

(3) To advance the relevant technologies through research and advanced development programmes, so enabling the organisation to improve its products and maintain its competitive position.

The following departments comprise the advanced engineering organisation.

16.2.4.1 Project management

Authorisation and financial control of components, rigs and research programmes are effected against the appropriate project, research or company private venture contract, or other sponsorship.

Management and financial control of these programmes are the responsibility of Advanced Engineering Project Management.

16.2.4.2 Control Systems

The activities of this department are divided into three functional groups:

Control Systems and Technology provides technical advice and performance and design data to assist other departments and suppliers with, for example, specification, design and development of electronic, hydromechanical and pneumatic systems, controls and heat exchangers. Fluid specifications are examined to ensure that they are compatible with the products and any additives are investigated for possible side effects.

Design and Suppliers Control is responsible for assisting in the design of prototype and production electronic control equipment and for the examination of proposed designs and design changes by suppliers and sub-contractors for all electrical, (including electronic) hydraulic, mechanical and pneumatic controls.

Project Engineering consists of specialist engineers who are appointed to each project, for which they provide a prime interface between Control Systems and the other engineering areas, to ensure that the available resources are used cost effectively and that suppliers' designs and development programmes are suited to the requirement of the project. In addition, they supply technical assistance, when required by the project, for the evaluation, development and operation of the various control systems involved.

16.2.4.3 Aerodynamics

This function is responsible for defining geometry, speeds and performance capabilities, for project design purposes, and for preparing specifications of, for example, profiles. Rig tests of full-size and scale models are used to explore the potential of advanced designs and to provide information to assist in development programmes. Improved theoretical methods are evolved and evaluated for design, and the analysis of performance.

16.2.4.4 Rig Test

Test Departments undertake the rig tests necessary to obtain data required by the Advanced Engineering area. Their functions include procurement of new test facilities and the maintenance of existing rigs and plant, in addition to the implementation of the test programmes required.

16.2.4.5 Performance and advanced projects

The Performance Department is responsible for defining the degree of accuracy required of the test measurement instrumentation used to determine the significance of test bed readings, and stipulating the calculation and correction procedures to be used.

It is also responsible for dealing with customer complaints and rejection from test beds. It maintains liaison with the Design and Development Departments on changes likely to affect performance, and is responsible for approval of standardisation documents for all modifications.

It is also responsible for analysing development flight test data and watching the effectiveness of the product in service, and for the content of acceptance schedules and operating instructions.

Advanced Projects Department keeps abreast of the needs of operators and manufacturing industry and maintains a leading position in the field of advanced technology.

New concepts are evaluated with the aid of computer programs are and design studies, and investigations are carried out of their potential performances and effects on costs, operating efficiencies and applications.

16.2.5 *Mechanical Engineering, Laboratories and Engineering Computer*

The Mechanical Engineering, Laboratories and Computing functions come within the jurisdiction of the Chief Mechanical Engineer. These functions are carried out through the Mechanical Research Department; Engineering Computing; Stress Engineering and Material and Product laboratories.

The responsibilities of the departments within the Mechanical Engineering, Laboratories and Engineering Computing functions are as follows.

16.2.5.1 Mechanical Research Department

This is responsible for a range of engineering programmes under the following main groups, and for ensuring that appropriate rig and laboratory facilities are provided for the task:

(1) Research aimed at improving the mechanical design of components and operating systems.
(2) The establishment of suitable programmes and provision of the necessary test evidence to support the case for product certification, to establish or extend component lives, and to validate new materials and processes.

(3) The solution of mechanical problems arising during development or in service and proving of corrective modifications.

16.2.5.2 Stress Engineering Departments

The basic function of Stress Engineering is to provide a structural and mechanical engineering service to optimise mechanical design, and ensure the overall reliability and integrity of all major components, the failure of which could jeopardise safety. A particular responsibility is the establishment of safe lives for low-cycle, fatigue-limited components.

Advanced computer-based methods of stress and vibration analysis are developed and programs written.

A specialist service is provided to the engineering department on all matters affecting materials and processes, in particular, the selection of suitable materials and/or processes for new designs.

Mass properties of parts, assemblies and installations are determined and weight and centre-of-gravity control exercised.

16.2.5.3 Materials and product laboratories

Materials laboratories provide engineering services as follows:

(1) materials/process research and development,
(2) new materials and processes evaluation,
(3) generation of material design data,
(4) component failure investigation,
(5) chemical and physical analysis, and
(6) materials specifications.

Laboratory services to manufacturing are provided in respect of:

(1) process research and development, and
(2) manufacturing development.

Product laboratories ensure that engineering material and process specifications and material standards requirements are fulfilled. They are also responsible for the metallurgical integrity of materials, semi-finished products and finished components.

Their operations are governed by the requirements of internal national and ministry specifications and instructions for material and process quality control.

Materials and specifications are grouped into material types such as:

(1) non corrosion-resistant steels and cast irons,
(2) corrosion-resistant stainless and creep resistant steels,
(3) heat resisting and refractory alloys,
(4) light alloys,
(5) copper alloys,
(6) titanium alloys,
(7) non-metallic materials,
(8) elastomers and jointings,
(9) miscellaneous metallic materials, and
(10) procedural documents.

Process specifications are a separate series of documents.

16.2.5.4 Engineering Computer Centre

The engineering computer centre provides facilities for other departments in engineering to write computer programs and offers a consultancy service on software and hardware.

Terminals linked to a multi-access system are sited throughout the areas served. While many users are linked to the larger mainframe network, some have dedicated microcomputers.

The network and other projects are sustained by the following departments.

The Programming Systems Department is responsible for computing development in the field of software. A programming service is provided for network users, and software aspects of externally-acquired applications programmes are also a responsibility of the department. Similar considerations apply to micro- and mini-computers.

The Computer Engineering Department is responsible for computing development in the field of hardware, including design, development and manufacture of computer hardware and associated electronic equipment. Services provided include technical appraisal of bought-out items, liaison with equipment suppliers, co-ordination and back-up support to maintenance sub-contractors.

The Computing Services Department is responsible for the operation of all computing and peripheral equipment and for the services available to users of the network. A data preparation service is also provided and liaison is maintained with suppliers of computer media, e.g. magnetic tapes and line printer stationery.

16.2.6 Development Engineering

The development department is responsible for evolving products from the original design stage up to a standard where reliability and performance are acceptable to the appropriate certification authority, and are also in accordance with the requirements of customer operators.

16.2.6.1 Development Programme Control

Programme plan: Development is basically a repetitive process of testing, examination, assessment, modification and re-testing until the requirements specified are satisfactorily achieved, within the framework of a development plan. The plan is reviewed and up-dated periodically. Following entry-into-service, the development team maintain close liaison with the Product Support Department, and remain responsible for verification and acceptability of the solutions to technical problems that may arise during the service life of the product.

Programme Management: Planning and execution of development programmes are controlled by the Project Chief Development Engineer, who is responsible to the Chief Engineer of the Project for all development activity. Teams of Development Engineers and Programme Engineers are available, uniquely, to each project and are responsible for achieving an adequate mechanical standard and programme.

16.2.6.2 Reliability Engineering Department

The design standard of each project is investigated in terms of both safety and reliability for the following purposes:

(1) To provide the Design Department with a basis for improving the design of the project as an addition to the normal development engineering methods.
(2) To alert the Development Department to special tests which may be shown to be necessary.
(3) To provide the Product Support Department with a basis for producing logical maintenance schedules.
(4) To provide formal safety assessments and fault analyses of the design standards of products in service.

Summaries of actual experience are maintained to enable reasonable reliability assessments to be made on new product types.

16.2.7 Engineering electronics

The Engineering Electronics Department provides electronic and electrical accessories or components, developed to a satisfactory standard, and undertakes research and development for advanced systems. Specialised equipment for monitoring critical parameters under arduous and/or difficult conditions is also designed and developed.

The department's organisation covers the following activities:

(1) engineering controls and accessories,
(2) research and advanced development,
(3) test instrumentation,
(4) engineering measurement,
(5) electronic design services, and
(6) project services.

16.2.8 Control of product costs

16.2.8.1 Procedures and functions

Cost reduction: Essentially a review of the production drawings of an existing production to identify unnecessary cost and the implementation of agreed changes to drawings and processes to eliminate them.

Product cost control: Ensures that components are designed and manufactured at a cost level commensurate with the market price.

16.2.8.2 Cost reduction

All engines are subject to the Cost Reduction Procedure, carried out by a Cost Control Manager, seconded to the Project Chief Engineer. Review Meetings, chaired by the Cost Control Manager, are attended by appropriate designers, detailers, development engineers and representatives from Production Engineering and Business Planning. Subsequently, an appropriate drawing change procedure proforma is raised and cleared by the Project Management teams. The Cost Control Manager must then ensure that the appropriate priorities are accorded to clearing and implementing the proposals to meet the cost reduction targets and timescales.

16.2.8.3 Product cost control

Most significant component manufacturing costs are created at the design scheme and detail drawing stage. In recognition of this, a Design Cost Control Group, headed by a Senior Designer and including representatives from Manufacturing, Business Planning and the Purchasing Department, is responsible for:

(1) establishing the product target factory cost, and allocating target costs to component level at the design stage,
(2) ensuring that the designer receives timely production engineering advice and cost estimates, and
(3) monitoring the emerging cost status and arranging corrective action.

During the planning stage, processes are chosen which enable the target cost to be achieved. Methods used and times achieved are monitored.

16.2.9 Engineering plans and costs

16.2.9.1 Function and organisation

The Plans and Costs Group provides the programmes and estimated costs for the development activity, and monitors and cost-controls all main development projects. It comprises four departments, all responsible to the head of plans and costs, as follows.

16.2.9.2 Engineering Plans Department

This department calculates and prepares plans to show the content and timescale for all development work, and technical and support plans required.

16.2.9.3 Project Estimating Department

Provides cost estimates for all development activity.

16.2.9.4 Development Cost Control and Administration Department

Responsible for ensuring maximum cost control over all departments' activities and for administering all development contracts and allocation of company funding.

16.2.9.5 Engineering and Cost Management Department

Responsible for ensuring on-site programming for in-service development activities, and relevant monitoring and cost control.

16.2.10 Engineering quality assurance

16.2.10.1 Objectives

To contribute towards meeting specified requirements cost-effectively and achieving the requirements of the controlling/certifying authorities, regarding, safety, reliability, performance, etc.

To this end, the facility must ensure that engineering departments produce departmental operating procedures which meet the requirements of the Engineering Quality Manual and which are compatible at interfaces. Work output of departments is subject to regular audits and any deficiencies exposed by the audit are corrected.

16.2.10.2 Organisation

The Engineering Quality Assurance Engineer is responsible for all aspects of quality assurance, within the engineering area, and for ensuring that product assurance objectives are achieved in engineering.

16.2.10.3 Engineering area audit procedures

Output of the engineering area is subject to two primary categories of audit:

Product audits: To confirm that the necessary design, development and production programmes will be completed within a timescale defined by the markets at which the project is aimed, and that the resultant product will be both commercially and technologically viable and competitive. Similarly, product audits may be instructed during design and development phases to confirm that a project continues to be capable of meeting the agreed specifications and requirements of customers, whilst remaining commercially viable.

Technical audits: These are sub-divided into two main types.

(1) *Technical procedures audits* confirm compliance with organisational procedures and the requirements of the various controlling authorities. In addition, the audits examine the extent to which procedures are being observed and applied and their effectiveness in defining and controlling their specific functions.

(2) *Technical quality audits* examine the quality and technical acceptability of the work of the departments comprising the engineering area. Audits are organised to examine key functions of departments' activities to ensure that required standards are met.

16.2.11 Engineering Management

16.2.11.1 Function

Engineering Management provides overall support for Personnel, Administration and General management matters within Engineering. It also forms an interface between Engineering and other functional areas, principally Accounts, Works General Services, Divisional P & A and Security.

16.2.11.2 Organisation

Personnel and Administration: Includes such activities as remuneration and salary structures, job description and ranking. Involves preparation and maintenance of organisation charts, departmental terms-of-reference manuals and appointments. Other P & A activities concern the operation of subsistences, travel and allowance systems, welfare and accommodation, employee relations and collective agreements.

Manpower Resourcing, Planning and Budgets: Concerned with the preparation of estimates and budgets for manning and capital revenue requirements. It is also responsible for monitoring actual strength and spend against budgets.

16.2.12 Engineering procedures

16.2.12.1 Introduction

The quality of engineering work output is controlled by various procedures. Audits, at pre-determined intervals, ensure compliance with the procedures described in the following paragraphs.

16.2.12.2 Company engineering procedures

Engineering procedures are issued to define principles of safety and technical integrity.

16.2.12.3 Engineering technical procedures

Engineering Technical Procedures Manual defines the performance of those technical functions which involve more than one department within Engineering, also any interfaces with Product Support, Manufacturing or Commercial Departments, etc. Procedures are specific to action at the boundaries of departmental responsibility; internal procedures are covered separately.

16.2.12.4 Manual of Operating Procedures

Each Department or Group produces a Manual of Operating Procedures, detailing its functions, method of operation and procedures. Each individual in a department must be familiar with, and adhere to, the systems and procedures defined, for requirements are mandatory.

16.2.12.5 Management systems engineering procedures

These are 'good housekeeping', defining non-technical requirements standardised within Engineering, to ensure that such activities as storage, distribution and maintenance of Engineering procedures, etc., are effectively undertaken.

16.2.12.6 Accessory (equipment) procurement control procedure

The objectives of the procedure are:

(1) to ensure selection of the most appropriate supplier or suppliers;
(2) to support the use of competitive tendering;
(3) to establish and control the standard of the product; and
(4) to monitor cost and time.

The accessories required are listed, and potential suppliers given a specification and invitation to quote. A purchase order is issued to the selected supplier, based on the agreed specification which the supplier must meet, in the timescale given in the associated accessory development programme.

All changes subsequent to the purchase order are based on formally-cleared design schemes applied by modification proposal forms, which contain details of maximum cost, weight, introduction date, etc.

A declaration of design and performance (DDP) defines accessory operational limits approved by an accessory supplier. On receipt of the DDP from the accessory supplier, copies are passed to specialist departments for approval. When fully agreed, the DDP is signed by the Chief Development Engineer and passed to the airworthiness authority for approval signature.

16.3 Summary

By complying with the policies, procedures and standards promulgated in engineering manuals, the organisation seeks to direct and control its endeavours towards achieving the declared objective — to produce effective, soundly-engineered products, on time.

Directory

The purpose of this directory is to provide a starting point from which to seek an answer to the ever-present question, 'Where do I find explicit information on . . ?'.

The directory is divided into several parts, each of which represents a distinct facet of a designer's requirements. It is not claimed to be comprehensive.

Part 1   Design office equipment
A   Furniture
B   Drawing boards and tables
C   Drawing instruments, pens and pencils
D   Drawing materials, paper, films and transparencies
E   Calculators
F   Lettering systems
G   Reprodrafting systems
H   Printing equipment

Part 2   Computer systems
A   Computers, systems, terminals, workstations
B   Monitors
C   Printers, plotters, scanners, electronic typewriters
D   Software
E   Microfilm equipment
F   Leasing facilities
G   Communication equipment systems
H   Computer peripherals

Part 3   Standards
DIN
ASMT
BS
ISO
AGS, etc.

Part 4   Design consultants

Part 5   Societies and institutions

Part 6   Common hardware
A   Fasteners
B   Adhesives
C   Bearings
D   Materials
    (a)   Ferrous
    (b)   Non-ferrous
    (c)   Plastics
    (d)   Ceramics
    (e)   Special films and coatings
E   Finishes
F   Hardfacing
G   Welding
H   Testing/inspection
I   Fluid power
J   Power transmissions

Part 7   Miscellaneous
A   Help for industry
B   Design publications

1A Furniture

Abbott Bros (Southall) plc
Beachmount Ltd.
Budgie Office Products Co.
Alan Cooper Ltd.
Dams Office Furniture
Ericsson Information Systems
Falcon Office Furniture
NKR Systems Office Furniture
Project Office Furniture plc
Solarbo Fitments Ltd.
Stralfors
Westra Office Equipment Ltd.

1B Drawing boards and tables

Admel Ltd.
Alkens Drawing Supplies Ltd.
BFE Business Furniture & Equipment Ltd.
Blundell and Harling Ltd.
British Thornton Ltd.
Cannon and Wrin Ltd.
Cox
Essex Drawing Equipment Co. Ltd.
Faber-Castell UK Ltd.
Harper and Tunstall Ltd.
Esmond Hellerman Ltd.
Jakar International Ltd.
Millington York Ltd.
Office Equipment (John Dale) Ltd.
Ozalid UK Ltd.
Reprodraft Ltd.
Rotorbord Ltd.
Rotring UK Ltd.
G. H. Smith & Partners (Sales) Ltd.
Staedtler (UK) Ltd.
Stanford Marsh Ltd.
UNO Sales
William Vere Ltd.
Westwood Stationery Ltd.

1C Drawing instruments, pens and pencils

Berol Ltd.
Blundel and Harling Ltd.
British Thornton Ltd.
Cannon and Wrin Ltd.
Chartpak Ltd.
Edding (UK) Ltd.
Faber-Castell UK Ltd.
Esmond Hellerman Ltd.
Harper and Tunstall Ltd.
Jakar International Ltd.
Letraset UK Ltd.
Ludwig & Sons Ltd.
Mecanorma Ltd.
Millington York Ltd.
Pentel Stationery Ltd.
Pilot Pen Co. UK Ltd.
Rotring UK Ltd.
Royal Sovereign Graphics
G. H. Smith & Partners (Sales) Ltd.
Staedtler (UK) Ltd.
Swan Stabilo Ltd.
UNO Sales
E. Whitmont & Co. Ltd.
Winsor and Newton

1D Drawing materials, paper, films and transparencies

Aarque Systems Ltd.
Admel Ltd.
Agfa Gevaert Ltd.
Alkens Drawing Supplies Ltd.
Amber Film Sales Ltd.
Daler Board Co. Ltd.
Daler Rowney
Faber-Castell UK Ltd.
Frisk Products Ltd.
Harper and Tunstall Ltd.
Kodak Ltd.
Ludwig and Sons Ltd.
Ozalid (UK) Ltd.
Peel and Co. Ltd.
Rhone-Poulenc Systems Ltd.
G. H. Smith & Partners (Sales) Ltd.
E. Whitmont & Co. Ltd.
Wiggins Teape (UK) plc
Winsor and Newton

1E Calculators

Daler Rowney Ltd.
Systema UK Ltd.

1F Lettering systems

Autologo Ltd.
Kroy (UK) Ltd.
Legendary Characters Ltd.
Letraset UK Ltd.
Mecanorma Ltd.
Spandex UK Ltd.

1G Reprodrafting systems

Agfa Gevaert Ltd.
Infotec Ltd.

1H Printing equipment

Agfa Gevaert Ltd.
Canon UK Ltd.
Gestetner Ltd.
Paul Hill Ltd.
Infotec Ltd.
Kern Ltd.
Kodak Ltd.
Mita Copystar UK Ltd.
Power Equipment Ltd.

Rank Xerox (UK) Ltd.
Ricas Ltd.
Ricoh UK Ltd.
Sharp Electronics (UK) Ltd.
Span
A. M. Varityper

2A Computers, systems, terminals, workstations

ABS Computers
Advent Systems Ltd.
Apollo Computers (UK) Ltd.
Autodesk (UK) Ltd.
British Olivetti Ltd.
Compel plc
Computervision Ltd.
Counting House Computer Systems Ltd.
CPT (UK) Ltd.
Data and Control Equipment Ltd.
Data General Ltd.
Dicomed (UK) Ltd.
Digital Equipment Co. Ltd.
Drafting and Design Systems Ltd.
Engineering Computer Services Ltd.
Genisco Computers Ltd.
Gould Electronics
Graphic Products
ICL
Imtec Group plc
Interactive Drawing Office Systems
Itek Graphic Products
McDonnell Douglas Information Systems
    International
Marconi CAE Systems
Mitsubishi Electric (UK) Ltd.
NEC Business Systems (Europe) Ltd.
Pragma Ltd.
Racal Redac Ltd.
Sharp Electronics (UK) Ltd.
Sintrom Electronics Ltd.
Sperry Ltd.
Sun Microsystems UK Ltd.
Tektronix UK Ltd.
Terminal Display Systems
Valid Logic Systems
Xenotron Ltd.

2B Monitors

Mitsubishi Electric (UK) Ltd.
NEC Business Systems (Europe) Ltd.

2C Printers, plotters, scanners, electronic typewriters

Benson Electronics Ltd.
Brother Office Equipment Division
Bytech Peripherals Ltd.
Hewlett Packard Ltd.
Impectron Ltd.
Imtec Group plc
LexiSystems Ltd.
Marconi CAE Systems
NEC Business Systems (Europe) Ltd.
Penta Systems (UK) Ltd.
RealTime Printers Ltd.
Silver Reed (UK) Ltd.
Sintrom Electronics Ltd.
Surveying and Scientific Instruments Ltd.
Versatec Ltd.

2D Software

Acorn
    SPICE electronic simulation
    CHIPSMITH VLSI design
Acoustic Technology Ltd.
    Software for machinery analysis
Applied Research of Cambridge
    MAPS mapping and planning
    BSDS building services detailing
    GDS general drafting systems
    RCDS reinforced concrete detailing
ASA Ltd.
    DIAMOND drafting and design
Atkins Research and Development
    ASAS finite element for structural analysis
Autodesk (UK) Ltd.
    AutoCAD drafting and design
Automation Ltd.
    CALAY pcb package
Autoscribe Ltd.
Biotest Folex Ltd.
Computational Mechanics Ltd.
BEASY engineering analysis
Computerline Ltd.
    PLANTRAC project control
Concept Computer Systems Ltd.
    CONCEPT production control
Data General Ltd.
    CEO drafting
    GABLE
    SMIDS
    DOGS
    DRAGON
    PRAGOM
    DEGAS
Drafting and Design Systems Ltd.
    MENSAR data analysis

Ecotech Design Ltd.
  SCRIBE 3-D modelling
Ericsson Information systems
  DR GRAPH graphics
  DR DRAW graphics
ESDU International Ltd.
  Engineering analysis packages
  DRAGON
  DEGAS
ESS Consultants Ltd.
  ESS 2-D drafting
GE Calma
  Design and drafting software
Genisco Computers Ltd.
  GRASP robot design
Gould Electronics
  ISMS solid modeller
  DCG dynamic core graphs
  DSS drafting system
  INTERACT pcb system
  MCAD solids modelling
Graphic Products Ltd.
Hallmark Associates (Computer Services) Ltd.
  MANUMARK manufacturing control system
Imtec Group plc
Intergraph (GB) Ltd.
  ADAMS kinematics
  DRAM kinematics
  NASTRAN finite element
  MOLDFLOW injection moulding design
  ISOGEN 3-D pipework
Itek Graphic Products
Jentech Services Ltd.
  DIGITMASTER drafting system
Kalamazoo plc
Kewill Systems Ltd.
  MLD 2-D drafting
Lexidata Ltd.
  SOLIDVIEW M solid modelling
McAuto (UK) Ltd.
Manufacturing and Consulting Services (MCS) Ltd.
  ANVIL 1000MD, 2-D CAD
  OMNISOLID solid modelling
  ADAM, CAD/CAM
Memory Computer UK Ltd.
  IMPACT manufacturing and production control
Moldflow (Europe) Ltd.
  Injection moulding
MPR Publishing Services Ltd.
  Powder metallurgy
Pragma Ltd.
  CAEPAC
Prime Computers UK Ltd.
  MEDUSA
  PDGS
  LOCAM
Rhone-Poulenc Systems Ltd.
Robinson Ford Associates Ltd.

Robocom Ltd.
  BITSTICK 2 technical drawing systems
Scicon Ltd.
  Robotic software
Sheffield Micro Information Systems Ltd.
  UNIPLAN order processing and material control
Silvar-Lisco Ltd.
Sperry Ltd.
  MAPPER management
Staveley Computing
Tangram Computer Aided Engineering Ltd.
Trilex International Marketing Ltd.
  DOODLE
Valid Logic Systems
  SCALD
  REALDRAW
  SCALSTAR
Xenotron Ltd.
  CADMASTER

2E Microfilm equipment

Finlay Microfilm Ltd.
Imtec Group plc
Kodak Ltd.
Microgen Ltd.
Microphase Ltd.
Profile Microfilming (Kent) Ltd.
Rhone-Poulenc Systems Ltd.
3M (UK) plc

2F Leasing facilities

Microlease plc
Power Leasing Ltd.

2G Communications equipment/ systems

NEC Business Systems (Europe) Ltd.
Sanyo Marubeni (UK) Ltd.

2H Computer peripherals

KPG Hardware House

3 Standards

American National Standards Institute (ANSI)
American Society for Testing and Materials (ASTM)

American Society of Mechanical Engineers
  (ASME)
British Standards Institution (BSI)
Deutsches Institut für Normung (DIN)
International Electrotechnical Commission (IEC)
International Organisation for Standardisation
  (ISO)
National Bureau of Standards (NBS)
Society of Automobile Engineers (SAE)
Système International d'Unités, Le (SI)

4 Design consultants

Atkins Research and Development Ltd.
Design Council (Register of Designers)
Industrial Design Consultancy
Institution of Engineering Designers (Register of
  Designers)
International Automotive Design
Systems Designers International

5 Societies and institutions

Aluminium Federation
BCIRA
British Gear Association
British Quality Association
Building Research Establishment
Engineering Council
Fire Research Station
Institute of Metals
Institute of Polymer Technology
Institution of Electrical Engineers
Institution of Engineering Designers
Institution of Mechanical Engineers
Institution of Production Engineers
Production Engineering Research Association
Welding Institute
Writing Instruments Association

6A Fasteners

A & W Fasteners Ltd.
Armstrong Fastening Systems
Avdel Ltd.
Camloc (UK) Ltd.
Dzus Fasteners Europe Ltd.
European Industrial Services Ltd.
Everbright Fasteners Ltd.
Fasteners Centre
Gesipa Fasteners Ltd.
Headland Ltd., Thomas P.
IEC Ltd.
Philidas Ltd.
Protex Fasteners Ltd.
PSM Fasteners Ltd.

Salter Springs and Pressings Ltd.
Snap-Tite Europe BV
Southco Fasteners Ltd.

6B Adhesives

B+T Polymers Ltd.
Dunlop Adhesives
Loctite UK
Permabond Adhesives Ltd.

6C Bearings

Ampep plc
Barden Corporation
BNL Ltd.
British Timken
Clevite (Hare Components)
Cooper Roller Bearing Co. Ltd.
Fafnir Bearing Division
FAG Bearing Co. Ltd.
GKN Bound Brook Ltd.
GKN Vandervell Ltd.
Glacier Metal Co. Ltd.
IEC Ltd.
INA Bearing Co. Ltd.
Industrial Unit of Tribology
Koyo (UK) Ltd.
Le Carbone (GB) Ltd.
Manganese Bronze Ltd.
MPB Corporation
Nadella Bearing Co. Ltd.
National Centre Of Tribology
Norton Performance Plastics
Nylacast Oilen Ltd.
Railko Ltd.
RHP Group
SKF (UK) Ltd.
SNFA Bearings Ltd.
SNR Bearings (UK) Ltd.
Tufnol Ltd.
Westwind Air Bearings Ltd.
Wyko Bearings and Transmissions Ltd.

6D(a) Ferrous materials

British Meehanite Group
BSC Stainless
BSC Strip Mill Products
Hepworth and Grandage Ltd.
Inco Europe Ltd.
Spunalloys Ltd.

6D(b) Non-ferrous materials

British Alcan Aluminium Ltd.
HDA Forgings Ltd.
IMI Rolled Metals Ltd.
Kaiser Aluminium Europe UK Ltd.
Magnesium Elektron Ltd.
Titanium International Ltd.
Zinc Development Association

6D(c) Plastics

Amari Plastics plc
BASF (UK) Ltd.
Bayer UK Ltd.
BP Chemicals International
Celanese Ltd.
Dow Corning
Du Pont (UK) Ltd.
Freeman Chemicals Ltd.
Hoechst UK Ltd.
ICI Chemicals and Polymers Division
Monsanto plc
Norton Performance Plastics Ltd.
Pilkington Reinforcements Ltd.
Railko Ltd.
Rehau Plastics Ltd.
Tufnol Ltd.

6D(d) Ceramics

Advanced Materials Engineering Ltd.
AE Developments Ltd.
Brush Wellman Ltd.
English Glass Co. Ltd.
Lucas Cookson Syalon Ltd.
Lucas Industries plc
Metco Ltd.
National Engineering Laboratory

6D(e) Special films and coatings

Arco Chemical Europe Inc.
B+T Polymers Ltd.
Berger Industrial Coatings
Borg-Warner Chemicals
Cabot Plastics Europe
Carrs Paints Ltd.
Thorn-EMI Panelgraphic Ltd.

6E Finishes

Berger Industrial Coatings
Canning Materials Ltd., W.
Hoechst UK Ltd.

ICI Paints Division
Paint Research Association
Plascoat Systems Ltd.
Plastic Coatings Ltd.

6F Hardfacing

Flame Hardeners Ltd.
Union Carbide UK Ltd.

6G Welding

British Federal Welder and Machine Co. Ltd.
Crompton Parkinson Ltd.
ESAB Ltd.
Sciaky Electric Welding Machines Ltd.

6H Testing/inspection

Infrared Engineering Ltd.
J. J. Lloyd Instruments Ltd.
Mettler Instruments Ltd.
Monsanto plc
    Rubber testing machines
Negretti Automation
Pacific Scientific Ltd.
    Colour matching
Plessey Assessment Services
Polymer Laboratories Ltd.
Zwick Testing Machines Ltd.
    Plastics and rubbers

6I Fluid power

Atlas Copco GB Ltd.
CompAir Industrial Ltd.
Hydrovane Compressor Co. Ltd.
Lucas Fluid Power Ltd.
Martonair Ltd.
Mecman Ltd.
Origa Ltd.
Parker Hannifin

6J Power transmissions

Powerdrive PSR Ltd.
Reliance Gear Co. Ltd.
Renold plc

7A Help for industry

Barbour and Builder Index
Confederation of British Industry

Department of Trade and Industry
Design Council
Engineering Industries Association
ESDU International Ltd.
Frost and Sullivan Ltd.
Her Majesty's Stationery Office
Inbucon
London Information (Rowse Muir) Ltd.
Manpower Services Commission
RAPRA Technology Ltd.
Technical Indexes Ltd.
Workers Educational Association

7B Design publications

CAD/CAM International
Design
Design Engineering
Design, Products and Applications (DPA)
Draughting and Design
Drawing and Graphics Today
Engineering
Engineering Materials and Design
Eureka
Materials + Manufacture
Original Equipment Manufacture (OEM)

Directory addresses

A & W Fasteners Ltd
Awel Works, Unit 3, Strawberry Lane Industrial
Estate, Willenhall, West, Midlands WV13 3RS
0902 635515

Aarque Systems Ltd
PO Box 70, Blackthorne Road, Colnbrook,
Slough, Berks SL3 OAR
02812 4567

Abbott Bros (Southall) plc
Abbess House, High Street, Southall, Middx
UB1 3HE
01-574 6961
936029

ABS Computers
North Street, Portslade, Sussex, BN4 1ER
0273 421509
87488 ABSBR 1G

Acorn
Fulbourn Road, Cherry Hinton, Cambridge
0223 245200

Acoustic Technology Ltd
58 The Avenue, Southampton SO1 2TA
0703 37811
47156 AT G

Admel Ltd
Dacre Works, Brooklands Road, Weybridge,
Surrey KT13 ORL
0932 47212
22848/929607

Advanced Materials Engineering Ltd
Bewdley Raod, Stourport on Severn,
Worcs DY13 8QR
02993 2271

Advent Systems Ltd
12 The Business Centre, Molly Millars Lane,
Wokingham, Berks RG11 2QZ
0734 784211
858893

AE Developments Ltd
Engineering Ceramics Unit, 40 Somers Road,
Rugby, Warks CV22 7DB
0788 7739

Agfa Gevaert Ltd
27 Great West Road, Brentford, Middx TW8 9AX
01-560 2131
28154

Alkens Drawing Supplies Ltd
Alkens House, 31 Sidcup Bypass, Sidcup, Kent
DA14 5BH
01-302 2535

Aluminium Federation
Broadway House, Calthorpe Road, Birmingham
B15 1TN
021-455 0311

Amari Plastics plc
24–30 Baker Street, Weybridge, Surrey KT13
8AU
0932 54803

Amber Film Sales Ltd
Unit 45, Gravelly Industrial Park, Birmingham
B74 8TG
021 327 1157

American National Standards Insitute (ANSI)
1430 Broadway, New York, NY 10018, USA

**American Society for Testing and Masterials
(ASTM)**
1916 Race Street, Philadelphia, PA 19103, USA

American Society of Mechanical Engineers (ASME)
345 East 47th Street, New York, NY 10017, USA

Ampep plc
Clevedon, Avon BS21 6QQ
0272-876021

Alan Cooper Ltd
Burnley Road, Todmorden, Lancs OL14 7ED
070 681 5111

Apollo Computers (UK) Ltd
Bulbourne House, Gossoms End, Berkhamsted,
Herts HP4 3LP
04427 75026

Applied Research of Cambridge
Wellington House, East Road, Cambridge
CB1 1BH
0223 314041
81153 ARCAMB

Arco Chemical Europe Inc.
Windsor Bridge House, 1 Brocas Street, Eton,
Berks SL4 6BW
0735 57157
847436

Armstrong Fastening Systems
Clough Road, Hall, North Humberside HU6 7PR
0482 41401

ASA Ltd
Brooklands House, 46 Kneesworth Street,
Royston, Herts SG8 5AQ
0763 47712

Atkins Research and Development Ltd
Woodcote Grove, Ashley Road, Epsom, Surrey
KT18 5BW
037 27 26140
266701 AB ATKINS G

Atlas Copco (GB) Ltd
PO Box 79, Swallowdale Lane, Hemel
Hempstead, Herts HP2 7HA
0442 61201
825963

Autodesk (UK) Ltd
47 The Cut, London SE1 8LL
01-928 7868
911686 ACAD UK G

Autologo Ltd
Clydebank Business Park, Scotland

Automation Ltd
Marbaix House, Bessemer Road, Basingstoke,
Hants RG21 3NT
0256 473141
858286

Autoscribe Ltd
7 Hawkes Close, Wokingham, Berks RG11 2SZ
0734 787917

Avdel Ltd
Welwyn Garden City, Herts AL7 1EZ
07073 28161
24254

B+T Polymers Ltd
Station Road, Birch Vale, Stockport, Cheshire
SK12 5BR
0663 46518
669258

Barbour and Builder Index
Phoenix Way, Cirencester, Glos GL7 1BR

Barden Corporation
Western Road, Bracknell, Berks RG12 1QU
0344 424511
848250

BASF (UK) Ltd
4 Fitzroy Square, London W1P 6ER
01-388 4200
28649 BASFLO G

Bayer UK Ltd
Bayer House, Strawberry Hill, Newbury, Berks
RG13 1JA
0635 39000
847205 BAYNEW G

BCIRA
Alvechurch, Birmingham B48 7QB
0527 66414
337125

Beachmount Ltd
31–33 Station Road, Gerrards Cross, Bucks
SL9 8ES
0753 880144

Benson Electronics Ltd
300 Park Avenue, Aztec West, Almondsbury,
Bristol BS12 4RG
0454 617777
444597 BENSON

Berger Industrial Coatings
Freshwater Road, Dagenham, Essex RM8 1UR
01-590 6030
24317

Berol Ltd
Oldmedow Road, King's Lynn, Norfolk PE30 4JR
0553 61221
817409

BFE Business Furniture and Equipment Ltd
16–17 Lower Square, Isleworth, Middx TW7 6BW
01-847 0992

Biotest Folex Ltd
19 Monkspath Business Park, GB-Shirley,
Solihull, Birmingham B90 4NY
021-744 9100
339628

Blundell and Harling Ltd
Regulus Works, Lynch Lane, Weymouth, Dorset
DT4 9DW
0305 783275

BNL Ltd
Manse Lane, Knaresborough, North Yorkshire
N65 8LF
0423 865621
57896

Borg-Warner Chemicals
20 Coventry Road, Cubbington, Leamington Spa,
Warwicks CV32 7JW
0926 34121
311077

BP Chemicals International
Belgrave House, 76 Buckingham Palace Road,
London SW1W 0SU
01-581 1388
266883

British Alcan Aluminium Ltd
Southam Road, Banbury, Oxon OX16 7SN
0295 4444
83645

British Federal Welder and Machine Co. Ltd.
Castle Mill Works, Birmingham New Road,
Dudley, West Midlands DY1 4DA
0384 54701
343416

British Gear Association
Institution of Mechanical Engineers, 1 Birdcage
Walk, London SW1H 9JJ
01-222 7899
917944

British Meehanite Group
38 Albert Road North, Reigate, Surrey RH2 9EH
07372 44786
28700 MEEHAN G

British Olivetti Ltd
PO Box 89, 86/88 Upper Richmond Road,
London SW15 2UR
01-785 6666

British Quality Association
54 Princes Gate, Exhibition Road, London SW7
2PG
01-584 9026

British Standards Institution
Sales Department, Linford Wood, Milton Keynes
MK14 6LE
0908 320066
825777

British Thornton Ltd
PO Box 3, Wythenshawe, Manchester M22 4SS
061-998 1311

British Timken
Duston, Northampton NN5 6UL
0604 52311
31620

Brother Office Equipment Division
Jones and Brother, Shepley Street, Guide Bridge,
Audinshaw, Manchester M34 3JD
061-330 6531
669192

Brush Wellman Ltd
4–5 Ely Road, Theale Commercial Estate, Theale,
Reading, Berks RG7 4BQ
0734 303733
848428 BECURD G

BSC Stainless
Shepcote Lane, PO Box 161, Sheffield S9 1TR
0742 443311

BSC Strip Mill Products
PO Box 10, Newport, Gwent NP9 0XN
0633 290022
497601

Budgie Office Products Co.
Alder Close, Eastbourne, East Sussex BN23 6QB
0323 641521

Building Research Establishment
Garston, Watford, Herts WD2 7JR
0923 674040
923220

Bytech Peripherals Ltd
2 The Western Centre, Western Road, Bracknell,
Berks RG12 1RW
0344 424444

Cabot Plastics Europe
Siulk House, Park Green, Macclesfield, Cheshire
SK11 7NA
0625 613556
667963 EPDIVE G

CAD/CAM International
30/32 Farringdon Lane, London EC1R 3AU
01-251 6222
32157

Camloc (UK) Ltd
15 New Star Street, Leicester LE4 7JD
0533 763161
34488

W. Canning Material Ltd
PO Box 228, Great Hampton Street, Birmingham
B18 6AS
021-236 8621

Cannon and Wrin Ltd
68 High Street, Chislehurst, Kent BR7 5BL
01-467 0935

Canon UK Ltd
Canon House, Manor Road, Wallington, Surrey
SM6 0AJ
01-773 3173

Carrs Paints Ltd
Westminster Works, West Heath, Birmingham
B31 3PG
021-475 5251
336653

Celanese Ltd
78/80 St Albans Road, Watford, Herts WD2 4AP
0923 33616
922446

Chartpak Ltd
Station Road, Didcot, Oxon OX11 7NB
0235 812607

Clevite (Hare Components)
Acorn House, High Street, Erdington, Birmingham B23 6QY

CompAir Industrial Ltd
Broomwade Works, PO Box 7, High Wycombe, Bucks HP13 5SF
0494 21181
837371

Compel plc
184 St Albans Road West, Hatfield, Herts
AL10 0TF
07072 73661
267448 COMPEL G

Computational Mechanics Ltd
Ashurst Lodge, Ashurst, Southampton SO4 2AA
042 129 3223

Computerline Ltd
118 Church Road, Addlestone, Weybridge, Surrey
0932 55757

Computervision Ltd
Central House, New Street, Basingstoke, Hants
RG21 1DP
0256 58133
858554

Concept Computer Systems Ltd
Bagshot House, High Street, Bagshot, Surrey
GU19 5AF
0276 76303

Confederation of British Industry
Centre Point, 103 New Oxford Street, London
WC1A 1DU
01-379 7400
21331

Cooper Roller Bearing Co. Ltd
King's Lynn, Norfolk PE30 5JX
0553 763447

Counting House Computer Systems Ltd
Fornham House, Fornum St Martins, Bury St
Edmunds, Suffolk
0284 68921

Cox
PO Box 255, Brentwood, Essex CM15 9AD
0277 224224

CPT (UK) Ltd
4th Floor, Trafalgar House, 2 Chalk Hill Road,
London W6 8DN
01-741 9050
893380 CPTUK

Crompton Parkinson Ltd
Woodlands House, The Avenue, Cliftonville,
Northampton NN1 5BS
0604 30201
31364

Daler Board Co. Ltd
Westminster Road, Wareham, Dorset BH20 4NT
092 956621

Daler Rowney
PO Box 10, Bracknell, Berks RG12 4ST
0344 424621
847618 ROWNEY G

Dams Office Furniture
Gores Road, Kirkby Industrial Estate, Kirkby,
Liverpool L33 7UA
051-548 7111

Data and Control Equipment Ltd
DCE House, Bessemer Crescent, Aylesbury,
Bucks HP19 3TH
0296 32971
837318 DATROL G

Data General Ltd
Hounslow House, 724/734 London Road,
Hounslow, Middx TW3 1PD
01-572 7455

Design
Design Council, 28 Haymarket, London SW1Y
4SU
01-839 8000
8812963

Design Council
28 Haymarket, London SW1Y 4SU
01-839 8000
8812963

Design Engineering
30 Calderwood Street, Woolwich, London
SE18 6QH
01-835 7777
896238 MORGAN G

Design Products and Applications (DPA)
Blair House, 184–186 High Street, Tonbridge,
Kent TN9 1BE
0732 359990
957329

Design Technologies Ltd
Bradfield Road, Finedon Road Industrial Estate,
Wellingborough, Northants NN8 4HB
0933 78871

Deutsches Institut für Normung eV (DIN)
Burggrafenstrasse 4–10, D-1000 Berlin 30, FRG

Dicomed (UK) Ltd
Coworth Park House, Coworth, Ascot, Berks
SL5 7SE
0990 27444

Digital Equipment Co. Ltd
Digital Park, PO Box 110, Reading, Berks
RG2 0TR
0734 868711
848327

Dow Corning Ltd
Reading Bridge House, Reading, Berks RG1 8PW
0734 507251

Drafting and Design Systems Ltd
3 Derby Road, Eastwood, Nottingham NG16 3PA
07737 65085

Draughting and Design
31/33 High Holborn, London WC1V 6BD
01-405 0564
912881 MFT G

Drawing and Graphics Today
18/19 Ludgate Hill, Birmingham B3 1DW
021-236 8112
338024

Dunlop Adhesives
Chester Road, Birmingham B35 7AL
021-373 8101

Du Pont (UK) Ltd
Maylands Avenue, Hemel Hempstead, Herts HP2
7DP
0442 61251
825713 DUPONT G

Dzus Fasteners Europe Ltd
Factory Estate, Farnham, Surrey GU9 9PL
0252 714422
858201

Ecotech Design Ltd
45 Harefield Road, Sheffield S11 8NU
0742 680982

Edding UK Ltd
North Orbital Trading Estate, Napsbury Lane,
St Albans, Herts AL1 1XQ
0727 34471

Engineering
Design Council, 28 Haymarket, London SW1Y
4SU
01-839 8000
8812963

Engineering Computer Services Ltd
Cooper House, Dam Street, Lichfield, Staffs
WS13 6AA
054 32 58751
336916

Engineering Council, The
10 Maltravers Street, London WC2R 3ER
01-240 7891

Engineering Industries Association
16 Dartmouth Street, London SW1H 9BL
01-222 2367

Engineering Materials and Design
Quadrant House, The Quadrant, Sutton, Surrey
SM2 5AS
01-661 3091
892084

English Glass Co. Ltd
Scudamore Road, Leicester LE3 1UG
0533 871371
34442

Ericsson Information Systems
City House, 7 Gresham Street, London
EC2V 7BX
01-606 0425
8814540 ERICSG G

ESAB Ltd
Beechings Way, Gillingham, Kent ME8 6PU
0634 34455
96145

ESDU International Ltd
251/259 Regent Street, London W1R 7AD
01-437 4894

ESS Consultants Ltd
35 Cheney Way, Cambridge
0223 351196

Essex Drawing Equipment Co. Ltd
120 Stratford Road, Plaistow, London E13 0JW
01-552 0921

Eureka
Franks Hall, Horton Kirby, Kent DA4 9LL
0322 77755
8954447 FINPUB G

European Industrial Services Ltd
Woden Road West, King's Hill, Wednesbury, West
Midlands WS10 7TT
021-556 1900

Everbright Fasteners Ltd
Stainless House, 4–6 Edwin Road, Twickenham,
Middx TW1 4JN
01-891 0111

Faber Castell UK Ltd
Crompton Road, Stevenage, Herts SG1 2EF
0438 66511
825049

Fafnir Bearing Division
PO Box 18, Wolverhampton WV2 4NT
0902 26101
337453

FAG Bearing Co. Ltd
Heath Mill Road, Wombourne, West Midlands
WV5 8AF
0902 894114
337414

Falcon Office Furniture
Falconer Road, Newcastle upon Tyne
0632 614529

Fasteners Centre, The
1 Station Road, Heathfield, East Sussex TN21
8LB
04352 4466
95332 FASTC G

Finlay Microfilm Ltd
Finlay House, 18 Woodside Road, Amersham,
Bucks HP6 6PA
02403 22126

Fire Research Station
Borehamwood, Herts WD6 2BL
01-953 6177
8951648

Flame Hardeners Ltd
Shorter Works, Bailey Lane, Sheffield S1 3BL
0742 768167

Freeman Chemicals Ltd
PO Box 8, Ellsmere Port, South Wirral
L65 0HB
051-355 6171
628213

Frisk Products Ltd
4 Franthorne Way, Randlesdown Road, London
SE6 3BT
01-698 3481

Frost and Sullivan Ltd
104/112 Marylebone Lane, London W1M 5FU
01-486 8377-79

GE Calma
Beech House, 373–399 London Road, Camberley,
Surrey
0276 682821

Genisco Computers Ltd
7 Notre Dame Mews, Northampton NN1 2BG
0604 24621
317215 GENCOR

Gesipa Fasteners Ltd
Dutton Lane, Keighley, West Yorkshire BD21
4JU
0535 607844

Gestetner Ltd
210 Euston Road, London NW1 2DA
01-387 7021

GKN Bound Brook Ltd
Lichfield, Staffs WS13 6HF
05432 54101
337606

GKN Vandervell Ltd
Norden Road, Maidenhead, Berks SL6 4BG
0628 23456

Glacier Metal Co. Ltd
Argyl House, Joel Street, Northwood Hills, Middx
HA6 1LN
09274 26100
936881

Gould Electronics
Grove Road, Sutton, Surrey SM1 1BY
01-643 8020
947707

Graphic Products Ltd
36 Manchester Street, London W1
01-486 4667
25247

Hallmark Associates (Computer Services) Ltd
15–29 Goldsworth Road, Woking, Surrey
GU21 1JY
04862 22111

Harper and Tunstall Ltd
Leto Works, Dennington, Wellingborough,
Northants NN8 2QH
0933 71166
31690

HDA Forgings Ltd
Windsor Road, Redditch, Worcs B97 6EF
0527-64211

Thomas P. Headland Ltd
Rose Kiln Lane, Reading, Berks RG2 0HW
0734 863131

Esmond Hellerman Ltd
Hellerman House, Harris Way, Windmill Road,
Sunbury on Thames, Middx TW16 7EW
093 27 81888

Hepworth and Grandage Ltd
Bradford Foundry, St. John's Works, Nevill Road,
Bradford, West Yorkshire BD4 8TU
0274 729595

Her Majesty's Stationary Office
PO Box 569, London SE1 9NH
01-928 6977

Hewlett Packard Ltd
Miller House, The Ring, Bracknell, Berks
RG12 1XN
0344 773100

Paul Hill Ltd
Imperial Way, Watford, Herts WD2 4JN
0923 33977

Hoechst UK Ltd
Hoechst House, Salisbury Road, Hounslow,
Middx TW4 6JH
01-570 7712
23284

Hydrovane Compressor Co. Ltd
Claybrook Drive, Redditch, Worcs B98 0DS
0527 25522
339843

ICI Chemicals and Polymers Division
Bessemer Road, Welywn Garden City, Herts AL7
1HD
0707 323400

ICI Paints Division
Wexham Road, Slough, Berks SL2 5DS
0753 31151

ICL
ICL House, Putney, London SW15 1SW
01-788 7272
22971

IEC Ltd
Robert Rogers House, New Orchard, Poole,
Dorset BH15 1LU
0202 67662

IMI Roller Metals Ltd
PO Box 703, Witton, Birmingham B6 7UP
021-356 8361

Impectron Ltd
Foundry Lane, Horsham, Sussex RH13 5PX
0403 50111
87722

Imtec Group plc
170 Honeypot Lane, Stanmore, Middx
01-204 3456

INA Bearing Co. Ltd
Castlevale Industrial Estate
Maybrook Road, Minworth, Sutton Coldfield,
West Midlands
021-351 3833
338304

Inbucon
Knightsbridge House, 197 Knightsbridge, London
SW7 1RN
01-584 6171
916533

Inco Europe Ltd
Thames House, Millbank, London SW1P 4QF
01-834 3888
918858

Industrial Design Consultancy
Portland Business Centre, Manor House Lane,
Datchet, Slough, Berks SL3 9EG
0753 47610

Industrial Unit of Tribology
University of Leeds, Leeds LS2 9JT
0532 31751

Infotec Ltd
Hoechst House, 50 Salisbury Road, Hounslow,
Middx TW4 6JH
01-577 5577

Infrared Engineering Ltd
Galliford Road, The Causeway, Maldon, Essex
CM9 7XD
0621 52244
995266 EMKAY G

Institute of Metals
1 Carlton House Terrace, London SW1Y 5DB
01-839 4071
8814813

Institute of Polymer Technology
University of Loughborough, Leics LE11 3TU
0509 263171
34319

Institution of Electrical Engineers
Savoy Place, London WC2R 0BL
01-240 1871
261178

Institution of Engineering Designers
Courtleigh, Westburyleigh, Westbury, Wilts BA13
3TA
0373 822801

Institution of Mechanical Engineers
1 Birdcage Walk, Westminster, London
SW1H 9JJ
01-222 7899
917944

Institution of Production Engineers
Rochester House, 66 Little Ealing Lane, London
W5 4XX
01-579 9411

Interactive Drawing Office Systems
IDO House, 16 Sansome Walk, Worcester
WR1 1LN
0905 26383
335294 CHACOM G

Intergraph (GB) Ltd
Albion House, Oxford Street, Newbury, Berks
RG13 1JG
0635 49044
848831

International Automotive Design
IAD House, Dominion Way, Worthing, West
Sussex BN14 8LU
0903 210131
877602

International Electrotechnical Commision (IEC)
3 rue de Varembé, 1211 Geneva 20, Switzerland

International Organisation for Standardisation (ISO)
1 rue de Varembé, Case Postale 56, 1211 Geneva
20, Switzerland

Itek Graphic Products
981 Great West Road, Brentford, Middx
TW8 9DN
01-568 9297

Jakar International Ltd
Hillside House, Friern Park, London N12 9BX
01-445 6377
268209

Jentech Services Ltd
Nordley, Bridgnorth, Shropshire WV16 4SU
07462 61458

Kaiser Aluminium Europe UK Ltd
Prudential Buildings, St Philips Place, Colmore
Row, Birmingham B3 2PW
021-236 777

KPG Hardware House
578–586 Chiswick High Road, Chiswick, London
W4
01-955 3575

Kalamazoo plc
Northfield, Birmingham B31 2RW
021-475 2191
336700

Kenrick PFS Ltd
PO Box 9, Union Street, Kenrick Way, West
Bromwich, West Midlands B7 6DP
021-553 2741
336470 KENRIC G

Kern Ltd
Unit B3, Woolborough Lane, Crawley, Sussex
RH10 2AG
0293 512023–7
877348 KERLTD G

Kewill Systems Ltd
Ashley House, 20–32 Church Street, Walton-on-
Thames, Surrey KT12 2QS
0932 248328

Kodak Ltd
PO Box 66, Kodak House, Station Road, Hemel
Hempstead, Herts HP1 1JU
0442 61122

Koyo (UK) Ltd
4 Northfield Drive, Northfield, Milton Keynes
MK15 0DQ
0908 664422
825611 KOYOUK G

Kroy (UK) Ltd
Worton Drive, Worton Grange, Reading, Berks
0734 861411

Le Carbone (GB) Ltd
AD Battery Works, South Street, Portslade,
Sussex BN4 2LX
0273-415701

Legendary Characters Ltd
34–36 South Street, Lancing, Sussex BN15 8AG
0903 765793

Letraset UK Ltd
St Georges House, 195–203 Waterloo Road,
London SE1 8XJ
01-928 7551/6351
27550

Lexidata Ltd
Weaver House, Station Road, Hook, Hants
RG27 9JY
0256 72 3411

LexiSystems Ltd
Apex House, West End, Frome, Somerset
BA11 3AS
0373 61446
44717

J. J. Lloyd Instruments Ltd
Brook House, Warsash, Southampton SO3 6HD
04895 4221
477042 JAY JAY G

Loctite (UK)
Watchmead, Welwyn Garden City, Herts RH1
6BG
0707 331277

London Information (Rowse Muir) Ltd
Index House, Ascot, Berks SL5 7EU
0990 23377
849426

Lucas Cookson Syalon Road
Cranmore Boulevard, Shirley, Solihull, West
Midlands B9 4LL
021-744 2234
338526

Lucas Fluid Power Ltd
Torrington Avenue, Coventry CV4 9AJ
0203 468111

Lucas Industries plc
Shaftmoor Lane, Hall Green, Birmingham B28
8SW
021-777 3232

Ludwig and Sons Ltd
71 Parkway, Camden Town, London NW1 7QJ
01-485 0025
27443

McAuto (UK) Ltd
Merion House, Guildford Road, Woking, Surrey
GU22 7QH
04862 26761
859521 MDCLON

**McDonnell Douglas Information Systems
International**
Maylands House, Maylands Avenue, Hemel
Hempstead, Herts HP2 4RL
0442 61266
8259688

Magnesium Elektron Ltd
Regal House, London Road, Twickenham, Middx
TW2 7AA
01-892 4488

Manganese Bronze Ltd
Elton Park Works, PO Box 19, Hadleigh Road,
Ipswich, Suffolk IP2 0HX
0473 215151
98248

Manpower Services Commission
Moorfoot, Sheffield S1 4PQ

Manufacturing & Consulting Services (MCS) Ltd
Marlborough Court, London Street, Andover,
Hants SP10 2TA
0264 50022

Marconi CAE Systems
Cobham Road, Ferndown Industrial Estate,
Wimborne, Dorset BH21 7PF
0202 891010
41358

Martonair Ltd
St Margarets Road, Twickenham, Middx
TW1 1RJ
01-892 4411
935562

Materials + Manufacture
Unit 1G, Coopers Industrial Estate, Littlehampton
Road, Ferring, Worthing, Sussex BN12 6PW
0903 65405

Mecanorma Ltd
10 School Road, Acton, London NW10 6TD
01-961 6565

Mecman Ltd
Mecman House, Suttons Park Avenue, Reading,
Berks RG6 1AZ
0734 664456–60
848410

Memory Computer UK Ltd
Britannia House, 96 High Road, London
N12 9RY
01-446 1441

Metco Ltd
Chobham, Woking, Surrey GU24 8RD
09905 7121
858275 METCO G

Mettler Instruments Ltd
Kingsmead House, Abbey Barn Road, High
Wycombe, Bucks HP11 1QW
0494 450202

Microgen Ltd
Watling Street, Radlett, Herts
09276 2233

Microlease plc
Forbes House, Whitefriars Estate, Tudor Road,
Harrow, Middx HA3 5SS
01-427 8822

Microphase Ltd
36 Nuffield Way, Abingdon, Oxon OX14 1TF
0235 25695
837991

Millington York Ltd
Leighswood, Aldridge, Walsall, West Midlands
WS9 8AL
0922 54121

Mita Copystar (UK) Ltd
Mita House, Hamm Moor Lane, Addlestone,
Weybridge, Surrey KT15 2SB
0932 58266
299268 MITAUK G

Mitsubishi Electric (UK) Ltd
Hertford Place, Denham Way, Maple Cross,
Rickmansworth, Herts WD3 2BJ
0923 77000
916756

Modular Robotic Systems
Cranfield Road, Lostock Industrial Estate,
Lostock, Bolton, Lancs BL6 4QN
0204 699745

Moldflow (Europe) Ltd
75 High Street, Chislehurst, Kent BR7 5AG
01-467 3434

Monsanto plc
Monsanto House, Chineham Court, Chineham,
Basingstoke, Hants RG24 0UL
0256 57288
858837

MPB Corporation
Cores End Road, Bourne End, Bucks SL8 5AS
06285 25222
848492

MPR Publishing Services Ltd
Old Bank Building, Bellstone, Shrewsbury
SY1 1HU
0743 64675
35213 MPR G

Nadella Bearing Co. Ltd
12/14 Woodfield Road, Welwyn Garden City,
Herts AL7 1JQ
07073 34694
261112

National Bureau of Standards (NBS)
US Department of Commerce, Washington DC
202234, USA

National Centre of Tribology
UKAEA, Risley, Warrington, Cheshire WA3 6AT
0925 31244

National Engineering Laboratory
East Kilbride, Glasgow G75 0QU
03552 20222
777888 NELEK G

NEC Business Systems (Europe) Ltd
35 Oval Road, London NW11 7EA
01-993 8111

Negretti Automation
Stocklake, Aylesbury, Bucks HP20 1DR
0296 5931

NKR Systems Office Furniture
73 Welbeck Street, London W1M 7HA
01-486 7051

Norton Performance Plastics
Chesterton Works, Loomer Road, Newcastle,
Staffs ST5 7HR
0782 563726
36389 PAMPUS G

Nylacast Oilen Ltd
Brighton Road, Leicester LE5 0HD
0533 768558

Office Equipment (John Dale) Ltd
Winchester Wharf, Clink Street, London SE1
9DQ
01-407 8511 and 01-403 0818

Origa Ltd
Ashchurch Industrial Estate, Tewkesbury, Glos
GL20 8TD
0684 298977
437217 ORIGA G

Original Equipment Manufacture (OEM)
Audit House, Field End Road, Eastcote, Ruislip,
Middx
01-868 4499
934171

Ozalid UK Ltd
Langston Road, Loughton, Essex IG10 3TH
01-508 5544
25475

Pacific Scientific Ltd
4 First Avenue, Globe Park, Marlow, Bucks
SL7 1YA
02684 74074
846447 PACSCI

Paint Research Association
Waldegrave Road, Teddington, Middx TW11 8LD
01-977 4427
928720

Panorama Office Systems Ltd
13 Garamonde Drive, Wymbush
Milton Keynes, Bucks MK8 8LB
0908 562525

Parker Hannifin
PO Box 192, Star House, 69–71 Clarendon Road,
Watford, Herts WD1 1DQ
0923 46611

Peel and Co. Ltd
Chartwell House, Jeymer Drive, Greenford,
Middx UB6 8PW
01-578 6861
934265

Penta Systems (UK) Ltd
15 Sheet Street, Windsor, Berks SL4 1AS
075 35 55513
848597

Pentel Stationery Ltd
Unit 1, The Wyvern Estate, Beverley Way, New
Malden, Surrey KT3 4PF
01-949 5331
929621

Permabond Adhesives Ltd
Woodside Road, Eastleigh, Hants SO5 4EX
0703 629628
477543 AVBOND G

Philidas Ltd
Monkhill Lane, Pontefract, West Yorkshire WF8
1RL
0977 704141

Pilkington Reinforcements Ltd
St Helens, Merseyside WA10 3TR
0744 24022
627441 PBSTH G

Pilot Pen Co. UK Ltd
Bethune Road, North Acton, London NW10 6NJ
01-961 6661
8952882 PILOT G

Plascoat Systems Ltd
Trading Estate, Farnham, Surrey GU9 9NY
0252 721131

Plastic Coatings Ltd
Woodbridge Industrial Estate, Guildford, Surrey
GU1 1BG
0483 31155

Plessey Assessment Services
Titchfield, Hants
0329 43031

Polymer Laboratories Ltd
Technology Centre, Epinal Way, Loughborough
LE11 0QE
0509 233300
341383

Power Equipment Ltd
Kingsbury Works, Kingsbury Road, London
NW9 8UU
01-205 0033
8952887

Power Leasing Ltd
The Coach House, 24 Church Street, Bathford,
Avon BA1 7RS
0225 859900

Powerdrive PSR Ltd
Sydenham Industrial Estate, Leamingston Spa,
Warks CV31 1PZ

Pragma Ltd
Pragma House, Weirvale Industrial Estate,
Denham Way, Rickmansworth, Herts WD3 2RL
0923 720326
922625 PRAGMA G

Pressflow Ltd
Unit 29, Planetary Road, Willenhall, West
Midlands
0902 726671
334070 PFLOW G

Prime Computers (UK) Ltd
Primos House, 2–4 Lampton Road, Hounslow,
Middx TW3 1JW
01-572 7400
938371/896535

Production Engineering Research Association (PERA)
Melton Mowbray, Leics LE13 0PB
0664 64133
34684

Profile Microfilming (Kent) Ltd
Image House, 344 High Street, Rochester, Kent
ME1 1JU
0634 813751

Project Office Furniture plc
Haverhill, Suffolk CB9 8QJ
0440 706001

Protex Fasteners Ltd
Arrow Road, Redditch, Worcs B98 8PA
0527 63231

PSM Fasteners Ltd
Longacres Industrial Estate, Willenhall, West
Midlands WV13 2JS
0902 68011
338565

Racal Redac Ltd
Tewkesbury, Glos GL20 8HE

Railko Ltd
Loudwater, High Wycombe, Bucks HP10 9QU
06285 24901
848406

Rank Xerox (UK) Ltd
Bridge House, Oxford Road, Uxbridge, Middx
UB8 1HS
0895 51133

RAPRA Technology Ltd
Shawbury, Shrewsbury, Shropshire SY4 4NR
0939 250383
35134

RealTime Printers Ltd
Compton Place, Surrey Avenue, Camberley,
Surrey GU15 3DX
0276 681444
858893

Rehau Plastics Ltd
Unit 1, Perth Avenue, Slough, Berks SL1 4XZ
0753 30266

Reliance Gear Co. Ltd
St Helens Gate, Almondsbury, Huddersfield
HD4 6SF
0484 39441
51573

Renold plc
Renold House, Styal Road, Wythenshawe,
Manchester M22 5WL
061-437 5221
669052

Reprodraft Ltd
Factory Road, Cordes Trading Estate, Newport,
Gwent NP9 5FE
0633 57740/57273

Rhone-Poulenc Systems Ltd
High Street, Houghton Regis, Beds LU5 5QL
0582 605551
826525

RHP Group
PO Box 7, Chelmsford, Essex CM1 1PU
0245 61722
99185

Ricas Ltd
2 Chandos Road, London NW10 6UP
01-961 1666

Ricoh UK Ltd
Ricoh House, 32 Stephenson Way, London NW1
2HD
01-388 3200

Robinson Ford Associates Ltd
The Chapel, 5 Salisbury Street, Cranborne, Dorset
BH21 5PU
07254 566

Robocom Ltd
Clifton House, Clifton Terrace, London
N4 3TB
01-263 8585/3388

Rotorbord Ltd
Unit 6, Building 2, Stanmore Trading Estate,
Bridgnorth, Shropshire WV15 5HP
074 62 4883/5605

Rotring UK Ltd
Building No 1, GEC Estate, East Lane, Wembley,
Middx HA9 7PY
01-908 2577

Royal Sovereign Graphics
Britannia House, 100 Drayton Park, London N5
1NA
01-226 4455
267668

Salter Springs and Pressings Ltd
Spring Road, Smethwick, Warley, West Midlands
B66 1PF
021-553 2929

Sanyo Marubeni (UK) Ltd
8 Greycaine Road, Greycaine Estate, Watford,
Herts WD2 4QU
0923 46363

Sciaky Electric Welding Machines Ltd
212 Bedford Avenue, Trading Estate, Slough,
Berks SL1 4RH
0753 25551
847254

Scicon Ltd
49 Berners Street, London W1P 4AQ
01-580 5599
24293 SCICON G

Sharp Electronics (UK) Ltd
Sharp House, Thorp Road, Manchester
M10 9BE
061-205 2333
668380 SHARP G

Sheffield Micro Information Systems Ltd
Victoria House, Rutland Park, Sheffield 10

Silvar-Lisco Ltd
Alpha House, London Road, Bracknell, Berks
RG12 2TH
0344 481888
848210

Silver Reed (UK) Ltd
Silver Seiko House, 19–23 Exchange Road,
Watford, Herts
0923 45976/35616
923029 SILVER G

Sintrom Electronics Ltd
14 Arkwright Road, Reading, Berks RG2 0LS
0734 875464

SKF (UK) Ltd
Sundon Park Road, Luton, Beds LU3 3BL
0582 503233
82205

G.H. Smith & Partners (Sales) Ltd
28 Berechurch Road, Colchester, Essex CO2 7QH
0206 48221
987801

Snap-Tite Europe BV
Industrial Estate, Whitemill, Wexford, Ireland
010 35353 41566

SNFA Bearings Ltd
Charfield, Wotton under Edge, Glos GL12 8SP
0453 843501

SNR Bearings (UK) Ltd
Grovelands Industrial Estate, Longford Road,
Exhall, Coventry CV7 9ND
0203 362088
311045

Society of Automobile Engineers (SAE)
400 Commonwealth Drive, Warrendale, PA
15096, USA

Solarbo Fitments Ltd
Commerce Way, Lancing, Sussex BN15 8TF
0903 761166

Southco Fasteners Ltd
Unit E, Gregory Bank Industrial Estate,
Gregory's Bank, Worcs WR3 8AQ
0905 612444
336494

Span
8 High Street, Wendover, Bucks HP22 6EA
0296 624887/891/941

Spandex UK Ltd
Backfields House, Upper York Street, Bristol
BS2 8QQ
0272 428473
444309

Sperry Ltd
Computer Systems Sperry Centre, Stonebridge
Park, London NW10 8LS
01-965 0511
8951141

Spunalloys Ltd
Northcote Street, Walsall, West Midlands WS2
8BJ
0922 24551

Staedtler (UK) Ltd
Pontyclun, Glamorgan CF7 8YJ
0443 222421
497025

Stanford Marsh Ltd
Orchard Works, Northwick Road, Worcester WR3
7DX
0905 51735

Staveley Computing
Blackpole Road, Worcester WR3 8TH
0905 53335
336064

Stralfors
Unit 11, Techno Trading Estate, Bramble Road,
Swindon, Wilts SN2 6HB
0793 37837

Sun Microsystems UK Ltd
Kings Ride Court, Kings Ride, Ascot, Berks
0990 25942
847743

Surveying and Scientific Instruments Ltd
Wootton Rivers, Marlborough, Wilts SN8 4NQ
0672 810776

Swan Stabilo Ltd
71 Parkway, Camden Town, London NW1 7QJ
01-485 0025
27443

Systema UK Ltd
12 Albury Close, Loverock Road, Reading, Berks
RG3 1BB
0734 502223

Système International d'Unités, Le (SI)
48 rue Gay-Lussac, F7 Paris 5, France

Systems Designers International
System House, 106 Fleet Road, Fleet, Hants
GU13 8NZ

Tangram Computer Aided Engineering Ltd
5 Siddeley Way, Royal Oak Industrial Estate,
Daventry, Northants
0327 705026

Technical Indexes Ltd
Willoughby Road, Bracknell, Berks RG12 4DW
0344 426311
849207

Tektronix UK Ltd
Fourth Avenue, Globe Park, Marlow, Bucks
SL7 1YD
06284 6000
847378

Terminal Display Systems
Philips Road, Whitebirk Industrial Estate,
Blackburn, Lancs BB1 5TH
0254 676921
635693

Thorn EMI Panelgraphic Ltd
Aden Road, Ponders End, Enfield, Middx
EN3 7SW
01-805 8944
8955228

3M (UK) plc
3M House, PO Box 1, Bracknell, Berks,
RG12 1JU
0344 426726

Titanium International Ltd
Thornhill Road, Solihull, West Midlands B91 2HF
021-704 3321

Trilex International Marketing Ltd
57 Church Street, Staines, Middx
0784 63771
8813487

Tufnol Ltd
PO Box 376, Perry Bar, Birmingham B92 7EX
021-356 9351
339730

Union Carbide UK Ltd
Coatings Service, Drakes Way, Swindon, Wilts
SN3 3HX
0793 488311

Universal Grids Ltd
PO Box 3, Liskeard, Cornwall PL14 6YZ
0579 20878

UNO Sales
684 Mitcham Road, Croydon CR9 3AB
01-684 6171
(51) 947938

Valid Logic Systems
Valid House, 39 Windsor Road, Slough, Berks
SL1 2EE
0753 820101
847318

A. M. Varityper
Maylands Avenue, Hemel Hempstead, Herts HP2
7ET
0442 42251

William Vere Ltd
Chapel Lane, High Wycombe, Bucks HP12 4BG
0494 22361
837102

Versatec Ltd
5 Oxford Road, Newbury, Berks RG13 1QD
0635 42421

Welding Institute
Abington Hall, Abington, Cambridge CB1 6AL
0223 891162
81183

Westra Office Equipment Ltd
The Green, Southall, Middx U2 4DE
01-843 1122
296768 WESTRA G

Westwind Air Bearings Ltd
Trading Park, Holton Heath, Poole, Dorset BR16 6LN

Westwood Stationery Ltd
54–58 Park Royal Road,
London NW10
01-961 5252
21581 WEB G

E. Whitmont and Co. Ltd
10 Warwick Street, London W1R 6LS
01-439 0230

Wiggins Teape plc
Chartham Paper Mills, Canterbury, Kent
CT4 7JA

Winsor and Newton
Whitfriars Avenue, Wealdstone, Harrow, Middx
HA3 5RH
01-427 4343
927295 ARTIST G

Workers Educational Association
9 Upper Berkeley Street, London W1H 8BY
01-402 5608

Writing Instrument Association, The
8 Wimpole Street, London W1H 8AS

Wyko Bearings and Transmissions Ltd
Queens Cross, Dudley, West Midlands DY1 1QN
0384 232171

Xenotron Ltd
Vinces Road, Diss, Norfolk IP22 3HQ
0379 4144
975278 EXENTEL G

Zinc Development Association
34 Berkeley Square, London W1X 6AJ
01-499 6636
261286 ZILECA

Zwick Testing Machines Ltd
Southern Avenue, Leominster, Hertfordshire
HR6 0QH
0568 5201–2
35692 ZWICK

Index

301

Alpha
Mathematics 1
New Edition

Compiled by

T. R. Goddard,

J. W. Adams and R. P. Beaumont

 Schofield & Sims Ltd Huddersfield

0 7217 2250 4

First printed 1979

Reprinted 1979

Reprinted 1980

Reprinted 1981

Reprinted 1982

Reprinted 1984

Revised and reprinted 1985

Reprinted 1987

Reprinted 1989

The books in the two series forming this programme comprise:

Ready for Alpha and Beta 0 7217 2266 0

Beta Mathematics 1 0 7217 2258 X	Alpha Mathematics 1 0 7217 2250 4
Beta Mathematics 2 0 7217 2259 8	Alpha Mathematics 2 0 7217 2251 2
Beta Mathematics 3 0 7217 2260 1	Alpha Mathematics 3 0 7217 2252 0
Beta Mathematics 4 0 7217 2261 X	Alpha Mathematics 4 0 7217 2253 9
Beta Mathematics 5 0 7217 2268 7	
Beta Mathematics 6 0 7217 2269 5	

Designed by Peter Sinclair (Design and Print) Ltd, Wetherby

Printed in England by Chorley & Pickersgill Ltd, Leeds

Contents   Alpha Mathematics 1

Counting to 20

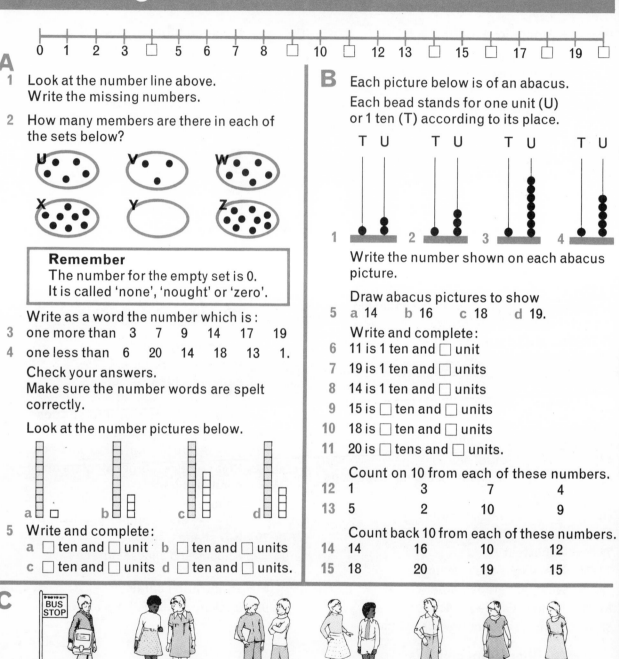

0 1 2 3 ☐ 5 6 7 8 ☐ 10 ☐ 12 13 ☐ 15 ☐ 17 ☐ 19 ☐

A

1 Look at the number line above. Write the missing numbers.

2 How many members are there in each of the sets below?

U V W
X Y Z

Remember
The number for the empty set is 0.
It is called 'none', 'nought' or 'zero'.

Write as a word the number which is:

3 one more than 3 7 9 14 17 19

4 one less than 6 20 14 18 13 1.

Check your answers.
Make sure the number words are spelt correctly.

Look at the number pictures below.

a b c d

5 Write and complete:
a ☐ ten and ☐ unit   b ☐ ten and ☐ units
c ☐ ten and ☐ units d ☐ ten and ☐ units.

B

Each picture below is of an abacus.

Each bead stands for one unit (U) or 1 ten (T) according to its place.

T U   T U   T U   T U

1   2   3   4

Write the number shown on each abacus picture.

Draw abacus pictures to show

5 a 14 b 16 c 18 d 19.

Write and complete:

6 11 is 1 ten and ☐ unit

7 19 is 1 ten and ☐ units

8 14 is 1 ten and ☐ units

9 15 is ☐ ten and ☐ units

10 18 is ☐ ten and ☐ units

11 20 is ☐ tens and ☐ units.

Count on 10 from each of these numbers.

12 1   3   7   4

13 5   2   10   9

Count back 10 from each of these numbers.

14 14   16   10   12

15 18   20   19   15

C

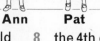

Alan **Jane Sally** **Tim John** **Mary Peter** **Tony** **Ann** **Pat**

1 How many children are there at the bus stop?

Write the name of
2 the first child   3 the last child.

Which child is
4 second   5 fifth   6 eighth?

Name 7 the 3rd child 8 the 4th child
9 the 7th child 10 the 9th child.

Write the place of
11 Mary   12 Tim   13 Pat.

14 Write the next two places after Pat.

Counting to 50

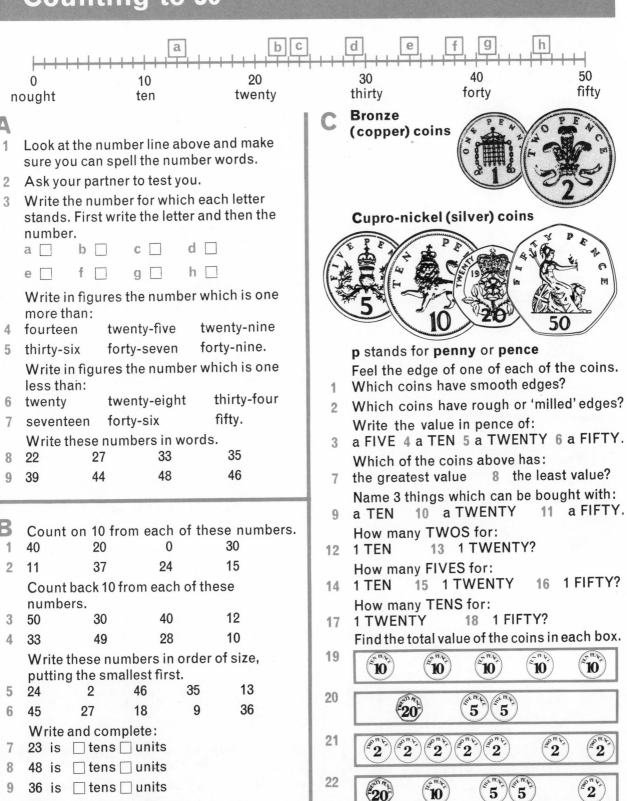

a   b c   d   e   f g   h

0	10	20	30	40	50
nought	ten	twenty	thirty	forty	fifty

A

1 Look at the number line above and make sure you can spell the number words.

2 Ask your partner to test you.

3 Write the number for which each letter stands. First write the letter and then the number.

a ☐   b ☐   c ☐   d ☐

e ☐   f ☐   g ☐   h ☐

Write in figures the number which is one more than:

4 fourteen   twenty-five   twenty-nine

5 thirty-six   forty-seven   forty-nine.

Write in figures the number which is one less than:

6 twenty   twenty-eight   thirty-four

7 seventeen   forty-six   fifty.

Write these numbers in words.

8 22   27   33   35

9 39   44   48   46

B

Count on 10 from each of these numbers.

1 40   20   0   30

2 11   37   24   15

Count back 10 from each of these numbers.

3 50   30   40   12

4 33   49   28   10

Write these numbers in order of size, putting the smallest first.

5 24   2   46   35   13

6 45   27   18   9   36

Write and complete:

7 23 is ☐ tens ☐ units

8 48 is ☐ tens ☐ units

9 36 is ☐ tens ☐ units

10 19 is ☐ ten ☐ units.

C

Bronze (copper) coins

Cupro-nickel (silver) coins

p stands for **penny** or **pence**

Feel the edge of one of each of the coins.

1 Which coins have smooth edges?

2 Which coins have rough or 'milled' edges?

Write the value in pence of:

3 a FIVE 4 a TEN 5 a TWENTY 6 a FIFTY.

Which of the coins above has:

7 the greatest value   8 the least value?

Name 3 things which can be bought with:

9 a TEN 10 a TWENTY 11 a FIFTY.

How many TWOS for:

12 1 TEN   13 1 TWENTY?

How many FIVES for:

14 1 TEN 15 1 TWENTY 16 1 FIFTY?

How many TENS for:

17 1 TWENTY   18 1 FIFTY?

Find the total value of the coins in each box.

19 (10) (10) (10) (10) (10)

20 (20) (5) (5)

21 (2) (2) (2) (2) (2) (2) (2)

22 (20) (10) (5) (5) (2)

Number to 10 addition and subtraction facts

A

The number of members in set **X** equals the number of members in set **Y**.

> The **equals** sign = means
> **is the same as**.

1 How many members in set **Z** are coloured?
2 How many members in set **Z** are white?
3 By counting, find the total number.

> The **plus** sign + means **add**.

4 Write and complete:
3 and 6 equal ☐   3 add 6 equal ☐
6 plus 3=☐   6+3=☐.

> The **minus** sign − means **subtract**.

5 Write and complete:
9 subtract 3=☐   9 minus 3=☐
9 take away 6=☐   9−6=☐.

B

Using the signs =, + and − write these four number facts about 9.

1

9
3   6

3+6=☐   9−3=☐
6+3=☐   9−6=☐

In the same way, write four number facts about each of the following.

2

8
6   2

3

8
3   5

4

9
5   4

5

9
2   7

6

10
8   2

7

10
7   3

C

Write and complete:

1 6+4=☐   2 10−4=☐   3 5+5=☐
4 4+6=☐   5 10−6=☐   6 10−5=☐
7 10−2=☐   8 3+4=☐   9 0+8=☐
10 8−8=☐   11 7−2=☐   12 2+5=☐
13 5+4=☐   14 9−8=☐   15 8−4=☐
16 8−7=☐   17 8+0=☐   18 7−6=☐
19 7−3=☐   20 8+2=☐   21 8−3=☐.

22 Write the value of each letter.
9+0=**a**   8−6=**b**   4+3=**c**
2+7=**d**   9−9=**e**   3+7=**f**
5+2=**g**   3+5=**h**   9−0=**i**

Write and complete:

23	24	25	26	27
6 +3	7 +2	0 +9	3 +5	4 +4

28	29	30	31	32
7 −3	9 −4	10 −9	7 −4	10 −3.

D

Number stories
Write the answers only.

1 There are 9 stamps. 7 are used. How many are left?

2 Richard is 10. Andrew is 3. What is the difference in their ages?

3 James had a FIVE and 4 pence. How much had he altogether?

4 Find the sum of 1, 2, 3 and 4.

5 Susan spent 2p and 5p. How much was that altogether?

6 Ann spent 6p and 3p. What change did she receive from 10p?

7 Make up five addition number stories. The answers should be less than 10.

8 Make up five subtraction number stories. Use 10 as the largest number.

Ask your partner to find the answers to your ten number stories.

Number to 20 addition and subtraction facts

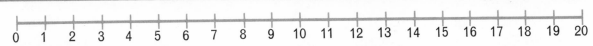

A

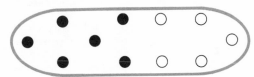

How many counters in this set are
1 coloured   2 white?
3 By counting, find the total number.
4 Write and complete:

$6+5=\square$ $11-6=\square$

$5+6=\square$ $11-5=\square$.

Use the number line if necessary to help
you to complete the following.

5 Begin at 8. Count on 3.
Write: $8+3=\square$.

6 Begin at 3. Count on 8.
Write: $3+8=\square$.

7 Begin at 11. Count back 3.
Write: $11-3=\square$.

11
8   3

8 Begin at 11. Count back 8.
Write: $11-8=\square$.

By counting on or counting back, write
four number facts about each of the
following.

9
11
7   4

10
11
9   2

B

Write these number facts about 12.

1 $3+9=\square$ $12-3=\square$

$9+3=\square$ $12-9=\square$

12
3   9

In the same way, by counting on or
counting back, write four facts about each
of these.

2
12
4   8

3
12
5   7

C

Write these number facts about 13.

1
13
4   9

$4+9=\square$ $13-4=\square$

$9+4=\square$ $13-9=\square$

By counting on or counting back, write
four facts about each of these.

2
13
6   7

3
13
5   8

4
14
5   9

5
14
6   8

6
15
6   9

7
15
7   8

8
16
7   9

9
17
8   9

Write and complete:
10 $6+6=\square$ $12-6=\square$
11 $7+7=\square$ $14-7=\square$
12 $8+8=\square$ $16-8=\square$
13 $9+9=\square$ $18-9=\square$
14 $10+10=\square$ $20-10=\square$.

D

1 From 11 take 9.
2 What number must be added to 7
to make 15?
3 Find the total of 8 and 6.
4 Add 3, 4 and 9.
5 How many more than 5 is 12?
6 Find the difference between 4 and 11.
7 Take 9 from 18.

Increase means 'make bigger'.
8 Increase 8 by 3.   9 Increase 10 by 8.

Decrease means 'make smaller'.
10 Decrease 17 by 9.   11 Decrease 20 by 7.
12 Find the sum of 6 and 7.
13 Subtract 6 from 14.

Money to 20p

A Which coin is equal in value to:

1 5 TWOS   2 2 TENS   3 4 FIVES   4 10 TWOS?

Write and complete these tables. Make sure they are correct. Ask your partner to test you.

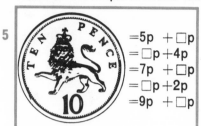

5
=5p + □p
=□p + 4p
=7p + □p
=□p + 2p
=9p + □p

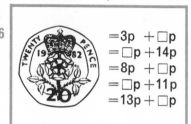

6
=3p + □p
=□p + 14p
=8p + □p
=□p + 11p
=13p + □p

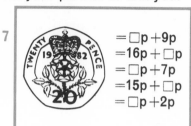

7
=□p + 9p
=16p + □p
=□p + 7p
=15p + □p
=□p + 2p

Find the change from a TEN after spending:

8 8p   9 6p   10 3p   11 9p   12 4p   13 7p.

Find the change from a TWENTY after spending:

14 4p   15 2p   16 11p   17 15p   18 13p   19 8p.

B By counting, find the value of the coins in each box.

1

3

6

2

4

7

5

8

C Look at the prices of the different flavours of iced lollipops.

Vanilla 8p   **Lemon 7p**    **Orange 5p**   **Banana 9p**

Find the total cost of the following lollipops.
1 a vanilla and a lemon
2 an orange and a banana
3 a vanilla and an orange
4 a banana and a vanilla
5 a lemon and an orange
6 a banana and a lemon

Find the change from a TWENTY after buying:
7 2 lemon
8 3 orange
9 2 banana
10 2 vanilla
11 2 orange and a banana
12 1 vanilla and a lemon.

D Which 2 coins make:

1 20p   2 15p   3 6p   4 11p?

Which 3 coins make:

5 17p   6 13p   7 9p   8 20p?

Number and money addition and subtraction

A

1. Copy these magic squares and find the missing numbers.

2	4	
	5	3
	1	

6	7	
	5	

Each row, down, across or from corner to corner, must add up to 15.

2. John has thrown 3 rings. What is his total score?

3. Total these scores.
   Ann   5, 6 and 7
   Alison   6, 2 and 9

4. Tony scored 17 with 2 rings. Which numbers did he get?

B

1. By how much is: the smallest pack cheaper than the largest

2. the middle size pack dearer than the smallest size?

3. Find the smallest number of coins needed to pay for the largest size.
   Write the value of each coin.

CHOC-BIX 14p
CHOC-BIX 9p
CHOC-BIX 5p

C

Find how much money each child has left after going shopping.

	coins in purse	money spent
Alan	10 5 1 1	8p
Anne	5 5 5 2 2 1	12p
Peter	10 2 2 1 1 1 1	10p
Joy	5 2 2 2 2 1 1	6p

D

1. Mary has a TWENTY. She spends 9p and 5p. How much has she left?

2. Joan went shopping with 1 TEN, 1 FIVE and 2 TWOS. She had 9p left. How much had she spent?

   After spending 8p, Paul had 3 TWOS and 2 pennies left.

3. How much did he have to start with?

4. Find the smallest number of coins which make this total.

Find the missing coins in each box.

5. 10 + 5 + ◯ + ◯ = 19p

6. 5 + 5 + 2 + ◯ + ◯ = 18p

7. 2 + 2 + 2 + ◯ = 17p

8. 5 + 2 + 1 + ◯ + ◯ = 20p

E

Write and complete using the sign + or − in place of ▲.

1. 15▲7=8
2. 4▲7=11
3. 12▲6=6
4. 5▲8=13
5. 8▲4=12
6. 14▲7=7
7. 3▲8=11
8. 13▲6=7

Write and complete:

9. □+8=14
10. □+7=12
11. 11−□=6
12. 9+□=14
13. □+8=16
14. □+9=17
15. 6+3+9=□
16. 13−□=9
17. 15−6=□
18. □+7=16.

> means **greater than**
< means **less than**

Write >, < or = in place of ▲.

19. 6+6▲4+8
20. 9+4▲2+9
21. 16−8▲13−4
22. 12−3▲14−7
23. 5+9▲7+7
24. 6+8▲8+3
25. 18−9▲4+6
26. 16−9▲3+4

Number addition and subtraction facts

0	1	2	3	4	5	6	7	8	9
1	2	3	4	5	6	7	8	9	10
2	3	4	5	6	7	8	9	10	11
3	4	5	6	7	8	9	10	11	12
4	5	6	7	8	9	10	11	12	13
5	6	7	8	9	10	11	12	13	14
6	7	8	9	10	11	12	13	14	15
7	8	9	10	11	12	13	14	15	16
8	9	10	11	12	13	14	15	16	17
9	10	11	12	13	14	15	16	17	18

Use this **ready reckoner** to help you to **add**.

Example 6+7	Place your ruler along the **6** line. Under **7** in the top row is the answer **13**. 6+7 = 13

Use the **ready reckoner** to help you to **subtract**.

Example 15−8	Place your ruler along the **8** line. In the top row above **15** is the answer **7**. 15−8 = 7

Using the ready reckoner, practise these addition and subtraction tests with a partner.

Then try to answer the tests without using the ready reckoner.

Place a strip of paper alongside test **A** and write the answers only.

Go on to tests **B**, **C** and **D** in the same way.

Time yourself for the four tests.

	A		**B**		**C**		**D**
1	7+2	1	0+9	1	8−5	1	7−3
2	6+4	2	3+5	2	9−4	2	8−8
3	9+2	3	9+6	3	16−8	3	18−9
4	7+6	4	8+4	4	15−9	4	16−7
5	8+3	5	7+7	5	13−7	5	14−6
6	9+8	6	6+5	6	17−9	6	12−9
7	6+6	7	5+8	7	12−7	7	14−9
8	7+4	8	3+9	8	11−9	8	11−3
9	6+9	9	9+9	9	15−8	9	17−8
10	4+7	10	8+6	10	13−5	10	13−9
11	8+9	11	7+5	11	12−4	11	11−8
12	6+8	12	9+4	12	14−7	12	13−6
13	4+9	13	6+7	13	11−4	13	16−9
14	9+7	14	5+9	14	12−6	14	15−7
15	8+5	15	4+8	15	11−7	15	12−3
16	7+8	16	9+3	16	15−6	16	11−2
17	5+6	17	7+9	17	14−8	17	13−8
18	3+8	18	8+8	18	13−4	18	12−5
19	9+5	19	5+7	19	12−8	19	11−6
20	8+7	20	2+9	20	11−5	20	14−5

Beat the clock

2 minutes for one test

10 minutes for the four tests

E Draw this table.

Keep a record of the time you take whenever you work the four tests together.

+ −	date				
time in minutes					
number correct					

Counting to 100

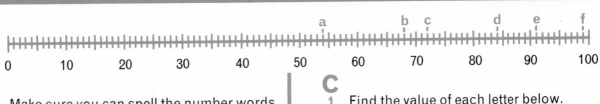

A

1 Make sure you can spell the number words for 60, 70, 80, 90 and 100.

2 Ask your partner to test you.

3 Look at the number line. Write the number for which each letter stands.

a ☐   b ☐   c ☐
d ☐   e ☐   f ☐

Write in figures the number which is one more than:

4 fifty-four   seventy   eighty-nine
5 ninety-nine   sixty-two   ninety-five
6 seventy-eight   eighty-seven   fifty-nine.

Write in figures the number which is one less than:

7 fifty-one   eighty   ninety-seven
8 sixty   ninety   seventy-three
9 eighty-six   fifty-eight   one hundred.

Write these numbers in words.

10 76   87   93
11 81   54   68
12 72   65   99

B

Count on 10 from each of these numbers.
1 60   80   50   70
2 83   77   65   89

Count back 10 from each of these numbers.
3 100   60   80   90
4 91   84   78   56

Write and complete each of these series.
5 10, 20, 30, ☐, ☐, ☐
6 90, 80, 70, ☐, ☐, ☐
7 37, 47, 57, ☐, ☐, ☐
8 63, 53, 43, ☐, ☐, ☐

How many 10s in:
9 30   70   100   90   50?

C

1 Find the value of each letter below.

$a + 80 = 83$ $64 - b = 60$ $c + 2 = 52$
$93 - d = 90$ $e + 6 = 76$ $68 - f = 60$
$g + 50 = 54$ $87 - h = 80$ $j + 9 = 99$

Write these numbers in order of size, putting the smallest first.

2 20   35   49   27   51
3 89   66   91   100   99

Write the answers only.

4 $10 + 10 + 5$
5 $10 + 10 + 10 + 10 + 8$
6 $20 + 10 + 10 + 10 + 1$
7 $20 + 10 + 9$

D

By counting, find the value of the coins in each box.

1

2

3

4

5

Find the total value of:
6 7 TENS and 3 FIVES
7 3 TENS and 4 TWOS
8 3 TWENTIES, 1 FIVE and 5 pence
9 1 FIFTY and 2 TWENTIES
10 1 FIFTY, 2 TENS and 2 FIVES.

Fractions   halves and quarters

A You will need two strips of paper of the same size.

1 Fold one of the strips into 2 **equal** parts.

$\frac{1}{2}$	$\frac{1}{2}$

Each part is called **one half** $\frac{1}{2}$.

2 How many **halves** in a whole strip?

Write and complete: $1 = \square$ halves $= \frac{\square}{2}$.

3 Fold the other strip into 2 equal parts and then fold it again to get 4 equal parts.

$\frac{1}{4}$	$\frac{1}{4}$	$\frac{1}{4}$	$\frac{1}{4}$

Each part is called **one quarter** $\frac{1}{4}$.

4 How many **quarters** in a whole one?

Write and complete: $1 = \square$ quarters $= \frac{\square}{4}$.

5 How many quarters in one half?

Write and complete: $\frac{1}{2} = \square$ quarters $= \frac{\square}{4}$.

6 Shade **three quarters** $\frac{3}{4}$ of your strip.

7 Name the part which is not shaded.

B Which of the shapes below have been divided into

1 halves   2 quarters?

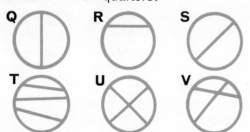

3 Draw the shapes below on squared paper.

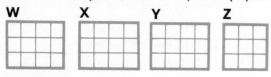

Shade

4 $\frac{1}{2}$ of **W**   5 $\frac{1}{4}$ of **X**   6 $\frac{3}{4}$ of **Y**   7 $\frac{1}{2}$ of **Z**.

C Each of the shapes below is a whole one which has been folded to show halves or quarters.

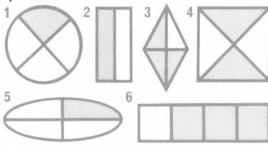

Name a   each of the shaded parts
      b   each of the unshaded parts.

In each case, make sure that the answers **a** and **b** add up to one whole one.

> **A part of a whole one is called a fraction.**

7 Write and complete:

$$1 = \frac{\square}{2} = \frac{\square}{4} \qquad \frac{1}{2} = \frac{\square}{4}.$$

8 Write a sentence telling how you would find $\frac{3}{4}$ of a cake.

How many times is

9 $\frac{1}{2}$ bigger than $\frac{1}{4}$ 10 $\frac{1}{4}$ less than $\frac{3}{4}$?

11 Tim, Ann, Alan and Judy share a prize equally. What fraction does each receive?

12 Susan has $\frac{1}{2}$ of a cake. The rest is shared equally between Pat and John. What fraction of the cake does each receive?

13 John had $\frac{1}{4}$ of a bar of chocolate and Peter had three times as much. What fraction did Peter have?

14 Janet had $\frac{1}{4}$ of a toffee bar and Bob had twice as much. What fraction was left?

15 Draw this diagram.

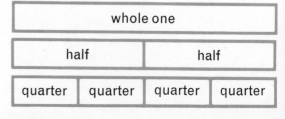

Telling the time

A

1 **a** What does the small hand on each clock tell you?
   b What does the large hand tell you?

The clock faces show 12-hour clock times.

Write the time shown on each clock face. The first one is done for you.

3 o'clock
3.00

C

> **a.m.** is short for '**a**nte **m**eridiem' which means 'before noon' or 'before midday'.
>
> **p.m.** is short for '**p**ost **m**eridiem' which means 'after midday'.

Write in figures the following afternoon times. Use a.m. or p.m.

1 half past 6   **2** quarter past 5
3 half past 2   **4** quarter to 3

Write in figures the following morning times. Use a.m. or p.m.

5 quarter to 2   **6** half past 8
7 quarter past 11   **8** quarter to 10

Write the following times in words.

9 10.15 a.m.   **10** 12.45 a.m.   **11** 6.45 a.m.
12 4.30 p.m.   **13** 8.15 p.m.   **14** 9.30 p.m.

Remember
There are 60 minutes (min) in 1 hour (h).
Every 30 minutes is half an hour.
Every 15 minutes is a quarter of an hour.

D

5 min to   5 min past
10 min to   10 min past
15 min to   **quarter   quarter**   15 min past
            to   past
20 min to   **half**   20 min past
                past
25 min to   25 min past
       30 min past

Use the clock to practise counting in fives:
1 the number of minutes past the hour
2 the number of minutes to the hour
3 the number of minutes round the clock
   5   10 . . . . 55 .

Write the following times as minutes past or to the hour.

4 1.20   **7** 10.35   **10** 3.05
5 4.50   **8** 6.05   **11** 9.30
6 7.40   **9** 11.55   **12** 8.45

Write in two ways the time shown on each clock.

13   **14**   **15**

B

Times can be written in words or in figures.

Write the time shown on each clock in two ways, first in words then in figures.

Three of them are done for you.

quarter   quarter
to   past
      half
      past

1   **2**   **3**

quarter past 4   half past 4   quarter to 5
4.15   4.30   4.45

4   **5**   **6**

Telling the time

A

Each of the pointers marked **w**, **x**, **y** and **z** shows the minute-hand of a clock in a different position.

How many minutes past the hour are shown by

1 pointer **w** 2 pointer **x**?

How many minutes to the hour are shown by

3 pointer **y** 4 pointer **z**?

Write in words, and then in figures the time shown on each of the clock faces below.

morning

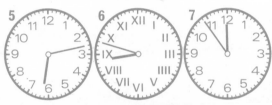

afternoon

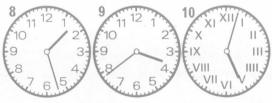

Clocks **6** and **10** have Roman numerals.

11 Write numbers 1 to 12 in Roman numerals.

Find another way of writing 4 in Roman numerals.

Write in two ways the correct time if:

12 clock **5** is 2 minutes slow

13 clock **6** is 3 minutes fast

14 clock **7** is 6 minutes slow

15 clock **8** is 2 minutes fast

16 clock **9** is 11 minutes slow

17 clock **10** is 5 minutes fast.

B

Write the following times in figures. Use a.m. or p.m.

1 half past four in the morning

2 quarter to nine at night

3 five minutes after midnight

4 ten minutes before midday

The digital clocks show Ann's usual daily timetable.

breakfast set out for school arrive at school

leave school arrive home bed-time

5 How many minutes after 7 o'clock does she have breakfast?

6 How many minutes before 9.00 a.m. does she arrive at school?

7 How many minutes does it take to walk from home to school?

8 Pat's bed-time is 20 minutes before Ann's. Write Pat's bed-time in figures. Use a.m. or p.m.

C

Write these times in figures. Use a.m. or p.m.

1 a quarter of an hour after 3.05 p.m.

2 seven minutes before 8.50 a.m.

3 ten minutes after 9.56 p.m.

4 ten minutes before midday

5 fifteen minutes before 8.05 a.m.

How many minutes are there between these times?

6 11.10 a.m. to 11.40 a.m.

7 7.15 p.m. to 7.45 p.m.

8 12.30 p.m. to 1.15 p.m.

9 10.50 a.m. to 11.10 a.m.

10 8.17 p.m. to 8.25 p.m.

11 9.05 a.m. to 10.00 a.m.

Tens and units

A This abacus picture shows 5 tens only.

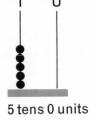

5 tens 0 units
50 + 0 = 50

Notice that 'nought' or 'zero' is used to show that there are no units in the units column.

Write the number shown on each abacus picture.

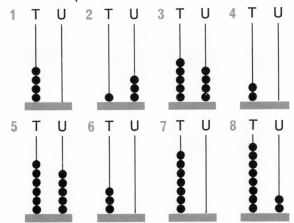

Draw abacus pictures to show each of these numbers.

9　29　　10　50　　11　41　　12　90

B Count on in tens from

1　4 to 54　　2　27 to 77　　3　53 to 93
4　11 to 61　　5　29 to 99　　6　8 to 88.

Count back in tens from

7　62 to 22　　8　73 to 33　　9　95 to 45
10　56 to 16　　11　42 to 2　　12　84 to 24.

Look at the example below.

> 3 tens 7 units = 30+7=37

Write and complete in the same way:

13　4 tens 6 units = ☐ + ☐ = ☐
14　8 tens 5 units = ☐ + ☐ = ☐
15　3 tens 3 units = ☐ + ☐ = ☐
16　9 tens 1 unit　= ☐ + ☐ = ☐
17　6 tens 7 units = ☐ + ☐ = ☐.

Write and complete:

18　28 = ☐ tens ☐ units = ☐ units
19　83 = ☐ tens ☐ units = ☐ units
20　30 = ☐ tens ☐ units = ☐ units
21　51 = ☐ tens ☐ unit　= ☐ units
22　77 = ☐ tens ☐ units = ☐ units.

C Draw the columns and write these numbers. The first is done for you.

H	T	U
	3	6

1　thirty-six
2　forty
3　sixty-two
4　8 tens
5　10 tens
6　100

What must be added to each of these numbers to make each up to the next 10?

7　31　　8　72　　9　95　　10　54

D Write the answers only.

1　30+40　　2　20+30　　3　60+20
4　40+50　　5　70+20　　6　30+50
7　40−10　　8　80−40　　9　60−50
10　50−30　　11　70−60　　12　90−20

13　10+20+5　　14　30+20+8
15　40+40+7　　16　20+70+1
17　50+20+3　　18　60+30+4
19　10+80+6　　20　30+30+5

21　Find out all you can about an abacus from books in the library.

Tens and units

A Write the number which is:

1. 1 more than 59
2. 9 more than 71
3. 2 more than 38
4. 4 more than 46
5. 5 more than 35
6. 7 more than 23.

Write the number which is:

7. 1 less than 90
8. 5 less than 50
9. 1 less than 100
10. 7 less than 70
11. 2 less than 60
12. 4 less than 40.

13. Find the value of each letter.

$a + 22 = 82$ $b + 35 = 75$

$91 - 41 = c$ $d + 64 = 94$

$28 + e = 68$ $83 - 60 = f$

$76 - 46 = g$ $17 + h = 47$

B

H	T	U
		1
	1	0
1	0	0

Read the numbers in the table.

Notice how the 1 moves to the left and '0s' (noughts or zeros) fill the empty spaces.

What is the biggest number which can be written in:

1. the units column
2. the tens column?

3. Write the biggest whole number less than 100.

C Find the value of the letters in these number series.

27,   37,   **u**,   57,   67,   77

v,   21,   31,   41,   51,   61

19,   29,   **w**,   **x**,   59,   69

98,   **y**,   78,   68,   58,   48

z,   15,   25,   35,   45,   55

D Write the answers only as quickly as you can. First add from left to right and then from right to left.

1. 8p + 2p + 6p
2. 7p + 9p + 1p
3. 7p + 4p + 3p
4. 5p + 5p + 9p
5. 3p + 7p + 9p
6. 5p + 4p + 5p
7. 2p + 6p + 4p
8. 7p + 2p + 8p
9. 4p + 5p + 6p
10. 1p + 3p + 9p

Find, by counting TENS and pence, the total value of the coins in each of these boxes.

11.

12.

13.

14.

15.

E Write and complete:

1. 17p = ☐ TEN ☐ p
2. 35p = ☐ TENS ☐ p
3. 47p = ☐ TENS ☐ FIVE ☐ p
4. 29p = ☐ TWENTY ☐ FIVE ☐ TWOS
5. 53p = ☐ TWENTIES ☐ TEN ☐ TWO ☐ p
6. 75p = ☐ FIFTY ☐ TENS ☐ FIVE
7. 87p = ☐ FIFTY ☐ TENS ☐ FIVE ☐ TWO.

Which three coins make:

8. 54p
9. 23p
10. 7p
11. 16p
12. 31p
13. 15p?

Which four coins make:

14. 20p
15. 18p
16. 82p
17. 29p
18. 56p
19. 75p?

Making sure

A

1 15   2 48   3 87   4 10

Write the number which is
a 10 smaller   b 10 greater
than each of the numbers above.
There will be two answers **a** and **b** to each.

By how many is the value of the figure
marked *x* greater than the figure marked *y*
in each of the following?

5 *xy*   6 *xy*   7 *xy*
   11   13   18

8 *xy*   9 *xy*   10 *xy*
   22   34   55

11 Find the value of each letter.

$3+$**a**$=9$ $7=3+$**b**   **c**$-6=6$
d$-8=7$ $14=$**e**$+8$ $9+$**f**$=18$

A	B	C	D	E	F	G	H

12 Write the letter which is the 7th, the 3rd,
the 8th, the 6th in the row.

13 Write the order of the letters which make
up the word BEAD.

Susan has only 10p coins in her purse.
What is the least number of TENS she
will need to pay each of these amounts?

14 37p   15 45p   16 81p   17 76p
18 12p   19 60p   20 19p   21 53p

Write the answers only.

22 $\frac{1}{2}+\frac{1}{4}$ 23 $\frac{1}{4}+\frac{1}{4}$ 24 $\frac{1}{4}+\frac{1}{4}+\frac{1}{4}+\frac{1}{4}$

25 $\frac{1}{4}+\frac{1}{4}+\frac{1}{4}$ 26 $\frac{1}{4}+\frac{1}{4}+\frac{1}{2}$ 27 $\frac{3}{4}+\frac{1}{4}$

28 $1-\frac{1}{2}$ 29 $1-\frac{1}{4}$ 30 $1-\frac{3}{4}$

31 $\frac{1}{2}-\frac{1}{4}$ 32 $\frac{3}{4}-\frac{1}{4}$ 33 $\frac{3}{4}-\frac{1}{2}$

B

Each of clocks **1-6** below is a quarter of an hour fast. Write in words the correct times.

Write, first in figures and then in words, the time shown on each clock face below.

C

Find the value of the missing coins in
each box.

5 How much had each child left
from the amounts shown?   **money spent**

1 $=36$p

Ann  12p

2 $=84$p

Bob   9p

3 $=51$p

Pat   8p

4 $=85$p

Tim   8p

Number and money   bridging tens

A

0   10   20   30   40   50

You have learnt that $7+8=15$.
Look at the number line.
You see that
$17+8=25$ $27+8=35$ $37+8=45$.
Write the answers to:

1 $47+8$ **2** $57+8$ **3** $67+8$.

Now do these.

4
$9+3$
$19+3$
$29+3$
$39+3$
$49+3$
$59+3$
$69+3$

5
$6+8$
$16+8$
$26+8$
$36+8$
$46+8$
$56+8$
$66+8$

6
$5+6$
$15+6$
$25+6$
$35+6$
$45+6$
$55+6$
$65+6$

7
$8+7$
$18+7$
$28+7$
$7+38$
$7+48$
$7+58$
$7+68$

8
$9+9$
$19+9$
$29+9$
$9+39$
$9+59$
$9+69$
$9+89$

9
$8+4$
$18+4$
$28+4$
$48+4$
$4+58$
$4+78$
$4+88$

C

0   10   20   30   40   50

You have learnt that $15-8=7$.
Look at the number line.
You see that
$25-8=17$ $35-8=27$ $45-8=37$.
Write the answers to:

1 $55-8$ **2** $65-8$ **3** $75-8$.

Now do these.

4
$11-5$
$21-5$
$31-5$
$41-5$
$51-5$
$61-5$
$71-5$

5
$12-7$
$22-7$
$32-7$
$42-7$
$52-7$
$62-7$
$72-7$

6
$14-8$
$24-8$
$34-8$
$44-8$
$54-8$
$64-8$
$74-8$

7
$13-4$
$23-4$
$33-4$
$43-4$
$63-4$
$83-4$
$93-4$

8
$11-6$
$21-6$
$31-6$
$51-6$
$71-6$
$81-6$
$91-6$

9
$17-9$
$27-9$
$37-9$
$57-9$
$67-9$
$87-9$
$97-9$

B   Write the answers only.

1 $23p+9p$ **2** $17p+8p$ **3** $46p+9p$

4 $4p+37p$ **5** $6p+28p$ **6** $65p+7p$

7 $25p$ **8** $9p$ **9** $38p$ **10** $7p$
  $+\ 8p$ $+37p$ $+\ 8p$ $+77p$

Add 8p to

11 $3p$ **12** $23p$ **13** $63p$ **14** $83p$.

15 Find the value of each letter.
  $m=29+16$ $n=34+17$ $p=45+39$

D   Write the answers only.

1 $21p-8p$ **2** $44p-5p$ **3** $56p-9p$

4 $32p-6p$ **5** $84p-7p$ **6** $72p-3p$

7 $56p$ **8** $64p$ **9** $41p$ **10** $93p$
  $-\ 7p$ $-\ 5p$ $-\ 7p$ $-\ 4p$

Subtract 7p from

11 $22p$ **12** $43p$ **13** $64p$ **14** $76p$.

15 Find the value of each letter.
  $a+6=25$ $37-b=28$ $c=46-8$

Number and money tens and units addition

First work Section **A**. Mark the answers and correct any mistakes.

Then work Section **B**. Do the same with Sections **C**, **D** and **E**.

Write the answers only.

First add upwards, then check by adding downwards.

A

1	52	2	76	3	54p	4	60p	5	35p
	+43		+21		+30p		+28p		+24p

B

1	45	2	68	3	74p	4	53p	5	31p
	+ 5		+ 2		+ 6p		+ 7p		+ 9p

6	57	7	16	8	39p	9	25p	10	42p
	+23		+74		+41p		+65p		+48p

11	51	12	72	13	10p	14	36p	15	23p
	7		5		22p		34p		63p
	+22		+13		+28p		+10p		+ 4p

C

1	46	2	27	3	28p	4	17p	5	39p
	+15		+67		+29p		+65p		+36p

6	58	7	55	8	36p	9	88p	10	14p
	+23		+ 8		+26p		+ 8p		+67p

11	19	12	38	13	17p	14	16p	15	25p
	26		13		14p		36p		46p
	+12		+44		+35p		+ 6p		+12p

D

1	29	2	48	3	19p	4	27p	5	18p
	19		17		18p		39p		9p
	+38		+28		+25p		+17p		+28p

6	17	7	23	8	38p	9	19p	10	7p
	49		29		27p		34p		18p
	+15		+29		+ 6p		+19p		+47p

E **First add from left to right, then check by adding from right to left.**

1	42p+15p	2	67p+30p	3	36p+14p
4	52p+33p+14p	5	41p+20p+9p	6	28p+35p+19p
7	13p+5p+16p	8	27p+18p+42p	9	68p+8p+17p

20

Number and money tens and units subtraction

First work Section **A**.   Mark the answers and correct any mistakes.

Then work Section **B**.   Do the same with Sections **C** and **D**.

Write the answers only.

Check each answer by adding to the line above.

A

| 1 | 26 −15 | 2 | 89 −36 | 3 | 75p −63p | 4 | 44p −31p | 5 | 39p −12p |

6 49 − 8   7 86 − 2   8 98p − 4p   9 67p − 3p   10 75p − 4p

11 87 −17   12 79 −49   13 95p −75p   14 43p −23p   15 88p −68p

16 72 −20   17 95 −30   18 61p −40p   19 89p −20p   20 63p −30p

B

1 50 − 7   2 70 − 6   3 30p − 8p   4 60p − 3p   5 40p − 9p

6 80 −54   7 50 −25   8 90p −11p   9 60p −16p   10 70p −52p

C

1 31 − 3   2 52 − 7   3 75p − 6p   4 93p − 7p   5 84p − 8p

6 84 −76   7 78 −69   8 91p −85p   9 63p −54p   10 56p −48p

11 91 −48   12 82 −15   13 73p −59p   14 54p −27p   15 95p −38p

16 74 −15   17 63 −48   18 82p −43p   19 91p −26p   20 76p −39p

D **Check each answer by addition.**

1 44p−12p   2 37p−21p   3 96p−43p   4 80p−27p

5 71p−27p   6 53p−26p   7 84p−29p   8 92p−34p

Numbers from pictures   graphs

A

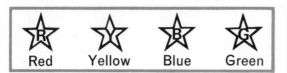
Red   Yellow   Blue   Green

In class 1 there were four teams, each having a different colour.
A star was given as a point for good work. Each star was placed on a sheet of paper in its proper column.

1   Which team was given the most points?

2   How many more points did the Red team score than the Yellow team?

3   Which team has twice as many points as the Blue team?

4   Name the teams in order, the team with the most points first.

5   How many points were given altogether?

B

In class 2, a point was shown by a coloured square.

1   Which team had the least number of points?

2   Which teams had the same number of points?

3   How many more points had the Red team than the Green?

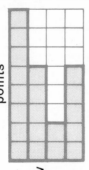
points

Red   Yellow   Blue   Green

4   Draw and fill in this table.

team	Red	Yellow	Blue	Green
number of points				

5   How many squares were coloured altogether?

C

This chart shows how many points were given to the children in class 3.
This kind of chart is called a **block graph**.

1   Which team had the most points?

2   Which team had half as many points as the Red team?

3   Which team had no points?

4   The team with the most points came first.
Name in order,
the second (2nd)
the third (3rd)
the fourth (4th) team.

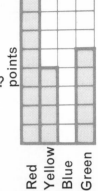
points

Red   Yellow   Blue   Green

5   Draw and fill in this table.

team	Red	Yellow	Blue	Green
number of points				

6   How many points were given altogether?

7   There were 8 children in each team and no child had more than one point.
How many children in each team did not receive a point?

D

The table below shows the number of points given each day to each of the four teams in class 4.

	Mon.	Tues.	Wed.	Thurs.	Fri.
Red	2	3	1	4	0
Yellow	4	0	1	0	3
Blue	2	2	2	2	2
Green	1	0	4	2	2

1   On squared paper, draw a block graph like the ones in sections **B** and **C**, showing the number of points each team received for the five days.

2   Which two teams had the same number of points?

3   Which team had the least number?

Numbers from pictures   graphs

A The block graph below shows how many days each of five children spent at school in two weeks.

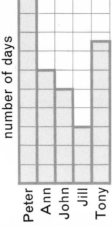

1 Write the names of the five children.

2 Which of the five children was at school
   a the most days
   b the least days?

3 Write the names of the children in the order of time spent at school, putting the child who spent the least time first.

4 How many more days did Peter attend than Jill?

5 Which child attended
   a half as many days as Peter
   b twice as many days as Jill?

6 Look carefully at the squares in Tony's column. How many days did Tony attend?

7 Draw the table below and show the number of days each child attended.

Peter	Ann	John	Jill	Tony

B The table below shows the number of days three children spent at school each week for three weeks.

	Michael	Thomas	Simon
1st week	5	3	4
2nd week	3	4	5
3rd week	4	3	4

1 On squared paper, draw a block graph to show how many days each of the three children spent at school in the three weeks.

2 Use your graph to find the name of the child with
   a the best   b the worst attendance.

C Here is the record kept by Class 4.
For each child absent a 'pin child' was drawn on squared paper.

children absent

Mon.	🧍 🧍 🧍 🧍 🧍 🧍 🧍 🧍
Tues.	🧍 🧍 🧍 🧍 🧍 🧍
Wed.	🧍 🧍 🧍
Thurs.	🧍 🧍 🧍 🧍
Fri.	🧍 🧍 🧍 🧍 🧍 🧍 🧍

There were 32 children in the class.

1 Draw and fill in the table below to show how many children were
   a absent   b present each day.

	number of children	
	absent	present
Mon.		
Tues.		
Wed.		
Thurs.		
Fri.		

2 Find the total number of absences for the week. Check the answer by counting the number of 'pin children'.

D Class 5 kept a record of the children absent by using shaded squares instead of 'pin children' to stand for absent children.
This is the graph they made.

children absent

Mon.	▨▨▨▨▨▨▨▨▨▨▨
Tues.	
Wed.	▨▨▨▨▨▨
Thurs.	▨▨▨
Fri.	▨▨▨▨▨▨▨▨▨

There were 35 children in the class.

1 Draw and fill in a table to show the number of children absent and present each day.

2 On squared paper, keep a record for your own class for two weeks.

Numbers from pictures graphs

A **Class 1 Collection for the Blind, first week**

Monday	/	/	/	/	/	/	/	/	/	/	/	/	/	/	/
Tuesday	/	/	/	/	/	/	/	/	/	/					
Wednesday	/	/	/	/	/	/	/	/	/	/	/	/			
Thursday	/	/	/	/	/	/	/	/	/	/	/	/			
Friday	/	/	/	/	/	/	/	/	/						

Class 1 decided on a target of 15p for each day. A daily record was kept so that they could see if the target had been reached. For every penny collected a stroke was made in a square.

1 Draw and fill in the table below.

	amount saved	amount short of target
Mon.		
Tues.		
Wed.		
Thurs.		
Fri.		

2 How much did the children save altogether?

3 By how much were they short of the target for the whole week?

4 Check the answers to **2** and **3** by counting from the daily record.

5 On which two days was the collection the same amount?

6 Why do you think the target was reached on Monday?

B The next week another record was kept, but instead of making strokes a shaded square was used to stand for one penny.

second week

Mon.
Tues.
Wed.
Thurs.
Fri.

pence

1 Draw and fill in a table to show the amount saved and the amount short of the target of 15p each day.

2 Find the total saved during the week.

3 Find the amount short of the target for the whole week.

4 Check the answers from the record.

5 How much less was collected in the second week than in the first week?

C For the third week another kind of record was kept. Instead of shaded squares, a line was drawn to show the number of pennies collected each day.
This is how the record looked.

third week

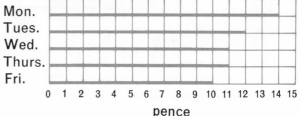

Mon.
Tues.
Wed.
Thurs.
Fri.

0 1 2 3 4 5 6 7 8 9 10 11 12 13 14 15

pence

1 Draw and fill in a table to show the amount saved and the amount short of the daily target of 15p.

2 Find the total amount saved in the week.

3 Find the amount short of the target for the whole week.

4 Check the answers from the record.

D 1 Look again at the record of the class collection in the first week.
Draw this record on squared paper using lines instead of strokes.

2 Draw the record for the second week using lines instead of shaded squares.

Puzzle corner

A Look at these numbers.

2,   4,   6,   <u>7</u>,   8,   10

The set of numbers starts at 2 and two more are counted on each time.
7 is underlined because it does not belong to the set.

In each set of numbers below, find the member which does not belong and write it as the answer.

1   5,   7,   9,   10,   11,   13

2   10,   20,   35,   50,   70

3   12,   9,   15,   16,   18

4   5,   15,   20,   23,   25,   30

5   10,   8,   5,   4,   2

6   1p,   2p,   4p,   5p,   10p

7   33,   44,   55,   66,   76,   77

8   $\frac{1}{2}$,   1,   2,   3,   4,   8

B

+	9	8	7	6	5	4	3
9	18						
8		16					
7			14				
6				12			
5					10		
4							
3							

Draw the diagram on squared paper.

Fill in the missing numbers.

C Find the number which follows next after those shown.

1   4, 5, 6, 7, ☐

2   8, 10, 12, 14, ☐

3   30, 25, 20, 15, ☐

4   1, 4, 7, 10, ☐

5   2, 4, 8, 16, ☐

6   7, 9, 12, 16, ☐

7   16, 8, 4, 2, ☐

8   4, 2, 1, $\frac{1}{2}$, ☐

> **> means greater than**
> **< means less than**

Write and complete using >, < or = in place of ●.

9   8+9 ● 9+8

10   3+4+5 ● 10+3

11   15−6 ● 12−4

12   9+7 ● 8+8

D Copy the puzzle on squared paper.

Then use the clues to complete it.

Across

1   5+5   2   1 ten 8 units

4   7 less than 60   6   9 twos+2

7   8 more than 30   8   4 less than 100

Down

1   5 more than 100

3   100 added 8 times

5   2 less than 400

6   19 more than 280

1			2	3
4	5		6	
7			8	

E

1   Write these letters of the alphabet.
the fifth, ninth and seventeenth letters

2   Each letter in the examples below stands for a number.
Find the value of each letter.

$x+x=18$ $y+5=13$

$7+w+2+5=22$ $\frac{1}{2}n=10$

Simon wrote a letter to Ruth in code. Here is part of his code.

A=1   B=2   F=6   K=11

3   Find the number he used for E.

4   Using the code, what word is this?

19   9   13   15   14

F

1   In seven years' time Simon will be twice as old as he is now. How old is Simon now?

2   When David and Anne shared 9 sweets, David had twice as many as Anne. How many did each have?

3   Half of a number is 2. Find three quarters of the number.

Addition and subtraction

A Mixed examples   Write the answers only.

1 26 +52	2 59 +30	3 20p +17p	4 39p +39p	5 19p +56p
6 50 +44	7 58 +12	8 64p +33p	9 36p +46p	10 42p +30p
11 15 4 +70	12 32 14 +44	13 17p 37p +29p	14 16p 7p +68p	15 50p 41p + 8p
16 85 +10	17 14 +39	18 57p +38p	19 34p +16p	20 20p +23p
21 11 42 +45	22 60 24 + 4	23 18p 39p +28p	24 23p 34p +13p	25 19p 29p +49p

B Mixed examples   Write the answers only.

1 86 −23	2 88 −29	3 70p −13p	4 74p −60p	5 94p −77p
6 60 −42	7 75 −56	8 50p −30p	9 59p −57p	10 83p − 9p
11 84 −75	12 82 −67	13 90p −26p	14 98p −54p	15 77p −20p
16 80 −59	17 96 −30	18 71p −41p	19 96p −69p	20 53p − 8p
21 63 −14	22 90 −31	23 65p −40p	24 42p −13p	25 96p −13p

When you have marked the answers to **A** and **B**, correct any mistakes. Show this work to your teacher. If you need more practice, turn to page 19 for addition and page 20 for subtraction examples.

C Write the answers only.

1 Increase 24 min by 17 min.
2 Decrease 63p by 16p.
3 Find the total of 18 cm and 25 cm.
4 How many pence less than 70p is 59p?
5 Find the sum of 23, 35 and 12.
6 Subtract 27 min from 1 hour.
7 Add 40 and 37.
8 Take 23p from 51p.
9 Find the difference between 47p and 35p.
10 What must be added to 63 to make 91?
11 16 plus 44
12 24+16+13+17

Addition and subtraction

A These are the amounts of money the children have saved.

Jane	46p	**Terry**	53p
Ann	37p	**Alan**	19p

1 How much have Jane and Terry altogether?

2 How much more has Terry than Alan?

3 Add Ann's and Alan's money.

4 How much more has Terry than Ann?

5 Who has 27p more than Alan?

6 How much less than 50p has Ann?

7 If Jane spends 18p, how much will she have left?

8 Terry wishes to buy a present for 90p. How much more must he save?

Mon.	adults	28
	children	44
Tues.	adults	24
	children	27
Wed.	adults	27
	children	19

These are the numbers of people who attended the school concert.

9 How many people attended on each day?

10 On Monday how many more children attended than adults?

11 Find the total number of children who attended the three concerts.

12 How many adults attended altogether?

13 How many more children attended on Monday than on Wednesday?

B

1 Janet read 26 pages on Monday and 39 pages on Tuesday. How many pages did she read altogether?

2 Tom saw two television cartoons. One lasted 25 minutes and the other 18 minutes. How many minutes was that in all?

The chart shows the number of children in each club at school.

	boys	girls
art	15	52
chess	19	18
games	45	27

3 How many boys are there in the clubs?

4 How many girls are there in the clubs?

5 How many more boys than girls are there in the Games Club?

6 How many fewer boys than girls in the Art Club?

7 How many more boys are there in the Games Club than the Chess Club?

8 How many children in the Chess Club?

9 James has 84 football-action cards. John has 46. How many more cards has James than John?

10 Jane had 90p. She gave Susan 36p. How much had Jane left?

11 Tim collects shells. He has 36 in one box and 24 in another box. How many shells has he?

The chart shows the amounts of money collected in one day.

class 1	48p	**class 4**	27p
class 2	32p	**class 5**	45p
class 3	19p	**class 6**	62p

12 Find the total collected by classes 1, 2 and 3.

13 How much less than 50p was collected by class 4?

14 Which class collected 30p more than class 2?

15 How much more was collected by class 5 than by class 3?

16 How much more than a FIFTY was collected by class 6?

Money   to £1

A

$$£1·00 = 100 \text{ pence}$$

From a real £1 coin, find and then write about:

1 its shape   2 its colour   3 its design.

Feel around the edge of the coin.

4 What do you find?

5 Has the £1 coin the same thickness as the other coins?

6 Make a list of three things which cost about £1.

Notes are used for larger numbers of £s.

7 Write their values and colours.

B

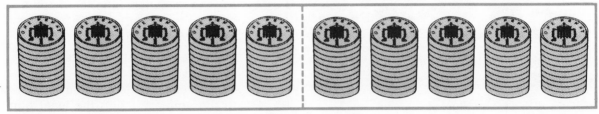

The drawing above shows 100 pence arranged in equal piles.

1 How many pence are there in each pile?

2 Name the coin which is equal in value to one pile.

3 Count the coins in groups of 10p.
Write: 10p   20p   30p . . . . . . 100p.

4 How many TENS can be changed for a £1 coin?

The coins are divided by a dotted line.

5 Into how many equal parts does it divide the 100 pence?

6 How many pence are there in each part?

7 Name the coin which is equal in value to one part.

8 Write and complete: £1 = ☐ FIFTIES
£½ = ☐ pence.

9 How many FIVES have the same value as:
1 TEN,   a TWENTY,   3 TENS,
2 TWENTIES,   a FIFTY,   £1?

10 Count in fives from 0 to 100 and back to 0.
Do this many times.
Ask your partner to test you.

C

Write these money tables. Find the missing numbers.

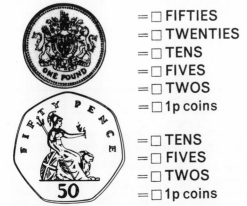

= ☐ FIFTIES
= ☐ TWENTIES
= ☐ TENS
= ☐ FIVES
= ☐ TWOS
= ☐ 1p coins

= ☐ TENS
= ☐ FIVES
= ☐ TWOS
= ☐ 1p coins

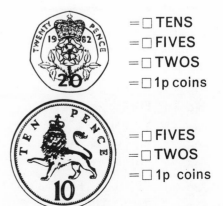

= ☐ TENS
= ☐ FIVES
= ☐ TWOS
= ☐ 1p coins

= ☐ FIVES
= ☐ TWOS
= ☐ 1p coins

Counting money

A Find the total value, in pence, of the coins in each box.

1. ⑤ ⑤ ⑤ ② ② ② ②

2. ⑩ ⑩ ⑤ ② ② ②

3. ㊿ ⑤ ⑤ ⑤ ⑤ ⑤ ① ① ① ① ①

4. ⑳ ⑳ ⑤ ⑤ ⑤ ② ②

5. ㊿ ⑳ ⑩ ⑤ ⑤ ② ②

Find the total value of :

6. 5 TENS and 3 TWOS
7. 1 FIFTY and 4 TENS
8. 3 TENS and 6 FIVES
9. 3 TWENTIES and 7 pence
10. 9 FIVES and 8 pence.

Which two coins together make these amounts?

11. 12p   **12** 25p   **13** 52p
14. 60p   **15** 55p   **16** £1·00

Which three coins together make these amounts?

17. 65p   **18** 60p   **19** 70p
20. 25p   **21** 62p   **22** 14p
23. 57p   **24** 75p   **25** 53p

B Find the least number of the given coins to make these amounts.

1. 45p = ☐ TENS   ☐ FIVE
2. 80p = ☐ FIFTY   ☐ TENS
3. 24p = ☐ FIVES   ☐ TWOS
4. 28p = ☐ TWENTY   ☐ TWOS
5. 56p = ☐ FIFTY   ☐ TWOS
6. 18p = ☐ FIVES   ☐ pence
7. 29p = ☐ TENS   ☐ FIVE   ☐ TWOS
8. 87p = ☐ TWENTIES   ☐ FIVE   ☐ TWO

C Draw the chart below.

		20p	10p	5p	2p	1p
1	18p		1	1	1	1
2	24p					
3	25p					
4	39p					
5	43p					

Write the smallest number of coins which make up each amount. The first one is done for you. Make sure it is correct.

6. Write five different amounts each less than £1.
Against each, write the coins which make up the amount, using the least number.

D Janet sorted the coins from her money-box.
1. How much had she altogether?

2. Tim saved the coins below.
How much had he altogether?

3. By how much were Janet's savings greater or less than Tim's?

The chart below shows the coins saved by Peter, Jane and Tony.
Find the total amount each saved.

		50	20	10	5	2	1
4	Peter		4			4	2
5	Jane		2	2	2	1	5
6	Tony	1		1	3		7

7. By how much were Peter's savings greater or less than Jane's?
8. By how much were Tony's savings greater or less than Peter's?

Counting money giving change

A

A shopkeeper may give change by 'counting-on' from the cost of the article.

If a TWENTY is given to pay for the toffees, which cost 12p, the shopkeeper gives the change like this.

He says: and **1p** make 13p
and a **TWO** make 15p
and a **FIVE** make 20p.

money given	price	change given
⬡20	△12p	◯ ◯ ◯

1 This picture tells the story.
Draw the three coins and write the value of each. Find the **total** change.

2 Find another way of giving this change using four coins.

B

Use the shopkeeper's method to find in each of the following
  a   the coins given in change   b   the **total** change.

1
money given		price	change given
⬡20	⬡10	21p	◯ ◯ ◯

2
money given	price	change given
⬡50	36p	◯ ◯ ◯

3
money given	price	change given
£1	△73p	◯ ◯ ◯

4
money given	price	change given
£1	47p	◯ ◯ ◯

Draw the coins required to give the change from:

5 2 TENS after spending 11p

6 3 TWENTIES after spending 44p.

C

Use the shopkeeper's method to give the change from:

1 a TEN after spending   a 4p   b 8p   c 6p

2 a TWENTY after spending   a 12p   b 14p   c 3p

3 a FIFTY after spending   a 42p   b 38p   c 45p   d 21p   e 13p   f 7p

4 £1 after spending   a 86p   b 65p   c 58p   d 49p   e 32p   f 17p.

D

Find the price in each of the following.

1
money given	price	change given
⬡20		②2 ②2 ②2

4
money given	price	change given
⬡50		⬡10 ②2

2
money given	price	change given
⬡20		②2 ②2 ⬡10

5
money given	price	change given
£1		⬡50 ②2 ②2 ②2

3
money given	price	change given
⬡50		②2 ⬡20

6
money given	price	change given
£1		⑤5 ⑤5 ⑤5

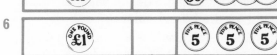

Money shopping

A

Which set of crayons is:
1 the most expensive
2 the cheapest?

Find the cost of these sets of crayons.
3 2 giant sets   4 2 slim sets
5 a mini-set and a stubby set
6 a giant set and a slim set
7 a stubby set and an assorted set?

How much more is the cost of:
8 a mini-set than a stubby set
9 a slim set than a giant set
10 an assorted set than a mini-set?

How much more does the assorted set cost than:
11 2 mini-sets   12 2 slim sets
13 2 giant sets   14 2 stubby sets?

15 What is the cost of one giant crayon?

Using the least number of coins in each case, which coins would you give to pay for:
16 a giant set   17 a slim set
18 a mini-set   19 an assorted set?

How much change from a FIFTY after buying:
20 a stubby set
21 a giant set   22 a mini-set?

23 Anne has 2 TWENTIES and a FIVE. How much more does she need to buy an assorted set?

24 Which two sets together cost 50p?

25 John gave two coins to pay for a stubby set and he received 6p change. Name the two coins.

B

Find the change from £1 after buying:
1 the fibre pens   2 the paints
3 the painting book   4 the paint sticks.

How much more than a FIFTY is the cost of:
5 the fibre pens   6 the paint sticks?

7 The fibre pens can be bought with three coins. Name the coins.

8 How much more do the paint sticks cost than the box of paints?

9 How much less is the cost of the painting book than the fibre pens?

10 How much must be added to 3 TENS and a FIVE to buy the painting book?

11 How much more than 80p do the paint sticks cost?

12 How much less than £1 is the cost of two painting books?

13 Jane must save 3 more TENS in order to buy the paints.
How much has she saved already?

14 John paid for a painting book with 2 TWENTIES and 3 other coins. Name the 3 coins.

Making sure

A Write the answers only.
1 Find the total of 6, 5 and 4.
2 Find the sum of 3, 4 and 9.
3 Find the difference between 7 and 15.
4 Subtract 5 from 12.
5 Increase 6p by 9p.   9 7 more than 6
6 Add 4p to 8p.   10 2p plus 9p
7 Decrease 13p by 5p. 11 14 cm minus 6 cm
8 5 less than 14   12 Take 3p from 12p.

D Find the value of each letter.

$16 - a = 9$	$11 - b = 7$	$14 - c = 9$
$9 + d = 17$	$7 + e = 14$	$7 + f = 13$
$g - 9 = 9$	$h - 4 = 9$	$i - 2 = 9$
$j + 5 = 11$	$k + 8 = 15$	$l + 8 = 16$
$13 - m = 5$	$14 - n = 6$	$15 - o = 7$
$9 + p = 13$	$3 + q = 12$	$5 + r = 12$
$s - 8 = 9$	$t - 9 = 6$	$u - 3 = 9$
$v + 8 = 12$	$w + 3 = 11$	$x + 9 = 17$

B The graph shows the amount each child has for spending money.

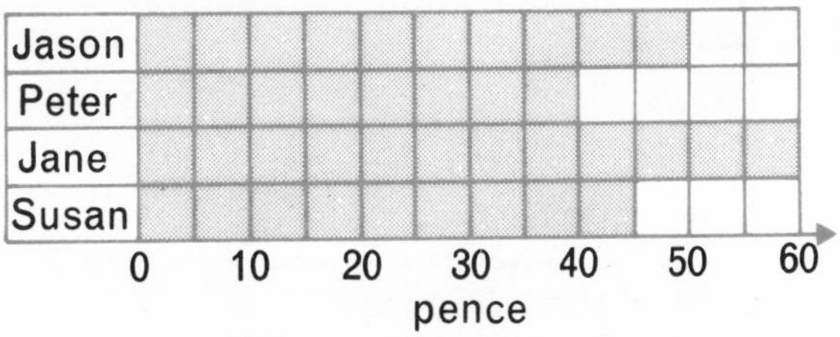

Jason	
Peter	
Jane	
Susan	

0 10 20 30 40 50 60
pence

1 How much does one shaded square on the graph represent?
2 Who has **a** the most   **b** the least spending money?
3 How much more does
  a Jason have than Peter
  b Jane have than Peter?
4 How much does Susan have?
5 Which two children have exactly £1 spending money between them?
6 How much less than £1 does each child get?

E

morning   afternoon   morning
x   **y**   **z**

1 Write in two ways the time shown on each of the clock faces above.
2 Write in figures, using a.m. or p.m., the correct time if
clock **x** is 4 minutes fast
clock **y** is 6 minutes slow
clock **z** is a quarter of an hour fast.

How many minutes are there between these times?

3	3.35 p.m. to 3.50 p.m.	4	7.59 p.m. to 8.35 p.m.
5	8.15 a.m. to 9.00 a.m.	6	7.25 a.m. to 8.30 a.m.
7	6.30 p.m. to 7.15 p.m.	8	noon to 12.25 p.m.
9	8.50 a.m. to 9.05 a.m.	10	11.40 p.m. to midnight

C Write the answers only.

	a	b	c
1	$36 + 20$	$49 + 40$	$21 + 50$
2	$40 + 19$	$60 + 17$	$20 + 62$
3	$55 + 15$	$27 + 13$	$32 + 18$
4	$74 - 30$	$96 - 50$	$42 - 20$
5	$58 - 38$	$76 - 16$	$59 - 39$
6	$100 - 40$	$100 - 70$	$100 - 30$

F How much change after spending:

	a	b	c	
1	18p	13p	11p	from a TWENTY
2	25p	22p	27p	from 3 TENS
3	29p	36p	25p	from a FIFTY
4	13p	19p	22p	from a FIFTY
5	55p	75p	45p	from £1
6	87p	74p	11p	from £1?

Table of twos

A

0 1 2 3 4 5 6 7 8 9 10 11 12 13 14 15 16 17 18 19 20

1 Begin at 0 and count on in **twos**. 0 2 4 — — — — — — — 20
2 Begin at 20 and count back in **twos**. 20 18 16 — — — — — — — 0
3 Do this many times. Ask your partner to test you.

B

| The sign × means **multiply by** or **times**. |

Look at the diagrams and complete the following.

1 2+2+2+2=☐
2 4+4=☐
3 4×2=☐
4 2×4=☐
5 8÷2=☐
6 8÷4=☐   11 4 multiplied by 2=☐
7 8=☐×4   12 8 divided by 2=☐
8 8=☐×2   13 2 times 4=☐
9 8÷☐=2   14 2(4)=☐
10 8÷☐=4   15 How many fours in 8?
                 16 4)8‾

| The sign ÷ means **divide by** or **share**. |

17 Write and complete four facts about 10.

$$\begin{array}{c} ^2 \\ 10 \\ _5 \end{array}$$

5×2=☐   10÷2=☐
2×5=☐   10÷5=☐

18 Write and complete four facts about 12.

$$\begin{array}{c} ^2 \\ 12 \\ _6 \end{array}$$

6×2=☐   12÷2=☐
2×6=☐   12÷6=☐

19 In the same way, write four facts about each of these numbers.

$$\begin{array}{c} ^2 \\ 14 \\ _7 \end{array}$$ $$\begin{array}{c} ^2 \\ 16 \\ _8 \end{array}$$ $$\begin{array}{c} ^2 \\ 18 \\ _9 \end{array}$$ $$\begin{array}{c} ^2 \\ 20 \\ _{10} \end{array}$$

20 Write the table of **twos**. Check and learn it. Ask your partner to test you.

C

1 Write and complete this series.
2, 4, 6, —, —, —, —, —, —, 20
These are called **even** numbers.

2 Write and complete this series.
1, 3, 5, —, —, —, —, —, —, 19
These are called **odd** numbers.

3 Write the set of even numbers between 19 and 29.

4 Write the set of odd numbers between 20 and 30.

5 How can you tell if a number is even or odd?

D Write the answers only.

1 18÷9	7 16÷2	13 14÷7	19 18÷2	25 16÷8	31 4÷2
2 5×2	8 0×2	14 2×9	20 2×4	26 2×5	32 9×2
3 6÷2	9 10÷5	15 2÷2	21 12÷6	27 6÷3	33 14÷2
4 2×7	10 6×2	16 3×2	22 2×2	28 10×2	34 8×2
5 8÷4	11 8÷2	17 12÷2	23 10÷2	29 0÷2	35 20÷2
6 2×6	12 1×2	18 2×8	24 7×2	30 2×10	36 4×2

Tables of fives and tens

A
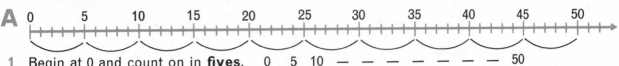

1 Begin at 0 and count on in **fives**.   0 5 10 — — — — — — — 50
2 Begin at 50 and count back in **fives**.   50 45 40 — — — — — — — 0
3 Do this many times. Ask your partner to test you.

B

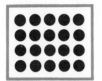

Look at the diagrams and complete the following.

1 $5+5+5+5=\square$
2 $4+4+4+4+4=\square$
3 $4\times5=\square$
4 $5\times4=\square$
5 $20\div5=\square$
6 $20\div4=\square$
7 $20=\square\times4$
8 $20=\square\times5$
9 $20\div\square=5$
10 $20\div\square=4$

11 4 multiplied by $5=\square$
12 20 divided by $5=\square$
13 5 times $4=\square$
14 $5(4)=\square$
15 How many fours in 20?
16 $4\overline{)20}$

17 Write and complete these facts about 35.

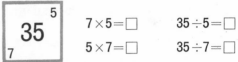

$7\times5=\square$ $35\div5=\square$
$5\times7=\square$ $35\div7=\square$

18 Write and complete these facts about 45.

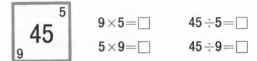

$9\times5=\square$ $45\div5=\square$
$5\times9=\square$ $45\div9=\square$

19 In the same way, write four facts about each of these numbers.

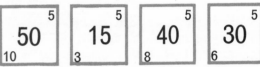

20 Write the table of **fives**. Check and learn it. Ask your partner to test you.

C
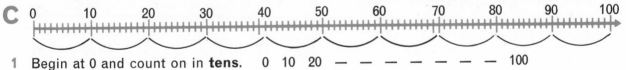

1 Begin at 0 and count on in **tens**.   0 10 20 — — — — — — — 100
2 Begin at 100 and count back in **tens**.   100 90 80 — — — — — — — 0
3 Do this many times. Ask your partner to test you.
Write four facts about each of these numbers.

4   5 80 6 30 7 70 8 90 9 40

10 Write the table of **tens**. Check and learn it. Ask your partner to test you.

D Write the answers only.

1 $45\div5$ 4 0×5 7 $30\div6$ 10 5×7 13 $40\div8$ 16 5×3
2 5×5 5 $35\div7$ 8 8×5 11 $25\div5$ 14 6×5 17 $20\div5$
3 $15\div5$ 6 5×4 9 $50\div10$ 12 1×5 15 $0\div5$ 18 5×9

Fractions fifths and tenths

A

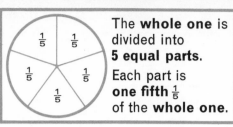

The **whole one** is divided into **5 equal parts.**

Each part is **one fifth** $\frac{1}{5}$ of the **whole one**.

A whole one

The **whole one** is divided into **10 equal parts.**

Each part is **one tenth** $\frac{1}{10}$ of the **whole one**.

1 Write and complete: $1 = \square$ fifths $= \frac{\square}{5}$.

The whole strip has been divided into 5 equal parts.

2 What fraction of the strip is shaded?

3 What fraction of the strip is unshaded?

4 Write and complete: $1 = \square$ tenths $= \frac{\square}{10}$.

5 Into how many parts has the whole strip been divided?

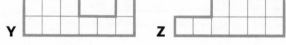

6 What fraction of the strip is one part?

7 What fraction of the strip is shaded?

8 What fraction of the strip is unshaded?

B

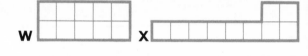

Each of these shapes stands for a whole one or unit.

1 What fraction of each whole one is
 a shaded   b unshaded?

Make sure that the two answers for each shape add up to one whole one, or unit.

2 Write a sentence telling how you would find
 a $\frac{2}{5}$ b $\frac{3}{10}$ of a whole one or unit.

C

1 Draw the shapes below on squared paper.

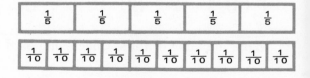

2 Shade the fraction given for each shape.

 W 2 fifths $\frac{2}{5}$ X 3 tenths $\frac{3}{10}$

 Y 3 fifths $\frac{3}{5}$ Z 7 tenths $\frac{7}{10}$

3 Write under each drawing the fraction which is
 a shaded   b not shaded.

D The two strips are of equal size and each represents a whole one or unit.

Look at the two strips then write and complete the following using the signs $>$, $<$ or $=$ in place of ●.

$\frac{1}{5}$	$\frac{1}{5}$	$\frac{1}{5}$	$\frac{1}{5}$	$\frac{1}{5}$

$\frac{1}{10}$	$\frac{1}{10}$	$\frac{1}{10}$	$\frac{1}{10}$	$\frac{1}{10}$	$\frac{1}{10}$	$\frac{1}{10}$	$\frac{1}{10}$	$\frac{1}{10}$	$\frac{1}{10}$

> **greater than**
< **less than**

1 $\frac{1}{5}$ ● $\frac{1}{10}$

2 $\frac{2}{5}$ ● $\frac{3}{10}$

3 $\frac{1}{5}$ ● $\frac{2}{10}$

4 $\frac{2}{5}$ ● $\frac{5}{10}$

5 $\frac{1}{5}$ ● $\frac{3}{10}$

6 $\frac{2}{5}$ ● $\frac{4}{10}$

7 $\frac{3}{5}$ ● $\frac{7}{10}$

8 $\frac{4}{5}$ ● $\frac{7}{10}$

9 $\frac{3}{5}$ ● $\frac{6}{10}$

10 $\frac{4}{5}$ ● $\frac{6}{10}$

11 $\frac{4}{5}$ ● $\frac{9}{10}$

12 $\frac{5}{5}$ ● $\frac{10}{10}$

Fractions   fifths and tenths

A

1   Get 20 counters and divide them into 5 sets of equal number.

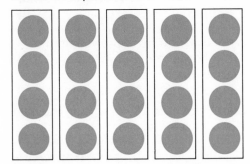

2   How many counters are there in each set?
Write and complete:

3   $\frac{1}{5}$ of 20 = ☐   4 $\frac{2}{5}$ of 20 = ☐

5   $\frac{3}{5}$ of 20 = ☐   6 $\frac{4}{5}$ of 20 = ☐.

7   Divide 15 counters into 5 sets of equal number.

8   How many counters are there in each set?
Write and complete:

9   $\frac{1}{5}$ of 15 = ☐   10 $\frac{3}{5}$ of 15 = ☐

11   $\frac{4}{5}$ of 15 = ☐   12 $\frac{2}{5}$ of 15 = ☐.

How many are there in:

13   $\frac{1}{5}$ of 10   14 $\frac{3}{5}$ of 10

15   $\frac{2}{5}$ of 10   16 $\frac{4}{5}$ of 10?

C

1   Divide 20 counters into 10 sets of equal number.

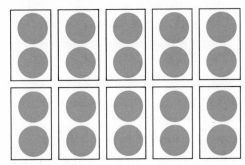

2   How many counters are there in each set?
Write and complete:

3   $\frac{1}{10}$ of 20 = ☐   4 $\frac{3}{10}$ of 20 = ☐

5   $\frac{7}{10}$ of 20 = ☐   6 $\frac{9}{10}$ of 20 = ☐.

7   Divide 30 counters into 10 sets of equal number.

8   How many counters are there in each set?
Write and complete:

9   $\frac{1}{10}$ of 30 = ☐   10 $\frac{2}{10}$ of 30 = ☐

11   $\frac{4}{10}$ of 30 = ☐   12 $\frac{6}{10}$ of 30 = ☐.

How many are there in:

13   $\frac{1}{10}$ of 50   14 $\frac{3}{10}$ of 50

15   $\frac{7}{10}$ of 50   16 $\frac{9}{10}$ of 50?

B   Find the value of:

1   $\frac{1}{5}$ of 30   7 $\frac{1}{5}$ of 40p

2   $\frac{2}{5}$ of 30   8 $\frac{2}{5}$ of 40p

3   $\frac{1}{5}$ of 25   9 $\frac{1}{5}$ of 50p

4   $\frac{2}{5}$ of 25   10 $\frac{4}{5}$ of 50p

5   $\frac{1}{5}$ of 35p   11 $\frac{1}{5}$ of 45p

6   $\frac{2}{5}$ of 35p   12 $\frac{2}{5}$ of 45p.

D   Find the value of:

1   $\frac{1}{10}$ of 40   7 $\frac{1}{10}$ of 60p

2   $\frac{2}{10}$ of 40   8 $\frac{2}{10}$ of 60p

3   $\frac{1}{10}$ of 10   9 $\frac{1}{10}$ of 90p

4   $\frac{5}{10}$ of 10   10 $\frac{5}{10}$ of 90p

5   $\frac{1}{10}$ of 80   11 $\frac{1}{10}$ of £1

6   $\frac{5}{10}$ of 80   12 $\frac{7}{10}$ of £1.

E

Look at the diagram.
Write and complete:

1   $\frac{1}{2} = \frac{☐}{10}$ 4 $\frac{☐}{5} = \frac{6}{10}$

2   $\frac{1}{5} = \frac{☐}{10}$ 5 $\frac{4}{5} = \frac{☐}{10}$

3   $\frac{2}{5} = \frac{☐}{10}$ 6   1 or $\frac{5}{5} = \frac{☐}{10}$.

The calendar

A

| Wednesday Saturday Thursday |
| Sunday Friday Monday Tuesday |

1. Start with Monday and write the days of the week in the correct order.
2. How many days are there in a week?
3. Learn to spell the name of each day. Ask your partner to test you.

Look at this page from a calendar.
4. Name the month.
5. How many days are there in April?

For the month shown, write the date of

April					
M		5	12	19	26
T		6	13	20	27
W		7	14	21	28
Th	1	8	15	22	29
F	2	9	16	23	30
S	3	10	17	24	
S	4	11	18	25	

6. the first Thursday;
7. the last Sunday;
8. the third Tuesday.

On which day is:
9. 5th April 10. 21st April 11. 15th April
12. 27th April 13. 11th April 14. 1st May?
15. Write the date of the first Saturday in the month and, by counting on in sevens, write the dates of the other Saturdays in the month.
Check, using the calendar.

B

Look at this page from a calendar from which some dates have been left out.

On which day is:

December				
M				
T		9		
W				31
Th				
F			26	
S		20		
S	7			

1. 1st December
2. 13th December
3. 17th December
4. 30th December?
5. Give the dates of all the Fridays in December.

6. Find the meaning of the word 'inclusive' before going on to questions **7** and **8**. Use the calendar in Section **A**. How many days inclusive from:
7. 4th April to 10th April
8. 18th April to 30th April?

C

March	July	May
September	August	January
December	November	June
February	October	April

1. Write the months of the year in the correct order and number them 1 to 12. Learn to spell them. Ask your partner to test you.
2. Learn the short way of writing the names of the months shown below.

| Jan. | Feb. | Mar. | Aug. |
| Sept. | Oct. | Nov. | Dec. |

Write the name of the month which is:
3. the 3rd, 4. the 7th, 5. the 11th,
6. the last month of the year.

David was born on 27th May and Joan was born on 27th October in the same year.
7. Which number is given to each of these months?
8. Who is older, David or Joan, and by how many months?

D

How many months inclusive from:
1. Jan. to May 2. April to Aug.
3. June to Nov. 4. Feb. to Oct?

| Wednesday 15th November |

The name and date of a day are given in the box.

In the same way, write the name and date of the day which follows:
5. Sunday 25th April
6. Saturday 29th May
7. Tuesday 10th June.

Give the name and the date of the day which comes before:
8. Friday 30th June
9. Thursday 13th July
10. Monday 24th August
11. Wednesday 1st November.

The calendar

A You will need a calendar or a diary.

> _____ days hath September, April,
> June and November.
> All the rest have _____ days
> excepting February alone which
> has _____ days clear but _____ days
> every leap year.

1 Write this rhyme of the months,
  filling in the blank spaces.
  Learn the rhyme.
  Ask your partner to test you.

  How many days are there in
2 August 3 March 4 June?
5 Copy and complete the table.

	name of the month	number of days
the 10th month		
the 11th month		
the 12th month		

6 How many days are there altogether in the
  last three months of the year?
7 Which of these are leap years?
  1984   1987   1990   1996

  How many days are there in the first
  three months of:
8 a leap year
9 a year, which is not a leap year?

B These special days are called
Public Holidays.

> **New Year's Day Good Friday**
> **Easter Monday Spring Holiday**
> **May Day August Bank Holiday**
> **Christmas Day Boxing Day**

1 Make a list of the Public Holidays and
  find from your calendar or diary the dates
  on which each falls this year.
2 Which of the Public Holidays have the
  same date every year?

C The seasons of the year

> **spring winter summer autumn**

1 Starting with **spring**, write the seasons
  in the correct order.
2 On which day is Christmas Day this year?
3 In which season does Christmas fall?
  Which season do you connect with:
4 Easter   5 holidays at the seaside
6 leaves falling from the trees?

D Andrew was born on 4th July 1974.
  This is written in a short form using
  figures only as 4.7.74.

1 Write your own birthday and that of your
  partner in figures. Check each other's
  answers.
  Here are the birthdays of four children.

name	date of birth		
	day	month	year
Joan Brown	15	5	73
Alan Smith	26	10	73
Susan Jones	17	6	74
Peter Black	22	12	70

2 Name the a oldest b youngest child.
3 By how many months is Alan older or
  younger than Joan?
4 By how many months is Susan older
  or younger than Alan?
5 How old was Joan on 15th May 1978?
6 In which year will Alan be 21 years old?
7 Peter will leave school when he is 16.
  During which year will he leave?
8 Susan will go to Canada three months after
  her 15th birthday. Find the date she goes.
9 Take each birthday in turn and find
  how many complete months there are to
  the end of the year.
10 How old in years and months will each
  child be on 31st Dec. 1990?

Measuring length

A From ancient times, measurements have been made by using parts of the body.

The picture shows a boy measuring length by **pacing**. You can do this in your class-room.

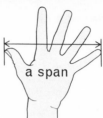

a pace

1 Stand with your heels against a wall. Walk forward counting the number of paces across the room to find its length and its width.

2 Write and complete:
The class-room is ☐ paces long.
The class-room is ☐ paces wide.

3 Draw the table below.

Find the measurements in paces and write them in your table. You can make other measurements if you wish.

		your paces	teacher's paces
class-room	length		
	width		
corridor	length		
hall	length		
	width		
playground greatest length greatest width			

4 How many paces does your teacher take to measure these distances? Write them in the table.

5 Compare your measurements with those of other children and those of your teacher. Some will be different from your own. Why is this so?

B Shorter distances may be measured in **foot lengths**.

a foot length

With a partner, measure the width of the corridor, the doorway and other small distances. Are your measurements the same as your partner's? If not, give a reason.

C

a span

Smaller lengths may be measured using **spans**.

Stretch your fingers as wide as possible.
A span is the distance between the thumb and little finger.

1 Your teacher can probably span the width of a page of this book. Can you?

2 Measure in spans:
the length of your desk
the width of your desk
the height of your desk.

3 Why would you not measure the length and width of the class-room in spans?

4 Draw a table like the one below.

object	measurement in spans
blackboard	
picture	
teacher's desk	

Measure suitable things in spans and record your measurements in the table.

D This body measurement is called a **cubit**.

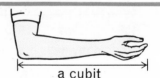

a cubit

1 Compare your body measurement of a cubit with your partner's and your teacher's.
What do you find?

2 More names of measures taken from parts of the body are

a **digit**   a **hand**   a **fathom**.

Find out all you can about each body measure.

Remember
Body measures vary according to the size of the person, so it has been necessary to bring into use a **standard measure** or unit which is always the same.

Measuring length   metre (m)

A

> The measure for length is fixed.
> It is a standard unit called
> a **metre (m)**.

1 Get a metre ruler. Place it on the floor.
   Mark distances of 1 metre, 2 metres,
   3 metres.

2 Is the length of your pace longer or
   shorter than 1 metre?

3 How many of your paces are the
   same as 3 metres?

   Place the metre ruler against the wall.
   Mark a height of 1 metre.

4 Is your height greater or less than 1 metre?

5 Is your height greater or less than
   2 metres?

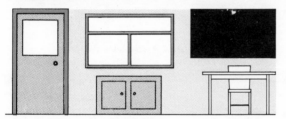

6 Look around you and choose four things
   which you think measure 1 metre in length
   or height.

7 Measure them and find which are
   longer than 1 metre, shorter than 1 metre,
   or exactly 1 metre.
   Draw a table and make a record of
   what you find, as in the table below.

object	longer than 1 m	shorter than 1 m	exactly 1 m
doorway width		✓	

B

1 Get some string and cut a piece
   exactly one metre in length.

2 By folding, find half of the length of the
   piece of string.

3 Using the half-metre length, measure a
   half metre on your metre ruler. Mark your
   ruler plainly to show a half metre.

C   Measuring to the nearest metre

1 Measure in metres the length and width
   of your class-room.

   Write and complete:
   The length of the class-room is ☐ metres.
   The width of the class-room is ☐ metres.

2 There is likely to be a short length at
   the end which has not been measured.
   This short length can be measured
   to the nearest metre.

3 Using your metre ruler, find if the short
   length you have not measured is
   less than half a metre or
   more than half a metre.

4 If the short length is
   less than half a metre – forget it;
   half a metre or more – count on to
   the next metre.

5 Write and complete:
   The length of the class-room to the
   nearest metre is ☐ m.
   The width of the class-room to the
   nearest metre is ☐ m.

D   Estimating and measuring to the nearest metre.

1 Draw this table.

	estimate m	measure to nearest m	c, l or s
corridor length			

2 Estimate in metres the length of a school
   corridor. Write your estimate in the table.

3 Now measure this distance to the
   nearest metre.

4 Write in the table whether your estimate
   was correct (**c**), too long (**l**) or too short (**s**).

5 Estimate and then measure to the nearest
   metre other distances.
   Write them in your table.

6 Compare each of the measurements
   to the nearest metre with those of other
   children and those of your teacher.
   They should be the same. Why is this so?

Measuring length   centimetres (cm)

A To measure a shorter length than one metre, a smaller measure than one metre is required. The metre is divided into 100 equal parts, each of which is called a **centimetre**.

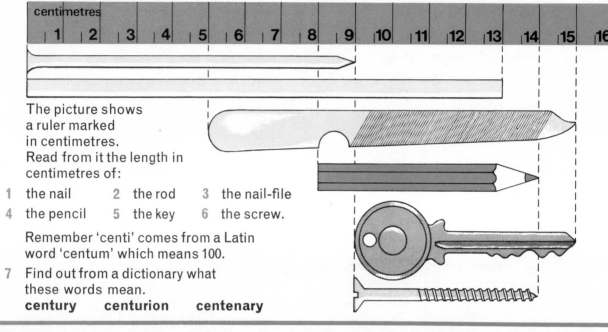

The picture shows a ruler marked in centimetres.
Read from it the length in centimetres of:

1 the nail   2 the rod   3 the nail-file
4 the pencil 5 the key   6 the screw.

Remember 'centi' comes from a Latin word 'centum' which means 100.

7 Find out from a dictionary what these words mean.
century   centurion   centenary

B Get a ruler marked in centimetres.
Measure each of these lines.

C **Drawing lines of given length in centimetres**

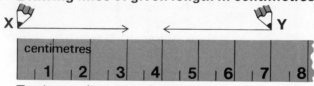

To draw a line 7 cm long:
1 hold the ruler with outstretched fingers
2 use a sharp pencil and draw clear lines
3 put the pencil point exactly on the point **X**, and draw inwards for part of the line
4 put the pencil point exactly on the 7 cm mark **Y**, draw inwards to complete the line.
Write the measurements as shown.

5 Draw lines of these lengths and write in the measurements.
8 cm   13 cm   19 cm   21 cm

6 Using a ruler marked in half centimetres, draw lines of these lengths.
Write in the measurements.
$4\frac{1}{2}$ cm $7\frac{1}{2}$ cm $16\frac{1}{2}$ cm $12\frac{1}{2}$ cm

7 Which of these measurements are less than a half metre?
29 cm   53 cm   91 cm   37 cm

Measuring length

A Measuring to the nearest centimetre

a It is longer
b
c

Look at the line marked **a**. It is longer
than 10 cm but shorter than 11 cm.

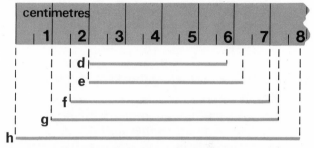

1 Write the length of line **a** to the nearest cm.

2 Write the length of line **b** to the nearest cm.

3 Write the exact length of line **c** and then
write its length to the nearest cm.

Write to the nearest cm the length of:

4 line **d**   5 line **e**

6 line **f**   7 line **g**   8 line **h**.

B

Measure and write the length to the
nearest cm of each of these lines.

1
2
3
4
5
6

C

Draw this table.

article	estimate cm	measurement to nearest cm	c, l or s
pencil			

Estimate in cm the length of a pencil.
Now measure it to the nearest cm.

Was your estimate correct? Was it too long or
too short? If so, by how much?

1 Write in the table what you find.

2 Estimate and then measure to the nearest cm the
lengths and widths of at least six other things
which are less than one metre.

Write in the table whether each estimate was
correct (**c**), too long (**l**) or too short (**s**).

3 Mark and measure 3 spans.
Find to the nearest cm the length
of one span.

4 Mark and measure 3 foot lengths.
Find to the nearest cm the length
of one foot length.

5 Mark and measure two paces.
Find to the nearest cm the
length of one pace.

6 Use the approximate
measurements of your span,
foot length and pace to estimate
suitable lengths and widths.

Length estimating and measuring

A

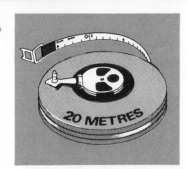

The picture shows a 20-metre tape which is used for measuring longer distances, e.g.
in the playground and on the playing-field.

Metre tapes may be 10 metres, 20 metres or 50 metres in length.

1 Get a 10 metre, 20 metre or 50 metre tape.

Work with a partner. Look at the measurements and find which units are shown.

2 Learn how to wind and unwind the tape.

B Go, with a partner, to the playground or playing-field.

1 Take the metre tape, a metre stick, chalk or pegs and paper and a pencil.

2 Mark a starting line and use the tape to measure a distance of 15 metres.

3 Use the metre stick to check the distance.

4 From the starting line, measure three separate distances of:
17 metres   24 metres   32 metres.

5 Check the distances with the metre stick.

6 Why is it easier to measure these distances using the tape instead of the metre stick?

C

1 Mark a distance of 10 metres.

2 Measure this distance in paces.

3 Draw and complete this chart.

distance	number of paces
10 metres	
20 metres	
30 metres	

4 By pacing, estimate distances of:
15 metres   25 metres   35 metres.

5 Check your estimates by measuring with the tape.

6 On Sports Day, running tracks measuring
a 60 m   b 80 m   c 100 m
are marked out.
How many 20 m lengths are required to measure each distance?

D

UPTON $4\frac{1}{2}$ km
DOWBY 12 km   **RIPTON $17\frac{1}{2}$ km**

Distances between villages and towns are measured in kilometres (km).

1 kilometre = 1000 metres

Write the distances from the signpost to:
1 Upton   2 Dowby   3 Ripton.
Find the distance in km:
4 from Upton to Dowby
5 from Upton to Ripton
6 from Dowby to Ripton.

E The drawing shows a road sign giving the distances to three towns.

A46
LINCOLN   19 km
NEWARK   45 km
LEICESTER   101 km

Find these distances:
1 from Lincoln to Newark
2 from Newark to Leicester
3 from Leicester to Lincoln.
4 Find the meaning of A in A46.
Name in this way some main roads near your school.
5 Find the meaning of M in M1.

Tables of fours and eights

A

1 Begin at 0 and count on in **fours**. 0 4 8 — — — — — — — 40
2 Begin at 40 and count back in **fours**. 40 36 32 — — — — — — — 0
3 Do this many times. Ask your partner to test you.

B

Look at the diagrams and
complete the following.

1 4+4+4=☐
2 3+3+3+3=☐
3 3×4=☐
4 4×3=☐
5 12÷4=☐
6 12÷3=☐
7 12=☐×3
8 12=☐×4
9 12÷☐=4
10 12÷☐=3

11 3 multiplied by 4=☐
12 12 divided by 4=☐
13 4 times 3=☐
14 3(4)=☐
15 How many fours in 12?
16 3)‾12

17 Write and complete four facts about 24.

6×4=☐   24÷4=☐
4×6=☐   24÷6=☐

18 Write and complete four facts about 28.

28

7×4=☐   28÷4=☐
4×7=☐   28÷7=☐

19 In the same way, write four facts about
each of these numbers.

32   36

20 Write the table of **fours**. Check and learn it.
Ask your partner to test you.

C

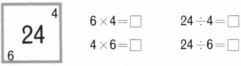

| multiples of 4 | 4 | 8 | 12 | 16 | — | — | — | — | — | 40 |
| multiples of 8 | 8 | 16 | 24 | — | — | — | — | — | — | 80 |

1 Copy and complete the **multiples of 4** shown above.
Then find from them the **multiples of 8** and write them underneath.
2 Count on in **eights** from 0 to 80. Count back in **eights** from 80 to 0.
Do this many times. Ask your partner to test you.

Write four facts about
each of these numbers.

3 24   **4** 48   **5** 56   **6** 72

7 Write the table of **eights**. Check and learn it. Ask your partner to test you.

D

Write the answers only.

1 3×4   **5** 5×4   **9** 4×9   **13** 4×7   **17** 8×4   **21** 0×8
2 24÷4   **6** 24÷8   **10** 16÷4   **14** 28÷4   **18** 8÷8   **22** 24÷
3 2×8   **7** 6×8   **11** 8×8   **15** 9×8   **19** 8×7   **23** 4×8
4 64÷8   **8** 32÷4   **12** 36÷9   **16** 56÷8   **20** 40÷5   **24** 72÷8

Fractions halves, quarters and eighths

A

1 Fold a strip of paper, first into two parts and then again to make four equal parts.

2 What is each part called?

3 Write and complete: $1 = \frac{\square}{2} = \frac{\square}{4}$.

4 Fold another strip of paper into four equal parts and then into eight equal parts. Each part is called **one eighth** $\frac{1}{8}$.

5 Into how many equal parts has the strip below been divided?

6 What fraction of the whole strip is one part?

What fraction of the whole strip is

7 the shaded part

8 the unshaded part?

Each shape below stands for a whole one or unit.

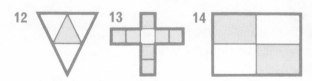

What fraction of each shape is
a shaded   b not shaded?

15 Draw the shapes below on squared paper.

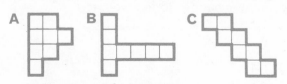

Shade half of shape **A**.
Shade a quarter of shape **B**.
Shade three eighths of shape **C**.

B

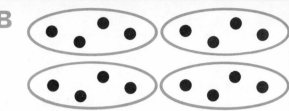

1 Put out 16 counters into 4 sets of equal number.

2 How many are there in each set?

3 Write and complete:
$\frac{1}{4}$ of 16 = $\square$ $\frac{3}{4}$ of 16 = $\square$.

Now divide the counters into 8 equal sets.

4 How many are there in each set?

5 Write and complete:
$\frac{1}{8}$ of 16 = $\square$ $\frac{5}{8}$ of 16 = $\square$.

Find:

6 $\frac{1}{8}$ of 80   7 $\frac{3}{8}$ of 80

8 $\frac{1}{8}$ of 24   9 $\frac{5}{8}$ of 24.

C

Draw a line 12 cm long.
Find the middle point of the line.

1 How long is each part?

2 How long is one quarter of the line?

3 How long is one eighth of the line?

4 Write and complete:
$\frac{1}{8}$ of 12 cm = $\square$ cm $\frac{3}{8}$ of 12 cm = $\square$ cm.

Find the value of:

5 $\frac{1}{2}$ of 20p   6 $\frac{1}{4}$ of 20p   7 $\frac{3}{4}$ of 20p

8 $\frac{1}{4}$ of 40 cm   9 $\frac{1}{8}$ of 40 cm   10 $\frac{3}{8}$ of 40 cm

11 $\frac{1}{4}$ of 32 m   12 $\frac{1}{8}$ of 32 m   13 $\frac{5}{8}$ of 32 m

14 $\frac{1}{4}$ of 24 km   15 $\frac{1}{8}$ of 24 km   16 $\frac{7}{8}$ of 24 km.

D

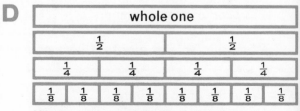

Write and complete the following using the signs >, < or = in place of ●

1 $\frac{1}{4}$ ● $\frac{3}{8}$ 2 $\frac{4}{8}$ ● $\frac{1}{2}$ 3 $\frac{3}{4}$ ● $\frac{5}{8}$

4 $\frac{1}{2}$ ● $\frac{3}{4}$ 5 1 ● $\frac{7}{8}$ 6 $\frac{6}{8}$ ● $\frac{3}{4}$

Tables of twos, fours, eights; fives and tens

Write the answers only.

A
1. 10×2
2. $35 \div 5$
3. 6×4
4. $40 \div 10$
5. 7×8
6. $28 \div 4$
7. 3×5
8. $16 \div 2$
9. 0×4
10. $64 \div 8$
11. 9×2
12. $40 \div 5$

B
1. $10 \div 10$
2. 7×5
3. $10 \div 5$
4. 8×10
5. $18 \div 2$
6. 3×4
7. $16 \div 4$
8. 0×8
9. $90 \div 10$
10. 1×2
11. $25 \div 5$
12. 4×8

C
1. 1×10
2. $0 \div 8$
3. 3×8
4. $4 \div 2$
5. 9×4
6. $30 \div 10$
7. 5×5
8. $32 \div 8$
9. 7×2
10. $30 \div 5$
11. 7×4
12. $12 \div 2$

D
1. $0 \div 5$
2. 10×10
3. $20 \div 2$
4. 5×8
5. $100 \div 10$
6. 2×4
7. $45 \div 5$
8. 2×2
9. $36 \div 4$
10. 3×10
11. $72 \div 8$
12. 8×8

E
1. 0×10
2. $4 \div 4$
3. 9×8
4. $0 \div 4$
5. 6×2
6. $48 \div 8$
7. 8×2
8. $20 \div 4$
9. 4×10
10. $14 \div 2$
11. 8×4
12. $16 \div 8$

F
1. $\frac{1}{2}$ of 10
2. $\frac{1}{5}$ of 20
3. $\frac{1}{8}$ of 56
4. $\frac{1}{10}$ of 60
5. $\frac{1}{4}$ of 32
6. $\frac{1}{4}$ of 24
7. $\frac{1}{8}$ of 40
8. $\frac{1}{5}$ of 15
9. $\frac{1}{8}$ of 8
10. $\frac{1}{10}$ of 80
11. $\frac{1}{10}$ of 50
12. $\frac{1}{2}$ of 8
13. $\frac{1}{4}$ of 12
14. $\frac{1}{4}$ of 40
15. $\frac{1}{8}$ of 24

G
1. $(9 \times 5) + 4$
2. $(6 \times 8) + 7$
3. $38 - (7 \times 5)$
4. $30 - (3 \times 8)$
5. $(4 \times 5) + 4$
6. $(8 \times 5) + 4$
7. $75 - (9 \times 8)$
8. $27 - (6 \times 4)$
9. $(4 \times 4) + 3$
10. $(2 \times 8) + 7$
11. $49 - (9 \times 5)$
12. $60 - (7 \times 8)$
13. $(7 \times 4) + 3$
14. $(8 \times 8) + 7$
15. $11 - (5 \times 2)$
16. $39 - (9 \times 4)$
17. $(7 \times 0) + 6$
18. $(6 \times 5) + 4$
19. $29 - (5 \times 5)$
20. $19 - (9 \times 2)$

H
1. How many pence are equal to 3 TENS?
2. 8 cartons each hold 5 bottles. How many bottles are there altogether?
3. Jane spent 32p on sugar bars. Each bar cost 8p. How many bars did she buy?
4. 28 children went to the zoo. 4 children rode in each car. How many cars were there?
5. Father works for 7 hours each day. How many hours does he work in 5 days?
6. Each table seats 8 children. How many children can sit at 7 tables?
7. Tim attends school for 5 days each week. How many days does he attend in 10 weeks?
8. How many sets of 5 are there in 40?
9. How many rows of 8 chairs can be made from 56 chairs?
10. John has 60 stamps. He sticks 10 stamps on each page. How many pages does he use?
11. There are 8 girls in each of 8 teams. How many girls are there altogether?
12. How much will 7 oranges cost at 4p each?

Find the value of each letter.

$8 \times a = 48$ $b \div 3 = 8$ $c \times 5 = 25$ $12 \div d = 4$ $5 \times e = 5$ $8 \div f = 1$

$g \times 10 = 100$ $h \div 2 = 8$ $i \times 4 = 32$ $j \times 9 = 72$ $6 \times k = 24$ $18 \div m = 9$

Making sure

A

1 Write the set of even numbers between 41 and 51.

2 Write the set of odd numbers between 30 and 40.

3 Which of the following numbers will divide by 2 without a remainder?
51 70 36 87 42

4 Which of the following numbers will divide by 10 without a remainder?
70 40 35 62 80

Find the total of each row.

5 $4+6+7+3+8+2+5+5$

6 $7+8+5+9+1+2+8$

Find the total of each row.

7 2 TWENTIES+3 FIVES+4 TWOS

8 1 FIFTY+1 TWENTY+6 TWOS

9 5 FIVES + 4 TWOS

Name three coins which make up each of the following amounts.

10 57p   11 23p   12 61p

13 16p   14 12p   15 90p

B

From this calendar page find which day is:

1 11th June

2 21st June

3 30th June.

June					
M	2	9	16	23	30
T	3	10	17	24	
W	4	11	18	25	
Th	5	12	19	26	
F	6	13	20	27	
S	7	14	21	28	
S	1	8	15	22	29

What is the date of :

4 the 2nd Monday in June

5 the 4th Saturday in June

6 the first Tuesday in July

7 the last Saturday in May?

8 Write the dates of all the Saturdays in June.

Write in full the names of these months:

9 the 3rd month   10 the 11th month

11 the 8th month   12 the 2nd month

13 the 5th month   14 the 9th month.

15 Write in full and in order all the days of the week.

C

1 Estimate in cm the length of each of these lines.

u _____

v _____

w _____

x _____

y _____

z _____

2 Measure each of the lines and find any error.

3 Estimate which of the following is more than one metre.
the height of your teacher   the height of the door   the length of your arm
the width of your desk   the length of your pace   your own height

How many cm are there in   4 2 m   5 5 m   6 3 m 50 cm   7 1 m 10 cm?

D

Write and complete the following using the sign >,< or = in place of ●.

1 $\frac{1}{5}$ ● $\frac{1}{10}$ 2 $\frac{1}{4}$ ● $\frac{1}{8}$ 3 $\frac{1}{8}$ ● $\frac{1}{2}$

4 $\frac{5}{10}$ ● $\frac{1}{2}$ 5 $\frac{2}{5}$ ● $\frac{7}{10}$ 6 $\frac{1}{2}$ ● $\frac{3}{8}$

7 $\frac{1}{5}$ ● $\frac{1}{8}$ 8 $\frac{10}{10}$ ● 1   9 $\frac{1}{5}$ ● $\frac{1}{2}$

10 How many fifths in a whole one?

11 How many eighths in a whole one?

How much greater is:

12 $\frac{1}{4}$ of 40p than $\frac{1}{5}$ of 40p

13 $\frac{1}{5}$ of 30 cm than $\frac{1}{10}$ of 30 cm

14 $\frac{1}{2}$ of 24 cm than $\frac{1}{8}$ of 24 cm?

Find:

15 $\frac{1}{10}$ of 60p   16 $\frac{3}{10}$ of 60p   17 $\frac{7}{10}$ of 60p

18 $\frac{1}{5}$ of 10 m   19 $\frac{2}{5}$ of 10 m   20 $\frac{3}{5}$ of 10 m.

Hundreds, tens and units

A Write the number shown on each abacus picture.

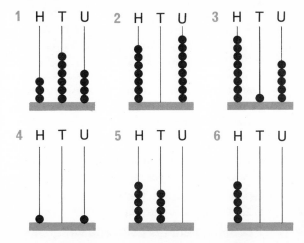

Draw abacus pictures to show these numbers.

7 569   8 303   9 990   10 800

B Read and write these numbers.

1 257 = ☐ hundreds ☐ tens ☐ units
2 530 = ☐ hundreds ☐ tens ☐ units
3 309 = ☐ hundreds ☐ tens ☐ units
4 466 = ☐ hundreds ☐ tens ☐ units
5 700 = ☐ hundreds ☐ tens ☐ units
6 999 = ☐ hundreds ☐ tens ☐ units

Draw this table and write in it these numbers in figures.

H	T	U

7 nine hundred
8 four hundred and four
9 five hundred and sixty-two
10 three hundred and thirty
11 nine hundred and nine
12 one hundred and eleven

Rearrange the figures 3, 8 and 5 to make
13 the largest possible number
14 the smallest possible number.

C

1 Look carefully at the diagram.

H	T	U
4	9	7

Then write and complete:

497 = ☐ hundreds ☐ tens ☐ units
497 = ☐ hundreds ☐ units
497 = ☐ tens ☐ units.

Write and complete:
2 153 = ☐ hundred ☐ units
3 806 = ☐ hundreds ☐ units
4 530 = ☐ hundreds ☐ units
5 307 = ☐ tens ☐ units
6 600 = ☐ tens ☐ units
7 962 = ☐ tens ☐ units.

8 Write and complete:
one thousand
= ☐ hundreds = ☐ tens = ☐ units.

D Which is the next number after:
1 299   2 709   3 491
4 269   5 500   6 999?

Which number comes next before:
7 400   8 610   9 100
10 560   11 801   12 950?

Count and write in hundreds from:
13 372 to 872   14 599 to 999
15 904 to 404   16 1000 to 500.

Count and write in tens from:
17 190 to 310   18 500 to 380
19 324 to 404   20 748 to 678.

What is the value of each figure underlined?
21 38<u>4</u>   22 <u>7</u>06   23 5<u>9</u>0

What is the value of the two figures underlined?
24 5<u>84</u>   25 <u>8</u>0<u>2</u>   26 <u>6</u>0<u>5</u>

Money £s and pence

A

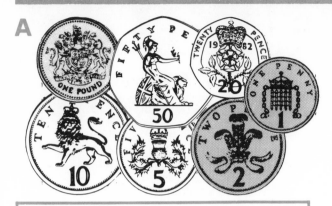

£1·00 = 100 pence

How many £1 coins have the same value as:

1 200p   2 300p   3 500p   4 700p?

How many pence have the same value as:

5 £4   6 £6   7 £9?

The table below shows the number of coins of each kind which have been saved by four children.

name	50	20	10	5	2	1
Peter	2		1	1	2	
Ann		3	4	2		
Tony	1	1	5		5	
Pat	3		3			5

B

Write and complete:

1 £2·76 = £☐ and ☐ pence

2 £3·40 = £☐ and ☐ pence

3 £6·08 = £☐ and ☐ pence

4 £4·05 = £☐ and ☐ pence.

Write the following as £s only.

5 £4 and 30 pence   8 £3 and 60 pence

6 £5 and 9 pence   9 £2 and 2 pence

7 £1 and 7 pence   10 £3 and 15 pence

Find the total of each of the following. Write the answers as £s.

11 3 FIFTIES a TWENTY and a TEN

12 2 FIFTIES and 4 TWOS

13 9 TENS and 4 FIVES

14 1 FIFTY and 3 TWENTIES

8 Find in pence the total savings of Peter. Check the answer.

9 He changes 100p for which he receives a £1 coin. How many pence are left? Peter now has a £1 coin and 19 pence which is written **£1·19.**

> When writing sums of money as £s, the dot or pennies point separates the £s from the pence.

10 Find in pence the total savings of Ann. Check the answer.

11 She changes 100p for which she receives a £1 coin. How many pence are left?

12 Put in the pennies point and write Ann's total savings as £s.

13 Find in pence the total savings of Tony.

14 Put in the pennies point and write his total as £s.

15 Find in pence the total savings of Pat.

16 Write her total as £s.

Peter has saved £1·19 which is read as **one pound and nineteen pence** or **one pound nineteen.**

17 Read in this way to a partner the total savings of Ann, Tony and Pat.

C

Sums of money less than £1·00 can be written in two ways, e.g. £0·18 or 18p   £0·04 or 4p.

> **Remember**
> 0 should always be placed in the £s column when there are no pounds.

Write the following as pence.

1 £0·25   2 £0·07   3 £0·90

4 £0·42   5 £0·06   6 £0·10

Write the following as £s.

7 64p   8 9p   9 38p

10 6p   11 20p   12 40p

Which coin has the same value as:

13 £0·50   14 £0·05   15 £0·10

16 £0·01   17 £0·02   18 £0·20?

Money £s and pence

A

doll £1·78

plastic car £0·87

puppet £0·45

football £4·84

truck £3·97

1 Read the price of each toy to a partner.

2 Which toys cost less than £1?
Write each price as pence only.

Which of the toys is

3 the cheapest   4 the most expensive?

5 a Which single coin can be given to pay
for the puppet?

b How much change will be given?

6 Tom bought a plastic car with a £1 coin.
How much change did he get?

7 Helen saved 2 FIFTIES. How much more
does she need to buy the doll?

How many TENS and pence are needed to

8 buy a plastic car   9 buy a puppet?

10 Draw a table like the one below and write
in the list of toys.

11 Then write the number of £1 coins, TENS
and pence required to pay for each.
The first is done for you.

toy	price	£1 coins	TENS 10p	pence 1p
doll	£1·78	1	7	8
plastic car				
puppet				
football				
truck				

B

Look at the bill below.
It shows the cost of three toys.

```
              £
truck      3·97
doll       1·78
car       +0·87
   total     ·
```

1 Copy the bill, making sure that the
figures and the pennies points are
in the correct columns.

2 Find the total cost of the toys.

Make out a bill and find the total cost of:

3 a football, a puppet and a doll;

4 a truck, a football and a plastic car.

Julie had saved £2·80.
She bought the doll.

```
                £
money saved   2·80
cost of doll −1·78
  money left    ·
```

5 Copy the example, making sure that the
figures and the pennies points
are in the correct columns.

6 Find how much money Julie had left.

Set down the following as in the example,
and find the difference between the price of:

7 the football and the truck;

8 the doll and the plastic car.

C Copy and work the following.
Make sure that the figures and the pennies points are in the correct columns.

```
1  puppet    0·45      2  football   4·84      3  money saved  5·00      4  money saved  5·00
   doll     +1·78         truck     +3·97         cost of doll −1·78         cost of truck −3·97
   total    _____          total    _____          money left  _____          money left  _____
```

Puzzle corner

A

Mr Brown had these coins in his pocket.
He paid a bill for 29p using 6 of the coins.

1 Which coins did he use to pay the bill?

2 How much money had he left?

Copy and complete the following examples.

3
```
  2 9
  3 □
+ □ 8
─────
  8 4
```

4
```
  5 4
- □ □
─────
  2 6
```

5
```
  □ □
-  4 9
─────
  3 1
```

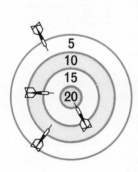

6 Jane has thrown 4 darts. How many has she scored?

7 She scored 15 more with her fifth dart. What was her total score?

8 John's total score with 5 darts was 60. His first 3 darts scored 25. Write the scores of his 4th and 5th darts.

9 Write two different ways in which 45 can be scored with 3 darts.

10 If 2 is added to 5 times a number the answer is 17. What is the number?

11 When a certain fraction is multiplied by 10 the answer is 5. What is the fraction?

B

Tim can choose any two of these fruits, an apple, a banana, a pear, an orange.

1 Write the different choices he can make.

2 How many choices are there altogether?

3 The product of two numbers is 36. Their sum is 13. Find the numbers.

In a certain code, letters stand for numbers.

D stands for 4, E for 3, F for 5 and G for 2, that is

$D=4$, $E=3$, $F=5$, $G=2$.

Write the letter in place of the ▲.

4 $E+G=▲$

5 $D-▲=G$

6 $(E+F)\div G=▲$

7 $F-▲=G$

Mr Brown gave these coins to his three children to spend.

John spent $\frac{2}{5}$ of the money,
Jane spent $\frac{1}{2}$ of the money and
Tim spent the remainder.

8 How much did each spend?

Write the number which comes next in each of the following series.

9 6, 10, 14, 18, □

10 20, 16, 12, 8, □

11 1, 2, 4, 7, 11, 16, □

12 3, 5, 4, 6, 5, 7, 6, □

13 20, 18, 15, 11, 6, □

Write and complete the following.

14 $\frac{6}{4}=1\frac{□}{4}=1\frac{1}{□}$

15 $\frac{15}{10}=1\frac{□}{10}=1\frac{1}{□}$

Number and money   addition practice

First work Section **A**.   Mark the answers and correct any mistakes.
Then work Section **B**.   Do the same with each section.
Write the answers only.

First add upwards and then check by adding downwards.

A
1 143	2 43	3 20	4 13	5 401
32	234	264	303	134
+120	+ 2	+105	+282	+202

B
1 208	2 108	3 249	4 17	5 269
14	330	15	318	17
+ 65	+ 57	+132	+256	+407

C
1 32	2 171	3 303	4 580	5 175
86	64	162	193	491
+ 70	+234	+ 94	+ 56	+262

D
1 44	2 66	3 98	4 80	5 79
65	58	34	98	87
+ 79	+ 23	+ 47	+ 53	+ 66

6 196	7 287	8 276	9 84	10 597
108	70	359	469	8
+155	+323	+105	+377	+259

E When the answer is **100p or more** you must **always** write it as **£s using a £ sign and a pennies point.**

1 38p	2 42p	3 26p	4 78p	5 89p
53p	78p	9p	15p	27p
+27p	+15p	+84p	+67p	+56p

F Set down the following and find the totals.
Make sure that the **figures** and the **pennies points** are written in the correct columns.

£	£	£	£	£
1 0·82	2 0·38	3 0·46	4 2·06	5 3·54
0·57	0·75	1·09	0·67	0·43
+0·06	+0·24	+0·82	+0·76	+1·05

£	£	£	£	£
6 1·96	7 2·06	8 5·90	9 0·68	10 2·98
2·38	1·37	1·06	0·77	0·50
+0·43	+0·49	+2·39	+0·85	+2·36

Number and money   subtraction practice

First work Section **A.**   Mark the answers and correct any mistakes.
Then work Section **B.**   Do the same with each section.
Write the answers only.

Check each answer by adding it to the line above.

A

1 285	2 552	3 599	4 696	5 876
−151	−141	−324	− 62	− 53

B

1 195	2 256	3 677	4 943	5 473
− 45	−126	−377	− 43	−271

C

1 284	2 178	3 389	4 566	5 746
− 30	−130	−240	−204	−403

D

1 60	2 80	3 340	4 670	5 507
− 29	− 53	− 37	− 42	− 94

6 806	7 700	8 600	9 710	10 550
−563	−371	−255	−602	−301

E

1 83	2 68	3 66	4 254	5 642
− 58	− 9	− 57	−129	−438

6 317	7 405	8 725	9 602	10 704
−209	−345	−397	−466	−108

F   Set down the following and find the answers.
Make sure that the **figures** and the **pennies points** are written in the correct columns.

1 £	2 £	3 £	4 £	5 £
0·74	1·83	3·57	2·00	3·86
−0·59	−0·74	−2·48	−1·36	−2·97

Write the answers only to the following.

6 £	7 £	8 £	9 £	10 £
1·66	3·07	0·92	1·30	4·00
−1·45	−2·80	−0·58	−0·88	−2·65

Number and money addition and subtraction

A Write the answers only.
First add from left to right, then check by adding from right to left.

1 203 + 79 + 156

2 48 + 317 + 190 + 85

3 9 + 115 + 80 + 36

Copy and complete:

```
4      2 0 3          5      8 9          6      □ 5
        □ □                  7 □                1 6 0
     + 1 4 2              +  □ 2              +  4 □
       ───────              ───────            ───────
       4 1 0                2 1 8              2 8 1
```

```
7      4 3 5          8    □ □ □          9    □ 4 6
      - □ □ □              -  8 6              - 1 □ 6
       ───────              ───────            ───────
         4 9                  7 4              3 8 0
```

Write the following sums of money in columns. Then find the totals.

10 68p + 35p + £1·07

11 42p + 19p + £1·84 + 8p

12 £1·15 + £3·09 + £0·70

Find the difference between:

13 207 and 971

14 537 and 469

15 £1·36 and 89p

16 62p and £2·50.

17 Increase £2·75 by 27p.

18 Decrease £2·04 by 18p.

19 How much greater is 176 than 90?

20 How much less than 120 is 63?

21 What must be added to 59 to make 111?

B

School

176 paces

Post Office   **Home**

230 paces

1 Peter paced the distance from school to home and drew this map.
The total distance was 475 paces.
Find the distance from the Post Office to the crossroads.

2 157 children in a school could swim.
Another 68 children learned to swim.
How many children could then swim?

3 Find the total number of children at the school.

BRANT SCHOOL
Number on roll

Boys 163	Girls 159

4 If 29 children are absent, how many are present?

5 If each child present gave 1p to the School Fund, find the total amount collected.

The chart below shows the number of children who were present on Monday, Tuesday and Wednesday at Axon School.

Class	Mon.	Tues.	Wed.	total
1	34	28	33	
2	31	30	29	
3	29	27	25	
4	27	26	28	
total				

Find:

6 the daily totals of children who attended

7 the total attendance for the three days

8 the total attendance for each class

9 the total attendance of the four classes.

If you have worked accurately answers to **7** and **9** should be the same.

10

Class 1	76p
Class 2	48p
Class 3	56p
Class 4	65p

The children collected these amounts for the Blind.
Write the total as £s.

Lines   straight and curved

A

There are six straight lines above. The straight edge of a ruler has been used to draw them. Test each of them with the straight edge of your ruler.

Notice that the lines are drawn in different directions.

1   Measure each line to the nearest cm.

X and Y are two points which are joined together by a straight line and a curved line.

2   Measure in cm the length of the straight line.

3   Use a piece of thin thread to measure the length of the curved line.

4   Which is shorter, the straight line or the curved line?

5   Mark two very small points S and T on your paper.
Draw a straight line and two curved lines between the points (make large curves).

6   Measure to the nearest cm the length of each line.

7   Which is the shortest line?

8   Which is always the shortest distance between two points, a straight line or any curved lines?

B

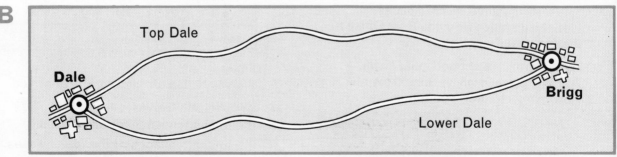

The map shows two towns, Dale and Brigg, joined by two roads.

Measure to the nearest cm the distance between the two towns:

1   by Top Dale   2   by Lower Dale.

3   Each cm on the map stands for 1 km on the road. Find the actual distance in km by each road.

4   Find the actual distance in a straight line from Dale to Brigg.

5   This distance is often described by the saying 'as the crow flies'. Can you see why?

Many centuries ago, the Romans built straight roads for their soldiers.

6   Today, motorways are built as straight as possible. Write a reason for this.

Lines vertical, horizontal and oblique

A Vertical lines

1 Tie a metal nut to a piece of string.

Hold it so that the string hangs in a straight line. The string makes a line which is upright.

Upright straight lines are called **vertical** lines.

The picture shows Peter testing the edge of the door to find if it is vertical.

2 In the same way, use the string and the metal nut to find six things which have vertical lines or edges.

Make a list of them.

3 Draw vertical lines of these lengths.
a $5\frac{1}{2}$ cm   b 9 cm   c $16\frac{1}{2}$ cm

4 Builders use a string and weight, called a plumb-line, to make sure that they are building vertically.
Why is this important?

B Horizontal lines

1 Try this experiment.
Get a glass or bottle half filled with water.
Tip the container in different ways.
Watch the level of the water.
What do you notice?

2 Straight lines which are level are called **horizontal** lines.

3 Find out what the word 'horizon' means.
Builders use a spirit-level.
Find a reason why.

4 Find out how a spirit-level works.
A simple spirit-level can be made by using a bottle containing water and a small air bubble.

5 Make a list of six examples of horizontal lines or edges you can see in the class-room.

6 Draw horizontal lines of these lengths.
a $7\frac{1}{2}$ cm   b 12 cm   c $10\frac{1}{2}$ cm.

C Oblique lines

Some straight lines are **neither** horizontal nor vertical.
They are **sloping** or **slanting** straight lines.
They are also called **oblique** lines.

Which of these straight lines are:

1 vertical   2 horizontal   3 oblique?

4 Draw five oblique lines in different positions.

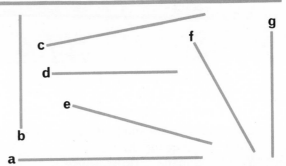

D

Using a pencil and a ruler, copy the drawings below on squared paper.
Then colour the vertical lines black, the horizontal lines red and the oblique lines green.

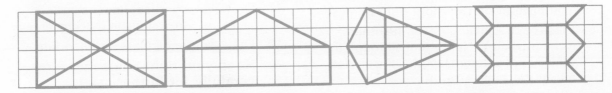

Right angles and perpendicular lines

A Look at the drawing below.
You see that a square corner is made when a vertical line and a horizontal line meet at a point.

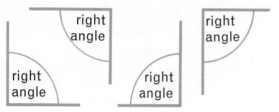

A square corner is called a **right angle**.

1 Draw a horizontal line and an oblique line which meet at a point.
Is a right angle made?

2 What do you find when a vertical line and an oblique line meet at a point?

Count the number of right angles in each drawing.

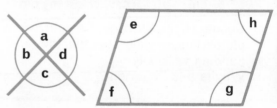

3   4   5

6 On squared paper, draw three right angles using horizontal and vertical lines. In each case make the arms (sides) of different lengths.

Work with a partner and find as many right angles as you can in

7 a window
8 the door   9 the blackboard.

B To draw and test right angles you will need a measure.

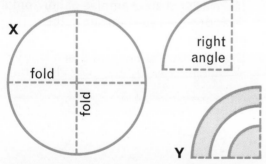

1 On thick paper, draw round the edge of a large, round tin lid.
You have drawn a **circle**.

2 Cut out the circle and fold it twice, as shown in drawing **X**.
You have made a **right angle**.

3 Use other lids to draw two more circles, one larger and the other smaller than the first.

4 Cut out and fold the circles as before.
You have made two more right angles.

5 Place each right angle over the other as in drawing **Y**. Notice that although the arms are of different lengths, the angles are of the same size.

6 Use the measures you have made to find which of these angles are right angles.

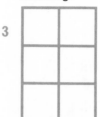

Which of the angles are
7 bigger than a right angle
8 less than a right angle?

> **Remember**
> When a line is at right angles to another line, it is **perpendicular** to it.

9 Draw a horizontal line 8 cm long.
Use your right-angle measure to draw three lines of different lengths which are perpendicular to it.

10 Now draw three perpendiculars on the other side of the line.

11 Draw   a   a vertical line 9 cm long
        b   an oblique line 12 cm long.

12 Draw perpendiculars to each line.

Keep your right-angle measures carefully for further use.

Parallel lines

A

1 Trace or copy on a piece of paper each pair of lines marked **a**, **b**, **c**, **d** and **e**.

2 Look at the pair of lines marked **a**.
   On your drawing, use your ruler and make the pair of lines longer at both ends.

3 What happens at one end?

4 What happens at the other end?

5 Do the same with the pairs of lines marked **b** and **c**.

6 Describe what happens at both ends in each case.

7 The pairs of lines marked **d** and **e** are curved.
   Continue the curves and describe what happens at both ends in each case.

B

The drawing is of a section of rail belonging to Tim's train set.

1 Measure the distance between the lines at the points **a**, **b**, **c** and **d**.

2 What do you discover about the measurements between the lines?

3 In the same way, measure the distance at the points shown between each pair of lines marked **x** and **y** below.

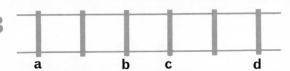

4 What do you discover about the three measurements in each case?

5 Draw, on squared paper, two pairs of lines like **x** and **y**, but make them as long as the paper allows.
   Find, by measuring, that the distance between each pair of lines is always the same.

> **Remember**
> Lines which are the same distance apart throughout their length are called **parallel lines**.

C

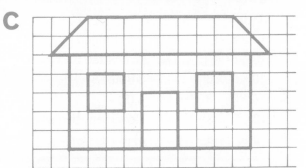

1 Draw the picture on squared paper. Then colour the horizontal parallel lines red and the vertical parallel lines blue.

2 Look around the class-room and see how many parallel lines you can find. Work with a partner checking each other.

3 Draw a horizontal line 8 cm long. Then use your right-angle measure to draw several lines of different lengths which are perpendicular to it.

4 What do you know about the lines you have drawn?

5 Draw a a vertical line 10 cm long
         b an oblique line 6 cm long.
   On these two lines use your right-angle measure to draw several parallel lines of different lengths.

6 Why is each line you have drawn a perpendicular?

Tables of threes and sixes

A

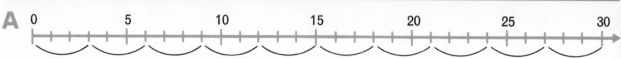

1 Begin at 0 and count on in **threes**. 0 3 6 — — — — — — — 30
2 Begin at 30 and count back in **threes**. 30 27 24 — — — — — — — 0
3 Do this many times. Ask your partner to test you.

B

Look at the diagrams
and complete the following.

1 3+3+3+3+3+3=☐
2 6+6+6=☐
3 6×3=☐
4 3×6=☐
5 18÷3=☐   11 6 multiplied by 3=☐
6 18÷6=☐   12 18 divided by 3=☐
7 18=☐×6   13 3 times 6=☐
8 18=☐×3   14 6 (3)=☐
9 18÷☐=3   15 How many threes in 18?
10 18÷☐=6   16 6)18

17 Write and complete these facts about 21.

21   3
7

7×3=☐   21÷3=☐
3×7=☐   21÷7=☐

18 Write and complete these facts about 27.

27   3
9

9×3=☐   27÷3=☐
3×9=☐   27÷9=☐

Write the answers only.
19 3×3   22 1×3   25 30÷3
20 9÷3   23 0÷3   26 5×3
21 0×3   24 3÷3   27 15÷3

28 Write the table of **threes**. Check and
learn it. Ask your partner to test you.

C

1 Copy and complete the **multiples of 3** shown below.
Then find from them the **multiples of 6** and write them underneath.

Multiples of 3	3 6 9 12 — — — — — — 30
Multiples of 6	6 12 18 — — — — — — 60

2 Count on in **sixes** from 0 to 60. Count back in **sixes** from 60 to 0.
Do this many times. Ask your partner to test you.

3 Write and complete these facts about 42.

42   6
7

7×6=☐   42÷6=☐
6×7=☐   42÷7=☐

4 Write and complete these facts about 54.

54   6
9

9×6=☐   54÷6=☐
6×9=☐   54÷9=☐

5 Write the table of **sixes**. Check and learn it. Ask your partner to test you.

D Write the answers only.

1 6×6   3 8×6   5 6×5   7 4×3   9 4×6   11 8×3
2 0÷6   4 24÷3   6 12÷6   8 36÷6   10 48÷6   12 24÷6

Fractions   thirds and sixths

A

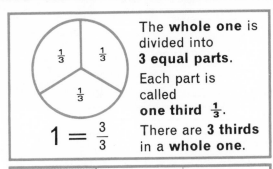

The **whole one** is divided into **3 equal parts**.
Each part is called **one third** $\frac{1}{3}$.
There are **3 thirds** in a **whole one**.

$$1 = \frac{3}{3}$$

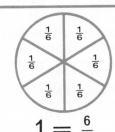

The **whole one** is divided into **6 equal parts**.
Each part is called **one sixth** $\frac{1}{6}$.
There are **6 sixths** in a **whole one**.

$$1 = \frac{6}{6}$$

The whole strip has been divided into 3 equal parts.

1 What fraction of the strip is shaded?
2 What fraction of the strip is not shaded?

The whole strip has been divided into six equal parts.

3 What fraction of the strip is shaded?
4 What fraction of the strip is not shaded?

B

 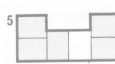

Each of these shapes stands for a whole one or unit.
What fraction of each strip is
a shaded   b not shaded?
Make sure that the two answers for each shape add up to a whole one or unit.

6 Write a sentence telling how you would find a $\frac{2}{3}$ b $\frac{5}{6}$ of a whole one.

7 Draw the shapes below on squared paper.

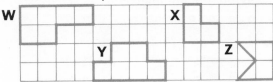

8 Shade the fraction given for each shape.
W 1 sixth $\frac{1}{6}$ **X** 1 third $\frac{1}{3}$
Y 5 sixths $\frac{5}{6}$ **Z** 2 thirds $\frac{2}{3}$

9 Write under each drawing the fraction which is a shaded   b not shaded.

C

1 Put out 12 counters into 3 sets of equal number.
2 How many are there in each set?
3 Write and complete:
   $\frac{1}{3}$ of 12 = ☐ $\frac{2}{3}$ of 12 = ☐.
4 Now divide the counters into 6 equal sets.
5 How many are there in each set?
6 Write and complete:
   $\frac{1}{6}$ of 12 = ☐ $\frac{5}{6}$ of 12 = ☐.

7   Find a $\frac{1}{3}$ of 30   b $\frac{2}{3}$ of 30.
8   Find a $\frac{1}{6}$ of 60p   b $\frac{5}{6}$ of 60p.
9   Find a $\frac{1}{3}$ of 27 cm b $\frac{2}{3}$ of 27 cm.
10 Find a $\frac{1}{6}$ of 24p   b $\frac{5}{6}$ of 24p.

whole one					
$\frac{1}{2}$			$\frac{1}{2}$		
$\frac{1}{3}$		$\frac{1}{3}$		$\frac{1}{3}$	
$\frac{1}{6}$	$\frac{1}{6}$	$\frac{1}{6}$	$\frac{1}{6}$	$\frac{1}{6}$	$\frac{1}{6}$

Write and complete the following, using the sign >, < or = in place of ●.

11 $\frac{1}{6}$ ● $\frac{1}{3}$ 12 $\frac{2}{3}$ ● $\frac{1}{2}$ 13 $\frac{3}{6}$ ● $\frac{1}{2}$
14 $\frac{5}{6}$ ● $\frac{2}{3}$ 15 $\frac{4}{6}$ ● $\frac{2}{3}$ 16 $\frac{1}{3}$ ● $\frac{1}{2}$

Tables of nines and sevens

A

1 Copy and complete the **multiples of 3 and 6** shown below.
Then find from them the **multiples of 9** and write them underneath.

Multiples of 3	3	6	9	12	—	—	—	—	—	30
Multiples of 6	6	12	18	24	—	—	—	—	—	60
Multiples of 9	9	18	27	—	—	—	—	—	—	90

2 To check the multiples of 9 try counting in this way:
1 nine=10−1 2 nines=20−2 3 nines=30−3 and so on.

3 Count on in **nines** from 0 to 90. Count back in **nines** from 90 to 0.
Do this many times. Ask your partner to test you.

B In the diagram,
how many:

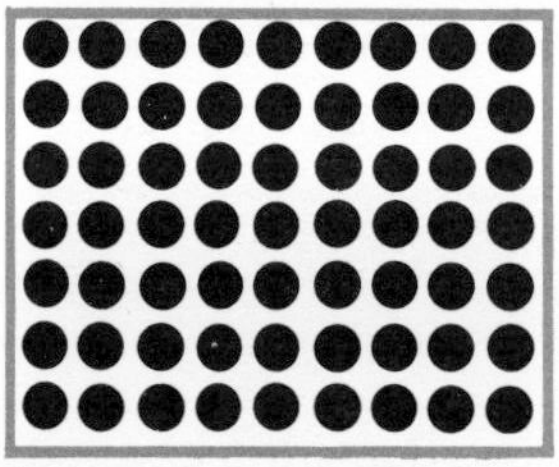

1 groups of 9
are there

2 groups of 7
are there?

Write and complete:

3 9+9+9+9+9+9+9= □
4 7+7+7+7+7+7+7+7+7=□
5 9×7=□   9 63=□×7
6 7×9=□   10 63=□×9
7 63÷7=□   11 63÷□=9
8 63÷9=□   12 63÷□=7

13 7 multiplied by 9=□
14 63 divided by 9=□
15 9 times 7=□
16 7(9)=□.
17 How many 9s in 63?
18 7)63‾

Write the answers only.

19 9×9   21 9÷9   23 81÷9
20 0×9   22 0÷9   24 1×9

25 Write in full the table of **nines**.
Check and learn it.
Ask your partner to test you.

C

1 Copy and complete the **multiples of 2 and 5** shown below.
Then find from them the **multiples of 7** and write them underneath.

Multiples of 2	2	4	6	8	—	—	—	—	—	20
Multiples of 5	5	10	15	20	—	—	—	—	—	50
Multiples of 7	7	14	21	—	—	—	—	—	—	70

2 Count on in **sevens** from 0 to 70. Count back in **sevens** from 70 to 0.
Do this many times. Ask your partner to test you.

Whilst learning the tables, 2s, 5s and 10s; 4s and 8s; 3s, 6s and 9s, you have also been learning
the table of **sevens** except 7×7=49 49÷7=7.

3 Write in full the table of **sevens**. Check and learn it. Ask your partner to test you.

D Write the answers only.

1 8×9	4 54÷9	7 6×7	10 27÷9	13 4×9	16 18÷9
2 56÷7	5 5×9	8 36÷9	11 4×7	14 35÷7	17 3×7
3 5×7	6 63÷7	9 6×9	12 72÷9	15 8×7	18 42÷7

Fractions

A

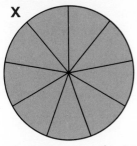

1 Into how many equal parts is the whole one **X** divided?

2 Write one of the equal parts as a fraction.

3 Into how many equal parts is the whole one **Y** divided?

4 Write one of the equal parts as a fraction.

Find the value of:

5 $\frac{1}{9}$ of 36   6 $\frac{1}{9}$ of 54p   7 $\frac{1}{9}$ of 81p   8 $\frac{1}{7}$ of 28   9 $\frac{1}{7}$ of 63 cm   10 $\frac{1}{7}$ of 35 cm.

11 Write these fractions in order of size, the smallest first. $\frac{1}{7}$ $\frac{1}{5}$ $\frac{1}{9}$ $\frac{1}{8}$ $\frac{1}{10}$ $\frac{1}{2}$

B

From a bag of sweets, Alan had $\frac{1}{4}$ and Susan had $\frac{1}{2}$ of the sweets. Paul had the remainder.

1 What fraction did Paul have?

Paul's share was 9 sweets. How many did

2 Alan have   3 Susan have?

4 $\frac{1}{8}$ of a number is 7. Find the number.

5 Jill had 36p. She spent $\frac{2}{3}$ of it. What fraction had she left?

6 How much money did she spend?

What must be added to each of these fractions to make a whole one?

7 $\frac{1}{6}$ 8 $\frac{7}{10}$ 9 $\frac{3}{8}$ 10 $\frac{4}{5}$ 11 $\frac{1}{3}$

C

Look at the diagram.

1 How many squares are there in each row?

2 How many rows are there?

3 How many squares are there altogether?

4 Copy the diagram on squared paper.

5 Shade $\frac{1}{4}$ of the squares blue, $\frac{1}{3}$ yellow and $\frac{1}{6}$ red.

6 How many squares are not shaded?

There are 15 counters.

7 If 3 counters are taken away, what fraction of all the counters is left?

8 If 5 are taken away, what fraction is left?

Write as fractions:

9 5 out of 15   13 1 out of 8

10 10 out of 15   14 3 out of 10

11 3 out of 15   15 2 out of 3

12 9 out of 15   16 4 out of 5.

D

John had 27 toffees. He gave $\frac{1}{3}$ of them to Tony, $\frac{1}{3}$ to Jill and $\frac{1}{3}$ to Peter.

1 How many toffees had John left?

How many toffees did he give

2 to Tony   3 to Jill   4 to Peter?

Ann spent $\frac{1}{2}$ of her pocket-money and then $\frac{1}{2}$ of what was left.

5 What fraction of her money had she left?

6 If she had 55p left, how much had she at first?

$\frac{3}{10}$ of the length of a line measures 21 cm. Find the length of:

7 $\frac{1}{10}$ of the line

8 the whole of the line.

Jane spent 25p which was $\frac{5}{6}$ of her pocket-money.

How much was:

9 $\frac{1}{6}$ of her pocket-money

10 all of her money?

11 Find the difference between $\frac{1}{7}$ of 63p and $\frac{1}{9}$ of 63p.

Tables of threes, sixes; sevens and nines

Place a strip of paper alongside each section in turn. Write the answers only.

	A		B		C		D		E
1	5×6	1	$27 \div 3$	1	9×3	1	$81 \div 9$	1	9×6
2	$24 \div 3$	2	7×9	2	$45 \div 9$	2	7×7	2	$18 \div 6$
3	8×9	3	$21 \div 7$	3	4×6	3	$27 \div 9$	3	10×9
4	$42 \div 6$	4	10×6	4	$18 \div 9$	4	6×3	4	$36 \div 9$
5	4×9	5	$0 \div 7$	5	5×7	5	$54 \div 6$	5	6×6
6	$56 \div 7$	6	5×9	6	$48 \div 6$	6	0×6	6	$28 \div 7$
7	7×6	7	$35 \div 7$	7	8×3	7	$63 \div 9$	7	8×7
8	$9 \div 9$	8	8×6	8	$90 \div 9$	8	4×7	8	$72 \div 9$
9	3×7	9	$63 \div 7$	9	9×7	9	$36 \div 6$	9	6×9
10	$54 \div 9$	10	0×9	10	$21 \div 3$	10	9×9	10	$42 \div 7$
11	3×9	11	$18 \div 3$	11	6×7	11	$30 \div 6$	11	3×6
12	$14 \div 7$	12	10×7	12	$49 \div 7$	12	2×9	12	$24 \div 6$

F

1	$\frac{1}{3}$ of 15	4	$\frac{1}{9}$ of 54	7	$\frac{1}{7}$ of 56	10	$\frac{1}{9}$ of 36	13	$\frac{1}{7}$ of 42
2	$\frac{1}{6}$ of 12	5	$\frac{1}{3}$ of 21	8	$\frac{1}{3}$ of 3	11	$\frac{1}{6}$ of 48	14	$\frac{1}{3}$ of 18
3	$\frac{1}{7}$ of 63	6	$\frac{1}{9}$ of 72	9	$\frac{1}{6}$ of 42	12	$\frac{1}{9}$ of 63	15	$\frac{1}{6}$ of 54

G

1	$(8 \times 7) + 6$	5	$(6 \times 6) + 5$	9	$(7 \times 3) + 2$	13	$(4 \times 7) + 5$	17	$(8 \times 6) + 5$
2	$(9 \times 3) + 2$	6	$(4 \times 9) + 7$	10	$(5 \times 9) + 7$	14	$(8 \times 3) + 2$	18	$(3 \times 9) + 4$
3	$57 - (9 \times 6)$	7	$68 - (9 \times 7)$	11	$59 - (9 \times 6)$	15	$54 - (7 \times 7)$	19	$28 - (4 \times 6)$
4	$24 - (2 \times 9)$	8	$20 - (6 \times 3)$	12	$17 - (5 \times 3)$	16	$80 - (8 \times 9)$	20	$70 - (7 \times 9)$

H

1 There are 9 crayons in a packet. How many crayons in 6 packets?

2 Each table seats 6 children. How many tables are required for 30 children?

3 7 cars each carried 3 people. How many people were carried altogether?

4 A box of 48 chocolates is shared equally among 6 children. How many did each child have?

5 How many lengths 9 cm long can be cut from a length of 72 cm?

6 There are 7 children in a team. How many children are there in 4 teams?

TIMOTHY wrote his name nine times.

7 How many times did he write the letter T?

8 How many letters did he write altogether?

I

Find the value of each letter.

$7 \times a = 21$ $b \div 8 = 9$ $c \times 4 = 12$ $24 \div d = 8$

$9 \times e = 54$ $27 \div f = 9$ $g \times 5 = 30$ $h \div 7 = 7$

$i \times 8 = 56$ $j \div 5 = 7$ $4 \times k = 36$ $24 \div m = 4$

Measuring mass

A

1   Get a brick and a large stone. Hold one in each hand and feel their **mass**.
    Which do you think is the heavier, the brick or the stone?

2   Collect six different things, some large and some small, e.g. a book, a stone, a wood-block, full boxes or tins.

3   Take them two at a time and by feeling their mass find in each case which of the two is the lighter.

4   Keep a record of your estimates in a table like the one below.

	lighter	heavier
brick stone	brick	stone

5   Get a pair of scales without the measures.
    Make sure that one side of the scales balances the other.

6   Put the brick on one side of the scales and the stone on the other. Which is the heavier, the brick or the stone?

7   Check the record you have made. Find out if the estimate you made about each pair of things was correct.

8   Now choose three of the things you collected.

9   Which do you think is the heaviest?

10 Write them in order, putting the heaviest first.

11 Use the scales only to find if your order is correct. Describe carefully how you used the scales to check the order.

B

sawdust   marbles   sand

1   Get three tins or jars all of exactly the same size and shape.

2   Fill one with sawdust, one with marbles and the other with sand.

3   Use the scales, but not the measures, to find:
    a   which of the tins is the heaviest;
    b   which of the tins is the lightest.

4   What have you discovered from this exercise?

5   Now fill one tin with dry sand and another with wet sand.

6   Which is the heavier?
    Write the reason why it is heavier.

C

1   Get two lumps of clay or plasticine of similar size. Work each of them between your hands into a ball.

2   Put them on the scales, one on each side. If they do not balance make the two balls equal in mass.

3   Work each ball into a different shape.

4   Put them on the scales again. Find if by changing the shape you have changed the mass.

Measuring mass

A

1 Draw this table.

	number of	
	marbles	cubes
stone this book my shoe		

2 Use the scales to find how many marbles will balance a large stone.
Write the number of marbles in the table.

3 Use marbles to balance
  a this book   b one of your shoes.
Write in the table the number of marbles used for each.

4 Now use wood or plastic cubes to balance each of the three things.

5 Write in the table the number of cubes used for each.

6 Look at the numbers.
What do you discover in each case about the number of marbles compared with the number of cubes?

7 Find the reason for the difference.

8 On squared paper, draw a block graph to show the number of marbles needed to balance each thing.

9 Draw another block graph to show the number of cubes needed to balance each thing.

B

You have discovered that when marbles and cubes were used for measuring, different answers were obtained each time. Therefore a measure for mass must be used.
The standard measure of mass is 1 kilogram (kg).

1 Get a pair of scales, the 1 kilogram mass and the $\frac{1}{2}$ kilogram mass.

2 Feel each mass in turn in your hand.

3 How many $\frac{1}{2}$ kg masses are equal to 1 kg?

4 Use the scales to measure a mass of 1 kg of sand and then a mass of 1 kg of sawdust.

5 Look at the quantity of each.
What do you notice?

6 Use the scales to find the number of
  a marbles   b cubes
needed to balance a $\frac{1}{2}$ kg mass.

7 Are there more, less or the same number of marbles as cubes?

8 Write the reason why the quantities are different, but the masses are the same.

C

1 Collect several things to estimate the mass of each.

2 Hold each one in your hand in turn and estimate which have a mass greater than $\frac{1}{2}$ kg ($>\frac{1}{2}$ kg) and those which have a mass of less than $\frac{1}{2}$ kg ($<\frac{1}{2}$ kg).

3 Make a record of your results as shown.

4 Use the scales and the $\frac{1}{2}$ kg mass to check your estimates.

5 Find three things which you think have a mass of about 1 kg.

	estimated mass
brick	$>\frac{1}{2}$ kg
empty jar	
jar full of sand	
wood-block	
box of pencils	
large stone	
small stone	

Measuring mass

A To find the mass of things and quantities which are not exactly 1 kg or $\frac{1}{2}$ kg, smaller measures of mass are required. These smaller masses are measured in **grams (g).**

These are the smaller measures of mass in common use.

1 kg = 1000 grams (g)
$\frac{1}{2}$ kg = 500 grams (g)

1 How many 200 g masses equal 1 kg?

How many 100 g masses equal

2 1 kg   3 $\frac{1}{2}$ kg?

How many of each of the following masses equal 100 g?

4 50 g   5 20 g   6 10 g

Which measures can be used to find the mass of:

7 600 g   8 300 g   9 800 g

10 250 g   11 70 g   12 130 g

13 360 g   14 780 g   15 670 g?

B

Portuguese Sardines Net Mass 125g	Carrots Net Mass 780g	Half Peaches Net Mass 820g	Caster Sugar Net Mass 450g

1 Read what is printed on the labels.

2 Find the meaning of **net mass.**

Write the mass contained in one tin of:

3 sardines   4 peaches.

How many grams less than $\frac{1}{2}$ kg is the mass of:

5 the sardines   6 the sugar?

How many grams less than 1 kg is the mass of:

7 the carrots   8 the peaches?

The mass of a large empty tin is 18 g.

Write the total mass of:

9 a tin of peaches   10 a tin of carrots.

This total mass is called the **gross mass.**

11 Add 97 g + 78 g + 150 g.

12 Add 135 g + 450 g + 235 g.

Find the difference between:

13 780 g and 440 g   14 900 g and 750 g

15 140 g and 230 g   16 $\frac{1}{2}$ kg and 325 g.

C The smaller measures of mass, shown in section **A**, are not used with many kinds of scales. Many shops use scales on which the dial is marked in units of mass. The dial shown is marked in grams.

0 50 100 150 200 250 300 350 400 450 500

a   b   c   d

Maximum mass 500 g

1 What is the greatest mass which can be measured on this scale?

2 What does one small division represent?

3 What masses are shown by the pointers **a, b, c** and **d?**

4 When you go shopping, look at the dials of different scales.

Find the maximum mass which can be measured on each and what each division represents.

Measuring liquids

A

Get three jars of different shape and size. Fill one of the jars with water.

1 By pouring the water from this jar into the others find which jar holds the most.

2 Arrange the jars in order, putting the one that holds the least first.

3 Notice that the water always takes the shape of the jar into which it is poured. For this reason water is called a **liquid**. Name six other liquids.

B

1 Get three containers, e.g. a large jug, a washing-up bowl and a large basin.

2 Using a jar as a measure, find the number of jarfuls of water which are needed to fill each container.

   Draw the table below and enter the numbers to the nearest full one.

3 Repeat the exercise, but this time use a cup as a measure.

container	jarfuls	cupfuls
jug		
bowl		
basin		

4 Make a record of your results by drawing block graphs.

C

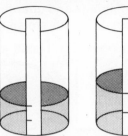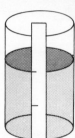

1 Get three containers which are of the same size and shape, e.g. large jars. You will need three long strips of paper for measuring.

2 Pour a cupful of water into the first container. Put a strip of paper alongside and mark the level of the water. Pour in more cupfuls of water, marking the level on the strip each time.

3 Repeat the exercise with the other two containers, using a small jar to fill one and a small bottle to fill the other, marking the strip each time.

4 Compare the marks on the strips.

5 Why are the markings different for each container?

6 If you had used sand would the records have been different?

7 From what you have discovered, give the reason why a standard measure is necessary.

D

The amount of liquid a container holds is its **capacity**.

The **standard measure** of liquids is **1 litre (ℓ)**.

Collect several containers of different size and shape.

Use the litre and the $\frac{1}{2}$ litre measures to find which of the containers hold approximately

a 1 litre   b $\frac{1}{2}$ litre   c 2 litres.

Practise estimating the capacity of different containers to the nearest $\frac{1}{2}$ litre.

Use the litre and $\frac{1}{2}$ litre measures to check your estimates.

Making sure

A

Write the number shown on each abacus picture.

1 H T U 2 H T U 3 H T U

Write and complete the following.

4 382 = ☐ hundreds ☐ tens ☐ units

5 382 = ☐ tens ☐ units

6 382 = ☐ units

7 £3·65 = £☐ ☐ ☐ TENS ☐ pence

8 £3·65 = ☐ TENS ☐ pence

9 £3·65 = ☐ pence

Write and complete these series.

10 180 190 — — 220 230

11 £2·70 £2·80 £2·90 — —

Write the value of each figure underlined.

12 28<u>6</u>   13 3<u>1</u>9   14 <u>4</u>57

Write the value of the two figures underlined.

15 <u>49</u>2   16 <u>5</u>0<u>7</u>   17 <u>6</u>0<u>8</u>

By how many is the figure marked x greater than the figure marked y?

	x y		x y		x y
18	232	19	159	20	111

By how much is the amount marked x greater than the amount marked y?

	x y		x y		xy
21	£1·53	22	£1·67	23	£2·49

Write the following as pence.

24 £0·37   25 £0·08   26 £0·70

Write as £s.

27 59p   28 70p   29 6p

30 £1 and 6 TENS   31 £1 and five pence

B

Look carefully at the lines below.

S T U V W X Y Z

1 Name the lines which are vertical and parallel.

2 Name the lines which are horizontal and parallel.

3 Name the lines which are oblique and parallel.

4 Which of the lines below are perpendicular to the line **AB**?

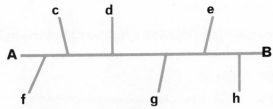

c d e A B f g h

5 How can you find if a line is perpendicular to another line?

Estimate which of the angles below are:

6 less than a right angle

7 more than a right angle

8 a right angle.

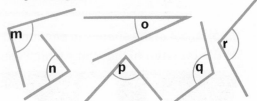

m o n p q r

The map shows two towns, Laken and Bilt, joined together by three roads.

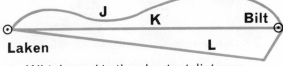

J K Bilt Laken L

9 Which road is the shortest distance between the two towns?

Measure in cm the distance

10 by road **K**   11 by road **L**.

Each cm on the map stands for 1 km.
Find the actual distance in km between the two towns:

12 by road **K**   13 by road **L**.

Shapes

A

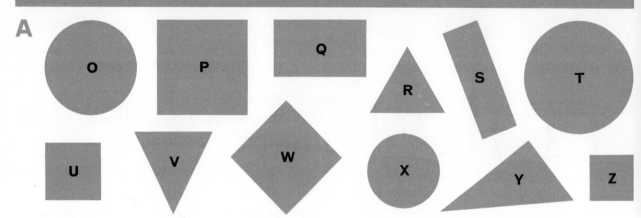

Look at the shapes above. There are **squares, rectangles, triangles** and **circles.**

Each of the shapes has a flat surface which has no thickness.

Write the letters of the shapes which are:

1 squares   2 rectangles   3 triangles   4 circles.

B   How many sides has:

1   a square   2   a triangle

3   a rectangle   4   a circle?

How many angles has:

5   a square   6   a triangle

7   a rectangle   8   a circle?

Write the letters of the shapes above in which there are:

9   no right angles   10   one right angle only

11   four right angles.

Use your right-angle measure to check the answers.

12   In which of the shapes are there parallel lines?

C   Look again at the shapes in section **A.**

Write the letter of the shape which you think fits exactly into each of the following.

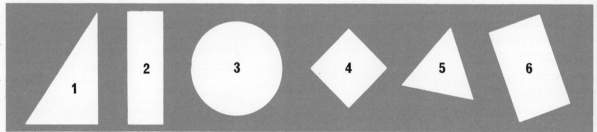

7   The circle is the easiest shape to fit. Give a reason for this.

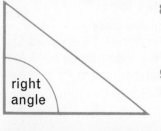

right angle

8   This triangle is a special triangle called a **right-angled triangle.**
Measure the two arms of the right angle and then draw the triangle.
Use your right-angle measure.

9   Draw four more right-angled triangles, making each one a different shape.
What must you do to alter the shape each time?

Shapes squares

A The picture shows two different **set squares.**
They are used for drawing and testing right angles.

1 Find the right angle on each drawing of a set square.
Ask your teacher for a set square.
Find the right angle.

2 Draw a horizontal line 8 cm long.
Use the set square to draw a right angle at each end of the line.

3 Do the same with a vertical line and then an oblique line.

B

 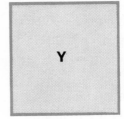

1 Measure in cm the sides of square **W**.
How long is each side?

2 Use the set square to measure each angle.

3 Copy and complete the following.
The ☐ sides of the square **W** are each
_____ in length.

The ☐ angles are_____angles.

Check the sides and angles of
squares **X**, **Y** and **Z**.

What do you discover about:

4 the four sides   5 the four angles?

6 Use a ruler and a set square to draw on a
separate sheet of paper the squares
W, **X**, **Y** and **Z**.

7 Cut them out carefully and place them one
on top of the other.

Which square has

8 the largest surface

9 the smallest surface?

The measurement all round a shape is
called its **perimeter**.

10 Find the perimeter of each of the squares.

C Draw squares with sides:

1 4 cm long   2 5 cm long
3 9 cm long   4 $7\frac{1}{2}$ cm long.
5 Find the perimeter of each square.

6 Draw and cut out a square of 10 cm side.
Fold the square into two equal parts.
There are four ways of doing this.
Can you find them?
Mark the fold lines clearly with your pencil.

7 On squared paper, copy these patterns. The patterns are called **tessellations.**
Find the meaning of the word **tessellation.** Make up some of your own, using squares.

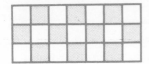  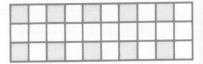

Shapes rectangles

A

Look at rectangle **P**. Measure in cm:
1. the two opposite long sides
2. the two opposite short sides.
3. What do you find about the opposite sides of rectangle **P**?
4. Use the set square to measure each angle.
5. Copy and complete the following.
   The _____ sides of a rectangle are _____ in length.
   The ☐ angles are _____ angles.

Check the sides and angles of **Q**, **R**, **S**, **T** and **U**.
What do you discover about:
6. their opposite sides
7. their four angles?
8. Explain why a square is a special kind of rectangle.

9. Use a ruler and set square to draw, on a separate sheet of paper, the rectangles **P**, **Q**, **R**, **S**, **T** and **U**. Cut them out. Make sure that you have drawn them correctly by fitting them on the drawings.

10. Fit rectangle **Q** on rectangle **P**. How many times is the surface of **P** greater than the surface of **Q**?

In the same way, find how many times:
11. the surface of **P** is greater than the surface of **R**
12. the surface of **T** is greater than the surface of **U**
13. the surface of **U** is greater than the surface of **S**.
14. Find the perimeter of each of the rectangles **P**, **Q**, **R**, **S**, **T** and **U**.

B Draw the following rectangles:
1. 8 cm long and 3 cm wide
2. 10 cm long and 7 cm wide
3. $5\frac{1}{2}$ cm long and $4\frac{1}{2}$ cm wide.
4. Find the perimeter of each rectangle.

5. Draw and cut out a rectangle 12 cm long and 8 cm wide. Fold the rectangle into two equal parts. How many different ways of doing this can you find? Mark the fold lines clearly with your pencil.

C Tessellations are made when bricks are laid to build walls of houses, garages, etc.
Each method is called a bond, three of which are shown below.
1. Copy them and then make up some of your own, using rectangles and squares.

Stretcher bond   Flemish bond   English bond

Shapes circles

A

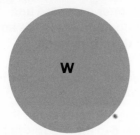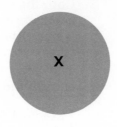

Which of the circles above has:

1 the largest surface
2 the smallest surface?

Get a 2p coin, a FIVE and a TEN.

3 Why do you think the coins are made in the shape of a circle?

4 Place the coins one on top of the other in order of size.
Write their order, putting the largest first.

5 Write one reason why you think wheels are made in the shape of circles.

6 Find some things in the class-room or at home which you can use to draw circles of different sizes. For example, you can draw round tin lids, plates, jars, etc.

7 On a sheet of paper draw and cut out some circles.

8 Place them one on top of the other to find which circle has the largest surface.

9 Number the circles in order of size, the smallest first.

B

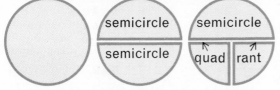

1 Take one of your large circles.

Fold it into two equal parts.

Cut it into two equal parts.

Each part is called a **semicircle**.

Fold a semicircle into two equal parts.

2 What part of a circle is half a semicircle?

A quarter of a circle is called a **quadrant**.

C

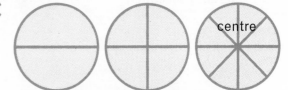

1 Take another of your large circles.
Fold it in half and draw a line along the crease.

2 Do this again in several places and each time draw a line along the crease.
If you have made the folds carefully all the lines cross at one point.
This point is the **centre** of the circle.
In the same way, find the centre of the other circles you have cut out.

D

1 Draw round different sized coins to make up the patterns below.

2 When a pattern covers a surface completely, without leaving any gaps, the pattern is a **tessellation.** Are these patterns tessellations?

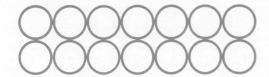

Table tests multiplication and division

A

1	2	3	4	5	6	7	8	9	10
2	4	6	8	10	12	a	16	18	20
3	6	9	12	15	18	21	b	27	30
4	8	12	16	20	24	28	32	c	40
5	10	15	20	d	30	35	40	45	50
6	12	18	24	30	e	42	48	54	60
7	14	21	28	35	42	f	56	63	70
8	16	24	32	40	48	56	64	g	80
9	18	27	36	45	54	h	72	81	90
10	20	30	40	50	60	70	80	90	100

1 Copy the ready reckoner on a card and complete it by writing numbers in the squares instead of **a, b, c, d, e, f, g** and **h**. Check your answers.

2 The ready reckoner will help you to **multiply** and **divide**. Learn how to use it.

Example 8×6	Place your ruler along the **8** line. Under **6** in the top row is the answer 48. $8 \times 6 = 48$
Example $63 \div 9$	Place your ruler along the **9** line. Above 63 in the top row is the answer **7**. $63 \div 9 = 7$

Keep the ready reckoner carefully.

Using the ready reckoner, practise these multiplication and division tests with a partner.

Then try to answer the tests without using the ready reckoner.

Put a strip of paper alongside test **B** and write the answers only.

Go on to tests **C, D** and **E** in the same way.

Time yourself for the four tests.

Beat the clock

3 minutes for one test

15 minutes for the four tests

	B	**C**	**D**	**E**
1	5×4	5×5	4×3	9×5
2	1×6	8×6	7×5	4×4
3	10×6	7×4	0×7	7×8
4	0×3	3×7	9×4	5×6
5	7×7	9×1	5×8	8×9
6	3×5	2×6	9×7	6×3
7	6×6	3×3	6×9	10×10
8	2×8	6×7	10×3	9×9
9	10×9	4×8	4×6	0×10
10	8×3	0×5	8×8	3×9
11	$14 \div 2$	$0 \div 3$	$20 \div 4$	$24 \div 3$
12	$30 \div 6$	$16 \div 4$	$18 \div 3$	$40 \div 8$
13	$4 \div 4$	$54 \div 6$	$45 \div 5$	$28 \div 4$
14	$12 \div 6$	$18 \div 2$	$16 \div 8$	$63 \div 9$
15	$0 \div 5$	$35 \div 5$	$30 \div 3$	$8 \div 8$
16	$21 \div 7$	$49 \div 7$	$48 \div 8$	$0 \div 7$
17	$12 \div 3$	$36 \div 6$	$25 \div 5$	$72 \div 9$
18	$32 \div 8$	$56 \div 8$	$24 \div 6$	$100 \div 10$
19	$27 \div 9$	$36 \div 4$	$80 \div 8$	$42 \div 6$
20	$15 \div 5$	$81 \div 9$	$0 \div 10$	$64 \div 8$

F Draw this table. Keep a record of the time you take whenever you work the four tests together.

X ÷ date				
time in min				
number correct				

Multiplication and division

A Find the value of each letter.

1	2	3	4	5
$2 \times a = 16$	$6 \times a = 48$	$4 \times a = 32$	$3 \times a = 3$	$7 \times a = 35$
$b \div 9 = 2$	$b \div 7 = 3$	$b \div 6 = 8$	$b \div 4 = 9$	$b \div 9 = 8$
$c \times 5 = 30$	$c \times 7 = 63$	$c \times 8 = 24$	$c \times 6 = 18$	$c \times 5 = 40$
$d \div 4 = 7$	$d \div 8 = 4$	$d \div 4 = 5$	$d \div 3 = 8$	$d \div 3 = 4$
$8 \times e = 72$	$10 \times e = 10$	$5 \times e = 20$	$4 \times e = 24$	$3 \times e = 27$
$f \div 7 = 9$	$f \div 7 = 6$	$f \div 8 = 10$	$f \div 8 = 7$	$f \div 9 = 6$
$g \times 3 = 27$	$g \times 9 = 90$	$g \times 9 = 36$	$g \times 9 = 54$	$g \times 6 = 24$
$h \div 6 = 4$	$h \div 3 = 6$	$h \div 5 = 9$	$h \div 6 = 5$	$h \div 8 = 5$

Practise multiplying two numbers and adding another number.

B
1. $(5 \times 5) + 4$
2. $(9 \times 4) + 2$
3. $(4 \times 8) + 3$
4. $(8 \times 3) + 2$
5. $(7 \times 8) + 6$
6. $(9 \times 5) + 4$
7. $(4 \times 6) + 5$
8. $(6 \times 7) + 5$
9. $(9 \times 9) + 7$
10. $(1 \times 9) + 8$
11. $(7 \times 0) + 6$
12. $(9 \times 6) + 8$
13. $(7 \times 6) + 4$
14. $(8 \times 5) + 3$

C
1. $2(7) + 6$
2. $6(9) + 7$
3. $2(8) + 5$
4. $7(5) + 4$
5. $6(6) + 5$
6. $3(3) + 2$
7. $7(7) + 3$
8. $0(8) + 3$
9. $8(6) + 4$
10. $7(4) + 2$
11. $6(5) + 3$
12. $4(9) + 7$
13. $(9 \times 2) + 1$
14. $(9 \times 6) + 5$

Practise multiplying two numbers and subtracting them from another number.

D
1. $20 - (6 \times 3)$
2. $67 - (9 \times 7)$
3. $53 - (8 \times 6)$
4. $23 - (3 \times 7)$
5. $19 - (4 \times 4)$
6. $35 - (9 \times 3)$
7. $44 - (5 \times 8)$
8. $65 - (10 \times 6)$
9. $6 - (9 \times 0)$
10. $17 - (3 \times 5)$
11. $35 - (8 \times 4)$
12. $31 - (4 \times 7)$
13. $69 - (9 \times 7)$
14. $26 - (6 \times 4)$

E
1. $78 - 8(9)$
2. $34 - 5(6)$
3. $14 - 4(3)$
4. $60 - 8(7)$
5. $39 - 9(4)$
6. $47 - 7(6)$
7. $22 - 5(4)$
8. $44 - 8(5)$
9. $39 - 5(7)$
10. $71 - 8(8)$
11. $34 - 8(4)$
12. $31 - 3(8)$
13. $74 - 9(8)$
14. $62 - 7(8)$

F What must 3 be multiplied by to give these answers?

1. 27
2. 0
3. 18
4. 21

Which numbers when divided by 6 will give these answers?

5. 5
6. 3
7. 8
8. 1

9. Find the value of each letter.

$(3 \times 9) + a = 30$ $38 - (7 \times 5) = b$
$(9 \times 6) + c = 59$ $70 - (8 \times 8) = d$
$(8 \times 4) + e = 36$ $41 - (6 \times 6) = f$
$(3 \times 7) + g = 25$ $40 - (7 \times 5) = h$

10. 6 children each ate 5 biscuits and there were 3 biscuits left.
How many biscuits were there at first?

11. There were 4 rows of 7 children and 1 row of 5.
How many children were there altogether?

12. Peter had 3 FIVES and 2 TWOS.
How much money had he altogether?

13. Alison walked 7 km each day for 4 days and 3 km on the fifth day.
How far did she walk in all?

Multiplication and division

A Division with remainders

There are
16 cubes.

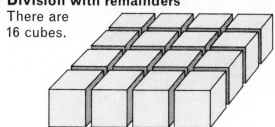

1 How many sets of 5 cubes can be made?
2 How many cubes are left over?
3 How many sets of 3 cubes can be made?
4 How many cubes are left over?
5 How many sets of 7 cubes can be made?
6 How many cubes are left over?

Divide the 15 counters into sets of two.
7 How many sets of two are there?
8 How many counters remain?
9 Write: 15÷2=7 rem. 1.

Divide the 15 counters into sets of four.
10 How many sets are there?
11 How many counters remain?
12 Write and complete: 15÷4=☐ rem. ☐.

B Work the following as quickly as you can. Write the answers only.

1 Divide by 2.
   a 9   b 13   c 7   d 19   e 11

2 Divide by 3.
   a 13   b 25   c 2   d 17   e 29

3 Divide by 4.
   a 17   b 11   c 30   d 23   e 37

4 Divide by 5.
   a 46   b 18   c 27   d 33   e 42

5 Divide by 6.
   a 5   b 26   c 45   d 58   e 40

6 Divide by 7.
   a 31   b 53   c 26   d 69   e 44

7 Divide by 8.
   a 33   b 51   c 44   d 22   e 59

8 Divide by 9.
   a 29   b 7   c 48   d 67   e 59

C There are 20 counters.

1 How many sets each of 2 counters
   can be made from them?

2 How many of the following sets can be made from the 20 counters?
   a sets of 4 counters   b sets of 5 counters   c sets of 10 counters.
   You could also make 20 sets each of 1 counter and 1 set of 20 counters.

   You have found that 1, 2, 4, 5, 10 and 20 will all divide into 20 exactly, without a remainder.
   These numbers are called **factors** of 20.

   Find the factors of   3 12   4 16   5 18   6 20   7 35.

D

1 52p was shared equally among 5 children.
   How much did each have?
2 How much remained?
3 37 sweets are shared equally among
   7 children. How many does each receive
   and how many are left over?

4 Which of the following have both 2 and 3
   as factors?
   6   9   15   18   24

5 Which of the following have both 4 and 5
   as factors?
   15   20   24   35   40

Number multiplication practice

A
First work Section **A**.　Mark the answers and correct any mistakes.
Then work Section **B**.　Do the same with Sections **C** and **D**.
Write the answers only.
You will learn later how to check the answers by dividing.

1　24
　×2

2　33
　×3

3　21
　×7

4　62
　×4

5　31
　×5

6　40
　×6

7　30
　×8

8　101
　×9

9　203
　×3

10　404
　×2

B
1　14
　×4

2　25
　×3

3　19
　×5

4　53
　×7

5　28
　×6

6　22
　×9

7　98
　×2

8　45
　×8

9　36
　×6

10　43
　×7

11　98
　×8

12　56
　×5

13　74
　×9

14　69
　×4

15　37
　×3

C
1　104
　×8

2　109
　×9

3　306
　×3

4　107
　×7

5　408
　×2

6　130
　×6

7　190
　×4

8　120
　×8

9　160
　×5

10　140
　×7

D
1　119
　×5

2　112
　×8

3　224
　×3

4　115
　×6

5　114
　×7

6　494
　×2

7　283
　×3

8　121
　×7

9　172
　×4

10　161
　×5

When you have marked and corrected the answers in Sections **A, B, C** and **D**, test yourself by working the mixed examples in Section **E**.

E
1　230
　×4

2　109
　×8

3　116
　×6

4　95
　×9

5　38
　×5

6　280
　×2

7　206
　×4

8　54
　×8

9　287
　×3

10　119
　×7

11　125×7
12　116×8
13　245×3
14　158×6
15　182×5

Number division practice

First work Section **A.**   Mark the answers and correct any mistakes.

Then work Section **B.**   Do the same with Sections **C, D** and **E.**

Write the answers only.

Check by multiplying the answers.

A
1 $6\overline{)42}$	2 $9\overline{)54}$	3 $7\overline{)35}$	4 $8\overline{)64}$	5 $4\overline{)36}$
6 $2\overline{)64}$	7 $5\overline{)55}$	8 $3\overline{)96}$	9 $4\overline{)84}$	10 $7\overline{)77}$

Show **remainders** as in this example.

$$\begin{array}{r} 7 \text{ rem. } 3 \\ 8\overline{)59} \end{array}$$

B
1 $3\overline{)28}$	2 $5\overline{)37}$	3 $7\overline{)46}$	4 $9\overline{)58}$	5 $2\overline{)17}$
6 $4\overline{)31}$	7 $6\overline{)40}$	8 $8\overline{)54}$	9 $7\overline{)53}$	10 $9\overline{)52}$

C
1 $3\overline{)156}$	2 $6\overline{)186}$	3 $4\overline{)248}$	4 $5\overline{)205}$	5 $2\overline{)146}$
6 $7\overline{)427}$	7 $8\overline{)328}$	8 $9\overline{)639}$	9 $4\overline{)368}$	10 $6\overline{)546}$

D
1 $3\overline{)165}$	2 $8\overline{)368}$	3 $6\overline{)132}$	4 $5\overline{)275}$	5 $4\overline{)336}$
6 $9\overline{)396}$	7 $7\overline{)455}$	8 $8\overline{)608}$	9 $6\overline{)432}$	10 $3\overline{)291}$

E
1 $2\overline{)160}$	2 $7\overline{)280}$	3 $5\overline{)350}$	4 $8\overline{)560}$	5 $9\overline{)810}$
6 $3\overline{)309}$	7 $4\overline{)804}$	8 $2\overline{)418}$	9 $3\overline{)615}$	10 $5\overline{)535}$
11 $7\overline{)763}$	12 $6\overline{)648}$	13 $9\overline{)954}$	14 $4\overline{)428}$	15 $8\overline{)832}$

When you have marked and corrected the answers in Sections **A, B, C, D** and **E,** test yourself by working the mixed examples in Section **F.**

F
1 $7\overline{)95}$	2 $3\overline{)157}$	3 $6\overline{)281}$	4 $3\overline{)921}$	5 $9\overline{)126}$
6 $4\overline{)216}$	7 $8\overline{)327}$	8 $5\overline{)492}$	9 $9\overline{)89}$	10 $4\overline{)516}$
11 $404 \div 5$	12 $843 \div 7$	13 $672 \div 6$	14 $817 \div 2$	15 $510 \div 3$

Puzzle corner

A

bowl   jug   bucket

A litre of water was poured into each of the containers.

1   In which container was the water the deepest?

2   Give a reason for your answer.

Copy the drawings below on squared paper and complete each one.

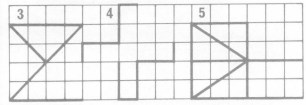

In jug **W** there are 4 litres of water.
In jug **X** there is 1 litre of water.

6   How many litres must be poured from jug **W** into jug **X** to make the amounts in both jugs equal?

Set **Y** (the circle)
Set **Z** (the square)

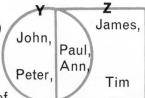

7   Write the names of the children in set **Y**.

8   Write the names of the children in set **Z**.

9   Which children's names are in both set **Y** and set **Z**?

B

Each letter below stands for a number.
$$w=5 \qquad x=7 \qquad y=9 \qquad z=6$$

Write the answers only to the following.

1   $x+y$
2   $y-z$
3   $(x+w)-z$
4   $y+y+y$
5   $3\times y$
6   $(z+y)-(z+y)$

Look at the drawings below.

7   How many rectangles are there altogether in the drawing **X**?

8   How many squares are there altogether in the drawing **Y**?

Look at the example. $\boxed{38\times5=190}$

Now write the answers only to the following.

9    $38+38+38+38+38$
10   $190-38-38-38-38-38$
11   $190\div5$ 12 37×5

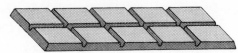

James bought this bar of chocolate. He gave $\frac{1}{2}$ of it to June, $\frac{1}{5}$ to Claire and $\frac{3}{10}$ of it to Tim.

13   How much of the chocolate had he left?

C

> The sign = means 'is the same as'.
> The sign ≠ means 'is **not** the same as'.

Write and complete the following using =, ≠, + or − in place of ●.

1   $3+6+9 ● 18$
2   $(5+5)+5 ● 20$
3   $19 ● 5=30 ● 6$
4   $18+5 ● 13=10$
5   $(15 ● 9)+4=10$
6   $(17-8) ● 2=11$

Write and complete using = or ≠ in place of ●.

7    $9+8 ● 8+9$
8    $15-7 ● 15-8$
9    $10+0 ● 10\times0$
10   $5\times6 ● 6\times5$
11   $42\div6 ● 42\div7$
12   $0\times4 ● 0\div4$
13   $10\times10 ● 10\div10$
14   $18-0 ● 0+18$
15   $4+28 ● 28-4$
16   $3\times3 ● 3\div3$

3-D shapes solids

A

Collect several boxes, jars, etc., which are like those in the picture.

1 Feel each one in your hand. Notice they all have **length** and **breadth** and **thickness.**
For this reason, they are often called **3-D shapes.**

2 Find what D stands for and the meaning of 3-D.

3 Which will take up more space,
an empty matchbox or a full one
an empty jam jar or a full one?

> In mathematics, all objects which have length, breadth and thickness and take up space are called **solids.**

B Cube

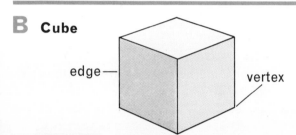

edge —

vertex

1 Get a large cube.
Each of its 'corners' is called a **vertex.**
Two or more are called **vertices.**
The cube also has faces and edges.

2 Count the number of:
a faces   b vertical edges
c horizontal edges   d vertices.

3 Place the cube on a sheet of paper and draw carefully round the bottom face.

4 What is the name of the shape you have drawn? Test it with a ruler and set square.

5 Cut out this shape and fit it, in turn, on each face of the cube.
What do you discover?

6 Get two more cubes, one larger and one smaller than the first.

7 For each cube, repeat **2, 3, 4** and **5** above.

8 Copy and complete:
A cube has ☐ faces each of which is a_____.
All the angles are_____ angles.

C

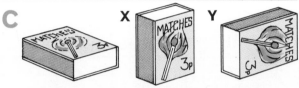

X   Y

1 Get an empty matchbox. Look at it and write how you know it is not a cube.

2 Count the number of:
a faces   b vertical edges
c horizontal edges   d vertices.

3 Place the matchbox flat on a sheet of paper and carefully draw round the bottom face. Name the shape drawn and test it with a ruler and set square.

4 Cut out the shape and find the other face that it fits.
Now do the same again, having placed the matchbox:

5 as in drawing **X**   6 as in drawing **Y.**

7 What have you discovered?
Copy and complete:
The matchbox has ☐ faces, each of which is a_____.
There are ☐ pairs of equal faces.
The opposite faces are_____faces.
All the angles are_____angles.

A matchbox is called a **rectangular solid** or a **cuboid.**

D

Make a list of ten things which are cubes or cuboids.
Think of small objects, as well as large ones - for example, a dice, a cupboard, a room at home.

3-D shapes

A Get a container of similar shape to the one in the drawing.

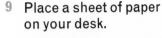

1 Count the number of
   a faces   b edges.

2 Place it upright on a sheet of paper and draw round the bottom face.

3 Name the shape you have drawn.

4 Cut out this face and fit it on the top face of the cylinder.

5 What have you discovered about the shape and size of the top and bottom faces? Solids of this shape are called **cylinders.**

6 Name the solid made by each pile of coins **X** and **Y.**

X   Y   Z

7 Write two ways in which solid **X** differs from solid **Y.**

8 Why is solid **Z** not a cylinder?

9 Place a sheet of paper on your desk.

Make sure that the paper has a flat rectangular surface.

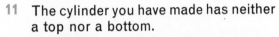

10 Bring together the two ends of the sheet of paper and stick them to make a cylinder. A cylinder has a curved surface.

11 The cylinder you have made has neither a top nor a bottom.

It is hollow, like a milk straw or a length of water pipe, but it is still called a solid.

12 Make a list of ten things, both large and small, which are cylinders.

Collect some pictures and drawings.

B The drawing shows another common solid called a **sphere.**

A ball is a sphere.

1 How many flat or curved faces has it?

2 Give a reason why a ball is usually made this particular shape.

3 Make a sphere from a lump of plasticine by rolling it between your hands.

4 Using a pencil point, make a line all round the sphere. Notice that the line comes back to the point from which it started.

5 Centuries ago it was believed that the earth was flat. We now know that it is a sphere. How do we know it is a sphere?

Collect three solids which are cubes or cuboids.

For each solid, measure to the nearest cm:
1 the length
2 the breadth or width
3 the height or thickness.

4 Get twelve matchboxes of the same size. Stack them neatly together to make a cuboid.

5 Rearrange them to make a different cuboid.

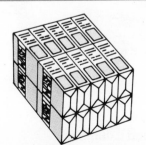

Many cartons are filled with boxes which are in the shape of cuboids or cubes.

6 Why are these shapes used?

D Collect several containers, tins and jars which are cylinders.

1 Take them in turn and measure to the nearest centimetre:
   a the height   b the distance round each container (use a piece of thread or a tape-measure).

2 Try to find a method of measuring the width across the top.

Making sure

A

Find the missing numbers in each of these series.

1	35	42	☐	☐	63	70
2	20	☐	28	☐	36	40
3	45	54	☐	72	☐	90
4	40	☐	56	64	☐	80

Six different numbers can be made by using the figures 4, 6 and 3.
They are:
463,   436,   634,   643,   346,   364.

5 Write in order, the smallest first, the six numbers you can make from the figures 5, 2 and 8.

6 Find the difference between the largest and the smallest of the numbers.

7 Using the figures 7, 2 and 9, write:
   a   the largest odd number
   b   the largest even number.

B

1 Write in two ways the afternoon time shown on the clock face.

2 How many minutes is it to 6.00 p.m.?

How many h and min to
3   8.00 p.m.   4   11.00 p.m.?

5 If the clock is 13 min slow, what is the correct time?

6 A train leaves the station at the time shown on the clock. It takes 48 min to travel to the next station.
At what time does it arrive?

7 Philip's date of birth is 29.3.73.
Write the date in full.

8 How old is Philip on the 29th December this year?

9 Kate is 7 months older than Philip.
Write the date of her birth.

C

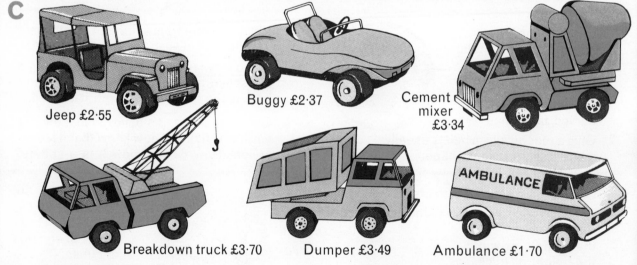

Jeep £2·55

Buggy £2·37

Cement mixer £3·34

Breakdown truck £3·70

Dumper £3·49

Ambulance £1·70

Find the total cost of:
1 a jeep and a buggy
2 a cement mixer and a dumper
3 a breakdown truck and an ambulance.
4 What is the difference in price between the cheapest and the most expensive of the toys?
5 Which toy can you buy with a £5 note and have £1·66 in change?

How much change from a £5 note after buying:
6   a jeep   7   a buggy   8   a dumper?

How much more does it cost to buy:
9   a breakdown truck than a dumper
10   a cement mixer than a jeep?

Use as few coins as possible to pay for:
11   a cement mixer   12   a dumper.

Money multiplication practice

A Write the following as pence. Use the 'p' sign.

1 £0·13   2 £0·46   3 £0·62   4 £0·80   5 £0·06   6 £0·99

Write the following as £s. Use the £ sign and a pennies point.

7 8p   8 27p   9 60p   10 5p   11 73p   12 10p

B Write the answers as pence. Use the 'p' sign.

1 23p ×4	2 19p ×5	3 48p ×2	4 29p ×3	5 14p ×7	6 16p ×6

7 12p ×8	8 18p ×4	9 17p ×5	10 12p ×6	11 9p ×9	12 13p ×7

Mark the answers and correct any mistakes.
Then write each answer as £s, using the £ sign and a pennies point.

C Look at the example. When the answer is **100p or more,** you must always write it using a **£ sign and a pennies point.** Work the following and write the answers as £s.

Example

49p
×4
_____
196p

=£1·96

1 37p ×3	2 26p ×5	3 48p ×4	4 19p ×7	5 20p ×9

6 13p ×8	7 24p ×5	8 37p ×7	9 28p ×9	10 52p ×6

11 12p ×9	12 15p ×7	13 25p ×8	14 17p ×6	15 51p ×4

D

Examples

£0·19
×4
_____
£0·76

£0·73
×5
_____
£3·65

Look at the examples and then work the following. **Make sure that the figures and the pennies points are in the correct columns.**

1 £0·06 ×4	2 £0·09 ×7	3 £0·07 ×3	4 £0·02 ×9	5 £0·08 ×6

6 £0·29 ×5	7 £0·37 ×4	8 £0·14 ×9	9 £0·59 ×2	10 £0·19 ×8

11 £0·87 ×3	12 £0·62 ×6	13 £0·70 ×7	14 £0·54 ×8	15 £0·40 ×5

E Work these examples.

1 £1·26 ×4	2 £1·30 ×6	3 £1·09 ×8	4 £1·24 ×5	5 £1·58 ×2	6 £0·25 ×7

7 £1·60 ×5	8 £0·94 ×3	9 £1·75 ×8	10 £1·04 ×4	11 £2·47 ×7	12 £2·52 ×6

Money division practice

A

Write the answers only.

1 5)35p   2 9)54p   3 7)63p   4 6)48p   5 8)56p   6 9)81p

7 2)74p   8 3)84p   9 4)92p   10 5)95p   11 7)91p   12 8)96p

B

Each of the following has a number of pence as a remainder.

1 7)59p   2 4)37p   3 6)50p   4 9)76p   5 8)43p   6 7)66p

7 6)86p   8 3)70p   9 5)77p   10 8)83p   11 7)87p   12 5)92p

C

Work the following. Some of the examples have remainders.

1 2)54p   2 4)56p   3 6)74p   4 8)91p   5 4)61p   6 5)62p

7 7)87p   8 6)80p   9 5)97p   10 3)73p   11 7)84p   12 6)90p

D

Look at the example and then work the following.
Make sure that the figures and the pennies points are in the correct columns.

Example
£2·12
4)£8·48

1 3)£6·93   2 2)£6·84   3 4)£5·68   4 7)£9·17   5 9)£9·45

6 8)£8·64   7 5)£7·00   8 6)£9·60   9 3)£5·22   10 7)£9·94

E

Look at the examples. **Remember the '0' in the £s place.**

Examples
£0·08
7)£0·56

£0·16
4)£0·64

1 2)£0·08   2 4)£0·36   3 7)£0·42   4 6)£0·36   5 9)£0·45

6 5)£0·40   7 3)£0·27   8 8)£0·64   9 7)£0·49   10 6)£0·54

11 3)£0·93   12 5)£0·65   13 7)£0·91   14 6)£0·96   15 2)£0·76

16 4)£0·76   17 7)£0·98   18 3)£0·81   19 9)£0·90   20 5)£0·80

F

Work the following.

1 2)£1·36   2 4)£1·76   3 6)£3·12   4 7)£2·24   5 9)£3·60   6 3)£1·65

7 5)£3·50   8 4)£2·96   9 8)£4·24   10 6)£4·74   11 7)£5·95   12 9)£7·11

Money   multiplication and division

A

Timco's Supermarket

Special Offers		Coffee	£1·25 jar	Jam	31p small jar
Sugar	30p kg	Salmon	93p tin	Jam	58p large jar
Tea	22p packet	Ham	87p tin	Peaches	26p small tin
Butter	34p packet	Fruit Salad	27p tin	Peaches	49p large tin

Find the cost, first in p and then in £s, of:

1 2 large jars of jam
2 7 kg of sugar
3 4 tins of fruit salad
4 5 packets of tea
5 6 packets of butter
6 2 tins of ham
7 5 jars of coffee
8 4 tins of salmon.

9 How much more than a FIFTY is needed to buy 3 packets of tea?

10 Find the change from £1 after buying 2 large tins of peaches.

11 How much less will 3 large jars of jam cost than 6 small jars?

12 How much more will 8 small tins of peaches cost than 4 large ones?

B

Copy the shopping lists below.
Find the cost of each item and then the total cost in £s of each list.

1 4 packets tea
   3 tins fruit salad

2 3 kg sugar
   2 small tins peaches

3 2 packets butter
   2 large tins peaches

4 3 small tins peaches
   5 kg sugar
   4 large jars jam

5 3 tins ham
   6 packets tea
   3 packets butter

6 2 jars coffee
   3 small jars jam
   3 tins salmon

C

3p

4p

5p

6p

Find the number of badges that can be bought for each amount given.

1 Swimming badges   60p
2 Avon Club badges   60p
3 Red Team badges   60p
4 Bird Club badges   60p
5 Red Team badges   £1·00
6 Avon Club badges   £1·00

Find the number of badges that can be bought and the change from each amount.

7   Swimming badges   50p
8   Avon Club badges   50p
9   Red Team badges   68p
10 Bird Club badges   70p
11 Swimming badges   80p
12 Bird Club badges   £1·00

Multiplication and division

A

Father bought 4 tickets for a concert.
He received 16p change from £1.

1 Find the cost of the four tickets.

2 Find the cost of one ticket.

Day trip to GATWICK AIRPORT	adult 78p return children half fare

3 How much will the trip cost for Father and three children?

Five boxes of sweets cost £3·50.

4 Find the cost of one box.

5 How much will 3 boxes cost?

6 Find the remainder when 82p is divided into 3 equal amounts.

7 How much is one fifth of £8?

8 Father gives Anne 30p each day, but 50p on Saturday and 50p on Sunday. How much is that for one week?

Peter, Jill, Tony, Susan and Tim divided a prize of £3 equally.

9 What fraction did each receive?

10 How much did each receive?

FAMOUS FOOTBALLERS
Card sets   £2·50 for 5 Sets

11 Find the cost of one set.

12 How much will three sets cost?

Four kg of apples cost £1·92.

13 Find the cost of 1 kg.

14 How much will $\frac{1}{2}$ kg cost?

Share these sums of money equally. There are no remainders.

15 £3 among 2 children

16 £5 among 4 children

17 £2 among 5 children

18 £6 among 8 children

B

1 Ask mother the cost of a small tin of baked beans and a large one.

2 Draw a table like the one below. Fill it in to make a ready reckoner. Ask your partner to check it.

Number of tins	1	2	3	4	5	6	7	8	9	10
large	p									
small	p									

Use the ready reckoner to find the cost of:

3 12 large tins   4 20 small tins   5 15 large tins   6 14 small tins.

7 Make another ready reckoner which will help Mother to reckon, for example, the cost of bottles of milk.

C

In multiplication, the answer is called the **product**.

1 Find the product of 38 and 7.

2 Find the product of 176 and 4.

Check this example: $27 \times 8 = 216$.
Now write the answers to:

3 $216 \div 8$ 4 8×27 5 $216 \div 27$.

6 First add and then check by multiplying.
$57 + 57 + 57 + 57 + 57 + 57 + 57$

D

In division, the answer is called the **quotient**.

1 Find the quotient when 256 is divided by 4.

2 Find the quotient when 675 is divided by 9.

3 There are 203 children in 7 classes of equal size. How many are there in each class?

Find the value of:

4 $\frac{1}{4}$ of 516 m   5 $\frac{1}{3}$ of 168 g

6 $\frac{1}{6}$ of 342 m   7 $\frac{1}{5}$ of 840 g.

Decimal number system

A Draw this table.
Write in the numbers
below, making sure
that each figure is
in the correct column.

H	T	U

1 three hundred and three
2 five hundred and fifty
3 nine hundred and nine
4 eight hundred and eighty
5 six hundred and twenty
6 four hundred and seventy
7 seven hundred and fifty
8 eight hundred and six
9 two hundred and twenty-two
10 six hundred and ninety

> **The value of each figure in a number
> is given by its place or position.**

Write the value of the figure underlined
in each of these numbers.

11 <u>5</u>98   12 7<u>6</u>4   13 80<u>9</u>
14 43<u>7</u>   15 <u>9</u>52   16 3<u>7</u>0

B Read the numbers in
the table.

Th	H	T	U
			1
		1	0
	1	0	0
1	0	0	0

> **Notice that '0' or
> zero is used as a
> placeholder.**

How many times is:
1   10 larger than 1
2   100 larger than 10
3   1000 larger than 100?

How many times is:
4   100 smaller than 1000
5   10 smaller than 100
6   1 smaller than 10?

Write and fill in the missing numbers.

7    $1 \times 10 = \square$ 10 $10 \div 10 = \square$
8    $10 \times 10 = \square$ 11 $100 \div 10 = \square$
9   $10 \times 10 \times 10 = \square$ 12 $1000 \div 10 = \square$

Write the numbers below, leaving out the
noughts which do not alter the value of
the numbers.

13 710   14 099   15 405
16 060   17 008   18 900
19 001   20 509   21 010

C How many times larger is:

1   50 than 5   7   800 than 80
2   70 than 7   8   300 than 30
3   90 than 9   9   290 than 29
4   60 than 6   10   530 than 53
5   400 than 40   11   710 than 71
6   600 than 60   12   940 than 94?

How many times larger is the figure
marked x than the figure marked y?

  x y   xy   xy
13 494   14 990   15 188

  xy   x y   xy
16 877   17 202   18 611

D How many times smaller is:

1   3 than 30   7   40 than 400
2   9 than 90   8   20 than 200
3   5 than 50   9   32 than 320
4   7 than 70   10   47 than 470
5   80 than 800   11   76 than 760
6   50 than 500   12   21 than 210?

How many times smaller is the figure
marked b than the figure marked a?

  ab   a b   ab
13 455   14 181   15 660

  a b   ab   ab
16 979   17 224   18 744

Decimal number system

A Watch the numbers getting **bigger**.

Th	H	T	U				Th	H	T	U
		7	0	←	10 ×					7
	5	3	0	←	10 ×	←			5	3
1	2	6	0	←	10 ×	←	1	2	6	

The numbers have been moved
one place to the left and a '0' put in
the empty space.

1 By how many times has each number
been made bigger?

Make each of these numbers 10 times
bigger.

2 5   3 20   4 68

5 97   6 132   7 105

Multiply each of these numbers by 10.

8 9   9 27   10 80

11 72   12 145   13 130

14 20   15 11   16 144

B Watch the numbers getting **smaller**.

Th	H	T	U				Th	H	T	U
		8	0	—	÷10	→				8
	4	7	0	—	÷10	→			4	7
1	1	5	0	—	÷10	→		1	1	5

The numbers have been moved
one place to the right.

1 By how many times has each number
been made smaller?

Make each of these numbers 10 times
smaller.

2 50   3 90   4 230

5 400   6 2000   7 1040

Divide each of these numbers by 10.

8 70   9 150   10 300

11 690   12 2050   13 1380

14 1070   15 120   16 2400

C Write the answers only.
1 26 × 10   2 330 ÷ 10   3 60 × 10
4 920 ÷ 10   5 52 × 10   6 190 ÷ 10

Divide each sum of money by 10.
Write the answers only.

7 90p   8 70p   9 60p
10 40p   11 80p   12 30p

Write the answers only as £s.
13 20p × 10   14 11p × 10   15 17p × 10
16 18p × 10   17 19p × 10   18 15p × 10

D Find the value of each letter.
1 $15 \times a = 150$ $b \times 27 = 270$
$151 \times 10 = c$ $222 \times d = 2220$
$350 \div e = 35$ $f \div 10 = 31$

Divide each of these numbers by 10.
Notice that the units figure becomes the
remainder.
Example: $347 \div 10 = 34$ rem. 7.
2 146   3 402   4 98
5 704   6 1098   7 1207
8 111   9 1006   10 2319

E

Th	H	T	U
1	0	0	0
	1	0	0
		1	0
			1

to the right

1 Look at the diagram.
What happens to the
value of the figure 1
each time it is moved
**one place
to the right**?

Th	H	T	U	tenths
			1	
				1

to the right

2 In this diagram, the figure 1 is moved
a further place to the right.
Its value is 10 times smaller than 1 unit,
$1 \div 10 = \frac{1}{10}$ (one tenth)
and it is written in the **tenths** column.

Decimal number system

A Look carefully at the table.

	H	T	U	tenths
1			1	1
2		1	8	4
3			3	2
4			5	7
5		2	0	5
6		3	2	9
7		1	9	8
8	1	0	4	2
9	6	6	6	6
10	2	5	0	3

Write the numbers in the table in the same way as shown in the two examples.

Example 1 1 unit 1 tenth = $1\frac{1}{10}$

Example 2 1 ten 8 units 4 tenths = $18\frac{4}{10}$

Draw similar columns and write these numbers in them.

11 $\frac{7}{10}$ 12 $4\frac{3}{10}$ 13 $9\frac{2}{10}$

14 $10\frac{5}{10}$ 15 $\frac{9}{10}$ 16 $31\frac{4}{10}$

17 125   18 $106\frac{6}{10}$ 19 $220\frac{8}{10}$

20 Copy the table below and make sure you understand it. It shows what you have learned so far about the **tens number system** which is also called the **decimal number system.**

'Decimal' means numbered by tens.

Th	H	T	U	t
1000	100	10	1	$\frac{1}{10}$
10×10×10	10×10	10	1	$\frac{1}{10}$

You have written **tenths** in this form.
$\frac{1}{10}$ $\frac{3}{10}$ $\frac{7}{10}$ etc.
These are called **vulgar fractions.**

When using money or making measurements, **tenths** are written as **decimal fractions**.

These are part of the decimal number system, as shown in the table.

> **A dot or decimal point separates the whole ones from the parts.**

Remember When writing measurements the decimal point is placed on the line.

B Look at the examples below.

3 tenths = $\frac{3}{10}$ = 0.3
(read as '0 point 3')

1 whole one and 7 tenths
= $1\frac{7}{10}$ = 1.7
(read as '1 point 7')

25 whole ones and 6 tenths
= $25\frac{6}{10}$ = 25.6
(read as '25 point 6')

Read these numbers to your partner.

1 24.6   2 0.3   3 60.5

4 10.1   5 101.9   6 200.4

Write as decimal fractions.

7 0 whole ones and 4 tenths

8 0 whole ones and 9 tenths

9 3 whole ones and 4 tenths

10 15 whole ones and 1 tenth

11 twenty whole ones and 8 tenths

12 forty-three whole ones and 7 tenths

13 ten whole ones and 1 tenth

14 sixty whole ones and 6 tenths

Mark the answers and correct any mistakes.
Read your answers to your partner.

Write as decimal fractions.

15 $\frac{1}{10}$ 16 $\frac{7}{10}$ 17 $\frac{9}{10}$ 18 $\frac{4}{10}$

19 $\frac{3}{10}$ 20 $\frac{5}{10}$ 21 $\frac{2}{10}$ 22 $\frac{8}{10}$

Write as vulgar fractions.

23 0.4   24 0.6   25 0.7   26 0.9

Decimal fractions

A Write as decimals the numbers shown on these abacus pictures.

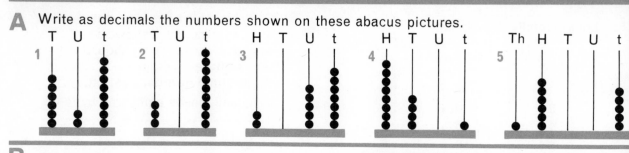

B

1 On squared paper, draw these shapes each of which stands for a whole one.

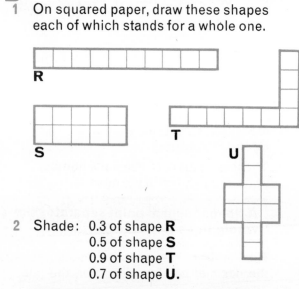

R

S

T

U

2 Shade: 0.3 of shape **R**
0.5 of shape **S**
0.9 of shape **T**
0.7 of shape **U**.

3 Write as a decimal fraction the part of each shape which is unshaded.

Each of the shapes **X**, **Y** and **Z** stands for a whole one.

4 Write as a decimal fraction the part of each shape which is
shaded   unshaded.

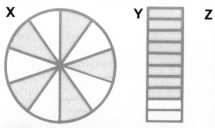

X   Y   Z

5 Write and complete: $\frac{1}{2}=\frac{\square}{10}$.

6 Write $\frac{1}{2}$ as a decimal fraction.

Write and complete:

7 $\frac{1}{5}=\frac{\square}{10}$ 8 $\frac{2}{5}=\frac{\square}{10}$ 9 $\frac{3}{5}=\frac{\square}{10}$ 10 $\frac{4}{5}=\frac{\square}{10}$

11 Write each of the vulgar fractions in questions **7**, **8**, **9** and **10** as a decimal fraction.

C

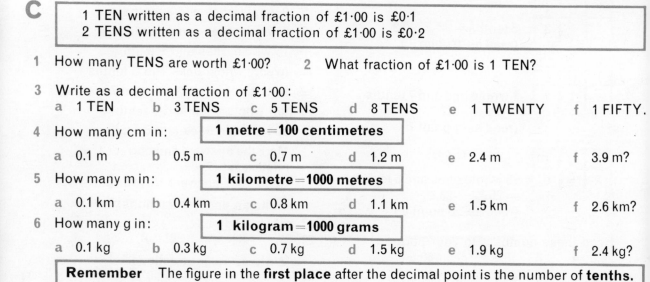

1 TEN written as a decimal fraction of £1·00 is £0·1
2 TENS written as a decimal fraction of £1·00 is £0·2

1 How many TENS are worth £1·00?   2 What fraction of £1·00 is 1 TEN?

3 Write as a decimal fraction of £1·00:
   a 1 TEN   b 3 TENS   c 5 TENS   d 8 TENS   e 1 TWENTY   f 1 FIFTY.

4 How many cm in: **1 metre = 100 centimetres**

   a 0.1 m   b 0.5 m   c 0.7 m   d 1.2 m   e 2.4 m   f 3.9 m?

5 How many m in: **1 kilometre = 1000 metres**

   a 0.1 km   b 0.4 km   c 0.8 km   d 1.1 km   e 1.5 km   f 2.6 km?

6 How many g in: **1 kilogram = 1000 grams**

   a 0.1 kg   b 0.3 kg   c 0.7 kg   d 1.5 kg   e 1.9 kg   f 2.4 kg?

Remember   The figure in the **first place** after the decimal point is the number of **tenths**.

Puzzle corner

A

code													
A	D	E	F	H	I	L	N	O	R	S	T	U	W
1	2	3	4	5	6	7	8	9	10	11	12	13	14

The following question is written using the code above.

14 5 1 12   6 11   12 5 3   12 9 12 1 7   14 5 3 8

9 8 3   1 8 2   12 5 10 3 3   1 10 3   1 2 2 3 2?

1 Write out the question in words.   2 Write the answer as a word and then in code.

3 Using this code, write this message, 'Treasure under floor'.

B

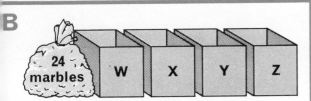

24 marbles

W   X   Y   Z

1 If an equal number of the marbles is put into each box and none is left, how many are there in each box?

2 If box **W** is left empty and an equal number of the marbles is put into each of the other boxes, how many are there in each of these boxes? Use all the marbles.

3 The marbles are put into the four boxes so that there are twice as many in **W** and **Z** as in **X** and **Y**.
How many marbles will there be in **X** and in **Y** if each has the same number?

4 This time, **Y** is left empty but 4 marbles are put into **Z**, half as many again into **X** and all but one of the rest into **W**.
How many are there in **W**?

C

1 Which number, when multiplied by 8, will give a product of 160?

2 Find the number nearest to 150 which will give a remainder of 6 when divided by 7.

3 5 posts are placed at equal distances apart in a straight line.
How many spaces are there between the posts?

4 If 8 posts are placed in a straight line 5 metres apart, find the distance between the first and the last post.

5 Three numbers, when added together, give a total of 555.
One of the numbers is 5 and another is 500.
Find the third number.

6 Paul paid for a toy, which cost 48p, with an equal number of 5p, 2p and 1p coins.
How many of each of the coins did he need?

D

Draw and complete these magic squares. If you have found the correct answers, each row down, across, and from corner to corner will add up to the given total.

1

5		3
	6	8
	2	

total 18

2

	7	7
8	5	

total 21

3

	12	
	11	6
9		

total 33

Shapes and space surfaces

A

1. On a separate sheet of paper, using a ruler and a set square, draw this rectangle. Mark it in squares.
2. Shade the surface of the rectangle.
3. How many squares cover its surface?
4. Cut out the squares. Then fit them together to make three different shapes.

One different shape is shown here.

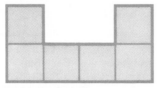

5. Draw on squared paper the shapes you have made.
6. What do you know about the amount of surface of the rectangle and each of the shapes you have made?

7. How many of the cut-out squares cover the surface of each of the following shapes?

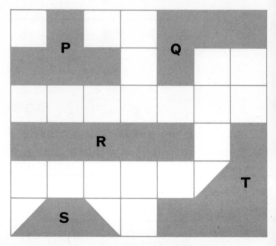

8. Name the shape which has the largest surface.
9. Which of these shapes have surfaces of the same size?

B

The amount of surface in a shape is measured by counting squares of equal size. The number of squares which cover a shape measures its **area**.

1. Which of these shapes has the largest area?
2. Which of the shapes has the least area?
3. Which of the shapes have surfaces which are equal in area?

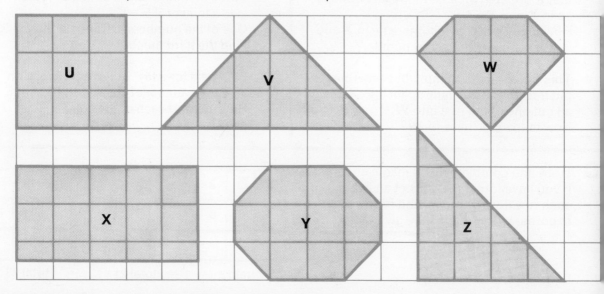

Plans and scales

A

Peter is holding his closed **Alpha** book so that he can look at it from above.

Get a book and look at it in the same way.

You can only see the top or front cover of the book.

1   Place it on a large sheet of paper and draw round the edge.

2   Write the name of the shape you have drawn.

3   Show on the drawing everything you can see on the book from above.

Your drawing is a **full-size plan.**

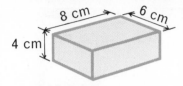

This is a drawing of a block of wood. The measurements are given.

What is:

4   the length   5   the width
6   the height   of the block?

7   Use a ruler and a set square to draw a full-size plan of the block.

8   Write the measurements on your plan.

9   Which measurement have you not used? Why?

The drawing is of an empty box without a lid.

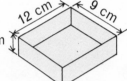

10   Draw a full-size plan of the box.

11   Write the measurements on your plan.

12   Which measurement have you not used?

> **Plans show the shapes of objects when looked at from above.**

B

This is a full-size plan of a box with a window in the top.

John uses it to collect insects which he takes to school.

Find, by measuring, the length and width of:

1   the box   2   the window.

3   Draw the plan in your book, using a ruler and a set square.

4   To make the plan smaller, you can halve the actual size.
Draw another plan making the measurements half the actual size.

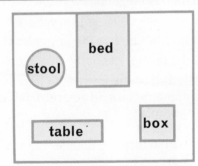

Jill lifts the roof from her dolls' house when she arranges the bedroom furniture. The plan shows what she can see from above.

It is drawn one quarter the actual size.

5   Find the actual length and width of the bedroom.

6   Find the actual length of the bed.

7   What is the shape of the top of the box?

8   What is the shape of the top of the stool?

9   If the plan is drawn so that 1 cm on the plan stands for 5 cm, what would be the actual length and width of the doll's bed?

Plans and scales

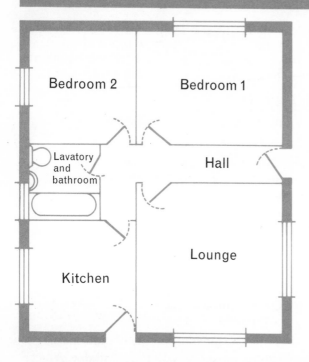

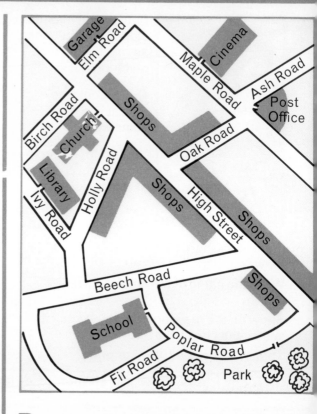

A This is a plan of a bungalow.

1 Which is the largest room?

2 Which is the smallest room?

3 How many bedrooms are there?

4 Estimate which is the larger bedroom.

5 Is the lavatory separate from the bathroom?

Entering by the front door into the hall, in which direction do you turn, left or right, to get into:

6 the kitchen   7 bedroom 2?

The plan is much smaller than full-size. It is drawn to a scale of
1 centimetre to 1 metre.
This means that **1 cm on the plan** stands for **1 m on the bungalow.**

8 Find the actual distance from the front door to the bathroom door.

9 Write the names of the rooms.

10 Find the length and width of each room in metres.

11 Which rooms are square?

12 Which rooms are rectangular?

13 Find the length and width of the bungalow. (Use the outside measurements.)

B This plan or map shows a school and the streets and buildings nearby.

1 Find the school.
Name the roads which form its boundary.

Write the names of the roads or streets in which the following are situated.

2 the church   3 the garage   4 the shops

5 the library   6 the cinema

7 Coming out of Beech Road into High Street, which way would you turn for the garage?

8 Peter lives on Ash Road, next to the Post Office. Describe his journey to school.

The map is drawn to a scale of
1 centimetre to 50 metres.

9 Measure in cm:
   a   the length   b   the width of the map.

10 Find the actual distances which these measurements represent.

11 Get a map showing the roads near your school. Practise finding your way from place to place and describing the route.

Making sure

A

Addition and subtraction to 10

	a	b	c	d
1	9+1	4+4	1+7	5+5
2	2+4	7+2	3+3	2+6
3	4+5	3+5	2+8	3+4
4	3+6	7+3	6+4	5+2
5	10−8	8−4	7−6	7−7
6	9−5	7−3	6−4	9−3
7	8−6	9−8	10−3	9−0
8	7−5	10−6	8−7	10−5
9	9−9	7−0	8−3	9−7

Addition and subtraction to 18

	a	b	c	d
10	9+2	7+6	6+5	5+8
11	7+5	9+9	4+8	8+6
12	8+8	9+5	8+7	7+7
13	6+9	9+7	9+4	9+8
14	17−8	15−7	13−4	11−6
15	12−5	11−9	14−8	13−6
16	11−7	18−9	12−8	16−8
17	13−8	12−6	16−9	14−7
18	12−9	14−9	11−8	15−9

B

Tables of twos, threes, fours and fives

		a	b	c	d	e	f	g	h	i	j	k
1	Multiply by 2	8	3	0	6	4	9	7	1	10	5	2
2	Divide by 2	6	20	12	4	8	0	18	10	14	2	16
3	Multiply by 3	4	0	5	3	8	6	1	9	10	7	2
4	Divide by 3	3	15	6	30	24	12	18	0	27	21	9
5	Multiply by 4	9	4	8	5	7	2	1	10	3	0	6
6	Divide by 4	24	4	12	32	8	20	28	36	0	16	40
7	Multiply by 5	5	8	0	9	3	6	10	4	1	7	2
8	Divide by 5	35	10	25	40	15	30	0	5	50	20	45

C

Tables of sixes, sevens, eights and nines

		a	b	c	d	e	f	g	h	i	j	k
1	Multiply by 6	4	7	0	10	5	2	9	6	1	8	3
2	Divide by 6	12	48	36	54	24	0	60	30	42	6	18
3	Multiply by 7	1	8	5	2	9	6	0	10	3	7	4
4	Divide by 7	0	42	21	63	49	28	7	56	35	70	14
5	Multiply by 8	6	9	3	8	5	1	10	4	7	0	2
6	Divide by 8	24	56	32	80	0	48	64	8	72	16	40
7	Multiply by 9	2	7	10	0	8	5	3	8	6	1	4
8	Divide by 9	36	90	63	81	27	54	0	72	18	45	9

Mixed examples

D

1. $(5 \times 5) + 4$
2. $(7 \times 4) + 3$
3. $(8 \times 9) + 6$
4. $(7 \times 7) + 5$
5. $63 - (7 \times 8)$
6. $51 - (5 \times 9)$
7. $26 - (3 \times 7)$
8. $40 - (6 \times 6)$

E

1. $9 \div 2$
2. $29 \div 3$
3. $41 \div 6$
4. $63 \div 8$
5. $97 \div 10$
6. $55 \div 7$
7. $62 \div 9$
8. $17 \div 2$
9. $16 \div 3$
10. $43 \div 9$
11. $53 \div 8$
12. $22 \div 6$

F

1. Multiply 9 by 7.
2. Find the product of 8 and 4.
3. Divide 100 by 10.
4. Decrease 50 by 24.
5. Subtract 6 from 15.
6. Increase 37 by 6.

Making sure

Money, giving change

A Find the change from a FIFTY after spending:

1	43p	5	18p	9	12p
2	30p	6	27p	10	11p
3	46p	7	9p	11	27p
4	24p	8	15p	12	18p.

Find the change from a £1 after spending:

13	75p	17	63p	21	24p
14	15p	18	31p	22	88p
15	82p	19	77p	23	49p
16	26p	20	14p	24	55p.

Changing coins

B How many TWOS have the same value as:

1	1 TEN	2	1 TWENTY	3	3 TENS	4	2 TWENTIES	5	a FIFTY	6	£1?

How many FIVES have the same value as:

7	1 TEN	8	1 TWENTY	9	3 TENS	10	2 TWENTIES	11	a FIFTY	12	£1?

How many pence have the same value as:

13	£0·50	14	£0·10	15	£0·05	16	£0·01	17	£0·20	18	£0·84?

Money addition

C Find the value of:

1 3 TENS and a FIVE

2 3 FIVES and 3 TWOS

3 5 TENS and 7 TWOS

4 5 FIVES and 4 TWOS

5 3 TWENTIES and 2 TENS

6 5 TWENTIES, a FIFTY and a TEN

7 a FIFTY, 2 TENS and 3 FIVES

8 a TEN, a FIVE and 6 TWOS

9 a FIVE, 2 TWOS and 8 pennies

10 a FIFTY and 7 FIVES.

Addition　　Money　　Subtraction

D Write each answer as £s.

1	30p + 80p	4	32p + 70p
2	40p + 90p	5	95p + 40p
3	60p + 48p	6	65p + 75p

Write each answer as pence.

7	£1·10 − £0·20	10	£2·00 − £1·05
8	£1·30 − £0·50	11	£3·00 − £2·75
9	£1·24 − £0·34	12	£5·00 − £4·25

Fractions

E Write and complete the following using the signs >, < or = in place of ●.

1 $\frac{2}{7} ● \frac{2}{9}$

2 $\frac{4}{4} ● 1$

3 $\frac{4}{5} ● 1$

4 $\frac{1}{5} ● \frac{2}{10}$

5 $\frac{1}{2} ● \frac{4}{10}$

6 $\frac{1}{2} ● \frac{2}{3}$

7 $\frac{7}{8} ● 1$

8 $\frac{2}{3} ● \frac{5}{6}$

9 $\frac{5}{5} ● \frac{8}{8}$

Write the answers only.

10 a $\frac{1}{5}$ of 35 cm　　b $\frac{3}{5}$ of 35 cm

11 a $\frac{1}{4}$ of 16p　　b $\frac{3}{4}$ of 16p

12 a $\frac{1}{3}$ of 15 ℓ　　b $\frac{2}{3}$ of 15 ℓ

13 a $\frac{1}{6}$ of 24 kg　　b $\frac{5}{6}$ of 24 kg

14 a $\frac{1}{5}$ of 50 g　　b $\frac{4}{5}$ of 50 g

Measures

F Write the answers only.

1	1 m = ☐ cm	2	$\frac{1}{2}$ m = ☐ cm	3	1 km = ☐ m	4	1 kg = ☐ g	5	$\frac{1}{2}$ kg = ☐ g
6	1 h = ☐ min	7	$\frac{1}{2}$ h = ☐ min	8	$\frac{1}{4}$ h = ☐ min	9	$\frac{3}{4}$ h = ☐ min	10	1 day = ☐ h

Making sure

A Number and money
Make sure you can add and subtract.

				£		£
1 $\begin{array}{r}37\\23\\+18\\\hline\end{array}$	2 $\begin{array}{r}346\\79\\+135\\\hline\end{array}$	3 $\begin{array}{r}56p\\38p\\+47p\\\hline\end{array}$	4 $\begin{array}{r}0{\cdot}26\\0{\cdot}95\\+0{\cdot}58\\\hline\end{array}$		5 $\begin{array}{r}1{\cdot}37\\2{\cdot}05\\+3{\cdot}59\\\hline\end{array}$	

				£		£
6 $\begin{array}{r}93\\-37\\\hline\end{array}$	7 $\begin{array}{r}405\\-196\\\hline\end{array}$	8 $\begin{array}{r}84p\\-37p\\\hline\end{array}$	9 $\begin{array}{r}1{\cdot}30\\-0{\cdot}65\\\hline\end{array}$		10 $\begin{array}{r}4{\cdot}26\\-1{\cdot}89\\\hline\end{array}$	

If you need more practice, turn to pages 51 and 52.

B

1 Find the total amount of these bills.

   93p   26p   43p   and 18p

2 The total amount is paid with 4 coins.
   Name the coins.

   Which three coins together have the
   same value as:

3 14p   4 22p   5 26p   6 53p?

   Which four coins together have the
   same value as:

7 75p   8 18p   9 9p   10 34p?

   Write the measurements below in cm.

11 1 m 45 cm   12 2 m
13 2 m 70 cm   14 3 m 9 cm
15 5 m 50 cm   16 2 m 22 cm

   The petrol tank in father's car holds
   60 litres.
   The gauge shows it is one quarter full.

17 How many litres are there in the tank?
18 How many more litres will it hold?

   A small car will travel 12 km on a litre
   of petrol. A large car will travel 5 km on
   a litre of petrol.

litres	1	2	3	4	5	10
small car (km)	12					
large car (km)	5					

19 Draw and fill in the table above to make a
    ready reckoner.

C Look at the scale on the balance.

1 What is the
   largest mass that
   can be measured on it?

2 Into how many
   equal parts is
   each kg divided?

3 How many grams
   does each small
   division represent?

4 The pointers a, b
   and c, show the mass of three parcels.
   Write the mass of each in kg and g.

5 Find the total mass of the parcels.

6 What is the difference in kg and g between
   the heaviest and the lightest parcels?

7 Measure each of the lines x, y and z to
   the nearest cm.

   x ──────────────

   y ────────────────

   z ──────────────────

8 Use a ruler and a set square to draw this
   rectangle.

9 Draw and
   measure the
   diagonal.

10 Draw and
    measure the
    other diagonal.

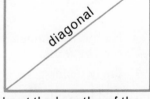

diagonal

11 What do you find about the lengths of the
    diagonals?

Making sure

A Number and money
Make sure you can multiply and divide.

| 1 | 86 ×9 | 2 | 193 ×5 | 3 | 23p ×7 | 4 | £0·28 ×6 | 5 | £1·53 ×8 |

6 $8\overline{)472}$ 7 $4\overline{)913}$ 8 $7\overline{)91p}$ 9 $6\overline{)£2·64}$ 10 $3\overline{)£4·71}$

If you need more practice, turn to pages 75 and 76 (number), pages 81 and 82 (money).

B
Write these fractions in order of size, the largest first.

1 $\frac{1}{3}$ $\frac{1}{2}$ $\frac{1}{4}$ $\frac{1}{6}$ 2 $\frac{1}{8}$ $\frac{1}{10}$ $\frac{1}{4}$ $\frac{1}{5}$

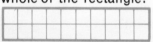

x

m

n

p

Which of the rods **m**, **n** or **p** is:

3 $\frac{1}{2}$ of rod **x**   4 $\frac{2}{5}$ of rod **x**   5 $\frac{7}{10}$ of rod **x**?

6 How many small squares are there in the whole of the rectangle?

Write the number of small squares in these fractions of the whole rectangle.

7 $\frac{1}{4}$, $\frac{3}{4}$ 8 $\frac{1}{5}$, $\frac{4}{5}$ 9 $\frac{1}{10}$, $\frac{9}{10}$

C
Write in figures:

1 thirty point six   2 eight point four
3 nought point nine   4 twelve point two.

Write as decimals.

5 7 tenths   6 11 tenths
7 19 tenths   8 43 tenths

Add 10 to each of these numbers.

9 64   10 192   11 7.8

Take 10 from each of these numbers.

12 203   13 170   14 20.2

Put these numbers in order of size, the smallest first.

15	0.3	0.5	0.7	0.8	0.2
16	1.7	1.4	1.0	1.9	1.1
17	2	20	2.2	0.2	22
18	4.3	3.9	4	2.7	1.8

D
A rectangle is 12 cm long and its width is $\frac{1}{4}$ of its length.

1 Find a the width
        b the perimeter of the rectangle.

2 Using a set square, draw the rectangle full-size.

Look at the drawing of the chocolate carton.

Name the shapes of:
3 the two ends
4 the two sides   5 the bottom.

The bottom is 19 cm long and 3 cm wide.
6 Draw a plan of the carton half-size.

E
Each line is drawn to the given scale. Measure each line and find the actual length it represents.

1 Scale: 1 cm to 1 m

2 Scale: 0.5 cm to 1 m

3 Scale: 1 cm to 10 m

Which of the shapes below has:
4 the largest area   5 the smallest area?

6 Write them in order, the largest area first.
7 Describe how you found the answers.

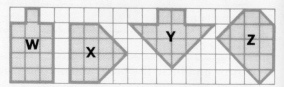